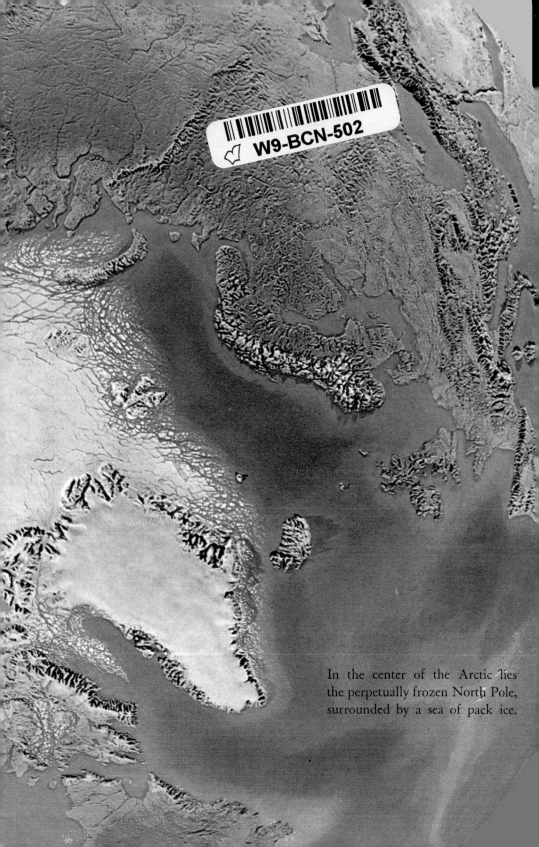

In the center of the Arctic lies
the perpetually frozen North Pole,
surrounded by a sea of pack ice.

THE EARTH & YOU

THE EARTH & YOU

A GEOGRAPHIC PICTURE
OF THE WORLD WE LIVE IN

by Norman J. G. Pounds, M.A., Ph.D.

Chairman, Department of Geography, Indiana University
and formerly of the Geography Department
of Cambridge University

Illustrated with Rand McNally Maps and Diagrams

RAND McNALLY & COMPANY

CHICAGO   NEW YORK   SAN FRANCISCO

*Rand McNally wishes to thank the following publishers for their permission
to reprint the material under copyright, found on the pages listed:*

Harcourt, Brace & World, Inc. for the quotations on pages 43 and 153 from
Land of the Free by Archibald MacLeish, copyright 1938 by Archibald Mac-
Leish; George Allen & Unwin Ltd for the quotation on pages 96–97 from
Travels in the North by Karl Capek; The Viking Press, Inc. and William
Heinemann Ltd for the quotation on pages 189–90 from *The Grapes of Wrath*
by John Steinbeck, copyright 1939 by John Steinbeck; Faber and Faber Ltd
for the quotation on page 275 from *Poems Chiefly Cornish* by A. L. Rowse;
Alfred Knopf, Laurence Pollinger Limited, and the Estate of the late Mrs.
Frieda Lawrence for the quotation on page 211 from *The Plumed Serpent* by
D. H. Lawrence; the Viking Press, Inc., Laurence Pollinger Limited, and the
Estate of the late Mrs. Frieda Lawrence for the quotation on page 91 from
Phoenix by D. H. Lawrence (copyright 1936 by Frieda Lawrence), and for
the quotations on pages 519 and 526 from *Kangaroo* by D. H. Lawrence
(copyright 1951 by Frieda Lawrence).

To

HERMAN B WELLS

Acknowledgments

No book is the work of its author alone, and this one is no exception. The author wishes to express his sincere thanks to all who have helped both by procuring data for him and correcting his errors. In particular he wishes to thank Dr. G. Etzel Pearcy of the Department of State, Professor Robert N. Taaffe of Indiana University, Mrs. Susan S. Ball, and the editorial and research staffs of Rand McNally.

CONTENTS

MAPS AND DIAGRAMS

INTRODUCTION

The Earth is rude, silent and incomprehensible at first—
Be not discouraged—keep on.

WALT WHITMAN

Politics today are wonderfully instructive in the facts of geography. Week after week, month after month, new, or at least little-known, territories break into the news: Laos, Nepal, Katanga, Irian, Kuwait. The press publishes little maps to show an uninstructed public just where these previously unconsidered territories are. As crises spread from continent to continent, so the layman's geography comes gradually to span the world. We cannot live today without some knowledge of the simple facts of geography, not only of our own locality and our own country, but also of the remotest areas of the earth.

There is a similarity, which is more than superficial, between the studies of geography and history. There has been no period in recorded human history when man was not interested in his own past. However heroic or legendary its expression may be, man has seen in history his own physical ancestry and the lineage of his own culture and society stretching back through the ages of his recorded past into the longer and more misty ages of his unrecorded origins. He has thought of influences from many ages and places as brought to a focus upon himself, upon his particular "bank and shoal of time." In Lincoln's words, he "cannot escape History." Yet geography is even less escapable, for it is all around us. Every event takes place, every crisis occurs at some point upon the earth's surface.

But from his study of the daily press what kind of geographical knowledge does the layman achieve? E. C. Bentley once quipped, "Biography is about chaps, but Geography is about maps." As a definition this leaves something to be desired, although geography does have much

12

to do with maps. Not long ago geography was not much more than a dull catalogue of names of continents, countries, and capitals, of capes and bays and rivers, of exports and imports. This still is useful knowledge, and we would each of us be able to follow the newscast or read the papers more intelligently each day if we knew in advance the location of each place that comes into prominence. But there are atlases to consult when our memories fail, as is likely to happen quite often. Geographic locations and maps are very far from being the extent of geography.

The philosopher Kant worked out a rule-of-thumb definition of and distinction between history and geography. He wrote: History, in the widest sense, is the ordering of events in time and the search for causal relationships between them. Geography is the ordering of phenomena of every kind, natural and human, in space.

Following Kant's definition, everything that has a distributional pattern over the earth's surface is grist to the geographer's mill. Mountains, plateaus, and plains; temperature, rainfall, and all other manifestations of climate are clearly geographical. So also are vegetation and soil, rivers and ocean currents. Each and all of these can be represented on maps. Take a map of types of vegetation and compare it with one of rainfall and another of temperature. The comparison suggests that the distribution of certain types of vegetation is in some ways connected with that of climate. And conclusions a great deal more subtle than these can be derived from the comparison of two or more patterns.

The examples given above are from physical geography; they are illustrations of the influence of one set of purely natural phenomena upon the distribution of another. But geography goes a great deal further than this. Geography has many times been defined as the study of the earth "as the home of man," or by some variant of this expression. The core of the subject is not so much the ways in which some natural phenomena depend upon others, important as these are, as the interdependence of the works of man with those of nature. This makes the subject infinitely broad, though its breadth must always be qualified. We are dealing only with human actions and human creativity in their spatial aspects, with those activities that are firmly anchored to place.

Man has always shown a deep interest in places beyond the horizon, and when he had little precise knowledge, he has often populated these remote areas with figments of his imagination. Travelers' tales, simple description, touched up by the hand of romance, long sufficed for his purposes. Geography began, as the name itself suggests, as description of the earth. During the past century the geographer's vision has deepened. Description is still necessary, and is still being written, but geographical science is now concerned more and more with analysis.

To understand the earth on which we live—its surface of land and sea, its minerals and agricultural land, the range of warmth and rainfall, of settlement and cities—involves techniques that have become the fields of specialists. The study of the earth's crust belongs to the geologist; of the oceans and the movements of their waters to the oceanographer; of the earth's cover of vegetation to the botanist; of the movements of the atmosphere to the meteorologist; and the origin and nature of the soils to the pedologist. So much does each aspect and facet of the earth's surface have its specialists, that one may wonder what there is left for the geographer to do. Yet the field of geography has not contracted as these specializations have ripened and dropped off. It has grown bigger and is more important than it ever was, for geography today is concerned with the *distribution* of these phenomena over the earth's surface.

The meteorologist is a familiar figure as he outlines the "highs," puts in the fronts, and suggests what the weather may be for the next few hours or days. His training has been in the physics of the atmosphere. Ask him when the monsoon breaks on the Ghats of India, or what brings the dry, gritty Sirocco wind to southern Italy, or how the Mediterranean climate influences agriculture, and he might be hard put to give an answer. Or again, the soil analyst who tests the soil sample in the field along the bottom land and recommends a fertilizer for it probably would not be able to tell you where else in the world soils of this general type are found and how important they are in the world pattern of agriculture.

The difference between these specialists and the geographer is that they are interested in air masses and fronts, in soil profiles and rock materials for their own sakes. The geographer, on the other hand, studies the distribution over the earth of these predominantly physical phenomena and examines the interplay of one with another, and he relates them, separately and together, to the pursuits of man. He views the pattern of human settlement in village and city against the pattern of hill and plain, of rivers and seas, of climate, soil and vegetation, and he discovers causal relationships and connections between them all.

The subject of geography is so immense, as we have seen, that it is broken up for purposes of study into a number of branches. We have physical geography, which studies distribution of climates and soils and types of vegetation, and the supply of water for urban and industrial use as well as for agriculture. We have economic geography—the study of man's economic or productive activities and the trade which results from his fields of specialization. Sometimes this vast field is broken down into more manageable units such as the specialized study of the geography of agriculture and the geography of manufacturing industry and of transportation. We have urban geography, the study of the distribution of cities and of the various functions within the cities. Then there is political geography, the study of politically organized areas, from the township to the nation state, their size, shape, the changes which they undergo, and the functions which they perform, and the ways in which they interact with one another. To this list many would add social or cultural geography, which is the study of the distribution of human societies and of the differences between them. It would include the study of poor societies no less than rich and developed. In fact it is likely to give more attention to the so-called underdeveloped peoples because they raise problems of development and economic growth which the developed do not.

No one can dispute that these are important subjects. They raise problems vital for our modern society which we would do well to study. The old-style geography, which so many of us learned in school, gave us a quantity of useful knowledge. But the new geography is an essential field to every citizen of the world, for it consists of a knowledge of the world around us.

These special branches of geography are often called systematic because they each single out and study intensively one element in the total environment of man; the climate, for example, or agriculture or urban development. It is no less important to have a broader knowledge of areas more restricted than the earth as a whole. This is regional geography. It attempts to put together the many branches of geography— the physical and economic, the geography of settlement and of political organization in so far as they relate to specific and restricted areas. The regional geography of a country takes the physical elements, the agriculture and industry, transportation, and synthesizes them into a whole, in which each element is related, in part as cause, in part as effect, with every other. This is the ideal of regional geography, the fullest understanding of some segment of the earth's surface. To acquire this knowledge and understanding is an immense task, as great if not greater than the understanding of the whole of human history.

It is an ambitious person who writes a world history, and a world geography is a task of similar magnitude. This book is merely an introduction. It sets out to review the elements of which our environment is made up, and goes on to survey each of eight arbitrarily set regions. In the compass of only a few hundred pages it can present nothing more than a thumbnail sketch of each of the two hundred or more political units (independent states and dependencies) which make up the modern world. But as far as possible in so small a space we shall attempt to trace the interaction of land, air, and water upon one another, and then their combined influence on man, and man's influence on them as he shapes this earth to meet his needs.

Bloomington, Indiana   Norman J. G. Pounds
April, 1962

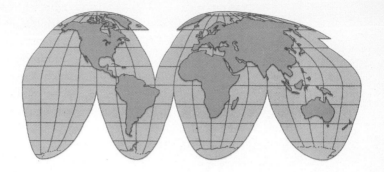

COMPARATIVE WORLD MAPS

Thousands of words would have to be written to impart all the facts and facets of world geography that can be gained by studying the following world maps. In this section the physical geography of the world is portrayed in the maps of land forms, climates, vegetation, and rainfall; the role of man in adapting the world to his needs, in the maps of the political units, the density of population, the spread of races and languages.

In the physical-geography maps you will note there is a close correlation between the types of climate and the pattern of vegetation and land forms. There is even correlation between these maps and the distribution of people on the land; and from the races and language maps the cultures which developed certain areas in certain directions can be traced.

Not only can the characteristics of the world as a whole be gained at a glance, but comparisons within a specific region can be made. How does the density of population in the northeast of the United States and the sparsity of human settlement in the western interior relate to the climate, vegetation, and land form maps? Or the high density of European population and the low density of South American settlement? Such comparisons, and others that will occur to you after reading this book, will enhance your understanding of the world we live in.

17

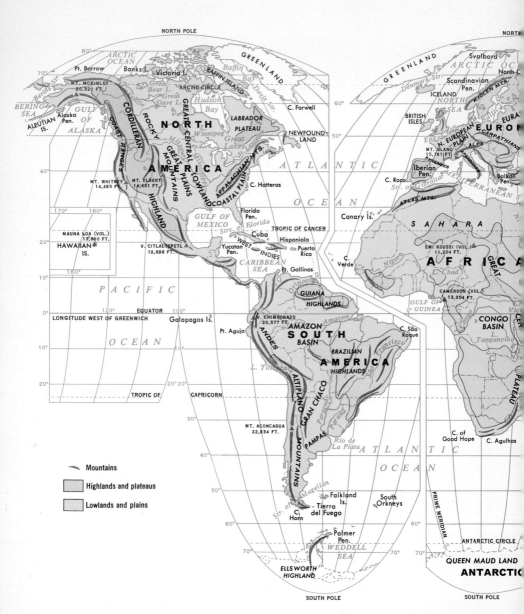

NORTH POLE

ARCTIC OCEAN

GREENLAND

Pt. Barrow · Banks I. · Victoria I. · Baffin Bay · Baffin ISLAND

MT. McKINLEY 20,320 FT.

Great Bear L. · ARCTIC CIRCLE

Great Slave L.

Hudson Bay

C. Farwell

NEWFOUND-LAND

GREENLAND

Svalbard · North · ARCTIC OC.

Scandinavian Pen. · KJÖLEN MTS.

ICELAND · NORTH SEA

Denmark Str.

BRITISH ISLES

EUROP · EURA

BERING SEA · ALEUTIAN IS.

GULF OF ALASKA · Alaska Pen.

COAST RANGES · CORDILLERAN

ROCKY MOUNTAINS

GREAT CENTRAL LOWLAND

Missouri · Winnipeg · Great Lakes

LABRADOR PLATEAU

ATLANTIC

NORTH AMERICA

GREAT PLAINS

APPALACHIAN MTS.

COASTAL PLAIN

MT. BLANC 15,781 FT.

Iberian Pen. · PYRENEES · ALPS · CARPATHIANS

C. Roca · APENNINES · Balkan Pen.

Str. of Gibraltar · MEDITERRANEAN S

ATLAS MTS.

OCEAN

MT. WHITNEY 14,495 FT. · MT. ELBERT 14,431 FT.

HIGHLAND

C. Hatteras

MAUNA LOA (VOL.) 13,680 FT.

HAWAIIAN IS.

GULF OF MEXICO

Florida Pen. · Strs. of Florida

TROPIC OF CANCER

Canary Is.

SAHARA

V. CITLALTEPETL 18,696 FT.

Yucatan Pen. · WEST INDIES

Cuba · Hispaniola · Puerto Rico

C. Verde

EMI KOUSSI (VOL.) 11,204 FT.

AFRICA · GREAT

L. Chad · Niger

PACIFIC

CARIBBEAN SEA · Pt. Gallinas

GUIANA HIGHLANDS

GULF OF GUINEA

CAMEROON (VOL.) 13,354 FT.

CONGO BASIN

L. Tanganyika · Vic

EQUATOR

LONGITUDE WEST OF GREENWICH · Galapagos Is.

V. CHIMBORAZO 20,577 FT.

AMAZON BASIN

Amazon

C. São Roque

OCEAN

Pt. Aguja

ANDES

SOUTH AMERICA

BRAZILIAN HIGHLANDS

San Francisco

PLATEAU

L. Titicaca · ALTIPLANO · GRAN CHACO

Orinoco

PAMPAS

TROPIC OF · CAPRICORN

MT. ACONCAGUA 22,834 FT.

Paraguay · Paraná

Rio de La Plata

ATLANTIC

C. of Good Hope · C. Agulhas

MOUNTAINS

Str. of Magellan

Falkland Is. · South Orkneys

OCEAN

PRIME MERIDIAN

Tierra del Fuego · C. Horn

Palmer Pen.

ANTARCTIC CIRCLE

WEDDELL SEA

QUEEN MAUD LAND

ANTARCTIC

ELLSWORTH HIGHLAND

SOUTH POLE · SOUTH POLE

⌒ Mountains

Highlands and plateaus

Lowlands and plains

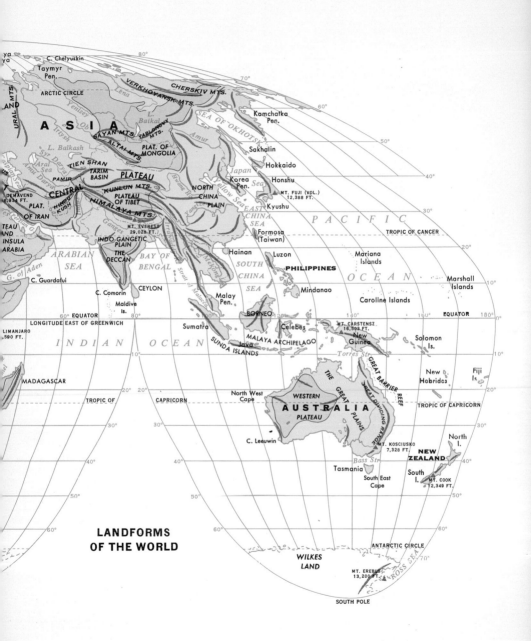

LANDFORMS OF THE WORLD

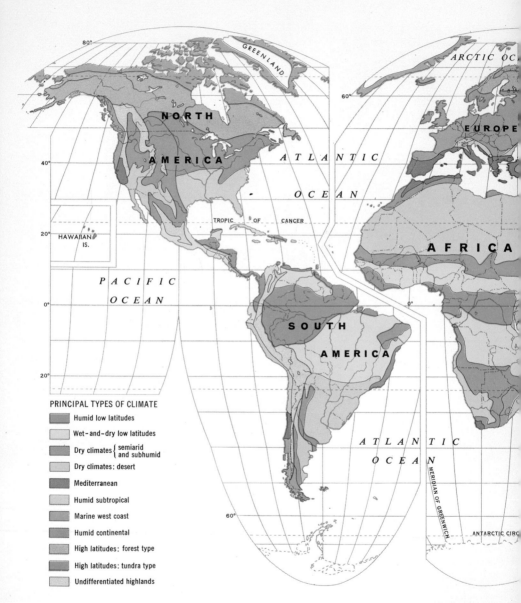

PRINCIPAL TYPES OF CLIMATE

- Humid low latitudes
- Wet-and-dry low latitudes
- Dry climates { semiarid and subhumid
- Dry climates: desert
- Mediterranean
- Humid subtropical
- Marine west coast
- Humid continental
- High latitudes: forest type
- High latitudes: tundra type
- Undifferentiated highlands

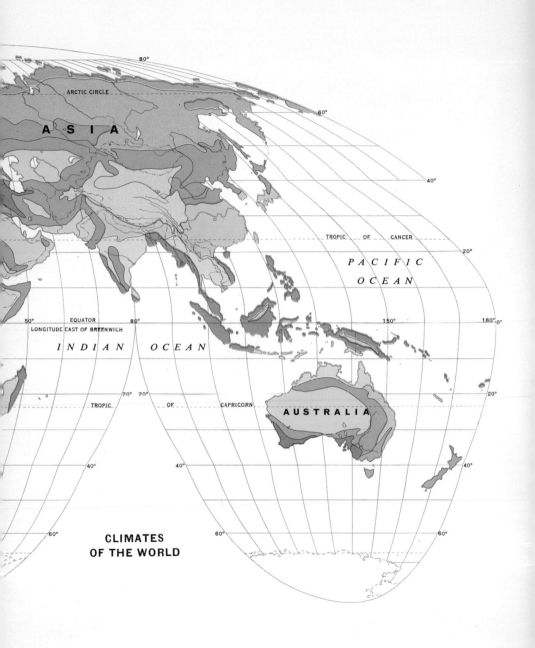

CLIMATES
OF THE WORLD

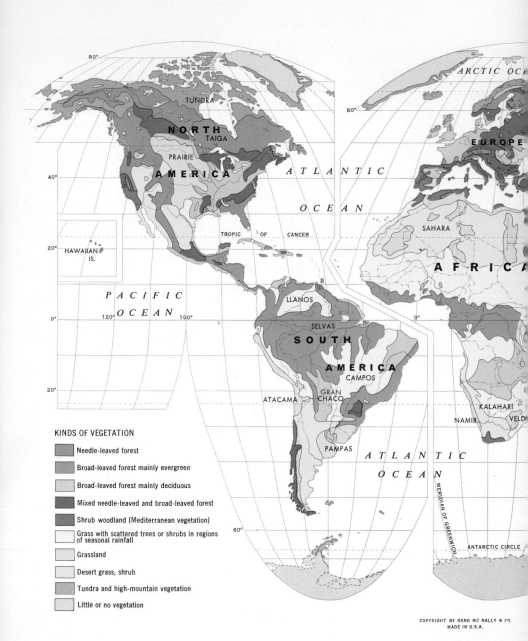

KINDS OF VEGETATION

- Needle-leaved forest
- Broad-leaved forest mainly evergreen
- Broad-leaved forest mainly deciduous
- Mixed needle-leaved and broad-leaved forest
- Shrub woodland (Mediterranean vegetation)
- Grass with scattered trees or shrubs in regions of seasonal rainfall
- Grassland
- Desert grass, shrub
- Tundra and high-mountain vegetation
- Little or no vegetation

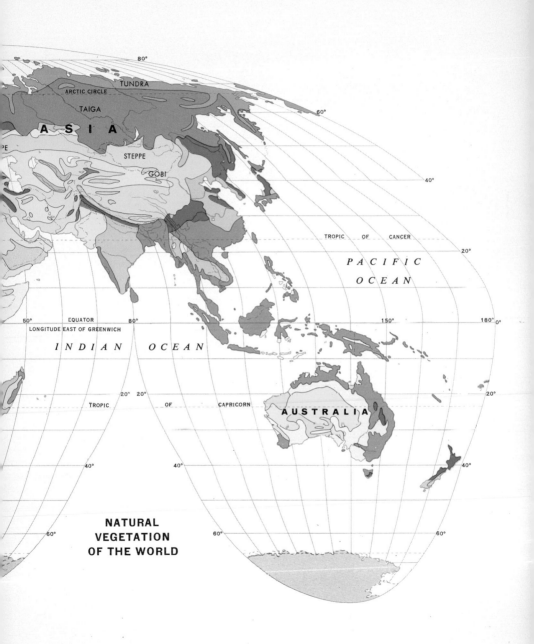

NATURAL
VEGETATION
OF THE WORLD

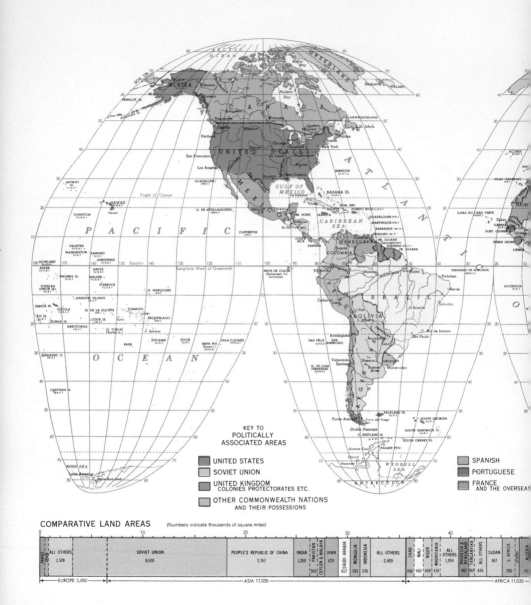

KEY TO
POLITICALLY
ASSOCIATED AREAS

UNITED STATES

SOVIET UNION

UNITED KINGDOM
COLONIES PROTECTORATES ETC.

OTHER COMMONWEALTH NATIONS
AND THEIR POSSESSIONS

SPANISH

PORTUGUESE

FRANCE
AND THE OVERSEA

COMPARATIVE LAND AREAS   (Numbers indicate thousands of square miles)

FRANCE	ALL OTHERS 1,528	SOVIET UNION 8,650	PEOPLE'S REPUBLIC OF CHINA 3,767	INDIA 1,269	PAKISTAN	CEYLON & MALAYA 365	IRAN 629	SAUDI ARABIA 617	MONGOLIA 591	INDONESIA 576	ALL OTHERS 2,409	CHAD 466	MALI 465	NIGER 459	MAURITANIA 419	RHODESIA & NYASALAND TANGANYIKA ALL OTHERS 1,054		487 362 646	SUDAN 967	S. AFRICA 790	ALGERIA 91

EUROPE 3,850 ─── ─── ASIA 17,035 ─── ─── AFRICA 11,635 ─

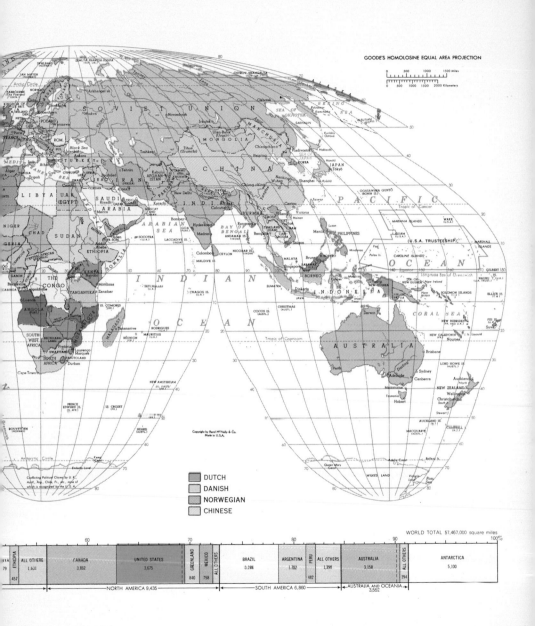

GOODE'S HOMOLOSINE EQUAL AREA PROJECTION

DUTCH
DANISH
NORWEGIAN
CHINESE

WORLD TOTAL 57,467,000 square miles

	ETHIOPIA 79	ALL OTHERS 1,631	CANADA 3,852	UNITED STATES 3,675	GREENLAND 840	MEXICO 758	ALL OTHERS	BRAZIL 3,286	ARGENTINA 1,702	PERU 482	ALL OTHERS 1,390	AUSTRALIA 3,158	ALL OTHERS 394	ANTARCTICA 5,100

NORTH AMERICA 9,435 ─── SOUTH AMERICA 6,860 ─── AUSTRALIA and OCEANIA 3,552

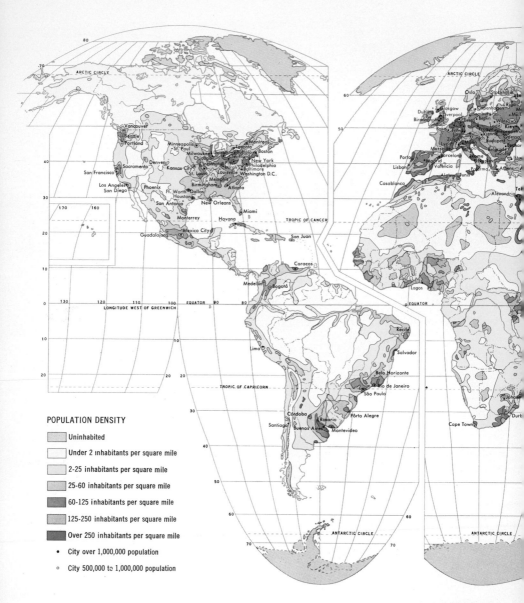

POPULATION DENSITY

- Uninhabited
- Under 2 inhabitants per square mile
- 2-25 inhabitants per square mile
- 25-60 inhabitants per square mile
- 60-125 inhabitants per square mile
- 125-250 inhabitants per square mile
- Over 250 inhabitants per square mile
- • City over 1,000,000 population
- ° City 500,000 to 1,000,000 population

**POPULATION
OF THE WORLD**

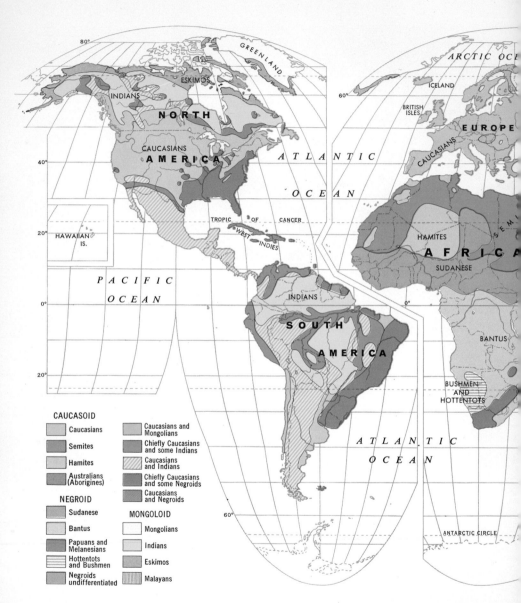

CAUCASOID

Caucasians

Semites

Hamites

Australians
(Aborigines)

NEGROID

Sudanese

Bantus

Papuans and
Melanesians

Hottentots
and Bushmen

Negroids
undifferentiated

Caucasians and
Mongolians

Chiefly Caucasians
and some Indians

Caucasians
and Indians

Chiefly Caucasians
and some Negroids

Caucasians
and Negroids

MONGOLOID

Mongolians

Indians

Eskimos

Malayans

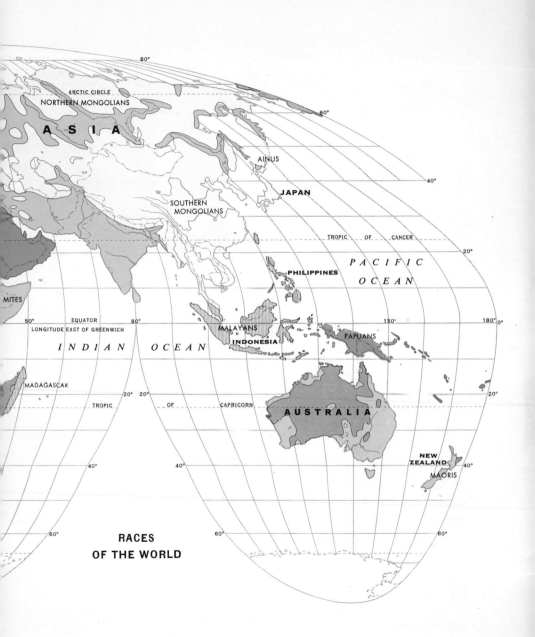

RACES
OF THE WORLD

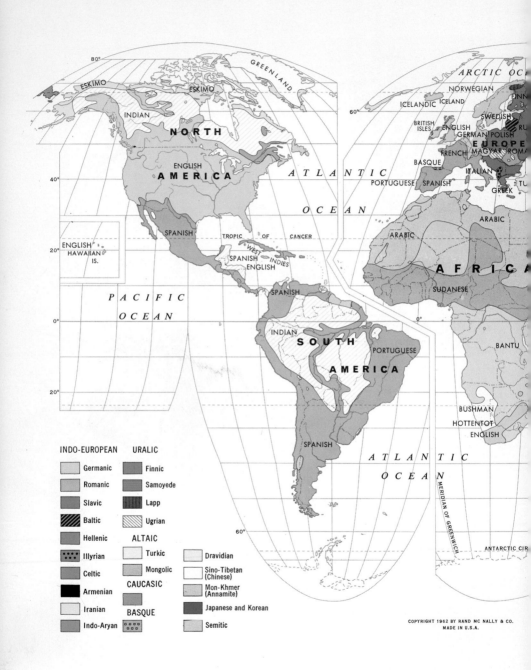

INDO-EUROPEAN

Germanic
Romanic
Slavic
Baltic
Hellenic
Illyrian
Celtic
Armenian
Iranian
Indo-Aryan

URALIC

Finnic
Samoyede
Lapp
Ugrian

ALTAIC

Turkic
Mongolic

CAUCASIC

BASQUE

Dravidian
Sino-Tibetan (Chinese)
Mon-Khmer (Annamite)
Japanese and Korean
Semitic

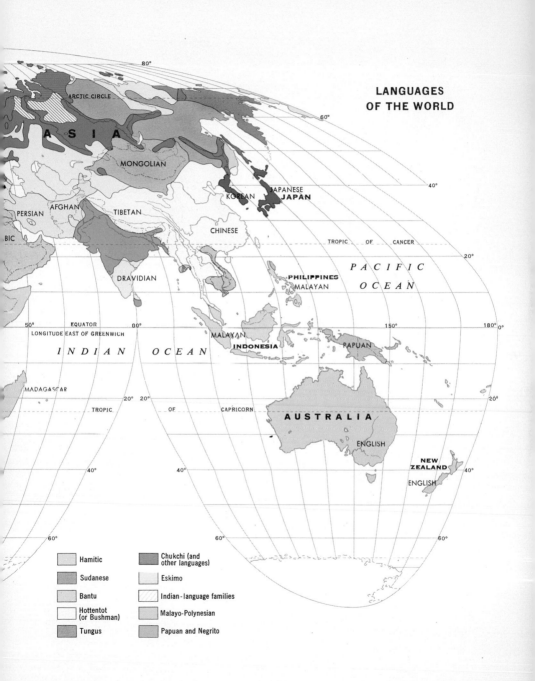

**LANGUAGES
OF THE WORLD**

	Hamitic		Chukchi (and other languages)
	Sudanese		Eskimo
	Bantu		Indian-language families
	Hottentot (or Bushman)		Malayo-Polynesian
	Tungus		Papuan and Negrito

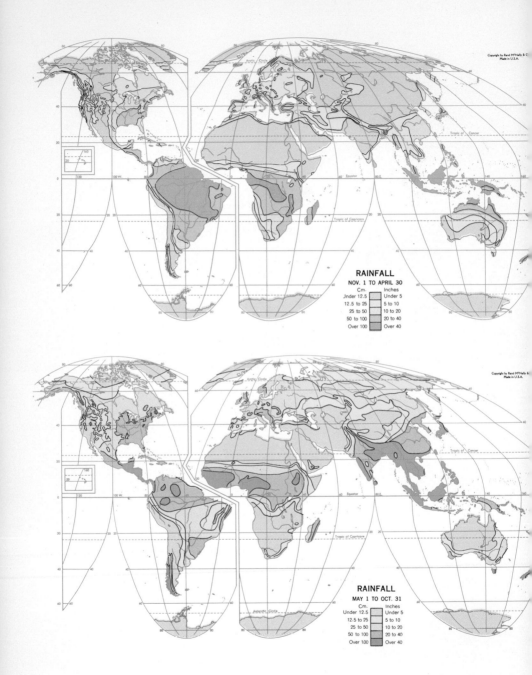

RAINFALL

NOV. 1 TO APRIL 30

Cm.	Inches
Under 12.5	Under 5
12.5 to 25	5 to 10
25 to 50	10 to 20
50 to 100	20 to 40
Over 100	Over 40

RAINFALL

MAY 1 TO OCT. 31

Cm.	Inches
Under 12.5	Under 5
12.5 to 25	5 to 10
25 to 50	10 to 20
50 to 100	20 to 40
Over 100	Over 40

THE EARTH & YOU

1 THE HOME OF MAN

Broad acres are a patent of nobility; and no man but feels more of a man in the world if he have a bit of ground that he can call his own. However small it is on the surface, it is four thousand miles deep; and that is a very handsome property.

CHARLES DUDLEY WARNER

Man lives in the thin skin of the earth. Below the surface of the earth rocks extend for almost four thousand miles to the earth's center. Man has penetrated less than two miles of this great distance, and what he knows about the depths beneath him he infers from the behavior of the earth, its gravity and the ways in which shock waves are propagated through it. Above him the atmosphere reaches out, becoming ever thinner and more difficult for him to breathe, for about two hundred miles. This he has explored with aircraft, balloons, and by direct observation. Beyond is space. Man reaches down into the earth for minerals and water; he rises above it in his tall buildings and in the controlled flight of aircraft. The span of his activity, from the deepest mines to the highest regular flights of aircraft, measures less than ten miles. This is the earth's skin, which is the concern of geographers and the chief subject of this book.

On the undulating surface of the globe, across and around its almost 197,000,000 square miles, where the earth and the atmosphere meet, man has made his home. His life is conditioned by both these elements. His roots, as it were, are put down into the earth. From the rocks he hews the stones for his building, and he extracts the minerals for his use. From the soil, a thin mantle covering the earth to a depth of at most a few feet, he grows his food. His well-being depends upon the content of the rocks and the soil. But man also moves in the atmosphere; he is enveloped by it. He is blown upon by the wind, rained upon, and scorched by the heat. His clothing, his home, his crops, his seedtime and harvest—all are adjusted to that layer of air, the atmosphere, which envelops him.

Mark Twain is said to have observed that everyone complains about the weather, but that no one does anything about it. It is true that this seems to be a one-way process; weather controls the man, and so far he has not learned to control the weather. He cannot hold back that mass of cold air that keeps pushing in from Canada; he cannot stop the frost that cuts off the citrus fruit in Florida or Texas or that grips the Russian rivers and puts a stop to navigation; and he cannot check the violent rainfall that floods the valleys or check the onset of the Indian Monsoon. But he does guard against them. Insulation and the furnace keep out the arctic cold; smudge pots spread a protective layer of smoke over the orange groves, and engineers build dams and straighten and control the rivers so that they can handle the run-off from sudden and violent rains. The conditions imposed by earth and atmosphere cannot be changed, but man can, as it were, get around them.

At the same time that the atmosphere and earth condition and even control the broad features of human existence, they also interact one upon the other. The wind storm strips away the topsoil and distributes it far and wide; the rainstorm gullies the hillside, carrying mud down to the rivers and to the sea. The earth itself, rearing its surface up into great mountain ranges, presents barriers to the circulation of the atmosphere; it causes air to pile up, to form towering masses of cloud, and to empty rain down upon its surface. In this eternal triangle of earth, air, and man, each influences the others and is influenced by them.

Man by his ingenious devices—more and more ingenious as the years go by—makes himself as comfortable as he can in his home of land and air. By means of air-conditioning and central heating he now makes the least hospitable areas at least habitable. If it is too dry he pipes in water; if too wet he drains it. If the climate is too severe for the crops he regularly cultivates, the plant breeders produce something that grows quicker or ripens with less sunshine; and if the soil lacks minerals, he manufactures chemical fertilizers and makes up the deficiencies of nature.

Man has been modifying his environment ever since human history began, but there are limits to what he can do. He cannot lengthen the summer or shorten the winter; his efforts to make artificial rain have not

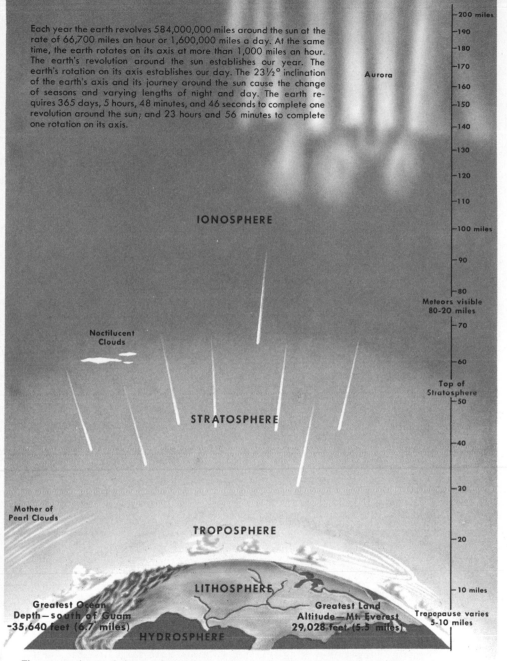

Each year the earth revolves 584,000,000 miles around the sun at the rate of 66,700 miles an hour or 1,600,000 miles a day. At the same time, the earth rotates on its axis at more than 1,000 miles an hour. The earth's revolution around the sun establishes our year. The earth's rotation on its axis establishes our day. The 23½° inclination of the earth's axis and its journey around the sun cause the change of seasons and varying lengths of night and day. The earth requires 365 days, 5 hours, 48 minutes, and 46 seconds to complete one revolution around the sun; and 23 hours and 56 minutes to complete one rotation on its axis.

Aurora

IONOSPHERE

Noctilucent
Clouds

STRATOSPHERE

Mother of
Pearl Clouds

TROPOSPHERE

LITHOSPHERE

Greatest Ocean
Depth—south of Guam
-35,640 feet (6.7 miles)

Greatest Land
Altitude—Mt. Everest
29,028 feet (5.5 miles)

HYDROSPHERE

—200 miles
—190
—180
—170
—160
—150
—140
—130
—120
—110
—100 miles
—90
—80
Meteors visible
80-20 miles
—70
—60
Top of
Stratosphere
—50
—40
—30
—20
—10 miles
Tropopause varies
5-10 miles

The atmosphere of the earth reaches up to two hundred miles through the troposphere, the dense air in which we live, on through the rarefied air of the stratosphere which spreads out horizontally, and on through the highly rarefied air of the ionosphere, where molecules are partially ionized by the sun. Between the troposphere and the stratosphere is a band, the tropopause, which averages about six miles in depth. Its thickness is greater over the equator.

been conspicuously successful, and he has not been able to increase the total precipitation in dry lands. He cannot now guide the tornado, or control the hurricane, or remove mountains. For all his cleverness and ingenuity, in spite of all the technical advances in recent centuries, nature still controls man far more than man has been able to control nature. "There is a destiny that shapes our ends, rough-hew them as we will," and that destiny is compounded of air and land and water.

But let us be precise. Man has available for occupation less than a third of his home, for on the oceans and seas of the earth's surface he can establish no permanent abode. The land, 57,225,000 square miles of the earth's area, is only the higher surface of platforms of rock which rise from the floor of the sea and are separated from one another by the expanse of the oceans. Despite an occasional earthquake, these platforms are remarkably firm and stable. Riding on them, we travel through space at a speed of 66,700 miles per hour without a sensation of movement; only by looking at objects fixed in the sky—the sun and the stars—can we perceive the immensity of our movement.

The continents are built of rocks, rocks which derive from the interior of the earth—rocks of every degree of hardness and softness, of every texture and mineralogical composition. As the earth slowly cooled from a molten state, they began to take shape, a hard crust covering a still liquid interior. This crust thickened and hardened as the earth continued to cool. The wind blew over its bare, hard surface; rain began to fall upon it, and to flow down into its basins and hollows. The rock was gradually broken up, sorted out by wind and water, and laid down in layers, compacted, and again hardened into rock. Coarse, gritty sandstone, fine-grained, impervious clay were formed. Then life appeared: first, animal life in the seas, which left its material remains as fossils to show us what it was like and through what phases living creatures evolved; later, plant life appeared, growing rich and luxuriant in those primeval swamps. The wealth of living creatures in the sea gave rise to immense accumulations of their dead remains on the sea floor, and these, hardened and compacted, produced man's limestones and marbles. The plant growth, dying and sinking into the swamps, gave man his peat, lignite, and coal in all their varieties. Organic remains, half-animal and half-plant, scattered through the beds of sand and clay, decomposed, disintegrated, and produced petroleum and natural gas.

Far below the solid platforms of rock the interior of the earth remains hot. Pressures build up many miles below the surface, to be relieved by some form of volcanic action. The semimolten mass, of which the deep interior of the earth is made, is squeezed upward through cracks in the overlying crust, toward the surface. Sometimes it flows out as a mass of red-hot lava, pouring down the slopes of Mauna Loa in Hawaii and making the sea boil; sometimes dropping down the flanks of Etna in Sicily, engulfing the lemon groves; sometimes exploding catastrophically, spreading ash and dust into the air to scorch and burn a little town like St. Pierre in Martinique or to bury and preserve the classical Pompeii and Herculaneum. The volcano is perhaps the most terrifying of all the more violent manifestations of nature. But in southern Italy, when Vesuvius has been belching smoke and dust, you may see an Italian farmer, small shovel and brush in hand, sweeping this fine dust from the road to put around the roots of his vines. Volcanic dust does wonders to the soil, and even a volcanic eruption has its positive sides.

Most volcanic activity, however, has been within not upon the surface of the earth. Molten rock has been injected into the crust, often lifting it just as a blister is lifted on one's finger. The crust is stretched and shattered in the process and is later readily stripped away. The earth's surface is dotted with bold forms of such rock masses. Usually they are of granite, a hard, crystalline, brightly colored rock, that lends an impression of stability to banks and public buildings. But such internal activities are not limited to the outpouring of rock in these immense quantities. Liquids and gases percolate upward through the myriads of tiny cracks and fissures that have opened in the crust. Sometimes the fissures are several feet wide, sometimes only a minute fraction of an inch. These fluids cool quickly as pressures force them upward and they solidify on the walls of these cracks. Often the fluids have nothing of value; sometimes they contain the ores of gold, silver, copper, lead, zinc, tin, and of the whole range of metalliferous minerals. The deposits on the walls of the wide cracks have provided man with the veins and lodes of mines.

Above the platforms of rock on which man lives lies the atmosphere, reaching outward into space, becoming ever more thin and diffuse, always in motion. "The wind bloweth where it listeth," and there seems little pattern or regularity in the turbulence of the atmosphere. Climate and weather have so far been inescapable and almost unpredictable.

The movement of the atmosphere is due in part to the spin of the earth on its axis, slowing the direction of the wind. But mainly it is caused by the sun, by the heating, expansion, and rising of the air here; the cooling, contraction, and sinking of the air there. The day-to-day,

hour-to-hour changes of the weather spring from this turbulence in the atmosphere: the majestic procession of the clouds; the towering white cumulus of summer, sharp-edged against the deep blue space beyond; the low, gray, broken clouds that scud along, spitting rain, as a front passes; the thin, filmy, translucent clouds which turn the sky a pale yellow and warn of bad weather to come; the splendor of sunrise and sunset, as scattered clouds are lit up like flames or thrown into purple shadows; the cold, clear nights of winter, when the temperature drops, and frost penetrates the soil. This ever changing pageant of the weather is part of the physical setting amid which we live.

Climate is defined as the average of weather: in the Midwest cold, snowy Januarys alternating with hot, humid Julys and mild dry days of fall when the leaves crisp and redden. Climate is what we expect, but weather is what we get. Central heating and antifreeze in the radiator, air-conditioning and the sleeping porch are geared to the extremes of

weather and climate. There are many crops that could stand a given climate if it were not for the weather. If a region experienced its average temperatures, and if it received its average rainfall, all would be well; the farmer would know what to grow and when to sow and harvest. It is the unpredictable extremes of weather that make life hard.

In the United States cotton is grown just about as far north as the farmer can be sure of growing it. Only a little farther north he may still be lucky, or he might get one of those late frosts in May that end his crop for that year. The heart of the Corn Belt is Iowa and Illinois, but corn is also grown in Wisconsin and Minnesota; in a hot summer it does well this far north, but in a cool, dry summer the farmer has to take a loss. In England farmers may plant their potatoes before the risk of frost is over, and be obliged sometimes to cover them with straw. As climate and weather influence man, forming an inescapable condition of his existence, so does he try to moderate their extremes, adjusting himself to them, sometimes playing the game of chance where he cannot adapt them to his needs, for man's success in controlling climate has its limits.

Another interplay in the triangle of geography is that represented by the mutual influence of the atmosphere and the earth. From the time when rain first fell on the earth these two have interacted. The rain has gathered to form small streams and these have joined to make rivers, which have flowed down to the sea. The wind, blowing over the face of the oceans takes back what the rivers have given, and precipitates it once again over the land. This endless cycle of cloud, rain, river, ocean, and evaporation performs work as it accomplishes its course.

Before me as I write is a muddy stream, flowing through its small valley, etched gently into this rolling Indiana countryside. At most times of the year it is brown or yellow, discolored by the burden which it is carrying. Fine particles of silt, of soil, clay, or rock waste, stripped from the fields of the Midwest, are diffused through it. Some may be dropped by the current along the river's bank; some may get lodged among the reedy undergrowth along the Ohio; they may be laid down by the river in flood over the bottom lands of Mississippi or Arkansas. But these will be only temporary resting places. Sooner or later the particles will again be gathered by the river and carried majestically down the Mississippi, out through the channels at its mouth, to be dropped at last on the outer margin of its delta. A particle of soil from the slope below my home may thus, perhaps quickly, perhaps after a period of many years, help to advance the shore line of Louisiana into the Gulf of Mexico, to extend the area of the United States, and, in doing so, to lower its altitude.

For many thousands of years this little stream has been slowly deepening its bed, using small stones and sand as tools with which to cut away the rock over which it flows. Both the tools which it uses and the minute particles of rock and clay which it cuts loose are carried away toward the sea. As the valley is deepened, the gentle slopes on each side are lowered by the run-off of soil with the rain water. A violent rainstorm may show some measurable result on the slope of the land and in the course of the stream, but to most of us fifty years of change reveal no alteration in the contours. Yet change there is: slow, imperceptible change, as the high land is worn away and silt is spread out over the flood-plains of the great valleys and is laid down to claim new land from the sea.

The deltas of the Mississippi, Niger, Ganges, and Nile were formed in this way. Gradually, as their level is raised, the newly made land is reclaimed and brought under cultivation. The bottom lands of the Mississippi, the Plain of Lombardy, the great plains of northern India and China were once deltas.

Not even the Rocky Mountains are permanent. Very slowly and unnoticed the material of which they are built is slipping away down the Colorado or the Missouri. One day they will become worn down to rolling hills, like the Ozarks. If any one doubts the capacity of a river to erode the earth's surface and transport it, let him look at the Grand Canyon. Enough rock has been removed by the action of this one river in ten to twelve million years—a period of time that a geologist would call short—to fill up Lake Superior and to turn it into flat cropland. There is something awe-inspiring in the immensity of the erosion process, carried on with slow deliberation through the whole duration of geological time.

These processes are so slow, you may say, that they scarcely affect us. What is a fraction of an inch of topsoil in a human lifetime? And although the soil is continuously being eroded and carried away, it is also continuously being created by the disintegration of the rock below, the breakdown of soil minerals, the growth of plants and their decay to form humus. In nature there is a balance; new soil is formed as old soil is worn away. The sea eats away at the coast line, causing cliffs to crumble, and it also distributes the rock waste, building up new land. But this balance is easily upset. The vegetation cover, grassland or forest, serves as a kind of regulator; cut down the trees, plow up the grassland, and the brake is released, and simple, normal erosion attains what we may call epidemic proportions, described so aptly by Archibald MacLeish:

> *Under our feet and our hands the land leaves us. . . .*
> *Worked out corn fields where the soil has left us*
> *Silent and secret; coloring little streams:*
> *Riling in yellow runnels after rainfall:*
> *Dribbling from furrow down into furrow and down into*
> *Fields fallow with winter and on down—*
> *Falling away to the rivers and on down*
> *Taking life with it. . . .*

Yes, nature sets limits to what man may do with the land; go beyond these limits and the land vanishes. It is for the geographer to hold out a warning light, and to say: Here it is too dry to plow—this is grazing land. Here it is too steep—keep the land under trees and their roots will

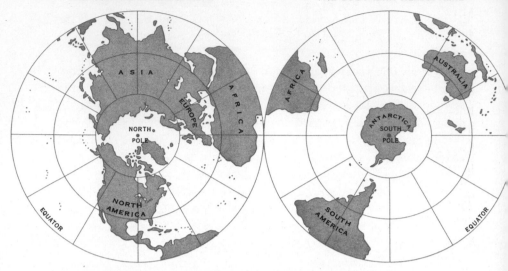

THE NORTHERN HEMISPHERE   **THE SOUTHERN HEMISPHERE**

Polar projections of the Northern and Southern Hemispheres show that a relatively greater proportion of land occurs in the Northern Hemisphere.

bind the soil together. Here are minerals—extract them so that the land is not ruined for other purposes. Do not always do with the land what seems profitable at the moment. Use it so that it will survive, for the land is not merely a priceless heritage; it is the source of life itself.

Nature does not recognize man's division of the earth into hemispheres, continents, or countries. Natural forces, operating at one point, influence all. Man cannot isolate himself from them, just as he cannot shut out the cold air that blows from the Arctic in winter, or cut off the supply of warm water to northwestern Europe. Crop failure in India, famine or flood in China, plant disease in the cacao plantations of Ghana are not merely local occurrences, of concern only to those directly affected. No natural disaster is limited in its results to one area.

And man's activities are not limited in their consequences to the geographical region where he lives and works. Unemployment in a mining town in Scotland, or the rise of a new industry in the American South in some degree affects everyone. The consequences in increased or diminished production and demand can be felt and measured. The building up of industry in India, the neglect of plantations in the Congo, the elaboration of synthetic and substitute materials in laboratory and factory have their repercussions everywhere. Every advance and every loss is like a stone thrown into a pond. Ripples spread outward, becoming ever smaller, but not disappearing until they reach its banks. Ours is, in Wendell Willkie's phrase, "one world," and no man can escape his dependence upon each and every part of it.

The moral of this is that every overcrowded West Indian island, every poverty-stricken village in India, every mineral deposit that goes unused, every acre of cropland that lies untilled, and every gullied hillside in the world, is mankind's business. "No man is an island, entire of itself; every man is a piece of the continent, a part of the main; if a clod be washed away by the sea, Europe is the less, as well as if a promontory were, as well as if a manor of thy friends or of thine own were; any man's death diminishes me, because I am involved in mankind; and therefore never send to know for whom the bell tolls; it tolls for thee."

2 THE FACE
OF THE EARTH

There rolls the deep where grew the tree
O earth, what changes hast thou seen!
There where the long street roars, hath been
The stillness of the central sea

Alfred Tennyson

Take one of those fine clear days of summer; climb a small hill and look out in each direction to the distant horizon. You can almost see the earth's surface curving away from you in the distance, dipping with its curvature out of sight. If it is a really good day and your view is not much obstructed by hills nearby, your eye might take in three or four hundred square miles, just about one-hundred-thousandth part of the populated land surface of the globe. And yet this would be a very much smaller fraction of the world's surface, for most of its 196,940,400 square miles is not land at all. The oceans and seas cover nearly three-quarters of it—73 per cent of its surface to be exact. And of that 27 per cent which lies above the sea, a part is deeply covered by ice, and in yet another fraction the temperature scarcely ever rises above freezing. We are all crowded onto less than one fifth of the earth's surface, for the deserts as well as the icecap can support no regular inhabitants.

As we have seen, the relationship of land and sea, however, is not constant. All around the coasts the sea is either eroding the cliffs, breaking them down by the impact of its waves and distributing the debris over the sea floor, or building up fresh land by its accumulation of silt, sand, and gravel. The silt brought down by every river ultimately drops to the sea floor. The past erosion of the mountains has created land for

47

millions to settle on and cultivate today. And this process continues still at its own slow, deliberate pace, wearing away the land here, adding to it there.

THE CONTINENTS

What sort of home does the land surface of the earth provide us? We customarily think of it as divided into continents. We usually count six of them: the two Americas, Africa, Europe, Asia, and Australia; and to these we add, as a kind of extra, the ice-covered land of Antarctica. We commonly think of the continents as separate, distinct from one another, as if one might have one policy for one continent, and a different policy for another.

Yet these divisions are arbitrary. North and South America appear clear-cut enough, though they are joined by Central America. Africa is joined to the rest of the Old World only by a narrow neck of land north of the Gulf of Suez, and this is now cut through by a canal. But the division between Europe and Asia is wherever you choose to put it. The traditional line of division follows the Ural Mountains, and then the Ural River to the Caspian Sea, but the Soviet Union, through which this imaginary boundary runs, knows no such division. Europe is in fact a peninsula stretching westward from the land mass of Asia.

It is also difficult to separate Australia from Asia. Between the two extends the immense island group which makes up Indonesia and New Guinea. These islands lie like closely spaced steppingstones, each one visible from the next, all the way from Southeast Asia to the coast of Australia. The biologist, Alfred R. Wallace, drew a line through the islands to separate the fauna and the flora that seemed to be typically Australian from those peculiar to Asia. But Wallace's line has not been a convenient division for other purposes, and has never been followed by the boundaries of political control. It is more convenient to say that New Guinea belongs geographically to Australia, which anyway controls half of it politically, and Indonesia to Asia.

The continents within their conventional boundaries are very unequal in size. Asia is the largest with about 30 per cent of the world's land surface; Australia the smallest, with only 5 per cent. And the size of a continent does not seem to bear any close relation to its population. Asia has well over half the human race within its limits; Australia has less than half of one per cent of all mankind. Crowded lands like the plains

On the familiar Mercator projection the six continents of the world can be viewed in their relative latitude (distance from the equator). Distortion increases away from the equator in this type of projection. Note the relative size of Antarctica, sometimes considered a seventh continent.

of India, and empty lands like the plateau of Tibet, lie side by side. Could the population not be spread a little more evenly? Must there be such congestion in parts of Asia; such wide, empty spaces in other parts, as well as in Australia and South America? On the answer to that question hangs the future of mankind on this earth of ours.

The continents are strangely spread over the surface of the globe. The North Pole is in the midst of an ocean; the South Pole occurs in Antarctica; but more than two-thirds of the land surface actually lies to the north of the equator. The Arctic Ocean is ringed with land: the North American, Asian, and European continents. Only Australia lies wholly to the south of the equator, although more than two-thirds of South America and over a third of Africa also lie south of it. An immense ocean, the Pacific, covering almost half the total surface of the globe, separates the Americas from Asia and Australia.

Several of the continents have a peculiar shape, tapering toward the south. South America looks as if it could be fitted, jigsaw fashion, into the west coast of Africa.

How did this pattern of continents and oceans originate? It was once supposed that the continents were formed by the break-up during an earlier geological time of a vast continent, the fragments of which drifted into their present positions. In this way has been explained the peculiar "fit" of South America into the west coast of Africa. If the continents did, in fact, drift in this way, we may ask ourselves are they still moving and what gigantic forces are there to propel them?

Answers to such questions can at best be conjectural. We just do not yet know enough about what lies only a few miles beneath our feet. It is hard to believe that continents do not move, for how otherwise can we explain the folding of the strata? Yet it is difficult to believe that the continents once formed a single land mass which broke up, like an ice floe in the polar seas, allowing the fragments to drift apart to form the continents as we know them. But unless we admit that there has been a quite extensive movement of the land masses, how can we explain the beds of coal—which are formed in humid, tropical forests—in icy Spitsbergen (Svalbard) or Antarctica; or oil in northern Canada? These questions are at the basis of physical geography, yet we cannot give firm answers to any of them. They excite our curiosity, they attract the attention of scientists, and one day we shall know the answers to them.

About the less fundamental matters of the components of continents and how their surfaces have been fashioned, we know a very great deal. No doubt in time we shall push the boundaries of the known back until we have revealed the origin of the continents and even of this earth.

THE SEAS AND OCEANS

We think of the continents as limited by the sea coast. This, however, is not so. Beyond the coast line the land slopes very gently for varying distances beneath the sea. It forms, in fact, an almost level plain until it reaches a depth of 600 feet, or 100 fathoms below the sea. Here its gradient steepens, and in a few miles its surface drops to the great depths of the ocean. This slope—known as the continental slope—is the real perimeter of the continents. The gently descending sea floor which reaches from the coast out toward the edge of the slope is the continental shelf, which ends abruptly most everywhere. It is as if the oceans were too full, and their water had overflowed the margins of the continents. If we could miraculously evaporate the seas and lower their surface by about 600 feet, then we should see the true margin of the continents.

The deep floor of the ocean lies at a depth of from 20,000 to 30,000 feet. Oozes, the remains of sea creatures, and dust that falls upon the ocean surface and slowly sinks accumulate here. It is dark on the ocean floor and there is little life. The immense pressure of the water restricts the varieties of life and has so far made it impossible for man himself to descend to these depths except with the aid of the Bathyscaphe.

The floor seems to be fairly level. Only rarely is it interrupted by rocky pinnacles which reach steeply upward to break, maybe, the surface of the Pacific Ocean, and wear a crown of coral with a tuft of palm trees. "Deeps" even more rarely sink below these immense plains of the ocean floors. The deepest point in the oceans, so far located, is the Challenger Deep, a narrow trench to the south of Guam, in the Pacific Ocean, which is known to reach a depth of 35,640 feet, nearly seven miles. Several such trenches are found close to Japan, Formosa, and the Philippine Islands. The mountains of Japan rise to over 12,000 feet above sea level. Only 160 miles away lies the Japan Trench, nearly 30,000 feet below the level of the sea. Between these two points the crust of the earth rises about 43,000 feet, an average gradient steeper than one in twenty, enough to make the surface rocks unstable and to contribute to the frequency of earthquakes.

Continental shelves vary greatly in width. Off Newfoundland, Argentina, and northwest Europe, they extend for 300 miles, and even more. From them rise groups of islands, like the Falkland Islands and the Hebrides. Off the coast of Southeast Asia the shelf underlies the South China Sea, and the islands of Indonesia and the Philippines rise from

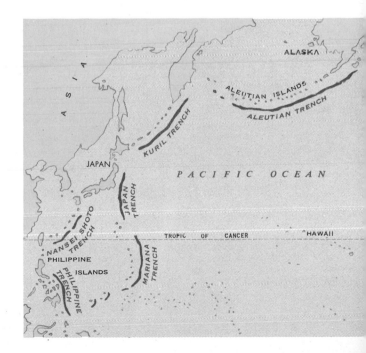

Some of the trenches of the Pacific. The Challenger Deep, lying south of Guam, in the Mariana trench, is the deepest.

its shallow depths. Along the coast of California and the west coast of South America the shelf is rarely more than 25 miles wide.

The presence of a shelf is important to the neighboring land. Most of the edible species of fish live in its shallow water; many of them breed and some live their lives close to the sea bed. The waters of the shelf, especially where there are "banks" at only a shallow depth beneath the surface, are thus the most important ocean fisheries. Advances in the study of the oceans show that it may some day be possible to extend the fisheries to areas of the oceans very far from land and even from the shelves, but today the Grand Banks of Newfoundland, the shallow waters around Iceland and the British Isles, along the Norwegian coast, and between the Japanese islands and the mainland of Asia are among the world's most important fishing grounds.

The shelves are important in another way: they belong to the continents, they are a continuation of the continents. And whatever the continents contain by way of minerals, they also are likely to contain. In September, 1945, President Truman turned geologist. "The continental shelf," he proclaimed, "may be regarded as an extension of the land mass of the coastal nation" and may contain "a seaward extension of a pool or deposit lying within the territory. . . ." In short, the oil fields of Texas, of Venezuela, of Arabia may, and probably do, extend out beneath the sea as far as the continental shelf itself extends. And President Truman went on to insure that the United States has first claim on all the resources that may be in the shelf around its shores. This principle, that every nation has the prior right to whatever minerals may occur in the continental shelf which borders its coast, has since 1958 been incorporated in the body of international law.

We know a good deal about the continental shelf; it is shallow enough to be inspected and for geologists to put down bores in search of minerals. But of the ocean floor we have little direct knowledge. We believe that the ocean floor is almost level for great distances, and we believe that it is floored with rock material that is denser than that which composes the continents. It is as if the continents were floating rafts, in a sea of this heavier rock. Over half the earth's surface is made up in this way; and this unknown half, that has never known the foot of man, appears to offer nothing for his use.

The continental slope is the real margin of the continents; it separates the lands and the shallow seas from the deep ocean floor. But the relationship of land and sea has not been always constant. Even in recent geo-

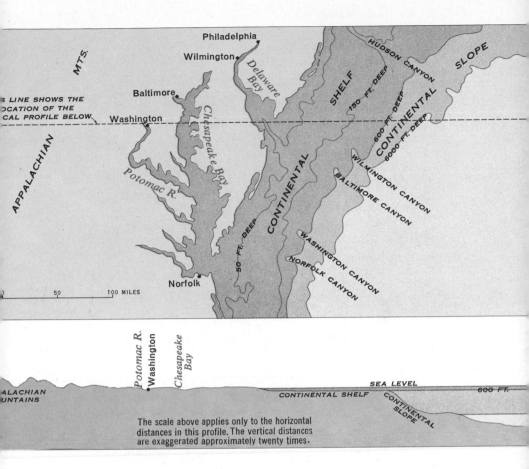

The scale above applies only to the horizontal distances in this profile. The vertical distances are exaggerated approximately twenty times.

logical times—since the advent of man upon the earth—there have been great fluctuations. Not only have the continents themselves been unstable, rising and sinking slightly like a raft from which weights have been removed and replaced, but the volume of water in the sea has also varied. There are many factors in these movements and changes, but the most important of them has been the formation and then the melting away of vast sheets of ice over parts of the land. The ice sheets depressed the continental rafts under their weight and, at the same time, lowered the level of the oceans and seas by abstracting water from them. As the ice sheets slowly melted away, the previous relationship was in time more or less restored. Around many of the coasts are evidences in "raised beaches" of the times when the sea stood higher in relation to the land than it does now, and buried beneath the waves is the evidence of lower sea levels than those which we now know.

The oceans and seas are in constant motion. Waves are driven by the wind across their surface. Their level rises and falls with the tide, and everywhere the water is in slow movement as currents carry masses of water from one area of the sea to another. We shall return in the next chapter to a consideration of these movements within the waters that cover nearly three-quarters of the surface of the globe.

THE SURFACE OF THE LAND

The complexity of land forms assumed by the surfaces, the continents, defies description. Yet we must find some order in the apparently chaotic pattern of hill and valley, mountain, plateau, and plain.

Mount Everest is high, the highest mountain in the world. With a pretension to accuracy the surveyors say that it soars 29,028 feet above the level of the sea. But this is short of the greatest depths of the ocean. An old wives' tale perpetuates the belief that the ocean is like the continents in reverse, that the heights of the mountains would fit neatly into the holes in the ocean floor. This is not so. All the mountains of the world would not suffice to fill in the few deeps there are. In contrast with the floor of the oceans, which is fairly level and regular, the surface of the land is highly irregular. Ranges of mountains are festooned across it. Between areas of lowland, many of them created from the silt laid down by the rivers, are plateaulike areas, neither plain nor mountain. Our key to the unraveling of the pattern of the land lies in the history of its formation.

The immense span of geological time was interrupted at intervals by intense movements of the earth's crust; the rocks were folded and piled upon one another, and the mountain ranges were built. During the intervening periods of geological calm, sediments accumulated in the shallow seas and were compacted and hardened before being folded during the next period of more violent movement. During each of the long periods of quiet, the mountains built during the preceding earth movements were slowly worn down as rivers and ice combined to lower their summits, gouge out their flanks, and spread the rock waste over the plains and the sea floor. The oldest mountains have been worn down so that only their flattened stumps remain, but written into the rocks is the evidence of their violent history of accumulation, folding, and erosion.

Today these oldest rocks, created perhaps a billion years ago, make up

In the first stage of mountain building alternating layers of hard and soft sedimentary rock were folded and fractured into high mountain ranges.

the rolling plains of Siberia and the Canadian North, the low plateau of western Australia, the higher, rougher, and more fractured plateaus of Africa, the Middle East, Tibet, and Mongolia, the highlands of Brazil and Guiana, and the Deccan plateau of the Indian Peninsula. They are smoothed and flattened, hardened by the pressures to which they have been exposed for hundreds of millions of years; they were faulted or fractured by the shock of subsequent movements of the crust, and intruded by igneous rocks and mineral lodes. These are not rugged or mountainous areas; their aspect is gentle and mature, as befits the oldest parts of the earth's surface.

The mountains that were piled up in the later movements have been worn down to a very much smaller degree, and some of them remain more conspicuously mountainous. They include the Appalachian Mountains, the mountains of New England and of the Ozarks, which were folded about one hundred sixty million years ago. In Europe they include the modest mountains of Scotland and Ireland, the more rugged coast line of Norway, and the hills of central France and Germany; in Asia, the Ural Mountains of Russia and the mountains of Central Asia such as the Hindu Kush and Tien Shan; in Australia, the Great Dividing Range that borders the Pacific. Nevertheless it is not always possible to tell merely from the look of the land the age of the rocks and the geological period when they were folded. The forces of erosion work faster in some areas than in others, and more easily in softer rocks than in hard, wearing some down to a rolling peneplain, while others remain hilly or even mountainous.

But the low mountains and hills which remain from earlier mountain-building periods are insignificant beside those created by the most recent. This movement which occurred about fifty million years ago affected every continent. It raised the highest mountains of the North American continent: the Rocky Mountains, the Sierra Nevada, the Cascades, and the Coast Range. The mighty wrinkles which this movement produced stretch all the way round the earth: from the Rockies southward through the mountains of Mexico, the Andes of South America, and into the Antarctic continent. From Alaska they stretch out across Asia; they envelop Tibet, Iran, and Turkey. In the high Himalayas they separate China from India, and they reach through the Carpathians and Alps, the Apennines and Pyrenees of Europe into the Atlas Mountains of North Africa. Branches from the mountains of Asia provide the skeleton around which are clustered the lands of Southeast Asia, and they are continued through the island festoons of Japan, Indonesia, and New Zealand.

These, the most recently created of mountains, are also the highest, the most spectacular and, in their influence on human affairs, the most important. Reaching high above the surrounding lowlands, they make their own climate; they influence profoundly the organization and economics of those societies which live among them. They obstruct human movement, they separate cultures, and they protect from invasion or attack. Capped with snow for much of the year, their upper valleys occupied by glaciers, they nourish the world's greatest rivers; they are a source of almost unlimited hydroelectric power; they are a resort of the skier and the climber.

Long before their building had been completed, the mountains were beginning to be destroyed. James Hutton wrote in 1795, "The ruins of the old land furnished the materials of the new." The rocks of which they were composed were shattered by the action of frost, of wind, of moving ice and water, and their particles have been carried slowly away to lower ground and to the sea. Most powerful of the agents of transportation have been the rivers. They have done the most both to erode the mountains and to carry the rock fragments away. But in this they have been powerfully assisted by the action of ice. At some time ice has filled the valleys of most high mountains, forming glaciers, and even during the last Ice Age it spread out as ice sheets over nearby lowlands.

As we have seen, the work of rivers goes on almost everywhere over the land. Frost and drought slow down its work only seasonally. Without ceasing, mountain torrents cascade down from the heights, with the power not only to turn the blades of a turbine but also to move boulders and to deepen and widen their beds. In their lower and slower courses the rivers often flow brown with the silt to which they have, by their slow attrition, reduced the coarser material of their upper courses. At last

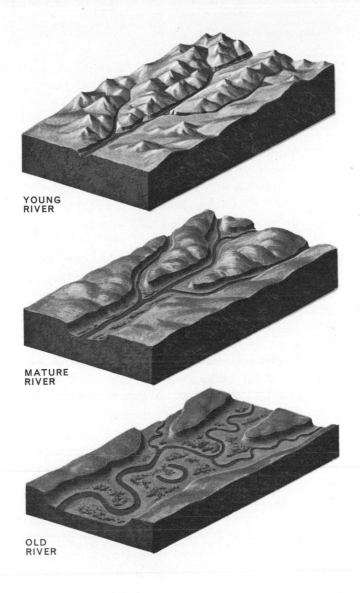

YOUNG
RIVER

MATURE
RIVER

OLD
RIVER

Young rivers flow swiftly, with rapids and waterfalls, through narrow, steep-walled valleys. Mature rivers course through wide deep valleys, marked by gentle slopes. Old rivers wend their way along broad, flat valley floors created by the deposit of the rivers' sediment. River valleys develop these characteristics in relation to the degree of the land's resistance to erosion. Often a long river will pass through all three stages as it flows from its source.

the material removed by erosion from the mountains and hills is laid down and goes to build the plains. Some is deposited along the lower courses of the rivers, where flood waters spread out over the land and, retreating, leave each time a thin veneer of silt behind; the rest makes its way to the sea and is dropped to build up islands in the river's delta and thus to extend the area of the land.

Around the margins of the continents alluvial plains, built from the silt brought down by rivers from the hills and mountains, are continuously being built forward—by the Mississippi into the Gulf of Mexico; by the Nile and Po into the Mediterranean; by the Tigris and Euphrates into the Persian Gulf; by the Indus and Ganges into the Indian Ocean; by the great Chinese rivers into the Pacific; and by thousands of smaller rivers everywhere. The plains which they create are made up of fine-grained materials which form a deep and generally fertile soil. The rivers which created the plains are used, where necessary, to provide water to irrigate them.

Some alluvial plains, like the great plain of the Amazon River in South America, are damp, ill-drained, and jungle-covered. Others, like those of the lower courses of the Indus, the Tigris and Euphrates, and the Colorado, are ringed with desert so wide that their waters are insufficient to irrigate them. Yet others broaden northward from the northern forests across the tundra of Canada and the Soviet Union to the Arctic Ocean through a climate that is too severe for their alluvial soils to be cultivated. But most of the other plains like those of the Po and the Rhine in Europe, the Ganges, Irrawaddy, and Mekong in Southeast Asia, the Hwang Ho, Yangtze, and Si of China, and many others—are densely peopled and intensively cultivated. Where the right climate is combined with the deep, rich soil of the alluvial plains, there we find the densest populations on the face of the globe.

Between the high hills and the mountains on the one hand, and the plains on the other, are the hills and plateaus. Most of the earth's surface is made up of hills: the hills of New England and the Laurentians of Canada; the Allegheny Plateau and the Ozarks; the plateaus of Brazil, of southern India and interior China; the low rolling hills of Europe and the almost level plateaus of Africa and Australia. These intermediate areas between the mountains and the plains are former mountains that have been worn down; or they are rocks lifted by earth movement only a few hundreds of feet above the sea. They are all in process of being dissected and eroded by rivers.

On the map the pattern of tiny threadlike streams joining to make rivers, which join with one another to make even larger rivers, forms an intricate filigree. Where they have been active for a long period of time, for millions of years, the valleys are wide, shallow, with gentle slopes, like that of the Mississippi. Where erosion has been active for a shorter period, the valley is often deeper and its sides steeper, like the mining valleys of Pennsylvania or the canyons of the West. The shape of the valley depends upon many things besides the period of years that has gone into its creation: the nature of the rock in which it is cut, its hardness or softness, and whether it is made up of strata lying horizontally or folded; and the climate, the rainfall, the wash of the rock and soil from the sides of the valley, all help to shape it. No two valleys are ever quite the same because in no two places are quite the same conditions of rock, climate, and river flow encountered. The uniqueness of each place on the earth's surface, and, at the same time, its broad similarity to other places, are facts of geography that we must always recognize.

Incessantly, from the beginning of geological time until the present, the surface of the earth has been modified. Mountains have been worn down to mere rises along the horizon; the material torn from them by river and ice has been spread out to make new land, or laid down in shallow seas to form the material from which future mountains will be raised. At intervals volcanic activity raises a volcanic crater or spreads lava or volcanic dust over the land.

Around the coast the waves of the sea beat ceaselessly against the land, the same today as when atmospheric moisture first condensed to form pools of water on the surface of the new earth. The cliffs slowly crumble and retreat beneath their impact, sometimes so slowly where they are built of hard rocks that there is no change to be seen in the span of a lifetime; sometimes so swiftly in soft rocks that homes vanish over the edge to be engulfed by the sea below. The sea undercuts the cliffs, the rocks above collapse in a heap of stones and earth onto the beach below, and the waves sort it all out, washing away the finer, lighter material, slowly rounding the stones to gravel, and reducing the gravel to sand that they can transport and deposit somewhere else. The debris of the cliff here goes to build the beach, the sandbar, or the chain of low islands that protects the shore from the heavy ocean surf.

Where did the gravel and sand of Cape Hatteras off the Carolinas come from, or that long bar of sand that protects Florida from the Atlantic, or Sandy Hook, or the sandbars that still make the approaches difficult to the African continent? From cliffs near and far, where the waves beat against and slowly erode them. There have been islands that waves have completely truncated, cutting them off only a few feet below the ocean surface.

In tropical seas, especially in the South Pacific, the small coral polyp, after swimming freely in the ocean for the earlier part of its life, anchors itself to the rocky coast of an island. Here, in time, it dies leaving its small, limey skeleton. Coral polyps live only in warm seas, near enough to the surface for the rays of the sun to penetrate to them. Here they attach themselves in their millions to the hard remains of the countless generations of corals that went before them, building up fantastic, multi-colored, treelike forms, amid which lives the prolific sea life of the tropics.

Sometimes the reefs form irregular, rounded shapes, a perimeter which encloses a shallow lagoon to which access can be gained only through gaps, often narrow, in the enclosing wall of coral. This is the atoll, the typical coral island of the Pacific Ocean. The coral breaks up in time beneath the constant pounding of the sea to form a coral sand which is heaped up over the reef by the waves. It is a poor enough soil, but one in which palm trees and a few other plants can germinate and grow from seeds that come floating in on the current. Coral lives only in the clean, clear water of the ocean. It is not common along the tropical coasts of the continents, and is never found where rivers bring silt down to the sea to muddy waters and make them dark and turbid.

Dead coral sometimes become compacted and hardened to make a kind of limestone. On the sea floor, too, limestone is accumulating from the remains—skeletons and shells—of sea creatures. Sometimes the lime of which they are made is dissolved and redeposited as small grains, known, from their fancied resemblance to the roe of a fish, as "oolites"; sometimes they retain their original form, and survive as the familiar fossils, embedded amid the material in which they were laid down millions of years earlier.

ROCKS OF THE EARTH'S CRUST

All the rocks which make up the earth's crust were first formed in one of two ways. As molten rock they were either injected into the crust or poured out over its surface as lava which slowly flowed, and then cooled and solidified. Or they originated as deposits in lakes or on the floor of the sea, which in time were compacted, hardened, and lifted up to make land in the course of one of the periodic disturbances of the crust. And the second group derived originally from the first, for the earth was once a ball of molten or semimolten rock perhaps torn off from the sun, sterile, lifeless, and slowly cooling. As soon as moisture could condense on its surface, rivers carried loose materials down to the lakes and seas. The work of erosion began; sand and clay started to accumulate in the depressions, and after life had appeared, the remains of living creatures came to be preserved as fossils, and sometimes came even to compose the whole body of a rock.

The lavas gave man the granites and basalts and the whole range of igneous rocks. They cooled slowly and formed crystals. They differ from one another in the range of minerals of which they are composed, in their color, their hardness, and in the kind and richness of the soils to which they give rise. The granites yield a sterile soil but a hard ornamental building stone; the basalts weather down to form a better soil but are of little use for building. Igneous rocks are almost all hard. They form the core of many of the greatest mountain chains, and outcrop as the jagged crests of some of the highest ranges. The Sawtooth Mountains in Idaho and Mont Blanc in the Alps, the rugged Cuillins of Skye in Scotland, and the Tatra of Czechoslovakia are all of granite.

The sedimentary rocks were laid down by water and wind. They consist of sand, worn from the hard quartz of granite; of fine particles of clay produced by the disintegration of feldspar, another crystalline mineral which goes to make up the igneous rocks, and of other minerals; and of the remains of creatures which came, millions of years later, to live in the sea. Thus the sandstones, clays, and limestones were created. These rocks differ greatly in their hardness, in the quality of soil they yield, and in the uses which man can make of them. Limestone often produces hills, rounded and grass-covered, sometimes honeycombed by caves created by the percolating waters that drop downward from the surface. Clay is soft and easily eroded and carried away; it usually forms areas of lowland, often damp and poorly drained, for water lies long on the surface of the impermeable clay. Sandstone often stands up in the hills with bizarre rock forms, such as those in Bryce Canyon.

The earth has known many changes. Rocks of whatever origin have been compressed and fractured, folded, twisted, and hardened. Sometimes the process of hardening has been accompanied by physical changes in the rock itself. Soft clays may have become hardened by the pressures generated in the movements of the crust to give shale, or further compressed, their particles oriented all the same way, to make the hard slate, which splits easily into thin sheets. Limestone may be crystallized by the heat and pressure of earth movements to give marble. The grains of sandstone may fuse together to produce the hard, flintlike quartzite. Even in the igneous rocks themselves similar changes may be brought about. The minerals may be fused and recrystallized with the long axes of the crystals lying at right angles to the pressure. The smooth, silky schist and the coarser gneiss, both of them built of crystals, are the products of such changes. All the very old land masses, like the Canadian Shield, the mountains of Scandinavia, and the plateaus of India and South Africa are built up partly if not wholly of such altered or metamorphic rocks. They are always old and, hard as they are, have often been worn down to a rolling and gentle relief.

Over much of the land surface of the earth the qualities of the rock have a profound influence on the contours of the land. In the Appalachians and the Rockies almost every ridge and valley can be traced back to the relative hardness or softness of the rocks of which it is built. Across the plains the low hilly ridges or the flat-topped buttes and mesas owe their origin to the protection given by some outcrop of harder rock. Everywhere the geological map provides the most important key to the unraveling of the complex history of the earth's surface.

Among the organisms that died and sank to the floor of the sea or lakes and swamps were plants and minute organisms without shell or skeleton to survive in fossil form. From these derived the mineral fuels, which are today dug or pumped from the sedimentary rocks.

FUEL FOR POWER

About three hundred million years ago there grew vast swampy forests, perhaps like those found in the United States in Georgia or the Great Dismal Swamp of Virginia, though the trees were of different species. Mostly they were giant ferns. They grew, died, and collapsed into the swamp, where their remains hardened and were converted into black carbon, the coal deposits of today. The accumulation of plant remains was intermittent, punctuated by changes in the relative level of land and sea and by the deposition of beds of sand and clay. Hundreds of beds of coal were formed, ranging in thickness from a fraction of an inch to thirty feet or more. After their formation they were compressed

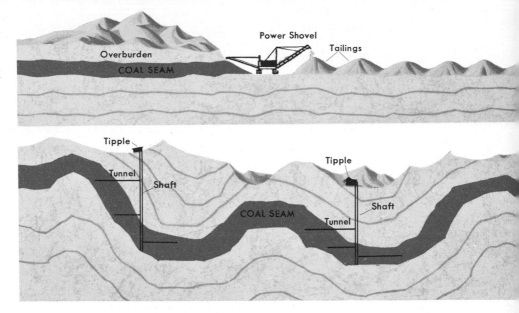

In strip-mining coal power machines remove the overburden and deposit it in tailings. In underground mining the tipple houses the necessary surface machinery.

by the great weight of overlying deposits, folded, fractured, and hardened.

The quality of a coal depends in part on the kinds of plant material from which it was made, in part on the degree of pressure to which it has been subjected. Anthracite or hard coal has usually been exposed to the greatest pressures; moisture and contained gases have been driven out, and what is left is almost pure carbon. It burns without smoke and gives out a great heat. It was excellent as bunker fuel in coal-burning ships and for central heating in big buildings. But oil and natural gas have put it out of business, and there is unemployment and distress in the hard-coal areas of Pennsylvania and the United Kingdom. Peat and brown coal, or lignite, have been least subjected to pressure. They contain a good deal of moisture, which reduces their value as fuel. Coking coal, so important in the iron-smelting industry is a coal which, when heated in a retort, yields a pure, firm, porous coke. This quality depends chiefly on its possession of just the right quantity of contained gas. The coals of western Pennsylvania, especially those around Connellsville, and of West Virginia have it. This coal is needed in increasing quantities, and the mining villages that produce it have not undergone the degree of depression of the hard-coal areas.

The quality of the coal restricts its usefulness; the thickness of the seams and the extent to which they have been folded and broken, or faulted, affect the ease with which it can be mined. In the valleys of West Virginia the seams of coal outcrop, or reach the surface, along the steep valley sides. The coal is mined from galleries driven into the hillside, brought to the mouth of the gallery and tipped down the hillside to waiting barges or freight cars. In Indiana or Illinois the seams lie level and only a few feet below the surface. Machines strip away the overlying soil and rock, scoop out the coal, and throw back the waste materials. In the Ruhr coal fields of northwest Germany, the seams lie at depths of up to four thousand feet. They are reached by vertical shafts, from which galleries run out to the working coal-face. Coal is hauled up the shaft to the surface and distributed to the consumer by freight car.

Only a minority of the countries of the world contain reserves of coal, and in many of these the coal is small in quantity and poor in quality. The occurrence of coal depends on the existence of rocks of the proper geological age, and even then there is the danger that the coal itself may mostly have been eroded away, as it has from over most of the Appalachian country. The world's production of coal is today almost two billion tons a year. Of this total more than three-quarters is supplied by only six countries:

China	420	United Kingdom	197
United States	392	West Germany	143
U.S.S.R.	375	Poland	104

(In millions of tons: figures for 1960)

These will remain the great producers. The majority of the countries which today produce none will never produce any. They do not have it in their geology to do so.

In the twenties and thirties of this century petroleum and natural gas began to displace coal. Oil and gas can be made to flow through pipes. They can be distributed more easily than coal; they can go to the factory, the factory need not come to them.

Oil and gas also derive from the remains of organisms. These, when they died and sank to the floor of the sea, were caught up and enclosed in the rocks that were gradually forming there. These organisms slowly decomposed, each to a minute particle of oily fluid. In porous rocks, like sandstones, the tiny droplets flowed and collected in pools. In impervious rocks, like shale, they remained as scattered particles, distributed through the rock. The geologist bores into the one, and if he is fortunate the oil is forced upward under its own pressures, and gushes out at the surface.

He quarries the other, the shale, and crushes it to an oily paste from which he extracts the oil.

Not infrequently the oily fluid of petroleum reserves evaporates within the rocks to produce natural gas. Sometimes the pressure of the gas forces the oil to the surface; usually the gas itself escapes into the air or is trapped and led away by pipe to serve industrial and domestic needs. Some natural gas occurs in all oil fields, but it is more common in some than in others. It is relatively unimportant in the Middle East, and very important in the oil fields of the American plains.

It is conceivable that all mineral resources of fuel will one day run out. Today there is coal for hundreds of years, and it does not seem as if we are going to need it; but future scarcity of other fuels may create a revival for it. Oil reserves, however, are more quickly exhausted. Through western Pennsylvania, where oil in North America was first discovered, the landscape is dotted with abandoned oil wells. Colombia, Trinidad, Burma, Indonesia, Romania, even the great Soviet oil fields of the Caucasus, have all declined in production. Future generations must reckon with the ultimate exhaustion of the world's supplies of mineral fuel. Nuclear power, you will say, will come to replace coal and oil. Already it is used for industrial power and on ships; soon it will be used for aircraft, perhaps also for automobiles. But fissionable uranium— the U-235 of the scientists—is also a mineral and it is among the rarer constituents of the earth's crust; its occurrence is highly localized and

A cross-section of Texas oil land shows typical subsurface formations in which oil is found—a pool atop a salt dome, another trapped in upthrust strata, one created by slippage along a fault line, another held in a sedimentary dome.

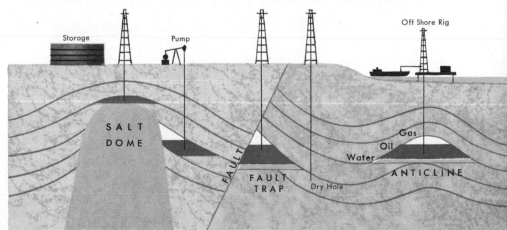

Storage   Pump   Off Shore Rig

SALT DOME

FAULT

FAULT TRAP

Dry Hole

Gas
Oil
Water

ANTICLINE

few of the known deposits appear to be large. It is possible that reserves of fissionable material may last for a very long time, but they, like coal and oil, are exhaustible too, and unless trade is developed in these materials, some countries are likely to be sadly short of what they may need.

This brings us back to where our ancestors started. Our earliest industrial power was the blowing wind and the running water. These will continue long after the others have been extracted, consumed, burned up, and dissipated as carbon dioxide into the atmosphere. There is immense power in the rivers as they descend from mountain to plain; in the tide as it flows and ebbs under the attraction of the moon and sun. Rivers are being used on an increasing scale; soon not a single river will be allowed to flow down to the sea without paying its toll of power to satisfy man's insatiable needs.

Today the Tennessee and the Missouri drop down by giant steps to the sea, each step a dam and a generator; little Alpine rivers that once cascaded down the mountain side, now flow unseen through steel pipes and between the blades of turbines; the Colorado River is ponded back between the chocolate-brown rocks of its canyon to provide a steady, high pressured flow to the generators set in Hoover Dam. These are models which the rest of the world tries to follow. The Kariba Dam on the Zambezi, the Aswan High Dam on the Nile, the Volta River Dam in Ghana, future dams on the Himalayan, Chinese, African, and Australian rivers will yield power for homes and factories. This will not be accomplished without problems—the supply of capital and skill and the technical problems of rivers drying up in summer and freezing in winter; but it will come. And when all the rivers are used, there still remain the tide and the wind.

METALS AND MINERALS

The old-time prospector knelt beside the small stream and panned the river sands for gold dust. He then traced the grains of gold back up the stream bed, up the mountain side to the spot where a vein or lode had through the centuries been slowly worn away, freeing particles of gold to slip down the hillside to the river. He then turned miner, and with drill and hammer cut into the vein, opened up a mine, floated a company, built ore-crushing and dressing equipment, and left his wealth to endow a philanthropic foundation. It has not all been as simple as

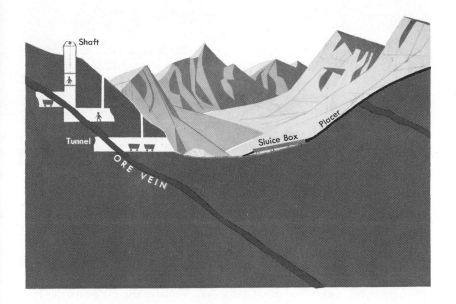

Gold is removed by deep shaft mining with the help of tunnels, or by placer methods which sluice gold-bearing sand and gravel through an inclined trough.

that. Very few metals can be found among the river gravels. Gold and tin are examples, but most of the others corrode and decompose and are borne away by the stream.

Metals and minerals occur as traces in the ocean, where marine organisms are able to extract and use them. But most metals we use have to be extracted from the rocks and crushed and smelted. They occur in many ways: as thin veins or lodes, to be followed wherever they may lead into the earth's crust; as thinly diffused particles, like the copper ores of Butte, Montana, or Bingham Canyon, Utah, spread through an immense mass of rock. Iron ore—the most abundant of all metalliferous ores—occurs in an even greater variety of ways; the iron in much of the ore that is mined and used today has already been taken down to the sea in an earlier geologic time, and here it was absorbed and secreted by marine organisms and incorporated into the rocks which they formed.

Some metalliferous minerals are usually found associated with one another. Lead, zinc, and silver are closely associated. In their lodes, tin and copper often go together. Some parts of the earth's crust have been highly mineralized; others not at all. Broadly speaking, the older rocks are more mineralized than the younger, chiefly because during the long

geological ages they have developed cracks and weaknesses up through which the fluid materials have been able to pass. The tablelands of very hard, ancient rocks, which make up much of northern Canada, Siberia, Australia, and South and Central Africa are comparatively richly endowed. The younger rocks associated with the young mountain folding have few mineral deposits of note. But it is unwise to generalize. A deposit or lode of some mineral of economic importance might be found in rocks of almost any variety and almost every age.

It does happen, however, that a small group of countries dominate the world production of most minerals. The United States is at present the leading producer of copper, zinc, molybdenum, and vanadium, and ranks in the first two or three in iron ore, lead, and tungsten. On the other hand, it scarcely counts in the output of chrome, manganese, nickel, and tin. Canada dominates the world nickel market; countries of Southeast Asia, that in tin; the Soviet Union, that in manganese; countries of South and Central Africa, that in chrome.

Just as the climatic variations from one part of the earth's crust to another make trade necessary in human foodstuffs, so the uneven distribution of mineral wealth makes it necessary to trade and exchange among nations the products of quarries and mines. The immense variety of the earth's surface, the uniqueness of each segment of it, makes it necessary that all parts should function as a whole, trading freely what each has in excess for what nature has provided in abundance in others.

Commerce in minerals raises problems of a political order. Many minerals have a high strategic value; they are not only necessary in the national economy, they are essential to national power. The German Empire, wrote Lord Keynes, was "built more truly on coal and iron than on blood and iron." If we admit that iron ore is itself a fairly widespread mineral, it is nevertheless true that several industrial countries— Poland, Czechoslovakia, and Germany among them—have very little, and that continuance of their supply from other sources is a matter of deep political concern. It is of some significance to the Western World that most of the manganese, essential for making high-quality steel, comes from the Soviet Union, and that much of the tungsten is mined in China. More serious than the danger of exhausting the store of minerals in the earth's crust is the danger of being denied access to what there is.

To some degree we of the Western World meet this danger by recovering scrap, and looking for alternative or substitute materials; to some extent also by stockpiling it while we may. The story of the political results of shortages of the metalliferous ores, like wolfram, tin, manganese, and nickel, and of fuels like high-quality coking coal and petroleum has yet to be told. It is a difficult story to piece together because the motives for political action are sometimes confused and nearly always secret.

The most critical minerals today are probably those which are described as "fissionable." They are those which, by means of a controlled nuclear disintegration, can be made to yield power. The power may be developed suddenly, as in a "big bang," or more slowly in a reactor, so that it can be used to raise steam and operate turbines. The cost of nuclear power remains high; on a cost basis it generally compares unfavorably with hydroelectric power and also with steam power produced by burning coal. But nuclear reactors have a value and importance far beyond their small contribution to power generation. The production of isotopes for medicinal and scientific purposes is desirable, and the prepa-ration of warheads a necessary employment of reactors, so fissionable minerals are perhaps the most strategic of all source materials.

Uranium, which forms the essential raw material, is a fairly rare mineral. Like most others, it occurs most readily in areas of ancient crystalline and metamorphic rock, like the Canadian Shield, the similar shield which covers much of Soviet Siberia, the African plateau, and the areas of old rock in Brazil and Australia. A few small, scattered deposits are found in Europe. Enough occurs in the old tin mines of Cornwall in England to mark a photographic plate with its radiation, but it takes more than this to operate even the smallest reactor. Uranium was found in the old rocks of Bohemia, at Jáchymov (Joachimsthal), and it was radium from this source that the Curies isolated as far back as 1898. Today the Jáchymov mines are one of the sources of radioactive materials for the Soviet Bloc. A blanket of secrecy is spread over this most strategic of all mining operations. It is difficult to find out the location of mines, and impossible to assess their output. In this, as in so many other fields, the great powers are playing a giant poker game, telling little and boasting much about their nuclear resources for both war and peace.

In this fog of secrecy it is difficult, if not impossible, to say whether the naturally occurring resources for nuclear power will outlast the coal, petroleum, and natural gas that have for several generations powered most of the world's industry. But, just as the longest day comes at last to evening, so the largest reserves of ore will some day run out. The earth's surface is scattered with the ruins of countless ghost towns, where now vanished minerals once were worked. The ancient Greeks mined silver at Cape Sunium, near Athens; the Romans worked lead in the Mendip Hills of southern England, and within living memory Cripple Creek, Virginia City, and Leadville were buzzing with activity and excitement. All are dead—or almost so—and only the untidy ground shows where the mining once was carried on. We can be confident that it is only a matter of time before the wealth of the Minnesota iron ranges or of the gold mines of the South African Rand will be exhausted; the economies based on them will have declined or turned to other sources of wealth.

Crowded lands lie side by side with empty lands. Why are people spread so unevenly? Why in some areas do people live so thick on the ground that the farmer barely has space to turn his plow, whereas in others, the land lies empty, uncultivated and unused? We have found that part of the answer lies in the nature of the earth's surface; in its relief, in the rocks of which it is built and the soils they yield, and in the concentrations of fuel and other minerals which attract the prospector and miner and give rise to manufacturing industries. These physical conditions themselves impose great inequalities upon the distribution of man over the earth's surface. Some parts are well, even overendowed; others poorly off, and their inhabitants, as it were, underprivileged from the start.

There is one more element to consider in this pattern of inequality, the climates which sometimes help or hinder, but always condition our activities. We shall gradually build up a picture of a grudging nature spreading its riches unequally, without, it would seem, any regard for man's needs. But has nature's parsimony been matched by man's improvidence; has man failed to make the best of what nature has given him? The chapter "Man on the Land" will take up this question.

3 THE ATMOSPHERE AROUND US

The empire of climate is the first of all empires.

Montesquieu—L'Esprit des Lois

The land constitutes only one element in the complex physical environment of man. Climate is no less important, for upon it depends in part the kinds of crops he grows, the amount of food he extracts from the land, the way he builds his home and how he organizes his life. The average of weather creates a climate, and weather is the product of forces at work in the atmosphere that surrounds man.

Our warmth comes from the sun. Continuously and without variation, the sun sends its rays toward the earth. Year after year the earth receives about the same quantity of heat from the sun and distributes it unevenly about its surface by means of the winds of the atmosphere and the currents of the seas. It is a commonplace that different parts of the earth receive differing quantities of heat or insolation. If the sun is overhead at the equator, its rays there are strong, and its heat intense; but at the same time from Canada the sun seems quite low in the sky, and its intensity is much reduced. Near the North Pole the sun is merely a glow on the horizon, contributing almost nothing to the warmth of the surface of the land. Thus the intensity of insolation varies at any one time with the distance from where the sun is overhead.

In its annual pilgrimage around the sun, the earth follows a path—its orbit—spinning as it goes upon an axis that is tilted to the plane along which it moves. The polar axis is inclined 23½° from the vertical, the North Pole always pointing away into space toward the Polar Star. In June the northern end of the axis is inclined toward the sun; the sun rises higher in the sky in the Northern Hemisphere; it shines more

73

brightly and days are longer. In winter, the Northern Hemisphere is tilted away from it; the sun is lower and days are shorter. The summer and winter solstices are moments when this inclination to or from the sun is greatest. At this time we see the sun standing as high—or as low —as it ever goes; in the Arctic the Midnight Sun is experienced or the period of perpetual darkness. In March and September the axis is inclined across the rays of the sun, which is overhead at the equator. These are the equinoxes, when the whole earth experiences equal periods of daylight and dark.

If the distance from the overhead sun and the change of seasons were all to consider, one might calculate with reasonable accuracy what would be the temperature at any place and at any time. But as we have noted, this we cannot do, for the sun pours down a certain amount of heat, but the movements of the atmosphere and of the seas and oceans determine its distribution over the earth's surface.

THE DRAMA OF WEATHER

The movements of the atmosphere, or winds, spring from the basic physical law that warm air is lighter than cold and is forced to rise, and conversely that cold air tends to sink. On a summer's drive we may see the air shimmering above the blacktop of the road. Over the parched ground little dust devils may rise upward into the air. The air, heated by contact with the hot ground, spirals upward. On a night drive on a still fall or winter's night, as we drop down into a valley, we may feel a chill in the air, and a patch of fog may lie in the valley bottom. There the cold air has sunk slowly downward, and falling temperatures have forced the moisture in it to condense into tiny water particles, until it has gathered in pools of fog in every valley and hollow. Why does the fruit grower plant his orchards on the slopes rather than in the bottom of the valley? Simply because the risk of frost is less on the higher ground.

Take these small-scale manifestations of the tendency of hot air to rise and cold air to sink, and magnify them many millions of times. We then have the upward rush of air on the summer day, heated by contact with the hot land, rising ever upward into the higher, cooler reaches of the atmosphere, until its contained moisture condenses out into fleecy white clouds piling up like cauliflowers and sailing slowly, majestically in the wind. The upward movement of the air continues, forcing the

THE CHANGE OF SEASONS

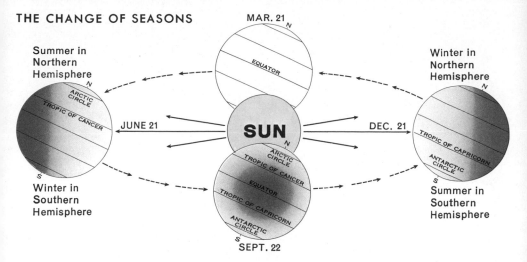

The solstices occur in June and December. During the equinoxes of March and September, the whole earth experiences equal periods of darkness and light.

clouds to rise ever higher, until their accumulated tensions are at last released in a thunderstorm.

Or look at the same phenomenon on a scale immeasurably larger even than this. At some latitude between the Tropics of Capricorn and Cancer the sun is overhead, or very nearly so, day after day. The land is heated, and the air, heated by contact with it, rises. A bright, clear dawn is followed by the convectional rise of the air. Heavy storm clouds form; a thunderstorm, with torrential rain, follows; and the air is cooled by the rain. The sun begins to sink, and the convectional process is slowed down as evening approaches. The towering clouds break up, contract, and melt away as the air is drawn back again toward the surface of the earth, and the setting sun shines brightly through the rain-washed air onto the sodden ground below.

In the latter example the heating of the land surface and the upward movement of the air are on a vast, continental scale. The upward movement is fed by an inrush of air from cooler latitudes, which gives us the trade winds, winds which blow, year in year out, along their regular trade or track, from north and south toward the focus of the perennial equatorial storm. John Masefield wrote of their ceaselessness—

> *And day-long, night-long, the cool and pleasant breeze*
> *Of the steady Trade Winds blowing.*

This is the first element in the general circulation of the atmosphere: the flow of air toward the equatorial zone where the heating is most

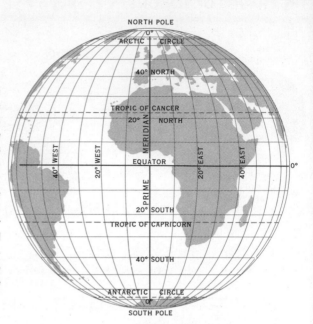

Longitude begins at the prime meridian and extends east and west 180°. Latitude begins at the equator and extends north and south to the poles, or 90°. On either side of the equator lie the tropic zones, limited by the Tropics of Cancer and Capricorn. Beyond the tropics the temperate latitudes extend to polar latitudes which are marked by the Arctic and Antarctic Circles.

intense. But the trade winds are themselves supplied by air masses from the so-called high-pressure areas which lie on each side of the equator. Here the air settles slowly down toward the earth's surface. In a sense it is pressing more heavily upon the earth, creating an area of high pressure. As this air mass gradually sinks, it becomes warmer; its capacity to hold moisture increases; and it readily absorbs the moisture which it finds. Clouds are evaporated back into the atmosphere, and the air dries up the land and parches the lips and throat, and helps to create the great deserts that are the most characteristic feature of the low latitudes. From the high-pressure areas the trade winds blow toward the equatorial low-pressure belt.

On the other hand the southwest winds of the Northern Hemisphere and the westerlies of the Southern blow very generally toward the poles; it is these winds that continental United States experiences when a warm wind blows up from the Gulf or in from the Pacific. In the middle latitudes these warm and moist winds from tropical areas alternate with cooler, drier winds blowing from the poles. The polar regions are in all ways the reverse of the equatorial. The land is cold; the sea is covered with floating ice. The air is chilled by contact with the earth's surface, becomes dense, and tends to flow outward around the globe, drawing more air behind it downward toward the earth. This outblowing polar air brings the arctic chill from Canada into the United States, to the Midwest or along the Atlantic seaboard in winter. It may carry snow into southern Texas or frost to blight the orange groves of Florida. But usually it is held back from coming so far by the opposite movement of warm air from the tropics.

We can predict weather at best for only a day or two in the middle latitudes, and even then the margin of error is considerable. Near the tropics weather forecasting is easier; the weather is more sure. The basic reason for this is that the equatorial "low" and the tropical "highs" are relatively stable, moving regularly with the procession of the seasons. In the middle latitudes the line of meeting of tropical and polar air masses, the front as we call it, has a regular movement, toward the poles in the summer, toward the tropic zones in winter, but it has also an irregular movement. It is like a rope that is shaken to send a wave along it. Wavelike curves pass irregularly along the front, so that any particular place lies alternately on one side and on the other of the front as it passes. The middle latitudes for this reason have weather that is changeable, without the daily rhythm that in general characterizes that of lower latitudes. The weather is unpredictable for more than a few days ahead just because there is no certainty where the front will lie a few days, or even hours, ahead.

The changing pageant of the sky announces the weather to come. Since earliest times weather lore has been largely based upon the patterns of the sky, and with good reason, for the clouds mirror the conditions of stability and humidity in the atmosphere upon which our weather hinges. Reduced to their simplest terms, clouds belong to three types. All are produced by the cooling of the air to the point at which moisture begins to condense into fine particles which hang poised in the air.

First and most familiar is the cumulus-type cloud, the heaped-up, sharp-edged masses of cloud which are the crowning glory of the summer day. Cumulus clouds are the simple product of the convectional rise and cooling of the air. They are the normal features of a fine, hot day. Broken cumulus is a fair-weather sky; it will dissipate toward evening. Only when the tufts of cumulus soar upward to immense heights and merge to cover the sky do they presage thunder, rain, and hail.

The stratus-type is a layer cloud. It is most familiar when it forms directly upon the ground, and we see and feel it as fog. It forms more often at some height above the ground, where it may give a milky color to the sky and make the sun look wan and misty. It may lie in

At the belt of equatorial calms, or doldrums, hot air rises upward and cooler air from north and south, the trade winds, moves in to replace it. Some of the hot air from the equator moves aloft toward the poles, and at 30° north and south descends as cooler air forming a high-pressure belt known as subtropical calms or horse latitudes. Also some of this descending cooler air flows from the southwest and northwest as the prevailing westerlies.

heavy, threatening rolls, or it may give a smooth unbroken canopy of gray. It may not always presage rain, but it is likely to thicken into bad-weather cloud. Stratus cloud often warns of the approach of a front and the atmospheric disturbances that bring rain.

The third is the cirrus-type, made up of light, delicate and feathery wisps of cloud floating at very great heights. These wisps may form a pattern of little tufts, like the scales of a fish, or they may be drawn out into long streamers which span the sky. Cirrus clouds are made of ice crystals and are usually white and without shadow, and at morning and evening they may glow pink in the rays of the sun. They do not yield rain, but they are evidence of disturbances in the higher atmosphere and are the harbingers of change.

Atmospheric circulation can be illustrated by diagrams; the one above, and the one on page 82, show the course and the destination of the air as it circulates. The earth has its constant supply of air which stays with it. Plants abstract part of it and return it to the atmosphere. We breathe in a lungful from the passing wind, and breathe it out again, and it passes on. Shall we ever breathe in those same particles of air again? Who knows? Perhaps after completing its vast journey over the surface of the earth and back again through the higher reaches of the atmosphere, it may again come our way, but the chances are very slight.

The sun appears to move north and south with the seasons. In June it is overhead at the Tropic of Cancer; in December, at the Tropic of Capricorn. As the sun apparently moves it takes the heat equator, or belt of greatest heating with it. The place where the trade winds converge is north of the equator in our summer, south of it in our winter.

This movement influences also the latitude of the tropical belt where air is settling down toward the earth in the form of high-pressure areas and that of the front which separates tropical from arctic air. These lie farther north in summer, farther south in winter. Land north of the equator gets more of the tropical air in the summer months, and of the arctic air in the winter. Lands south of the equator experience the same situation in reverse, and hence their seasons have a reverse cycle to that of the Northern Hemisphere.

The winds, however, do not blow directly from south to north or north to south. They are given a twist by the fact that the earth is rotating at a great speed beneath them. In the Northern Hemisphere they are diverted to the right; the trade winds become the northeast trades; the south wind becomes a southwest or even westerly wind, and the polar winds come out of the northeast. This pattern is reversed in the Southern Hemisphere, where the winds are diverted to the left of their objective. Of course, wind directions are not always regular. The shape of the land, the different heating of land and sea, all introduce irregularities and unevennesses.

In the pattern of movement of the great wind systems we have the key to the world's pattern of climate. The winds carry the temperature of one place into another. They also carry moisture. The warmer the air, the greater is the quantity of water it can hold. When this air is cooled sufficiently, it liberates the moisture in the form of clouds or fog, dew or frost. A warm dry air, as it blows across a sea, has an immense capacity to pick up moisture. The trade winds, which start as dry winds, become very wet ones and deliver immense quantities of rainfall to the equatorial regions. The southwest winds of the United States and the southwesterlies of Europe are all wet winds. They release this moisture when they are cooled. The heavy rains on American mountains and the violent summer downpour with its accompaniment of thunder claps, are both borne northward by warm winds from the tropics, which gather the moisture from the Pacific Ocean or the Gulf of Mexico.

These winds are cooled as they rise to pass over hills and mountains. But rain falls over low, flat land where there are no hills to make the wind rise. Here too the warm, moisture-laden winds are cooled by being made to rise, this time over the invisible barrier formed by masses of cooler and heavier air. This is how most of our rain comes; cold northern air pushes south, and warm air rises and flows on above it. This is what a front is made of. The line along which these air masses meet fluctuates

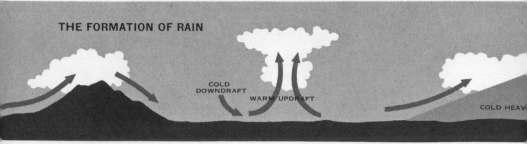

COLD
DOWNDRAFT

WARM UPDRAFT

COLD HEAV

Over mountains   By convection   Over heavy air

and wanders. A cold front, where a mass of arctic air is cutting in under the warm moist air from the south, may move in over the Pacific Northwest. It crosses the continent, leaving in its wake snow, rain, or even tornado damage, according to the season.

Temperature falls as heights from the land into the atmosphere are attained, usually at the rate of about 3°F. for each thousand feet of ascent. On a hot summer's day, when the ground temperature is about 90°, a rise of nearly 20,000 feet must be made before the freezing point is reached. This lapse rate, however, is neither even nor uniform. Convection and turbulence influence it, so that temperature is not a sure measure of altitude, nor altitude of temperature. There is nevertheless a height at every place and at all times above which moisture condensing from a saturated air will form, if not minute droplets of water, then small and beautifully formed ice crystals, which grow into snowflakes and fall slowly toward the ground. If the snowflake passes downward into warmer air, this may cause it partly to melt and give sleet, or even to turn wholly into rain.

Snow is a winter phenomenon, but hail belongs more to summer. The hailstone is literally a frozen raindrop. It began as a globule of water, falling toward the earth. A careful examination of a hailstone, if one can be kept long enough without melting, discloses its history. It is made up of a series of concentric layers of ice, like those children's toys which consist of a series of boxes or cubes fitting neatly inside one another. The innermost of the boxes represents the frozen raindrop. As it fell it encountered a rising convectional current. It must have hung for a while, like a ping-pong ball poised on a jet of water, before being swept upward to colder regions of the atmosphere where it froze. Again it fell, gathering moisture around itself, and again it was carried upward for the fresh moisture to freeze as a fresh coating around the original droplet. And so the process continued, until the hailstone at last fell out of the cloud and down to earth. It takes a powerful convection current to do this, and, in general, such currents come only on hot days. It is paradoxical that the biggest hailstones come in the hottest weather, and those giants, "as big as hens' eggs," if we may believe the press, demand an almost tropical heat for their formation.

Hail often accompanies the passage of a front, because of the rapid rise of air that takes place as the cool air mass undercuts the warm. But the hail storm is far from being the most violent manifestation of frontal activity. When the front is very strongly marked, and the temperatures of the tropical and arctic air masses widely separated—as they are in spring and early summer—the air may spiral upward in small, tight whirlpools, like those which pass along the surface of a flooded river. This is the tornado, the most concentrated in its violence of all the manifestations of weather. Tornadoes can occur almost anywhere, but they do have their familiar and well-beaten paths. Hills seem to interrupt the flow of air into the vortex; the plain country facilitates its formation. Scarcely a front passes across northern Texas, Oklahoma, and Kansas in late spring without at least the threat of a tornado.

Hurricane, the American word for the typhoon of the China Sea and the cyclone of the Indian seas, is also a frontal storm, but one more typical of late summer and fall. The first usually strikes the eastern or southern coast of the United States in August, and by the time that the Weather Bureau has run through its birthday book and given them all names, some half-dozen have been christened. They are more concentrated than ordinary storms that accompany the passage of a front; but far less concentrated than the tornado. The damage which they do is nevertheless often much greater, in part because they cover a larger area than the tornado, in part because they usually originate at sea and add to the damage by wind the greater harm done by the tide and waves.

High above these movements of the air are the more violent motions of the upper atmosphere which we call the jet streams. These are, as it were, rivers in the atmosphere, narrow belts of air moving very rapidly from west to east around the globe, one in each hemisphere. They move north and south with the seasons. They probably control the interplay of warm and cool air at the surface of the earth, and they often help to propel high-flying aircraft to their destination.

Warmth from the sun is not only distributed by the winds. The currents of the oceans play an important role. The sea differs from the land in heating up more slowly and holding its heat longer. The land has

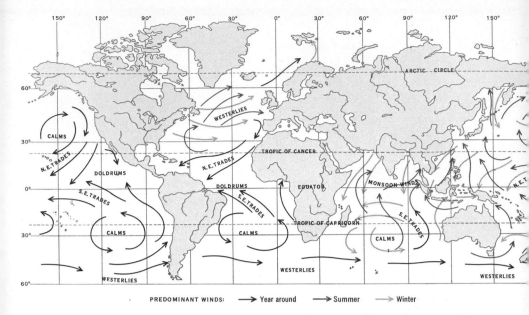

PREDOMINANT WINDS: → Year around → Summer → Winter

The distribution of the heat of the sun is dependent on the planetary winds. Some winds blow year round. Others like the monsoon winds blow only in summer, while others blow only in winter. Another medium for the distribution of warmth and cold is found in ocean currents. The Gulf Stream or North Atlantic Drift warms the coasts of Northern Europe and moderates the temperature. The North Pacific Drift from Japan brings warm waters to Alaska's shore.

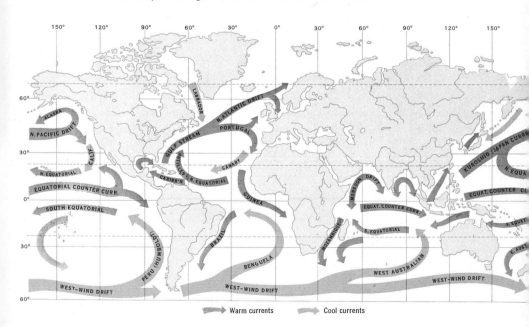

→ Warm currents → Cool currents

already cooled off during the fall while the sea is still relatively warm, and in spring and early summer, the land is warming up while the sea remains cool. The effect of the seas and oceans, and even of lakes and small ponds, is to moderate the temperature of the nearby land in summer and to raise its temperature in winter. Frost is less frequent and less intense on the shores of lakes and near the sea than it is only a few miles away inland. In summer it is cooler on the coast, and the sea breezes are more refreshing than the hot winds over the land.

The seas have currents, slow movements of the water driven under the impulse of the wind. The trade winds impel the surface waters of the oceans toward the equator, they tend to pile up on the western edge of the oceans and to escape by flowing back toward the east approximately along the equator. This gives us the Northern and the Southern Equatorial Currents. In higher latitudes the westerly or southwesterly winds drive the surface waters of the oceans from the tropical latitudes toward the eastern edge of the great water bodies. Thus the warm waters of the Caribbean Sea are driven by the southwest winds in a slow, surface drift, sometimes called the Gulf Stream, northeastward toward the continent of Europe, bearing with them just a little of the warmth of those seas from which they came. This warmth spreads out and becomes diffused, but still remains sufficient to keep ice away from the coasts of Great Britain, Ireland, and Norway. Norway lies in the latitude of Greenland, and yet its ports remain open throughout the year for shipping. The Gulf Stream is the most valuable gift ever given by the New World to the Old. In the North Pacific Ocean the Kuroshio or Japan Current and the North Pacific Drift fulfill a similar role, bringing warm ocean water to the coast of Alaska and British Columbia. In the Southern Hemisphere, less obstructed by land masses, there is a steady movement of the ocean—the West Wind Drift—around the continuous southern ocean.

Why is San Francisco cool most of the year, and why do the fog banks roll in through the Golden Gate to blanket the city, while less than an hour's drive to the east the climate is hot and dry? Off the California coast the water is cool. The winds, blowing offshore for much of the year, drive the surface water southwestward, where it merges into the North Equatorial Current. Its place is taken by cold water which comes welling upward from the ocean depths. Air is chilled by contact with this water. Fog is formed and is often blown inland until it is dissipated by the greater warmth.

Such cold water coasts are a regularly recurring feature of the earth's surface, like the regions of equatorial low pressure and of tropical high pressure. They are found off the coast of Chile and Peru, of western Australia, and of northwest and southwest Africa.

THE CLIMATES OF THE WORLD

There are no sharp divisions in nature. Just as mountains merge gradually into hills and hills into plains, so each of the climatic types which it is possible to distinguish merges gradually, almost imperceptibly into the next. Within each of the great climatic divisions of the world all is not uniform. There is an infinity of local variations, determined by the configuration of the land, by exposure to wind and frost, by the dampness of the ground and the vegetation cover. We divide the surface of the earth into a small number of large regions. None of these is completely uniform or homogeneous, and their boundaries are imprecise.

Most clear-cut and distinctive of all these regions is the *Humid Low Latitudes,* sometimes referred to as the Equatorial Rain Forest. This vast belt of territory which lies on both sides of the equator in South America, in Central Africa, and in southeastern Asia is characterized by temperatures that are uniformly high throughout the year. At Belém (Pará), for example, near the mouth of the Amazon River, the hottest month has an average temperature of 80°; the coolest 77°. Djakarta in Indonesia ranges from 78° to 80°; Luluabourg in The Congo, from 76° to 77°. By contrast, Chicago has an average in January of about 26°, and of 74° in July. There are no seasons in the humid lowlands, and the difference between the hottest and the least hot months is generally so slight that the human body cannot detect the difference.

Rain occurs in all months; one can distinguish only between wet months and very wet months. Belém, with an average total rainfall of nearly 100 inches, has about 2.5 inches in its driest month, and over 14 inches in the wettest. Singapore has on average 6.7 inches in its driest month and 10.6 in its wettest. Clearly, there is almost as little variation in rainfall as there is in temperature. The humidity remains high all the time, and this more than the heat itself is the cause of the exhaustion which visitors to these regions usually feel.

The nineteenth-century traveler, Henry W. Bates, described a day in the forests of the Amazon. "First, the cool sea-breeze, which commenced to blow about 10 o'clock, . . . would flag and finally die away . . . while clouds would appear in the east and gather into cumuli, with an increasing blackness along their lower portions. The whole eastern horizon would become almost suddenly black, and this would spread upward, the sun at length being obscured. Then the rush of a mighty wind is heard through the forest, swaying the tree-tops; a vivid flash of lightning bursts forth, then a crash of thunder, and down streams the deluging rain. Such storms soon cease, leaving bluish-black motionless clouds in the sky until night. . . . Towards evening life revives again, and the ringing uproar is resumed from bush and tree. The following morning the sun rises in a cloudless sky, and so the cycle is completed."

And so, of course, it begins again the next day. There is no alternation of warm and cool air masses; no stimulus from the rapid changes of weather, no need to guard against extremes which do not occur.

This is a hot-house climate. Plants grow fast, and know no season when life is dormant. Chemical changes in the soil are faster here than anywhere else. Minerals are broken down to their simpler and more soluble components, and are swiftly carried away by percolating waters to the rivers and the sea. Humus, produced by the decay of plants does not remain, as it does in cooler latitudes, to fertilize the soil; it is decomposed and washed down to the subsoil. The soil remains poor; often it consists only of a sterile red or yellow clay known as laterite.

Yet the vegetation which grows here is rich and lush. Tall trees send deep roots to tap the deposits of plant food far below, and a high canopy of leaves reaches upward as plants compete for light, cutting out the sunshine from the damp soil; and the jungle plants extract some nourishment from the rapidly decaying leaf fall. But this is not uniform. Even before man began to cut down the forest, to establish plantations and to plant crops, there were breaks in the continuity of the forest. Hills, rising above the heat and the humidity of the plains and valleys, were clothed with a less dense vegetation, and at a few thousand feet above sea level the forest gives way to more open country, grass covered with scattered trees.

Nothing is more deceptive than the apparent richness of the equatorial forest. It hides a poor soil, unsuited without elaborate precautions for the cultivation of crops. For the most part this region has only a small population, and much of it ranks as one of the least populous in the world. Much of its agriculture is shifting. The native peoples clear a small patch of forest, burn the trees, harvest a few crops for two or three or perhaps as many as five years, and then abandon the impoverished soil, which is reoccupied in a few weeks by dense tropical growth. Plantations—rubber, palm oil, bananas, cacao—can be maintained more easily than ordinary field crops, because the trees send roots deep into the subsoil to utilize some of that plant nutriment which is washed downward from the surface.

Toward its northern and southern margins the forest begins to thin out, as the rainfall and the temperature gradually, imperceptibly take on a seasonal character. Near the equator the sun is overhead in March and September, and for the rest of the year is not too far away. But at 10° (about 700 miles) from the equator a distinct hot season and cool season have begun to separate themselves from the uniformity of the equatorial region. At Salisbury in Southern Rhodesia the hottest month of the southern summer has an average of 71°, and the coolest in winter, 56°. The range of temperature has risen from an almost imperceptible two or three degrees to fourteen. The rainfall diminishes during the dry season which gradually makes itself apparent as one travels outward from the equatorial forest. In summer the temperature and humidity may be as oppressive as near the equator, but one knows that they will not last more than a few months, and that for the rest of the year the air will be dry and the temperature warm. This is the *Wet-and-Dry Low Latitude* climate.

Vegetation reflects the change in climate. Away from the equator, the forest becomes more open, first over the higher, cooler, and better drained land; then in the valleys. A parklike landscape, with tall grass and scattered trees, replaces the forest. Trees may cluster along the water courses and then thin out over the intervening higher ground. They are of species which can endure a dry season. Many of them lose their leaves in winter, and put them on again in summer. This vegetation is sometimes called savanna. It is the haunt of big game; the elephant, giraffe, zebra, and the thousand different species of deer which feed on grass and other forms of plant life, and the carnivores, headed by the lion and the leopard, which feed on them.

This type of climate with its resulting vegetation is found on the margins of each of the regions of equatorial forest. It stretches through Central America from Venezuela and Colombia, into southern Mexico; it covers the southern half of Brazil; and it extends across Africa skirting the equatorial forest of the Congo basin. Northern Australia and much of India and Southeast Asia also experience climates of the same general type.

The wet-and-dry climate is easier on man than the humid equatorial. It is less monotonous; disease is less rampant; insects and reptiles are less prevalent. The presence of a dry season slows down chemical change in the soil, and the products of the decay of vegetation are no longer removed as soon as they are formed. The soils are better, and more suited to the cultivation of crops. The local peoples have formed large settled communities, and they cultivate their fields continuously. The croplands do not wear out as quickly; nor do they have to be abandoned periodically to recover their lost fertility. Population is denser, and in some of the higher and cooler areas of the savanna, like those of East Africa, Europeans came and settled. Coffee plantations have been established in the savanna lands of Brazil, Central America, and East Africa. The sugar cane has become an important crop in many of the moister areas. Corn and sorghum, millet and barley, peanuts and fodder crops are also grown; and where enough water is available rice, the staple with the immense power of producing great quantities of food from a small area, takes over.

The boundary between the evergreen forest and savanna is difficult to draw because the two interpenetrate one another. (Compare maps on pages 20–21 and 22–23.) Nowhere is this distinction more difficult than in Southeast Asia. A feature of the wet-and-dry climate here is the monsoon. This is an Indian word meaning season, and it refers to the summer season when the rains come. Here the summer rains which would be normal in this latitude are immeasurably intensified. Over the interior of Asia, the land becomes heated and the air expands and rises. Winds are drawn in, as if by a huge suction pump, toward the low-pressure area that develops. These winds strike the west coast of India in June and continue into September. They pile up over the mountains, and pour down the heaviest, most violent, most continuous rain that the world knows. For months the rain clouds roll up the face of the Himalayas. Trees are washed of the winter's accumulation of dust; dirt roads are churned to mud, the paddy fields are full of water, and the young, green rice springs up. At Bombay about 70 inches of rain fall in the four months from June to September, and less than 4 in all the remainder of the year. Cherrapunji, in northeastern India, has an average rainfall of 426 inches. It has to rain continuously, violently, for weeks and months for all this water to fall to the earth.

In West Africa evergreen forest occurs in a narrow belt along the coast. Inland it merges into savanna. Northward the scattered trees become fewer and the grass drier; the rivers remain dry for longer periods of the year. Then sagebrush and other drought-resisting plants take over. At last even this evidence of life disappears, and the *Semiarid* climate gives place to *Desert*.

The Sahara Desert of North Africa is the most extensive in the world. It is reckoned to cover about 3,000,000 square miles, about 6 per cent of the earth's total land surface, and desert conditions are continued eastward over Arabia and much of the Middle East and into Pakistan and India and on through the interior of China to Mongolia. Desert covers much of South-West Africa and parts of the Republic of South Africa. The whole interior of Australia is desert. A narrow strip of desert—one of the driest in the world, the Atacama—lies between the Andes of South America and the Pacific Ocean in northern Chile and Peru; southern Argentina, or Patagonia, is desert. In North America desert conditions begin in Mexico and extend north into the United States.

Not all deserts are hot all the time. Most heat up under the sun during the day, but at night, with no vegetation cover and little cloud in the sky, the burning rocks radiate their warmth back into the atmosphere. The daily range of temperature, between the daytime maximum and the night's minimum, is greater in the deserts than in any other region of the globe. The highest temperature ever recorded under natural conditions, 136°, was measured in the Libyan Desert. It would be not uncommon for the night following such a day as this to drop to 40°. Deserts generally have a considerable annual range of temperature; it seems that in the Sahara the winters have a pleasant temperature from 20° to 40° cooler than the summers. In the deserts of Central Asia winters are very cold indeed. In the Gobi Desert January has an average temperature well below zero, and winters are by no means warm in parts of the western deserts of the United States.

What all these deserts have in common is their dryness. In some rainfall has never been known, yet all bear the visible traces of rain: deep, steep, rugged, rock-strewn valleys—wadis they call them in Africa and the Middle East—scoured out by the violent storms of long ago. No one remembers the storms, but there is always that slim chance that they will occur again. Dunsany tells the story of the desert traveler who was given a charm which would insure that he would never die of thirst. His last water bottle emptied, parched and dying, he lay down in a wadi— and was drowned by the sudden, violent surge of water that rushed down it after such a storm.

In some desert areas, Patagonia and the Great Basin of Nevada and Utah, for example, the dryness is due to the fact that they are cut off by high mountain ranges from rain-bearing winds. However, the deserts of Mexico and the American Southwest, of North Africa and the Middle East, of Australia and South-West Africa are due primarily to the fact that these areas are regions of high pressure, where the dense, dry air evaporates every trace of moisture that it encounters.

Despite its dryness the desert is a rich and varied place. Much of the desert areas of the world is made up of bare rock, slowly being broken up into sand which is whirled away by the wind. The bare desert floor is studded with sand; blobs and crescents of sand, moving, creeping slowly forward as the wind pushes the sand grains up the backside, over the top, and down in front of the moving heap of sand. Then the dunes merge into a sea of sand. Their waves are like the waves of the sea, but pale yellow in the sun, black in the shadow, frozen as it were, with little ripples climbing up the sides of the great, still waves. Sometimes these waves of the desert move slowly outward to beat on the surrounding areas that are settled and sown, engulfing them in the advancing sea of sand.

The desert is a harsh environment, but is no longer as intractable as it once was. Agriculture, once limited to natural oases, where water was made available from underground reservoirs, is now being extended to areas where water can be piped in from distant mountains. The chance of discovering minerals in the desert is as great as in any other part of the earth, and a good deal easier, because the rocks are laid bare by nature for the geologist. The desert of northern Chile has long been a leading source of nitrates. The Arabian desert is now a foremost source of petroleum. Gold and silver and lead are mined in the Australian desert; diamonds in the desert of South-West Africa; copper, silver, and other minerals in the deserts of Arizona and Mexico.

On the outer or poleward margins of the desert regions the winds blow away from the deserts and toward the middle latitudes. This atmospheric circulation is interrupted by the occurrence of land masses, which tend in winter to build up high pressure systems and in summer to form low pressures. The former tend to push the normal wind systems away from them; the latter attract them. The resulting climatic regions lose the relative simplicity which has characterized them hitherto in this discussion. Climatic change from place to place is more abrupt and frequent, and the classification and definition of climatic regions becomes more difficult.

Take the change in climate that occurs along the west coast of the United States from San Diego to Seattle, a distance of about twelve hundred miles. In southern California summers are long, hot, and dry; the July average temperature in San Diego is almost 70°, and is a good deal higher a few miles inland from the ocean. The winters are mild and pleasant, and San Diego has a January temperature average of 55°. The rain comes mainly between December and March, and the rest of the year is dry. The essential feature of this climate is that the hot season is also the dry season. Plants grow and leaf in the winter. The season of flowers is late winter and early spring. By late spring vegetation is beginning to die back, and through the long, hot summer it is dormant.

The seasonal rhythm is to be explained by the fact that the southwest winds blow onshore here only in the winter months. In summer they

As the moist prevailing westerlies are quickly cooled at high altitudes, they bring heavy rainfall or snow to parts of the Coast Ranges of California and the western flanks of the Sierra Nevada. Warmed again as they descend to the valleys, they become a hot dry wind helping to create the arid conditions of the San Joaquin Valley and of eastern California and western Nevada. Note the variations in average annual rainfall of six selected locations.

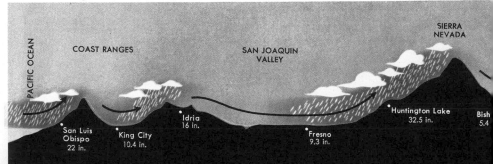

have been pushed northward by the seasonal shift in the wind belts and their place is taken by the high pressure and the hot, dry conditions which we associate with the belt of tropical deserts.

Compare this climate with that of Seattle, where the winters are cool, with an average temperature of about 38° in January, and the summers are warm, with a July average of 62°. Total rainfall is higher than in San Diego, with a very different distribution. July and August have less rainfall than other months, but there is no dry season; rain may occur at any time during the year, and summer storms may be as violent as those of winter. Here the dormant season for plants is winter. Trees shed their leaves in the fall and put on fresh foliage in the spring. Spring and summer are the seasons of flowers and of growth. The reason again is simple. Here the southwest winds, forced from the tropical high-pressure systems, blow northeastward throughout the year, gathering moisture from the Pacific Ocean and dropping it over the Coast and Cascade ranges.

Between San Diego and Seattle there is a gradual transition from one extreme to the other, from the *Mediterranean* climate to the *Marine West Coast* climate, as the long, dry summer of southern California contracts and disappears as it is traced northward and, with it, the whole cycle of plant life is reversed.

It is the same in Europe, in South America, in Australia—wherever, in fact, the land faces westward across the oceans in latitudes between about 30° and 60° North or South. As between the Pacific Northwest and southern California, the contrast between Western Europe and Italy is the same. As D. H. Lawrence observed: "North of the Alps, the everlasting winter is interrupted by summers that struggle and soon yield; south of the Alps, the everlasting summer is interrupted by spasmodic and spiteful winters that never get a real hold, but that are mean and dogged. North of the Alps, you may have a pure winter's day in June. South of the Alps, you may have a midsummer's day in December. . . ."

Southern Spain corresponds with southern California; Lisbon with San Francisco; northern France and southern England with Seattle. The whole Mediterranean Basin has a climate similar to that of southern California, and it is, indeed, the type area which gives its name to this climate of hot, dry summers and warm, moist winters; it is the region of Mediterranean climate par excellence. But this climate occurs also, and under similar conditions, in central Chile, around the cities of Valparaíso and Santiago; in the Cape Town area of South Africa; and near Perth and Adelaide in Australia.

In terms of vegetation and land use, the Mediterranean climate is one of the most distinctive. It is less suited to crop farming than most because of the lack of rain in summer when plants usually grow most vigorously. On the other hand, it is well suited to trees which flower in the spring and form fruit which ripens through the summer. The olive and the grape are the typically Mediterranean crops, though lately the modern techniques of irrigation have allowed the cultivation of other crops to be greatly extended. Western civilization was cradled in a Mediterranean climate. The literature of classical Greece and Rome is redolent of the blue skies, the vineyards, and the outdoor life which this climate makes possible.

The cooler, damper Marine West Coast climate of the Pacific Northwest extends through British Columbia into the Alaska Panhandle, becoming cooler and moister. In northwestern Europe it spreads over the British Isles, Germany, Denmark, and coastal Norway. In contrast with the Mediterranean lands, it is a chill, ungrateful climate. The winter's cold is never intense, but it is damp and raw, and the summers are cloudy and cool. This is no land for the vine. Its typical fruit is the hardy apple; its crops are oats, barley, potatoes, and fodder crops. Wheat is grown, though summers are often too damp for it. Broadly similar types of climate are met with in southern Chile, southeastern Australia, and New Zealand. They are all lands of broad-leaved trees, like the oak, beech, and elm, and of meadows which remain green and lush throughout the year. They are best suited to the growing of fodder crops and grass, and the raising of dairy cattle.

Now turn to the Atlantic seaboard of the United States and look at the climate of, let us say, Georgia. Atlanta has a mild winter with a 44° average temperature in January, and a hot summer with a July average of 78°. This does not differ greatly from the climate at similar latitudes in California; only the winter is a little cooler. But the rainfall distribution is quite different; Atlanta has no dry season. Rainfall is spread evenly through the year, and is fully adequate for crops which can be sown in spring, mature through the summer, and be harvested in late summer or early fall. Cotton, though no longer of much importance in Georgia, is typical of the crops of this climatic region. Such a climate extends westward from the Atlantic coast states to Texas and Oklahoma, where it becomes dry and merges gradually into the desert. The northward limit of this climate is set where the length of winter and the intensity of frost cease to permit the growth of "southern" plants such as cotton, tobacco, peanuts. It is difficult to draw a precise boundary, but the line runs roughly through Kansas, Missouri, and Kentucky and on to the coast in Virginia or Maryland.

This humid climate of mild winters and hot summers, the *Humid Subtropical* we call it, covers substantial areas of the world. Most of China and northern India has this type of climate; so has southern Japan, eastern Australia, the southeastern coastlands of Africa, and the Plata lands of Argentina and Uruguay as well as southern Brazil. These regions all lie on the eastern side of the continents between the latitudes roughly of 20° and 35° from the equator. They are in general slightly closer to the equator than the regions of Mediterranean climate, and they lie in the track of onshore winds from the Atlantic for most if not all the year. In Southeast Asia the monsoon effect intensifies these winds in summer and increases the amount of summer rainfall relative to that which falls in the rest of the year. In China much of the total rainfall comes in the three months of summer. At Sydney, Australia, Buenos Aires, Argentina, or New Orleans no month is much wetter or much drier than the rest.

North of the humid subtropical belt of the United States the climate becomes more extreme, more continental. Summers remain hot. Chicago in summer is only a degree or two cooler than New Orleans, New York only slightly cooler than Atlanta; but the winter temperatures are from twenty to thirty degrees cooler. The first severe frost of the fall comes in September rather than November, and the last in the spring is in April or even May instead of February. Total rainfall diminishes from 50 or more inches in much of the South to 30 inches or even less in the driest parts of the Midwest. The eastern seaboard remains quite humid north into New England and the eastern provinces of Canada, but toward the west the rainfall tapers off and imperceptibly this region merges into the deserts and semideserts of the West.

This is the region of *Humid Continental* climate, of hot summers and cold winters, of violent summer thunderstorm and winter blizzard. This is where the farmer can afford to leave his farm and his fields after his corn or his wheat has been harvested in the fall, and only return in time for spring plowing. During the winter the top foot of the soil is frozen and no plow can penetrate it. This is the region where the soil lies black and rich when the plow has turned it; where the natural fertility

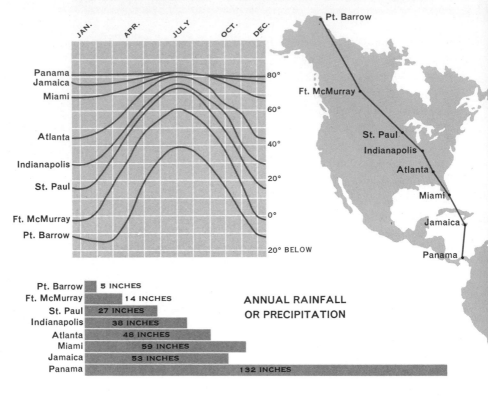

THE YEARLY MARCH OF TEMPERATURES IN NORTH AMERICA

ANNUAL RAINFALL OR PRECIPITATION

Pt. Barrow	5 INCHES
Ft. McMurray	14 INCHES
St. Paul	27 INCHES
Indianapolis	38 INCHES
Atlanta	48 INCHES
Miami	59 INCHES
Jamaica	53 INCHES
Panama	132 INCHES

is as high as anywhere on the earth, and crop after crop can be grown without using fertilizer.

But not all of the humid continental region has these characteristics. The range of temperature is less along the eastern seaboard than it is inland. There are small areas of relatively mild climate close to the Great Lakes, where the grape and the peach can be grown commercially. There are many areas also where the soil is poor, where abundant fertilizer is needed if crops are to be grown and the land is best left under forest or grass. Toward the western limits of the region the amount of rainfall falls below that needed for corn, then below the demands of wheat until the land is cultivated only if irrigation water is available; and the rest is left to grass and grazing cattle.

This climatic belt which reaches from the Atlantic Coast to the Rocky Mountains and reaches far north into Canada is by no means the most extensive region of humid continental climate. In the Old World, another such belt begins in Germany and reaches to Central Asia, where it merges into the high mountains and deserts. It appears again in northern

China and extends into Korea, eastern Siberia, and northern Japan. The climatic features of the American humid continental climate are found here too: winters of extreme severity, and hot summers. The range of temperature increases from Germany, where 30° to 40° separate summer from winter, eastward to the Urals where the range is about 60.° In Soviet Central Asia it reaches 70°, about the same as in North Dakota. There too the total rainfall diminishes as the climate becomes more extreme, and the grasslands of Central Asia correspond with those of North Dakota or Manitoba.

The vegetation of the humid continental region is one of broad-leaved forest gradually passing through tall-grass into short-grass prairie. The broad-leaved forest occupies the moister east in the United States. In Germany and eastern Europe the natural vegetation before most of it was cleared by man was oak and beech; with conifers on the higher ground and the poorer soil. This merged eastward into a belt of mixed forest with both deciduous and coniferous forest, which in turn passed gradually into steppe or prairie. The Russian steppe resembles in its level expanse of rich black the cornlands of Illinois and Iowa. The Russians have recently pushed the limits of cultivation eastward from the steppes of Ukraine into the so-called "virgin lands" of Kazakhstan; this is a project of Khrushchev's. The Chinese have similarly advanced into the grasslands of Manchuria and Inner Mongolia. Geographically considered, this phenomenon is identical with the cultivation of the high plains of Oklahoma, Kansas, Colorado, and Nebraska, and the Canadian practice of extending the wheatlands northwestward to the limits of the humid continental climate in the Peace River Valley of northern Alberta.

The word *chernozem* is Russian, and it means "black earth." It was the name which the Russian scientists who pioneered the study of the soil gave to the rich, dark soil of Ukraine. In the United States the word has been taken over and given to the similar soils of Illinois and Iowa. In this relatively dry margin of the continental climate, humus is formed from the living tissues of plants. But it decomposes only slowly. During the long, cold winter bacteriological action is restricted or brought to a stop. The products of plant decay are not removed by percolating waters because there is in fact very little downward movement of moisture. The dry air and the continuous evaporation from the surface of the soil is always drawing moisture up to the ground level. Here it evaporates, concentrating the soluble chemicals of the soil in the top few inches, where the roots of plants may reach them. Plant matter and the products formed by its decay are thus held in the surface layers of the soil, giving it the dark, even black color which we associate with the best of the midwestern soils.

Out on the arid frontier of the humid continental region the climate becomes increasingly unreliable. As the average rainfall drops, so does its reliability. An average of 40 inches in the humid east may mean a certainty of getting each year between 35 and 45 inches. An average in western Kansas of 15 inches may in fact mean anything from less than 10 to over 20; the latter is abundant for wheat, the former is totally inadequate and the crop will be choked by drought. This was demonstrated in the United States in the bitter thirties of this century, and it was learned by harsh experience that there is a limit beyond which it does not pay to plow the plains without reaping a heritage of soil erosion and dust storms. It is probable, even certain, that in Soviet Central Asia and in Mongolia and Manchuria there is also a limit beyond which crops will be less sure than the resulting perils of blowing soil. Today the Russians are pressing boldly forward into the virgin lands. How long will it be before they recoil from the dust storms they have created?

Across the top of North America and the Old World stretch the cold regions, the *High Latitude Forest* and the *High Latitude Tundra* climates. From Alaska to Labrador, from the coast of northern Norway right across Siberia to the Pacific Ocean thousands of miles away, is a great belt of forest, the taiga, the only really great expanse of virgin timber left, and second only to the deserts, the most extensive climatic region in the world. Its summers are short and cool; only rarely does a July average rise to over 60°. Fall comes early, and freezing temperatures are widespread in September. Winter temperatures plunge below zero; the average for January is more than –10° over much of northern Canada and all of eastern Siberia. The celebrated station of Verkhoyansk in Siberia has a January average of –59°, and it's not unusual for a place to have four months or more of temperatures continuously below freezing.

Yet the short summer is quite warm. Although the sun never gets very high above the horizon, it stays above it the whole day and at midnight just rolls along the northern horizon. Karel Čapek thus described the arctic summer in northern Scandinavia: "Here there is no night, and there is not even day; here are only the morning hours, when the sun is still low, all golden with the dawn and silvery with the dew, the sparkling sun of early day; and then without a break came the hours of late afternoon, when the sun is already low, turning gold with the

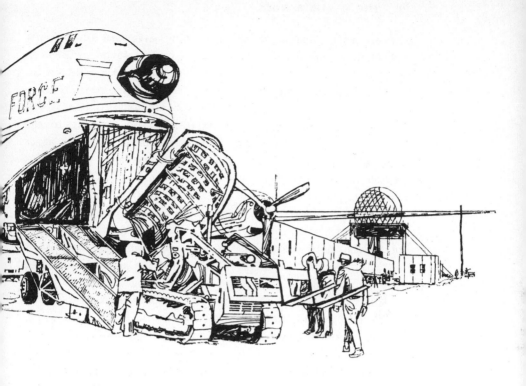

sunset, already purple and misty with the sweet melancholy of evening . . . never does the high bright arch of the steep moon raise its vault aloft, and the golden evening without an end in the fiery midnight dissolves into the silvery morning without a beginning, and it is again day." This is the landscape of northern Sweden, of Finland, of northern Canada, and the Soviet Arctic.

Grass grows, and flowers bloom in the open tracts amid the forests, and mosquitoes could not be more numerous in the equatorial forest. Occasionally a hardy, quick-growing crop of rye, barley, or fodder crops can be reaped, but the wealth of the region does not lie in its agriculture. It lies in its forests, its minerals, and its fur-bearing animals. Formerly the last were the most important, because they alone could be carried out of the region by the fur trapper who moved on foot or by canoe. More recently the forests have themselves come to be exploited. The lumber is coniferous softwoods, with occasional stands of hardy deciduous trees like the birch. It is in demand for building and for pulp and paper manufacture, but the difficulty in the way of its use has always been that of transportation.

The rivers of the subarctic region mostly flow northward to the Arctic Ocean. Though their upper courses may be open and navigable all summer and into the fall, their mouths lie farther north and are frozen for longer periods. At the same time sea ice makes them inaccessible to ocean-going freighters without incurring the high cost of using icebreakers. The Russians use such means to open up shipping to the mouths of some of their northern rivers, but icebreakers have never been used regularly along the northern coast of Canada.

Lastly, along the shore of the Arctic Ocean, in North America and in northern Europe and Asia, and spread out over the islands of the Arctic Ocean, is the tundra. Point Barrow, in northern Alaska, is typical. July has an average temperature of 40°, and only three months have temperatures above the freezing point. For five months the average is below zero. Precipitation is slight, as is usually the case in very cold climates, and most of it falls as snow. The growing season for plants lasts only for the two or three summer months. This is too severe even for the coniferous forest. Along its northern edge the conifers die away, just as the broad-leaved trees fade on the edge of the prairie. A few stunted conifers struggle against the wind and perpetual cold in sheltered hollows, and then they too give up the unequal struggle. Only mosses, lichens, and a few small, bright flowering plants, like the "alpines" of the mountains, continue to live, making a brave show when the snow melts away for the few weeks of summer.

The same physical environment extends around the remaining shores of the Arctic Ocean from the north of Norway to the Bering Strait, which separates Siberia from Alaska. It covers Svalbard, much of Iceland, and the arctic islands of the Soviet Union, and in Greenland the tundra forms a narrow strip between the ice sheet that covers most of this huge island and the ocean.

Despite the hardships, there is human life in this region. Small groups of Eskimo or of the similar Tungus, Chukchi, and other arctic peoples of Siberia live here. Agriculture is impossible, but they fish and hunt, selling their skins to traders who in turn make life easier for them by selling them modern tools and hunting weapons.

Most of the land surface of the earth lies in the Northern Hemisphere —about two-thirds, in fact—and in the latitude of Canada there is far more land than sea. The continents taper away toward the south, and between the latitudes of 55° and 65° south of the equator there is no land at all, beyond a few small, rocky, and almost uninhabited islands.

Yet at the poles themselves this relationship is reversed. The North Pole lies in the midst of the Arctic Ocean; the South Pole, high on the icecap which covers most of the Antarctic continent. Antarctica, almost twice as large as the continent of Australia, has no permanent inhabitants, though today it seems never to be without its parties of explorers and scientists. Most of it is covered with ice, and the rock appears in savage cliffs only around its margin. It has no soil; no crops could grow out-of-doors, and unless some wealth in minerals or fuel is discovered, Antarctica is likely to remain exclusively for the scientist.

We are now one step farther toward answering the question to which we addressed ourselves at the beginning of this book: Why is mankind spread so unevenly over the earth, and what remedy is there? The pattern of climates and the incidence of weather play a role no less—perhaps more—important than the surface relief of the land and the rocks of which it is made. Climate sets limits to the growing season and restricts the crops that can be grown. Through its influence on the soil it determines the fertility of the land. Climate would appear to set a rigid framework within which man has to live and grow his food, with some regions of the earth remaining forever of small importance in supporting human life, and others of no importance at all. Yet this frame may not be so rigid after all. Man's ingenuity is proving to be a match, locally at least, for parsimonious nature.

4 MAN
ON THE LAND

*There are no necessities, but everywhere possibilities;
and man, as master of the possibilities, is judge of
their use.*

LUCIEN FEBVRE

The population of the world is more than three billion, and each day adds another one hundred fifty thousand to the total. When a man now retiring from active work was born, there was only half this total. A century and a half ago there were only a quarter as many people, a generation ago there were only two-thirds as many people, and if the present trend continues, the world's population will reach five billion within this generation. Yet the world is still very far from having standing room only. There are today a little over fifty people to every square mile of land; on average, every inhabitant of this earth has about ten acres. English farm workers once demanded "two acres and a cow." If that is what is needed to support a family, then this earth has land for all needs and more to spare.

But the problem is not as simple as this. The land itself, as we have seen in the last two chapters, is of very unequal value. Two acres of English lowland is one thing; two acres, or even fifty acres, of equatorial forest, of tundra, or of desert are quite a different matter. And secondly, people are themselves not equal in skill and ability. As far as concerns farming, they range from the farmer trained in a land-grant college, who knows plant biology and soil chemistry and can use a tractor and a harvester, to the primitive cultivator with nothing more elaborate than a digging-stick. In terms of human progress, thousands of years separate the farmer who calls upon a rainmaker and one who uses irrigation.

101

Agriculture is the fundamental human occupation. With the exceptions only of hunting and fishing, it provides us with all our food, and about three-quarters of the human race are tillers of the soil. The curse of Cain has rested heavily upon mankind, and if in this book we give a lot of space to land, soil, and crops, it is because these in the last analysis determine our welfare. The basic reason for human inequality is the unevenness both of the fertility of land, and of man's use and misuse of it.

But about a quarter of mankind lives, or at least works, in cities. As we know all too well, a majority of the population of the United States now lives in cities; it was very different even a generation ago. Cities serve many functions, but looked at broadly, they serve as centers of specialized industry and commerce. The world's population has grown fast; that of its city dwellers, much faster. This reflects one thing: the increasing efficiency of the farmer over the world at large, so that agriculture has come to require the labor of a diminishing proportion of those whom it feeds. At the same time, it reflects the growing demand for the products of the factories and the services of the cities.

We must start in with the population map on pages 26–27. The most densely peopled areas show more than 250 persons to the square mile, and the least have less than two. But these figures are not the extremes. Population densities range from no people at all over parts of the desert regions and of the Arctic and Antarctic to over a thousand to the square mile on the most congested lands of India, China, Egypt, or the island of Java—the highest densities anywhere except, of course, in the great cities. In these crowded lands there is only about half an acre, not a great deal more than a suburban building lot, to support each man, woman, and child. How much food could you grow on a piece of land this size? That is as much as a large part of the human race gets to eat.

The map shows three large areas of very dense population, together with numerous quite small areas. One is in eastern Asia: it includes China, with neighboring Korea, Vietnam, Formosa, and Japan. A thinly peopled land which is mainly high mountain and thick forest separates this from the second area of dense population: India, Pakistan, and Ceylon. This region of teeming humanity is also cut off by high mountains and empty desert from other such areas. The third covers much of Europe. Starting in the United Kingdom, it stretches beyond the narrow seas which separate England from the continent, across France, the Low Countries, Germany, and Italy. Unlike the populated areas of India and

China, which end abruptly at the foot of the mountains or the edge of the desert, this European region of dense population gradually fades out through the less densely peopled lands that border it, in Spain and Scandinavia, in the Balkan Peninsula, and the European parts of the Soviet Union.

The densely populated regions of India and Pakistan and of eastern Asia resemble one another; most people cultivate the land. In the European region they do not. If one were to drive across much of England by night, the landscape would never be without the twinkling lights of villages and towns. Reflected against the clouds there would always be seen the glow of the next city. England is a land of cities, and this predominance of cities extends through Europe until they become fewer and less frequent on the borders of this region of dense population. The contrast between densely populated rural countries and densely populated urban countries is vital for our discussion.

The rest of the world is very much less densely peopled. Look at the United States. The map shows clusters of dense population in the northeast of the country: from Boston to Baltimore and Washington, around Pittsburgh, Cleveland, Detroit, and Chicago. But most of the land has no more than the average density and much has a great deal less. Most of Canada is very sparsely peopled. In South America nine-tenths of the population lives around the margin of the continent, and except in a few fertile upland basins, the vast interior is little known, underdeveloped, and almost uninhabited. Spread through the African continent are small areas of dense population, like oases, each surrounded by the bush, the desert, or the jungle. Of the whole, huge land mass of Asia, only about a fifth of the area contains all the populous lands we have already discussed. The rest has only a very thin scattering of people, with larger knots and groups here and there. Australia is the smallest and most empty of all the land masses, with the exception of ice-covered Antarctica which has for inhabitants only the small masculine society of groups of scientists and explorers.

RURAL POPULATION

At first glance there is neither rhyme nor reason in this pattern which people make upon the globe. In this chapter we are concerned with the reasons for the inequality, not of man, but of the distribution of man. To what extent, we must ask ourselves, has nature determined this pattern for us? Does the pattern of people on the land spring from the pattern of those physical elements—the relief, soil, and climate—that we have already examined? Or does it arise from man's own volition; has he himself made this pattern of people what it is? Nature, we have already seen, has not always been liberal in her giving, but man has rarely been as provident as he should in using nature's gifts. Can it be said, as Shakespeare did, that

> *The fault, dear Brutus, is not in our stars*
> *But in ourselves, that we are underlings.*

We can answer these questions only by examining the regions and divisions of the world. Let us look closely, as if with a magnifying glass, at a half-dozen scattered and contrasted fragments of the earth. At the same time let's compare the population map with the vegetation map on pages 22–23.

In the equatorial forests of the Amazon live the Boro people. They are not a numerous people, but there are other tribes like them not only here in South America, but also in Africa and Southeast Asia. They live in the territory where Brazil meets Colombia and Peru, but for these political divisions the Boro care little or not at all. They are an agricultural people, and one of the most primitive of the agriculturists on the earth. None of the refinements of agricultural science have reached them.

The Boro live in small tribes which move and work together. They make a small clearing in the forest, ringing the trees to kill them and pulling up and burning the creepers and smaller plants. The soil is scratched with a digging-stick, made of hardwood and further hardened by being charred in a fire. This "plowing" penetrates only the top inch or two of the soil, and here they plant their manioc, yams, sweet potatoes, and pumpkins. The land gets no fertilizer except what the burned vegetation contributes. The rainfall is heavy and the tilled soil very quickly deteriorates. The valuable soil chemicals are dissolved and carried downward by the percolating rain water. Deep plowing would return some of them to the surface, and tree crops would send deep roots down in search of them; but the digging-stick and the yams of the Boro can do neither. The soil wears out, and the Boro tribe packs its few belongings and moves on to make a fresh clearing in the forest and to use up the meager store of fertility in another patch of soil. Meanwhile the forest closes in on the abandoned clearing. In a year or two no one would ever know that here a Boro tribe had rested a while; and the growth and decay of jungle plants and trees gradually gives back a little fertility to the wasted soil.

In a similar environment in Malaya the damp, equatorial forest grows in a similar, poor soil. Forest tribes once lived in the innermost recesses of the forest, avoiding contact with outsiders. Then came the Europeans with young seedlings of the rubber tree. The rubber was a native of those Amazonian forests where the Boro lived, but its usefulness was unknown to them. Along with the seedling rubber trees, the Europeans brought in the tools to clear the forest, to tear out the roots so that they would not grow again, and to build roads, railroads, and houses. They recruited Chinese labor, hardworking, intelligent, and quick to learn, in order to plant the seedlings, to protect them during their period of growth, and to tap the rubber from their trunks when they had fully developed.

Trees could live and flourish in this climate and soil, where plants could not, since their roots tapped the precious minerals of the subsoil; and when the soil showed the need of a fertilizer, it was supplied. A square mile of Malayan plantation supported far more people than a square mile of Amazonian forest, and kept them at an incomparably higher level of welfare. In this area developed by the ingenuity of man, the plantation workers are better fed, better housed, and better educated; they have the services of doctors, and their food supply is brought in by truck or freight car.

Now turn to the level alluvial plains and gentle hills that make up the most densely populated part of China. The land is cultivated here today just as it has been for the past four thousand years. A pattern of agriculture and of human existence has been evolved that remained, until very recent years, impervious to change. It has been a successful pattern because it has supported more people to the square mile than almost any other. To begin with, the land is good. Over the Great Plain of China there is deep, rich alluvial soil, brought down through the centuries by the Chinese rivers and spread out over the plain. The climate is also good; heavy rains in the summer when growing plants need them most, and irrigation waters from the rivers at other seasons; mild winters in the south so that crops can continue to grow, and three harvests can be made in a year in some areas, two in others.

Yet soil and climate do not alone explain the success with which Chinese society has adjusted itself to its natural conditions. The Chinese have themselves shown an extraordinary skill in fitting their pattern of agriculture into its physical setting. It is a kind of gardening. It is, in R. H. Tawney's words, "The agriculture of a pre-scientific age, raised by centuries of venerable tradition to the dignity of an art. Compared with that of most parts of Europe, in any period before the nineteenth century, it is a prodigy of efficiency."

The land is tilled and irrigated with almost an artist's sense of perfection; water is led onto it, the rice plants are set out in the paddy field, and the ripened grain is harvested with economy and precision and care for the last minutiae. As all food comes from the soil, so to the soil must everything return. There are no sewers and septic tanks; all goes back whence it came. These farmers of forty centuries have maintained undiminished the fertility of their fields, not by the use of factory-made fertilizer, but by the constant application of consummate patience, skill, and industry.

A different people would have reacted differently to the challenge of this environment. Many, like the Boro, would have extracted less from it. Some, by exploiting more fully its power resources, might have built up an urbanized and industrialized society, capable of supporting even more people to the square mile; Belgium, Great Britain, West Germany, and a few other states are inhabited by societies which have done just this. In each the great majority of the population lives in cities, and, if it does not actually work in factories, is nevertheless dependent upon manufacturing industries. In this way people live even thicker on the ground. The industrial regions, such as the Ruhr in West Germany, and the English Midlands have a population density unknown in the overcrowded agricultural countries of Asia. These industrial areas may be drab, dirty, and depressing, but they are not overcrowded. Work may be hard and people poor, but people do not live on the margin of subsistence, as they do amid the paddy fields of Asia.

By contrast to the plain of China the taiga and tundra are regions of sparse population and of no significant agricultural possibilities. Here, one may be tempted to say, nature has offered little scope; here the good life is not possible. The population has been limited to a handful of seminomadic peoples, whose traditional mode of life depends upon hunting and fishing. Land travel is not easy. The terrain is rough; in winter it is deeply covered by snow, and it is difficult if not impossible to keep roads open for motor vehicles. In spring the snow melts and makes its way slowly to the rivers. But for much of the summer the melt water lies in pools over the land. The sun is too weak to dry it up,

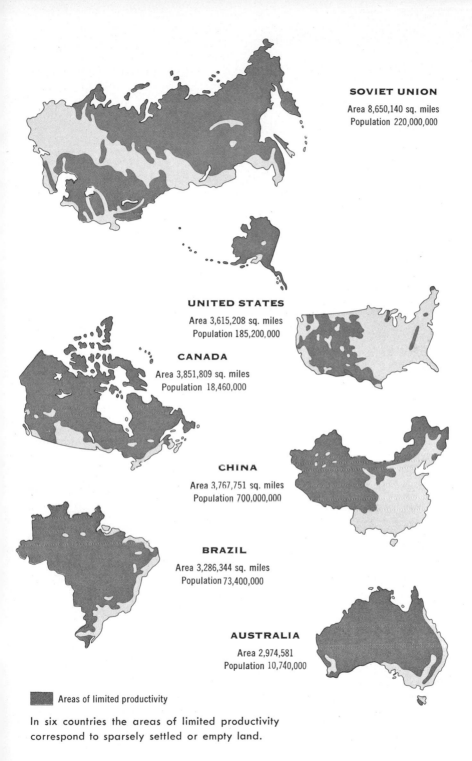

SOVIET UNION

Area 8,650,140 sq. miles
Population 220,000,000

UNITED STATES

Area 3,615,208 sq. miles
Population 185,200,000

CANADA

Area 3,851,809 sq. miles
Population 18,460,000

CHINA

Area 3,767,751 sq. miles
Population 700,000,000

BRAZIL

Area 3,286,344 sq. miles
Population 73,400,000

AUSTRALIA

Area 2,974,581
Population 10,740,000

Areas of limited productivity

In six countries the areas of limited productivity
correspond to sparsely settled or empty land.

and the permanently frozen subsoil, or permafrost, prevents the water from soaking in and draining away. Land travel is, in fact, easiest in winter when sled and snowshoes facilitate movement.

Now the search for minerals is doing more than any other development to open up this region, just as it is attracting people to those other empty regions, the hot deserts. But only the more valuable minerals are sought. Mining equipment is flown in, and in extreme cases the ore is itself flown out again. In recent years the subarctic has acquired yet another importance. It borders the Arctic Ocean, and the shortest route from the United States to the Soviet Union is across the Arctic. Running through the subarctic region is the Distant Early Warning system—the DEW line—and doubtless in the subarctic region of Europe and Asia is to be found the Russian variant of the same. Modern technology is revealing possibilities in these regions that were undreamed of a generation or two ago.

One might go on drawing such little vignettes of the world's cultivators and underdeveloped areas. What concerns us is the differing ways in which the cultivators bring their skill and techniques to the land; how they fit their agriculture into the framework which nature has prescribed for them; how they modify this framework by draining the land, spreading fertilizer, cutting irrigation canals, so that it better suits their needs. In a rough way we can rate these societies according to the skills they have shown in using their environment, and to the resulting levels at which they live. But we must not think of the level of human welfare as merely the result of man's skills and techniques on the one hand, and of the physical environment on the other.

A traveler in Eastern Europe, let us say in Poland or Romania, sees a farmer leading his cow along the road, pausing while it browses on the dusty grass by the roadside. A friend accompanies him, and they chat while the cow eats, and a shepherd dog runs in and about with all the appearances of frenzied activity. Wherever two men and a dog are employed to watch one cow, there is overpopulation. The same amount of work could be performed by one man; in fact, he might do several times as much, as he could watch several cows as easily as one. But here cows are scarce and men are not. There are more than enough people to do all the work that has to be done in the village and its fields, and the surplus labor just engages in busy work. Yet the food needs of the community are proportionate, not to the amount of work performed but to the number of workers who are engaged in its performance, however slight may be their individual contribution. "They also serve who only stand and wait," was not said with subsistence agriculturists in mind.

In most of the communities mentioned so far, would fewer hands accomplish as much and eat a good deal less? Clearly this is so in China; it is also true of India, of Egypt, of Java, and to some degree of the lands of Eastern Europe and the Middle East, of North Africa, the West Indian Islands, and much of Latin America. In each of these lands, despite the richness and the bounty of nature in most, man himself is not well off, and if mankind were not so numerous, he might be better off. For many of these peoples life is "poor, nasty, brutish and short." And in each instance, the reason for the poverty, the nastiness, and the brutishness of human existence lies, in part, in the way they use or misuse their natural environment; in part, also, in their numbers, whether they are fully employed or just underemployed; and, lastly, in the resources with which nature has itself endowed them. Technology, population, and natural resources—these are the keys to the understanding of the variations in the human condition, and only through understanding them can there come any improvement in the lot of man.

We have been making an erratic pilgrimage over the earth looking for ways in which man and nature are adjusted to one another. Anyone who leaves for a moment the well-beaten tourist routes will find poverty, and even the tourist is escorted through areas of poverty, provided it is picturesque enough. For the majority of mankind, want is a normal condition; the specter of starvation is always before him, whether because of nature's parsimony or man's improvidence is for us to inquire. But before we do so, let us look at some more successful and satisfying ways in which man has come to terms with nature.

At the opposite extreme from the crowded, toiling peasantry of China or India are the great corn and cattle farms of the North American Midwest, the wheat farms of Kansas, the fruit farms of California, or the dairy farms of Wisconsin. Each in its own way is blessed with the right physical conditions. The soil is good, and the climate, notwithstanding the everlasting complaints, is nevertheless suited to what the farmer grows, and usually gives him rain and sunshine when he needs them. These are specialized farms, cultivated with all the aids and refinements that science can offer. Here too there is space; people are not so crowded that they must cultivate that last square inch or two of soil, cost what it may in terms of labor, nor so numerous that we find two people doing the work of one.

The great corn-growing, cattle-fattening farms of Illinois or Iowa are large. The land is level, or nearly so; it is well drained, deep, black, and fruitful; it is plowed by tractor, and the crop is harvested by a corn picker. The beef cattle stamp and churn their feed lot to mud, putting on weight in the fastest possible way, fed by the corn and the silage channeled down to them. And when they are heavy enough, they are moved on to the equally streamlined and efficient packing factories in Omaha or Kansas City.

There are many other types of farm where the maximum yield is extracted from the soil with a minimum expenditure of effort: the huge cotton fields of Texas and California, where the seed is sown, the soil tilled, and the cotton picked by machines; the vineyards and fruit farms of California. The United States does not possess a monopoly of such streamlined and efficient farming. The sheep farms of New Zealand yield to none in the efficiency with which they fatten sheep and export them as lamb and mutton. Australia produces wool as cheaply as any country in the world. In each of these a few workers with big machines produce quantities that would be inconceivable to the subsistence farmer

in Asia or Africa or Latin America. As we saw in the case of the Malayan rubber plantation and even in the examples of the urbanized industrial societies of Europe, man's technology and skill, though in some
degree dependent on resources, are most instrumental in raising the
level of human welfare

These efficient farmers and producers have three features in common.
First, they are all specialists, whether it is beef or lamb, wheat or cotton
that they produce. Secondly, they are highly capitalized; their heavy
reliance upon mechanical equipment, upon fertilizers, and upon highly
developed skills and techniques lifts them far above the technical level
of the nearly self-sufficing peasant. Lastly, as a general rule, these farmers
have space; there is no crowding, and they can make their farms as large
as it seems desirable to make them. If we examine the volume of output
in relation to the input of labor, production appears staggeringly high,
because labor can call upon all the resources in technology and land that
it thinks desirable.

If, on the other hand, we compare the yield in crops or in animals
with the area used to produce them, the result is a great deal less impressive. The Indian or the Chinese farmer sometimes gets more out of
an acre than the wheat farmer of Kansas extracts from a single acre of
his spreading wheat fields. The American farmer, in general, is not called
upon to be sparing in his use of land; he has plenty, and can afford to
invest his surplus in the soil bank.

The farmer in the crowded lands of Asia and elsewhere has labor in
abundance, but his skills are only the traditional ones of his neighborhood, and his tools and equipment may well be primitive. Above all he
is crowded; he has pressed the area of his cultivation to the limits—and
beyond. Of course he would use better tools if they were available, but
no amount of machinery would get more rice from his paddy field than
he gets. He makes up for the lack of machines by the untiring labor of
his own arms. Better strains of seed and more fertilizer would give him
bigger yields, but what he wants is more land, wider fields, space to plow
and go on plowing for days. Where to find it is the problem.

Tomorrow's population will be bigger than today's; but already much
of the world's cropland is producing almost as much as it seems capable
of doing. How to feed tomorrow's billions is the greatest problem before
the world. When one looks at the terraced hillsides in the Philippines,
cut and built with immense labor merely to get a little extra land for
crops, or at the irrigated fields of Egypt where all the land and all the

water that comes down the river Nile are put to use, it would seem that here there is very little room to expand agriculture and to produce more food.

The equatorial forest has often been heralded as a natural storehouse of food. Its exuberant forest growth, it has been claimed, must denote a fertile soil, and many early explorers, judging only by the richness of the forest, have declared its soil to be immensely rich. As we have already seen, fertility proves not to be the case. Yet the old myth of its wealth dies slowly and only through the bitter experience of crop failure and financial loss has it been learned that the soil that can support the jungle does not necessarily produce corn or rice.

A nineteenth-century pioneer who tried to use the equatorial soils discovered to his dismay and loss that "newly-cleared forest land will only produce one crop of miserable grain." Plantation trees can be made to grow well—rubber, cacao, palm oil—but these will not support the hungry masses of Asia and Africa; and furthermore they require an amount of capital and skill to establish that poor, land-hungry subsistence farmers cannot hope to command.

The remedy for the physical conditions of the equatorial regions has not yet been found, except locally, yet the problem is not insuperable; it has not really been faced. Equipment is needed for clearing the land and for tearing out the roots of the trees on a scale undreamed of elsewhere. Fertilizers must be custom-made to fit the soil, and labor must be brought into the equatorial regions, for it goes without saying that there is little already there. Too often methods of large-scale cultivation, that have proved successful elsewhere, have been applied to the equatorial forest region; they have proved to be unsuitable, and the forest has been condemned as uncultivable.

As far as human settlement is concerned, the equatorial forest is still mostly an empty land, but the savanna, that country of tall grass and scattered, parklike trees, of big game and well-marked seasonal change, is dotted with widely scattered centers of population. Clearly it has potential, and, as L. Dudley Stamp has said, "of all the underdeveloped or undeveloped lands in the world the tropical savannas call most urgently for careful study."

Yet the problems of settling the savanna lands are only a degree less formidable than those of the equatorial forest. The wet season occupies only a part of the year, and the dry season is long and hot. The growing season is short, and intense evaporation during the rest of the year leads to the formation of alkali salts in the soil. The problems inherent in the management of the savanna may not be as insuperable as those of the rain forest, but they also would defy the skills of the peasant farmer.

In the years following the Second World War the British government decided to grow peanuts, then needed for their fat content, on the savanna of East Africa. This was to be mechanized farming in a big way: bulldozers to clear the brush, disc plows to break up the soil. All the skills that agricultural science could command were enlisted, and the scheme was a dismal failure. Its cost amounted to over $100,000,000, averaging $2.00 for every man, woman, and child in the United Kingdom. In the words of the London *Times*, "the forces of nature are strong in the tropics and the conversion of bush into productive farming land is more than a task for bulldozers. The soil and its defects have to be clearly studied. Usually there are good reasons why the natives have left the bush to nature." Yet some solution will—and must—be found. In the equatorial forest and the savanna lands of the tropics there is empty land for tomorrow's billions.

The fact that we can list the things that are wrong with the savanna country from the agricultural point of view suggests that we are on the way to a solution. The diagnosis is almost complete; next come prescription and cure. Already agriculture is making a slow and halting advance in regions of equatorial forest and savanna—in Brazil, in Nigeria, in Ghana, the Congo, Malaya, and Indonesia.

The potentialities of other regions must not be forgotten. The desert, for example, is as deceptive as the equatorial forest, though in the opposite way. The bare rock and drifting sand have no value, but here and there long vanished rivers have laid down large expanses of alluvium. No rainfall has leached away their inherent fertility, and they await only a life-giving stream of water. In Genesis we read that "a river went out of Eden to water the garden." In mid-latitudes the rivers usually do not water the land; they drain it, but Eden was conceived of as an oasis, in the words of Tennyson,

> *Where falls not hail, or rain, or any snow,*
> *Nor ever wind blows loudly....*

where the water comes as a perennial stream from the distant mountains, and the sunshine is bright and the soil deep and rich.

The land of Egypt is such an Eden, though the life of modern Egyptians may be something less than idyllic. So too is the Imperial Valley in southern California, where the Colorado River irrigates the vast, dry, fertile cotton lands, and so are the fruit orchards along the Gila Valley of Arizona and the land that Brigham Young settled at the foot of the Wasatch Range. Ribbons of bright-green irrigated land lie along the Platte, the Kansas, and the Arkansas rivers where they cross the high, dry plains. In the dry savanna and on the desert margin in Africa and India, irrigation is today extending the area under crops. In Australia a river has been made to flow through a tunnel cut across a mountain range to bring irrigation water to lands that lacked only the life-giving water. In irrigation lies the best hope of extending the area sown with crops and producing food. But irrigation works—and all new irrigation schemes which require elaborate engineering—are costly. The current project in India and Pakistan, to enable the fullest use of the water of the river Indus and its tributaries, is made possible only by a very large grant from the World Bank.

The pushing out of the frontier of cultivation into the equatorial forest, the savanna, and the desert is slowly being accomplished. At the same time more food is being obtained from the old fields that have long been cultivated. Better strains of seed and a more careful selection of the seed; the greater use of fertilizer, and the more careful suiting of fertilizer to soil; the introduction of better farm tools and improved farming methods—all contribute to heavier crops. In Denmark, farmers reap more than 40 bushels of wheat to the acre of land; in India less than 10. The United States averages over 30 bushels of corn; the Soviet Union, less than 20; and Java, less than 10. It is not surprising that Khrushchev, who is quite a farmer in his way, has shown an intense interest in the varieties and the performance of hybrid corn.

In these ways food production may keep ahead of food needs, but the price of complacency, of carelessness, and of waste in using the soil is starvation and want. We cannot afford the luxury of soil erosion and dust storms, of soil inadequately cultivated, and of rivers flowing down to the sea unused.

In the United States less than a quarter of the total area is cultivated, and total farm land, including grazing land, makes up about 60 per cent of the total. This is above the average for the world as a whole. Yet much of the country must remain uncultivated because it lacks both moisture and soil. In the rest of the world much larger areas are in this condition. Roughly estimated, there is in the world today a little more than one acre of cropland together with about twice as much more of grazing, for each single member of the world's population. The average level of the world's feeding therefore cannot possibly be high.

URBAN POPULATION

Three-quarters of the world's population lives and works on the land, producing food, not only for its own needs, but also for the remainder of humanity. The remaining quarter lives for the greater part in cities and its population is employed mainly in factories, mines, transportation, and services.

Cities range from the vast conurbations of New York, London, and Tokyo to small towns that have not severed their direct and immediate connection with their surrounding rural areas. They include mining cities, where everything is subordinated to the extraction of minerals or fuel, and the future of the community depends on how long the resources last. They include mill towns, dominated by a group of tall, gaunt cotton or woolen mills; heavy and light industrial cities; cities in which the primary business is to run a big country; and those which have grown up around transportation centers and ports. Most recent to develop have been the resort cities, dedicated to that hardest of tasks, making people enjoy themselves.

Scattered around and between these larger and more specialized cities, like the stars of low magnitude which serve to accentuate the brilliance of the greater, are the hundreds of small towns. Each has only a few thousand people. There may be a small factory, but the life of the small town is bound up still with that of the surrounding rural areas, a place where farmers can bring their goods and purchase the few tools of their trade. There may no longer be a public market once a week in American cities, where the rural produce is sold or exchanged for the products of the city, but in most continents the weekly gathering in the public square of the small town is still the direct link between farmer and factory.

In the whole course of human history, no changes have so altered life and landscape as the agricultural and urban revolutions. The first was the discovery of the practice of cultivating the soil; it led to settlements, to permanent homes, and to an immense expansion of available food. The second was the discovery of the value of a city as a place of specialized craftsmanship, industry, and commerce.

The first cities were probably those built in the Middle East, about 2000 B.C. The institution spread—to Egypt, Greece, Italy, and all over the

Western World. The city arose also in India and China. The early city was guarded by walls and gave shelter and protection to craftsmen and artists. The close association of peoples within the city, their joint participation in government, and the civic pride that was engendered lifted its citizens above the level of mere workers and food producers. Modern civilization is mainly a product of the city. No one ever epitomized more aptly the role of the city than Pericles in his Funeral Oration over the Athenian dead: "Our city is thrown open to the world, and we never expel a foreigner or prevent him from seeing or learning anything. . . . Because of the greatness of our city the fruits of the whole earth flow in upon us. . . . Athens is the school of Greece."

The most ephemeral of cities is that founded upon a wasting mineral wealth—the mining city. It is a highly functional city. Its citizens are devoted to one task, pulling as much out of the bowels of the earth as possible in the shortest time. All its services are ancillary to mining, and the slightest decline in output or fall in the value of metal is reflected in barroom and shop, and on the railroads which bring in fuel and other materials and carry out the products of the mines. Such were the gold mining cities of Cripple Creek in western United States and Coolgardie in Australia, rising to a sudden prosperity, living their brief, roaring lives, and gradually decaying until only their ghostlike image survives to entertain the tourist. Such has been the fate of most.

Some mining cities have kept going a very much longer time, like Johannesburg, South Africa, Broken Hill, Australia, and Sudbury, Canada; their respective ore deposits of gold, lead and zinc, and nickel have proved to be larger and more lasting than most. A few have attracted other industries, based either on the product of the mines or on the needs of the miners. The coal mines, in particular, have attracted industries to them whenever it seemed more profitable to bring other materials to the fuel, rather than to distribute the fuel.

The industrial city has a longer life than the mining city. One industry tends to bring others until a self-perpetuating complex of factories, housing, transportation, and services is created. The industrial landscape is a familiar one. It is made up of factories, blackened by smoke, of a forest of tall chimneys, of row upon row of workers' housing, laced by the shining steel of railroads. It is the landscape of the cotton and the woolen cities of England; of the cities of the German Ruhr; of the French and Italian, Indian, and Japanese industrial centers; of Pittsburgh, Detroit, Gary, and Birmingham in the United States. Such centers of industry commonly grew up near the source of the power that turned their wheels. Coal was often the mainspring of their activity, and in time they have grown to be almost the color of coal dust.

The factory is where raw materials are gathered to be processed or fabricated into finished articles. Of necessity it is specialized, as specialized in its different way as the Malayan rubber plantation. It must have power to operate its machines, a transportation network to convey its raw materials and finished products, and labor to supervise its processes. Its life-blood is trade, the exchange of its products for the materials of which they are made and for the requirements of its workers.

This dependence upon the products of other peoples' fields and mines and upon their needs as consumers introduces an element of risk. The cycle of boom and depression has no impact on the self-sufficing agriculturist in the Amazon forest or China, and but little on the West African peasant cultivator; but on the industrial city its impact is immediate and intense. Any falling-off or change in demand for automobiles or new clothing, for structural steel or household goods, is reflected at once in the industrial city. The world's demand for factory-made goods is always changing, as public taste alters and new technical advances make new articles available. The income of the factory worker is higher than that of the agricultural worker, but he faces risks of lay-offs and short time that the agricultural worker does not know.

The factory worker is better off in terms of wages and the food and the pleasures he can buy with them. And the industrial country is richer than the agricultural. The poorer countries today aim to become more highly industrialized, to employ their surplus population in factories, and to increase their total wealth. Factories can be established anywhere that the raw materials, the power, the labor, and the equipment and skills can be brought together. But some areas have greater advantages than others. In some there is coal, as in Britain, or hydroelectric power, as in the Pacific Northwest; the metalliferous ores may be found, and agricultural raw materials grown. Others like the new industries of Argentina and Brazil must rely on trade to secure these, and pay highly also for the transportation of them. That country which can produce the goods most cheaply is likely to secure the market. Many underdeveloped countries have high hopes of building up industries, but many of these hopes may be doomed to disappointment. The facts of geography most often determine where the advantages lie.

Newer forms of power are slowly creating a new pattern of industry.

A characteristic of earlier forms of industrial power was that they could be used most profitably where they were produced; workshops gathered along the streams that provided water power, and steam-operated factories were built near the coal mines. But the new centers of industry stand in sharp contrast with the blackened old mill towns of England or the steel towns of Germany. In Switzerland and Sweden, in the new South of the United States, factory cities, Zürich or Stockholm for example, are cleaner and brighter. They are not permanently shadowed by a pall of smoke, and a thin encrustation of dirt has not covered their walls. They are powered by electricity; they are heated by gas or oil; and even the railroads are operated by diesel or electric locomotives.

Electric power, generated from coal on or near the coal fields, or from the force of running water, can be carried by cable to places where it is needed. There remains some technical restriction on the distance that such power can be transferred, but this distance is already several hundred miles and it may become possible to transfer it over even longer distances. The use of nuclear power, still only in its infancy for industrial purposes, will break what bonds still remain between manufacturing industry and the reserves of mineral fuel and water power. Already many of the small towns in North America have shining new factories, where they cut gears, assemble radios, or make plastic table goods, using only power piped in by overhead power lines. The future holds out prospects of building factory industry over much of Africa and South America, where there is neither coal nor oil, and over much of Asia, where fuel resources are small.

All industries, indeed all urban growth, imply transportation, for their essence is specialization and exchange. Many years ago a distinguished geographer, Mark Jefferson, wrote of the "civilizing rails," civilizing because they permitted exchange and encouraged specialization and thus a better and fuller use of labor and resources. In North America this role is devolving in part on the trucks, and we might speak of the civilizing results of four-lane highways. But over most of the world the railroads are still supreme in providing the means of moving and exchanging goods overland.

Water transportation is always cheaper than movement by rail or road. It is by far the easiest way to shift bulk goods—oil or iron ore or wheat or coal—over great distances. That is why seaways, like the St. Lawrence, are constructed, and rivers, like the Rhine, Mississippi, and Danube are improved for deep-water navigation. But however much

rivers and canals are extended and improved, there comes a point where goods must be transferred from water to land, from ship to freight car or truck. This is the specialized function of the port city.

Many ports are just the intermediaries between sea and land. In Africa some of them, like Accra in Ghana, serve merely to ship the cacao or the rubber. But most ports attract industries because the port is a natural convergence of routes, where different materials can be assembled with a minimum of effort. A particular group of industries tends to grow up in ports. Bulky materials are often processed there as they are unloaded from the ships that bring them; wheat is milled, oil seeds crushed, sugar refined, ores smelted. All recently built iron-smelting plants in this country have been located where freighters can unload ore within a few yards of the furnaces. The rapid industrial growth of the New York and Philadelphia metropolitan areas, of Houston-Galveston and Mobile and, outside North America, of London and the lower Thames and Liverpool, of Genoa in Italy, Marseille in France, and Calcutta and Bombay in India, are merely a few instances of the power of ports to attract to themselves those industries which are based on bulky materials imported by sea.

The development of industry in cities has been a factor contributing to the rise of another kind of city, the governmental or administrative city, free—or at least relatively so—from the distractions and pressures of industry and commerce. Such are Canberra, Australia; Brasília in

Brazil; New Delhi in India; Ottawa in Canada; and, above all, Washington, D.C.

As society grows more affluent, more money becomes available for the pursuit of pleasure. The large cities sometimes have a whole sector devoted mainly to entertainment, like Broadway in New York City and the West End in London. Entertainment even can become, in a few rare instances in the richer countries, the dominant pursuit and the mainstay of a city. In their very different ways, Miami Beach, Las Vegas, and Sun Valley in the United States exist to entertain and to amuse. The cities of the French and Italian Rivieras, the Swiss and Austrian mountain resorts, the hill stations of India, and the languid beaches of Acapulco and Biarritz are resort towns, supported by the affluence of either a rich society or a privileged class.

The city, strictly considered, is a legal entity. Within its limits it has a different structure of government and level of taxation from the territory which surrounds it. It probably differs also in its economic base and in the way of life of its inhabitants. But the "city limits" rarely constitute a clear-cut boundary between the urban functions which in general characterize a city, from the rural functions of the surrounding area. In the United States there are few large cities that are not ringed by smaller incorporated cities, and beyond these there is usually a residential fringe reaching far out into the surrounding countryside, building lots becoming larger and oftentimes the houses becoming more expensive and select with increasing distance from the center of the urban area. The whole complex of big city, lesser incorporated cities, and suburban fringe together make up an outspreading entity defined as the metropolitan area.

The legal structure of great cities differs from one country to another. In some there is an over-all controlling authority for the metropolitan area like the London County Council for London, England; in others, this authority has limited functions; and in others, again, the competing authorities form a near anarchic pattern, with the larger striving to annex or incorporate the smaller. But in function there is a broad similarity between all great cities. They are centers of specialized industry and commerce. The larger the city, the more varied is the range of industrial activity. Many of the branches of industry are interrelated, like steelmaking, manufacturing, and steel construction. A textile industry attracts the manufacture of dyestuffs, and this brings other and related branches of the chemical industry. With the growth of industry and the expansion of the industrial population there come, of necessity, those branches of industry which supply food, prepare clothing, build and equip offices, factories, and homes, and provide the services essential to the smooth running of all. Once started, an industrial complex tends to snowball.

Above all, the great city requires a complex network of transportation, without which it could neither come into existence nor continue to operate. It produces no food, though it may—and commonly does—refine or process crude foodstuffs that are imported. It produces few of the raw materials of its industries, and, according to the kind and variety of its specialization, it has to bring in by land or sea fuel and lumber, ores and metals, crude or partly processed chemicals, and the raw materials of a thousand other specialized branches of industry. These must be distributed within the metropolitan area, and workers in these industries and in the commercial, insurance, and other businesses which accompany them, must be got to work each morning and home each evening.

Each office, factory, and home must be linked with a source of water supply and with a system of sewers to get rid of its waste. The city must have power stations, motivated by coal, oil, gas, or water power, to supply electricity for factory and home; and it must have also, in some form, the means of mass education, of mass entertainment, and of mass information. And it must have, lastly, the instruments for its own government and protection. Such is any great city: New York, Chicago, Los Angeles, London, Tokyo, Calcutta, or any other of the several hundred great metropolitan centers of the world.

The function of these greater cities is so varied that it is difficult to fit them into industrial, commercial, or any other category. Each is a microcosm of the industrial life of its own country, and each derives strength from the variety of its pursuits. These pursuits are not all likely at one time to be depressed or to have severe unemployment. Generally speaking, if automobiles are down, household appliances may be up, and labor turned away by chemicals may be taken on by clothing. What is lost on the roundabout is likely to be recouped on the swings.

Mere size has its obvious advantages; it has its no less apparent problems. The bigger the city the greater becomes the difficulty of transportation in all its forms, from the movement of freight to the movement of commuters. How to park the cars or cope with the rush-hour peak is a headache in every great city. Other less apparent but more menacing problems come with size. Providing water supply necessitates the tapping of ever more distant sources. Not every city has, like Chicago, an inexhaustible supply right beside it. New York draws on the streams of the Catskill Mountains, and Los Angeles on the Colorado River and soon on the remote rivers of northern California. And all large cities are faced with sectors of the city on which time has laid its corroding hand and with others which have come to be monopolized by a sectional group. Urban renewal and "tough" districts are not specifically American problems; they are city problems, and thus are world-wide.

It is not difficult to see what factors have encouraged the growth of the world's great cities. They are focally situated; the routes of commerce link them with other cities. They have space over which workshops and homes can spread, long waterfronts for the building of docks and waterside factories; and around and behind them in every case stretch populous hinterlands, able to supply foodstuffs to the cities and to utilize manufactured goods from them, and dependent on the cities for a variety of services.

Smaller cities are, of necessity, less varied in function. Their range of industry is smaller, and many have only one significant industry: textiles in the mill towns of England, both New and Old; iron and steel working in Youngstown, Ohio; pottery in the English city of Stoke; tweed in the Scottish cities of Hawick and Galashiels; and ball-bearings in the German city of Schweinfurt. Such a city has few of the problems that result from sheer size. The handling of materials and products is generally simpler; the commuter problem is less. But so great a dependence on a single brand of industries gives too many hostages to economic misfortune. When depression and unemployment strike, they strike hard. A whole city becomes a distressed area.

In the Western World the city is a place where specialized industry and commerce are carried on. It houses a large percentage—in most countries a majority—of the population. It has a complementary relationship with rural areas, based upon the exchange of their respective products. In many Asian and some African and Latin American countries, the city does not wholly fulfill this role. Where the rural communities are as self-sufficing as they are in some of these areas, there is little room for specialization and exchange between city and village, factory and farm. The city is large, not so much because it is a center of industry, as because it has become a refuge for the poor, the outcast, and the dispossessed of these crowded lands. It is easier to beg and to pilfer in the city; there is always a sidewalk, a temple, or a railroad station to provide a sleeping place.

GREATER CHICAGO

Built-up areas

+++++ Railroads

——— Main highways

0   5   10 MILES

Highland
Park

Barrington

Arlington
Heights

Elgin

Des Plaines

Evanston

St. Charles

Wheaton

Elmhurst

Oak
Park

Cicero

Chicago
River

Lake

Michigan

Downers
Grove

La
Grange

Aurora

Oak
Lawn

Calumet Harbor

Calumet River

Whiting

Indiana Harbor

East
Chicago

Gary
Hbr.

Harvey

Hammond

Gary

Joliet

Homewood

ILL.

IND.

Park Forest

Chicago
Heights

Great cities of the world continue to expand into their hinterlands. Chicago
spreads out for miles from its original settlement near the Chicago River.

It seems natural to suggest that, in those countries where farm land
is scarce, and a family has to support itself on the produce of an acre or
two, that the surplus go to live and work in the cities. This is no remedy.
The cities are as overcrowded as the countryside, and unemployment is
often a good deal greater. Bigger cities, by themselves, will not solve the
problem unless their factory industries are expanded more than proportionately. These cities require more factories, both to employ fully the
vast horde of unemployed and half-employed, and also to make those
goods which are likely to add to the productivity of the farmer. By
intensifying the bond of specialization and mutual exchange between
city and village the best interests of both are going to be served.

For many centuries the population of the world has been increasing, and through most of this time that section of it which dwells in cities has been increasing faster than the rest. Cities have grown larger and more numerous. Not only has this been conspicuously so in the United States, but it has also been a significant feature of Europe for the past thousand years, and in the Middle East and southern and eastern Asia for an even longer period of time. The increase in the size of the city has been made desirable, if not necessary, by the advantages which many industries derive from being closely associated with one another geographically and from sharing transportation and shipping facilities and public services.

Nearly all the great cities of the world are growing steadily larger. There is a certain civic pride in this growth, and some pleasure is derived from it; Chicago was exuberant when its population overtook that of some of the east coast cities, and now Los Angeles enjoys the fact that it has drawn ahead of Chicago in the population of its metropolitan area. But such pride in growth and size is always tempered by the problems it creates. With rising standards of housing, fewer and fewer people can live on an acre of land. The suburban sprawl spreads ever deeper into the countryside, and the journey to work grows longer. Problems of water supply, sanitation, and health increase.

We could argue that sooner or later the disadvantages of increasing size and the rising cost of providing the services which they need, would bring this process to a halt. It has not done so yet, and the great metropolitan areas, like New York, Chicago, Los Angeles, and many others, continue to grow and spread, to eat up the countryside, to digest it with their bulldozers and draglines, and then to bury it under concrete and blacktop. The operation of economic forces has not checked the expansion of large cities. Their advantages for manufacturing and business concerns continue to be overwhelming; all that has happened is that firms which were established in the often blighted core of the city, now shift their operations to the suburbs. There is even a danger that these cities will become an expanding wave of housing and business, hollow in the middle.

Until a generation ago no one thought seriously of the military dangers of these overgreat cities. The events of the Second World War showed that they could be destroyed, though only at great cost to the enemy. Our present knowledge is that they can be obliterated in a few minutes or even seconds. In any future war they are likely to be primary targets, and the larger they grow, the easier will it become to hit them, and the more difficult to evacuate their inhabitants if ever an attack appears to be imminent. Already there is a move to decentralize certain sensitive and highly important government functions, though fears of nuclear attack do not appear so far to have deterred industrialists from expanding their operations in the already overexpanded metropolitan areas.

In the United Kingdom legislative action has been taken to stop the expansion process. By law a "green belt" has been reserved for farming and rural pursuits alone around London and other large cities. This area may not be urbanized. If further urban growth is needed—as it is—then it is obliged to go to "new towns," established beyond the green belt. Farther growth of big cities is checked; the formation of more cities of medium and small size is promoted, and what the industrialist and businessman may perhaps lose, is offset by the public gain in health and amenities. Could this be a model for the planned great cities of the future? Could they be broken up, their parts separated by green belts and smaller, newer towns created to circle like satellites around the great city which has grown as large as it should be allowed to grow? The alternative is chaos.

In the first chapter of this book we described the field of geography as the triangular relationship of earth, atmosphere, and man, each interacting with the other two. The succeeding chapters have examined the relationship of weather and climate with the rocks of the earth's crust, the mutual relationship of man and the earth, and the role of weather and climate in conditioning man's activities. But the world, as we know it today, is the product no less of man's relations with man. Patterns of race and of culture are bound up—in harmony or in conflict—with those of political organization. Rich peoples live side by side with poor, the former giving grudging aid to the latter; the latter accepting it with suspicion and envy. It is now time to look at what man has made of man.

5 MAN

IN HIS WORLD

It is man who reveals a country's individuality
by moulding it to his own use. . . . Only then does
a country acquire a specific character differentiating
it from others, till at length it becomes, as it were,
a medal struck in the likeness of a people.

VIDAL DE LA BLACHE

The pattern of climatic regions forms a useful framework on which to hang our discussion of man and his relationship to his environment, as we have done in preceding chapters. All inhabitants of, let us say, the equatorial forest or the desert, face similar physical conditions. They may respond to them in very different ways, but at least they are confronted by problems that are broadly alike. But laid across this pattern of physical regions is another of political groupings, or states, which influence man's life no less profoundly than the elements which make up the physical environment. In North America, according to where he makes his home, man may live in a region of humid continental, humid subtropical, marine west coast, or Mediterranean climate. But he also lives in the United States, and he shares its cultural traditions and political obligations. Through governmental action—taxes, import duties, bonuses, and price supports—it influences the choice of crops, the location of industry, the nature of trade both within the limits of the United States and without. The sovereign state is the most important unit for the organization and development of resources, and our discussion of the geography of the world must be organized on the basis of countries.

Before we turn to the political organization of the world, however, there are other divisions of mankind which must be examined, if only briefly. People belong to groupings which we call races, and they are divided further according to their languages, religions, and cultures. None of these divisions are precise; they have not got the clear-cut character of political allegiance. In fact, it is commonly said that there is no such thing as a pure and distinct race. Be this as it may, there are many—far too many—people who are deeply conscious and deeply concerned about race. To most people "race" is a vague term, with strongly emotional overtones. The idea that the family group or the wider tribal or clan group are all interrelated, of the same "blood," is a very old one. It came to be extended to the nation, and the terms "race" and "nation" are often, though erroneously, used as if they meant one and the same thing. But such looseness does not help us. There is not necessarily any blood relationship among all the members of a tribe, and certainly not among those of a nation.

To be precise, the term "race" denotes a biological relationship. A race is a group of people who have inherited certain conspicuous physiological characteristics, and are likely to transmit them to their children. A race, assuming that such exists, is similar in such biologically inherited characteristics as shape of head; such features of the skull as the nose and chin, skin color, and the color and texture of the hair. The highest degree of purity of race is probably to be found among peoples who have been cut off from outside contacts for a long period of time. It is to be found in the Indians of the Amazon forest, the tribes of the Russian and Canadian Arctic, and among such primitive peoples as the Pygmies and Bushmen, who have been driven by stronger peoples into the Kalahari Desert and Congo forests. A relative purity of race seems, then, to be accompanied by such a primitive level of culture that it is surprising that so many peoples have boasted of their race.

Most conspicuous of the attributes of race is skin color. In fact, most people think of race almost exclusively in terms of color. Yet color is one of the more fallacious of guides. There is every graduation of color from almost white to almost jet black. Any attempt to differentiate between peoples on the basis of color must be arbitrary, and may prove embarrassing to those who do it. A distinguished European diplomat, when called upon, on entering the United States, to complete a blank giving certain details of himself, answered the question "Race" with the word "Human."

Although the arbitrary division of mankind according to his color has just as much significance as a classification of cats into black, white, tabby, and so on, the idea that there is a fundamental difference between peoples based on their differences in color, dies hard. It was formerly held—and not only in Nazi Germany—that blond hair and blue eyes denoted an intellectual and moral excellence and were, in fact, the distinguishing marks of a "Master Race" or a *Herrenvolk*.

More enlightened thinkers, bolstered by the results of the psychologists' tests, know there are no superior, and no inferior, races, only that there are privileged and underprivileged peoples. The alleged backwardness of certain "colors" is due not to their color as such, but to the segregation and the poorer educational and cultural facilities to which their color has exposed them. Yet a map of the races of the world turns out invariably to be one based mainly on the distribution of skin color, since it is skin color which we first recognize and react to, and, therefore, in our social organization it is the most important aspect of race.

We know little about race; we are far from sure that we know where the human race originated, though we are certain that it was neither in the New World, nor in Australia, and we suspect that it was not in Europe. We are, by and large, ignorant of the routes by which man migrated and the stages by which, in the course of perhaps the million years since Homo sapiens emerged, he has peopled most of the habitable earth. We know only that at the very beginning of man's cultural history he had spread over most of the Old World and had secreted skulls and other anatomical fragments as far away from one another as Peking and Kenya, Java and Neanderthal in the lower Rhineland.

By a process of natural selection, dark-skinned peoples perpetuated themselves in Africa—the Negroid race; the yellow-skinned, in eastern Asia—the Mongoloid. We know that Asiatic peoples spread, perhaps by way of a now sunken land bridge, from Asia to North America and so through Central to South America. The South American Indians are descended from the earliest Americans; the North American Eskimo from the most recent and most Mongoloid of the invaders before the arrival of the Europeans themselves. After the coming of the Eskimo, no more peoples came to America from Asia by way of the Bering Strait until, during the last century, a few Russian fur traders made their appearance in Alaska.

The so-called Caucasoid peoples may have acquired their dominant characteristics in the general area of the Middle East, from which they spread to India and to Europe, and from Europe to the New World, Africa, and Australia.

These three racial groups—Mongoloid, Negroid, and Caucasoid—in origin perhaps distinct in both their physical features and their habitat, have so intermixed with one another and have given rise to so many subgroups that any neat, schematic diagram of the human race and its divisions breaks down. The map on pages 28–29 shows what anthropologists recognize as the predominant racial types or mixtures of types in each area. It cannot show the range of types that have resulted, because these are infinite.

Man spread over the earth at a time when the lands and oceans had more or less assumed their present shape. But the sea level has risen since, drowning many straits, the depressions across which our ancestors like the Israelites in the Red Sea were able to cross by foot. Britain was not cut off from the continent of Europe until about 5000 B.C.; and the aboriginal Australians reached that continent when it was separated from Asia only by narrow straits, easily navigated. Deserts which now constitute a barrier to human movement in North Africa and the Middle East, were formerly less formidable; during the closing phases of the Ice Age they were probably lightly wooded grassland, in which peoples moving from Asia into Africa could settle for a while and hunt the game that must have been abundant. Mountain ranges must, then as now, have thwarted movement and caused circuitous routes. Man must have entrusted himself to the sea in frail, unseaworthy craft, and allowed himself, as on the Kon-Tiki raft, to be carried across the oceans by wind and tide. The voyage of Columbus was very far from being the first venturing into the unknown in search of land.

By a process of natural selection the racial characteristics that we recognize and exaggerate began to emerge. Facial and respiratory, these characteristics were a response to high temperature or high altitude. Racial characteristics have nothing to do with human cultures. The latter are made up of folkways and folklore, of attitudes, preferences, and prejudices, of religious beliefs and spoken languages. In some degree culture is adjusted to the physical setting. Climate may dictate the amount of clothing that should be worn; it may suggest the materials of which it might be made; but it does not account for the style and decoration used. The bright peasant costumes of Eastern Europe, the ceremonial dress of the Indians, of African warriors, and of Hindu dancers and Buddhist priests are the essence of culture; these manifestations may be indigenous, or may be a trait acquired from trader or missionary, or just picked up from neighboring peoples.

Modes of social organization also belong to culture. Sometimes they are firmly rooted in the requirements of agriculture or in physical conditions. As often as not they appear to have no simple rationale; they are just the ways in which a particular group of people have, over a period of centuries, come to manage their lives. People acquire, quite naturally, strong emotional feelings toward the customs and traditions which, however unimportant they may be in reality, nevertheless serve to distinguish them from other human groups. Upon such differences, reinforced sometimes by an illusory belief in blood-kinship, is based the unity of the tribe and of the nation.

The history of mankind has been one of fitful progress toward ever larger units of social and political organization. During the last four or five centuries the self-governing nation-state emerged in Western Europe,

and the concept of the independent sovereign nation has now spread to most parts of the world. In the beginning stages it was a group awareness, based mainly on language, but also on other aspects of popular culture. The Swiss rebelled in order, in Friedrich Schiller's words, "to be one single nation of brothers." The quarrelsome Dutch were welded into unity by the oppression of Spain. France was shaped by the hammer blows of the English invaders. The Italians awakened slowly and gradually to the beauty and the glory of their classical and Renaissance past. The Germans were aroused to their common traditions by the clarion calls of Fichte only a century and a half ago, and then joined only sluggishly and piecemeal to make the German state. In such ways did the European nations come to conceive of themselves as separate and distinct groups of humanity, and thus did they learn to give political expression to this community of feeling in the organization of the nation-state.

Also in the past countries and empires have emerged, created by military conquest and held together by force; the ancient empires of the Middle East, India, and China; the Roman and Carolingian empires in Europe; the widespread possessions of Hapsburgs and Bourbons, and the conquests of Napoleon; the colonial empires of France and Britain, Portugal and Spain; the empire created by the Russian Tsars, and inherited and added to by Soviet Commissars. All these rested upon naked force. Most have decayed and disintegrated; only the last of them remains. They broke up because of a weakening of the military power which held them together, or because the administrative structure failed to operate successfully, or because invaders from without combined with internal weaknesses to overthrow them.

The break-up of an empire in modern times has been followed by the emergence of national groups. The defeat of Napoleon in 1813-15 was accompanied by the collapse of the empire which had been put together largely by his armies, and was followed by the emergence of the nation-states of today—Italy, Hungary, the Slav states, and even Germany itself. During the First World War, three European empires were at stake, the Russian, German, and Austro-Hungarian, as well as the Turkish Empire of the Middle East. In 1918, Woodrow Wilson, announcing his formula for a peace that would terminate the conflict, had no doubt that the opposing empires would collapse, and that in their place would emerge countries held together by the bonds of nationhood: "The peoples of Austria-Hungary . . . should be accorded the freest opportunity of autonomous development . . . nationalities now under Turkish rule should be assured an undoubted security of life and an absolute unmolested opportunity of autonomous development. . . . An independent Polish State should be erected which should include the territories inhabited by indisputably Polish populations . . . ," and so on.

The basis of the new countries was to be not racial and historical, but cultural; they were to be made up only of the peoples who wanted to be together. It was as if each had declared, again in the words of the founding fathers of the Swiss Republic in Schiller's play: ". . . We are all one heart, one blood, one race! We are one people and will act as one."

To implement the formation of new countries on a cultural basis, boundaries were drawn separating language group from language group, with the purpose of achieving in each country a uniformity of speech that would make communication easy and unity inevitable. But language is not the only index of culture, although it is unquestionably one of the most important. And it is not a certain guide to the feelings of men and women; it sometimes conflicts with other aspects of culture.

Language, as we know it today, is of very recent growth, and it is continually changing and evolving, absorbing new words and simplifying older grammatical forms. Languages spread with a remarkable speed, not only because their bearers migrate from one region to another, but also by the imposition of language by a dominant group within a society. Only a minority of the population of the United States derives from the English speaking world; the rest has acquired English in a short span of years. Few of the German-tongued of Eastern Europe were descended from German settlers; their ancestors were probably Slavs, who picked up German which became the language of commerce and of government. Furthermore, boundaries between language groups are rarely simple. On the margins of each, rival groups live intermixed, and which language is spoken not infrequently becomes a symbol of status and class.

It proved to be impossible in Europe to satisfy the national aspirations of each group, and the holding of plebiscites to discover a national preference merely made the ethnic confusion seem more confused. Unfortunately, boundaries drawn impartially to separate linguistic societies proved in many instances to be unsatisfactory in every other respect, too. They failed to follow defensible physical barriers, long regarded as political divides, as in the Balkan Peninsula; they broke up coal fields that were better left undivided, as in Silesia; they cut off nations like Hungary and Austria from the sea, and separated village communities from their market centers, as on the border of the Hungarian Plain.

It is easy to exaggerate the political significance of language. Maps show the broad language groups of the world, groups of languages which are related in syntax or vocabulary and which are supposed to have derived from a common origin, but such a map faces the same kinds of difficulties as the compilation of one of the world's races; the immense number and the confused relationship of the languages to one another. It is claimed by linguists that there are no less than four thousand distinct languages spoken in the world today, and within these an almost infinite number of dialects. We can group languages, as we do races, into a number of families, but the family resemblances within each of these groups are not always easy to detect. The American child who is beginning to learn German derives little help or encouragement from being told that German and English are very closely related.

Many languages are spoken by only a handful of people, and one language, Chinese, if we include all its dialect forms, by almost a quarter of the human race. It is of some help to group the world's languages into large language families. The Indo-European comes out as by far the most important, and is spoken by almost two-thirds of the human race. It has its own subfamilies, distinguished on the map on pages 30–31, and among these the Germanic subgroup which includes English, the Romanic with Spanish, French, and Italian, and the Slavic with Russian, are the most important.

Next in importance come the Sino-Tibetan group, with Chinese and its related languages; the Uralic and Altaic groups, which include Finnish, Hungarian, Turkish, and Mongolian; Japanese and Korean; the Semitic languages of the Middle East; and the Sudanese and Bantu languages of Africa. Such distributions are of academic interest; they help to explain the spread of cultures, but in themselves these broad language families have little practical importance.

Pan-slavism was an instrument of Russian policy, but not a very effective force among the many disparate peoples who spoke a Slavic tongue. The Arabic-speaking peoples have been notoriously disunited; the Germanic group has never known any kind of unity; in Europe, following the First World War, it proved impossible to use language consistently as a basis for nationhood. At best the linguistic argument merely lends an emotional weight to a thesis already well grounded on other principles.

Outside Europe, language does not even seem to be the dominant aspect of culture; it is superseded by religion. Even in Europe religious affiliation rivals language as the important aspect of culture, and through the mechanism of a national church, it is used to reinforce the concept of national unity. The Serbs and the Croats have been held apart far more by their respective allegiance to the Orthodox and Roman Catholic churches than by linguistic barriers. Devotion to the Catholic Church is an important feature distinguishing the Poles and the Irish from their neighbors. Islam is a common bond among the countries of the Middle East and North Africa; Lamaism formerly constituted a theocratic society in Tibet; and when the British Empire of India disintegrated in 1947, it was along religious, not linguistic lines that the split occurred; the result was the creation of the Hindu Republic of India and the Islamic Republic of Pakistan.

But over most of the more advanced parts of the world, society is secular. Religious affiliation—if any exists—bears no relationship to the loyalty owed to the state. There is no official religion, and complete liberty of conscience and of belief is the only common article of faith. These are the states within which national coherence is so strongly developed that it no longer requires the adventitious aid of priest and presbyter. But such is not the case among some of the newer nation-states: India and Pakistan, which originated in a religious split, must necessarily emphasize the religious factor which separates them; Burma has formally adopted Buddhism as the state religion; and Israel is predicated upon Judaism. Only the most sophisticated of modern states have been able to renounce the religious bond as a cement to their unity.

The distribution of the main religions of the world shows a certain similarity to the map of languages. The Romance-speaking world, with certain notable exceptions, like Romania, is Roman Catholic; the Arabic world is predominantly Islamic; the Germanic world is heavily Protestant; the Slavic world mainly, though not wholly Orthodox, and the Chinese have their own peculiar composite of Taoism, Confucianism, and Buddhism.

The similarity of distribution of religion and language springs primarily from the fact that the forces which spread the religions brought also the languages. Western Christianity was propagated from Rome, the source also of the Latin language from which the Romance tongues derived; Islam was spread by the Arab invasions, and missionaries of the Eastern or Orthodox church played an important role in shaping the Slav languages and providing them with an alphabet. Protestantism derived chiefly from the German Reformation, and remains truly important only in those countries where languages of Germanic origin are widely spoken.

The state is an area of land, with people and a government. It is autonomous and self-governing. It makes agreements, or treaties, with other countries. It controls its own citizens, conscripting them for its armies, shaping their traditions, and guiding their lives. Each acquires a distinctive character, and, by the interaction of government and nation, land and people, takes on its own specific qualities distinguishing it from all others. Before the First World War there were about 60 independent countries. Today, there are about 125. If we exclude Antarctica, they cover about nine-tenths of the land surface of the globe. Their number has about doubled during the present century, and before 2000 A.D. the number of independent nations will certainly go higher. The remaining tenth is made up of colonies and dependencies of one kind and another. Some of these are so empty or so backward that we cannot conceive of them ever becoming independent and self-governing; others are on the verge of statehood and independence.

The geographical pattern of sovereign states is indeed confusing. Look, for instance, at the variety of flags that adorns the United Nations, or turn the pages of a postage-stamp catalogue, or merely examine the displays in the nearest travel agent's window. The largest in area is the Soviet Union, two and a half times as large as the United States. Next come Canada and China, both a little larger; then the United States, followed by Brazil and Australia. The size of countries ranges downward, through large ones like the United Arab Republic (Egypt), Nigeria, and Bolivia, to medium-sized, like Japan, Morocco, and France, and small countries like the United Kingdom, Nepal, and Laos, and to minute states such as Luxembourg and Lichtenstein, Cyprus, Lebanon, and Monaco.

Statehood is all that the 125 states have in common. The largest is twenty-two million times the size of the smallest. They range in population from China with almost 700,000,000 people, down to the minute, fairytale countries like Monaco (23,000 people), San Marino (17,000 people), and Liechtenstein (17,000 people), with their embattled walls, their rich pageantry, their colorful military guards, and their immense output of postage stamps. They include compact, populous, industrialized states like West Germany and Japan; and also tracts of desert in eastern Arabia, ruled by a nomadic sheik who has heard of none of the refinements of congress, cabinet, and diplomatic representation.

Nations vary in resources no less than in population. One might expect those countries which are large in area to have a proportionately larger share of natural resources. In general the volume of such resources is a function of size, though agricultural resources depend far more on location, climate, and relief than on area. Much of the Soviet Union's huge extent has only negligible agricultural value, and the Netherlands or Hungary has a food producing capacity out of all proportion to its area. The distribution of minerals, however, is dependent only on rock structure; there are areas richly mineralized, and also areas poorly endowed with minerals, but there are few countries without some mineral wealth upon which to base extractive and manufacturing industries.

This immense range in size, population, and resources seems unrealistic in this modern world of alliances and blocs and regional plans. What policy can the minute states pursue; what weight have they in the councils of the nations? Individually they have none. Some are too small and poor to be able to maintain normal diplomatic relations with other countries or to support the cost of membership in the United Nations. Their armies, like the papal guard at the Vatican, are symbolic only, and as if to emphasize this fact, are accoutered still with the uniforms and weapons of several centuries ago.

Yet all these states exist to express the ideals of the people who inhabit them. Nationalism is the force that drives peoples to demand the right to establish independent and self-governing societies. It is a healthy instinct which gives coherence and power to the state. In Europe the nation emerged as a self-conscious, self-confident group several centuries ago. National feeling, beginning usually with a politically mature and cohesive group, spreads gradually through the mass of the people who make up the population of the nation. In Europe the creation of a nation was immeasurably helped by the appearance of a literature, by the translation of the Bible into its own language, by the collection and dissemination of the heroic myth and story of the nation's past, and by the study of the nation's history. In most states the national consciousness has grown gradually to fill out the boundaries provided by the state. Like a new wine fermenting in old bottles, it has occasionally split asunder these bounds, and set out to conquer and absorb neighboring lands.

The nation possesses a complex system of signs, customs, and ritual, which, growing through the centuries, serves as an outward and visible symbol of an inherent and spiritual unity. The flag is foremost among these; but heraldry, songs, literature, ceremonies, and national monuments all serve to reinforce the feeling of togetherness, of belonging to one another, which is the essence of the nation.

The nineteenth century was in Europe the "springtime of the nations," when they broke the bonds of empires and established their rights to exist. In some ways these young nation-states were like children, jealous and quarrelsome, always ready to snatch some prized possession from one another. But in time the edge wore off this brash young sense of nationhood; the state began to wear its statehood with less arrogance, and learned to co-operate with neighboring nations. By this time the spirit of nationalism had accomplished its purpose; it had made the state into an essential unit of political and economic organization.

The fact is that the spirit of nationalism has operated to produce states that are on the whole too many and too small, and unhappily, their number is not likely to diminish; the future may well see the number of sovereign states increased from 125 to 140, as colonies achieve statehood and a few existing states, rent by the conflict of national groups, break up. The union of several small states into a larger federation may be the desirable solution, but this is farther than many of the young nations are prepared to go. However, there is a remedy which some small states are showing an eagerness to adopt: the acceptable compromise of participation in some kind of an economic union which provides the advantages of a wider market, without the sacrifice of national sovereignty.

The European Common Market, a union of six countries, creates a market of about 174,000,000 people. The European Free Trade Association, smaller and less ambitious, nevertheless forms a free trading area with 90,000,000 inhabitants. There is talk of the creation of similar associations in Central and South America. The British Commonwealth itself constitutes a very widespread market within which tariffs are reduced, and economic matters within the Communist Bloc are regulated by their pact of mutual economic assistance.

But it is not always possible to draw a clear-cut line to separate people of one national allegiance from those of another. Sometimes they live intermixed, as they do on the borders of the Hungarian Plain; occasionally national loyalties may be imperfectly developed, and on rare occasions national feeling may run counter to the ties of language. The German-speaking Alsatian is a loyal Frenchman; the Macedonian has been somewhat uncertain whether his allegiance should be to the Yugoslav or the Bulgarian nation. In Belgium it is by no means certain that the linguistically distinct Walloon and Fleming have yet merged their difference in a common Belgian nationhood.

There are few nations, even in Europe, where there is no national minority, no small group that has remained incompletely assimilated to the national ideals of the majority. Outside North America and Europe, such groups may even constitute a danger to the integrity and cohesion of the nation. The Kurds in the Middle East, the Nagas in the hills of northeastern India, the Tibetans within greater China are all groups for whom the national aspirations of their respective states constitute no great attraction. If the opportunity presented itself they probably would attempt to break away and found separate states of their own.

Among the sovereign states today, a rough division can be made between those states which have crystallized around a national concept, around the idea of a linguistic, religious, and cultural unit, and those whose origin has been more arbitrary. The countries of Europe and North America and many of those of Asia like Iran, Turkey, Burma, India, Pakistan, and Japan, are nation-states existing in order to express the will to live together, and be ruled together, of a coherent body of people, a nation.

But many of the new states of Africa have no such origin. They have arisen within boundaries laid down by European peoples in the course of their colonizing and empire-building. These boundaries are artificial; they bear no relationship to the cultures of the African peoples; they were drawn usually in ignorance of the land and its peoples; they threw hostile tribes together and separated friendly peoples. They represented only the power balance between the imperial powers which were European. What sense of cohesion, of belonging together, of nationhood, may be expected to grow up here?

The break-up of the French and Belgian empires has merely revealed a group of tribes, with little more conception of the nation and of its political expression in the institution of the state than they had before the arrival of Europeans. The state in Africa is the creation of a Western-educated African elite, which has not in every instance succeeded in imposing its ideas on the remainder of the population.

A commission appointed to report on the degree of unity existing in Nigeria on the eve of its independence found many tribes that feared for their welfare and even for their lives when Nigeria should be left to the Nigerians, and each demanded some kind of independent status that would protect it. A sense of nationhood, of forming an integral society had not yet emerged in Nigeria. Nor has it done so in The Congo, Tanganyika, the Sudan, and in many other of these plural societies.

The compromise represented in the federation of Nigeria, the creation and the dissolution of political ties in West Africa, the chaotic situation of The Congo, all reflect the failure of the majority of the population of the new African states to conceive of themselves as a nation, bound by a common culture and by ties of loyalty to a single state. Many of the new states have proved to be merely congeries of tribes.

On the other hand, it must be remembered that such integrated and cohesive nation-states as France, the United Kingdom, those of Scandinavia and the Low Countries, and North America have grown together and created their present sense of unity only slowly. In each of them the resistance of subnational groups had to be broken down, and their peoples gradually drawn into the stream of national life. It takes longer to break down beliefs and prejudices that are irrational than those based on reason, and thus amenable to rational discussion. The cohesion of the old nations stands as an object lesson for the new, but it just cannot be achieved overnight.

In 1788 the United States became a federal republic, with an important range of political action left to the individual states, and has remained a model of how to organize and govern large and varied areas. All the really large countries, with exception only of China, are federal, and in most of them the influence of American experience is clear. Federalism has been called the most geographically expressive of all forms of government. All really large countries are of necessity varied in both their physical make-up and in their population. In many of them federalism has been a concession to the linguistic and cultural communities that are found there.

Canada, one of the earliest to follow the example of the United States, had the problem of the English-speaking and the French-speaking communities, each with its distinct social and even legal systems. Here the federal system of government was found to give an over-all political unity while at the same time permitting each community to develop along its own lines. This pattern has been followed in the Soviet Union, where each of the soviet republics is founded—theoretically at least— upon the cultural unity of a single people; in Yugoslavia, and in India, which is now made up of fifteen states, each with its own language. Thus federalism allows large countries to exist in spite of the obvious differences among their peoples. It gives self-expression to nations with-

out causing them to fragment into separate and distinct nation-states.

Each nation is cut off from its neighbors by boundaries. This is where we show our passports and allow our bags to be inspected, before the barrier is opened to allow us through. Boundaries are marked on the land, sometimes by simple stone markers, or by more massive barriers of wire; sometimes the boundaries follow the lines of rivers or mountain crests, or they thread their way through marshes and forests, and sometimes there is nothing in the landscape at all to show that here the sovereignty of one state ends and that of another begins.

It is commonly supposed that a country is better off if it has a boundary that is etched into the physical landscape. A river or a mountain range is supposed to make the best kind of boundary. In part this idea developed because in the past such a boundary could be defended more easily than any other; it was itself a deterrent to an invader. In part, also, such features made easy boundaries; they were usually already marked on maps; they could be agreed upon in the conference room, and in the field there could be no question of their location. When the first boundaries of the United States were defined in the Treaty of 1783, they were found to follow, for no less than 83 per cent of their distance, the line of rivers, lakes, and mountains, not because these features provided any protection to the young republic, but because there could be no mistaking them.

But there is no feature of the earth's surface which makes a really good boundary between one country and another: every boundary attempts to divide what is indivisible. Always there are technical objections to the course of any proposed boundary; it will make land reclamation difficult; it will prevent flood control measures from being adopted; it will obstruct movement to ports or access to mines and factories. And very rarely does it perform properly its avowed objective—to separate nation from nation—because people are too intermixed for this to be possible. Anything that divides people from one another and restricts movement is bad; the guarded boundary is one of the greatest evils in the modern world.

To most Americans the most familiar boundary is the unguarded border which separates them from Canada. It was made to run westward from the Lake of the Woods along the 49th parallel, between the United States and British North America, and was continued by later agreements to the shore of the Pacific Ocean. It is one of the few boundaries in the world that has never been the subject of dispute that led to war and is not now patrolled by guards or protected by soldiers.

When it was chosen as a political boundary, the 49th parallel ran through virgin forest or open prairie. The Plains Indians, the herds of buffalo, the fur trapper, and the hunter crossed it at will, but there were no settlers. These came later, after the boundary had been established; and they adjusted themselves to it, the Canadians on one side, the Americans on the other.

There was no mixing of the two peoples, only a meeting along their mutual boundary. This is not to say that there were no problems: the use of water from the prairie rivers that flowed from one country to another; conversely the drowning of valleys in one country as a result of dams built on rivers in the other; and the sharing of the power potential that lay in the rivers, like the Niagara, that formed the boundary. But the boundary was established without friction, and it engendered a good will that has led to the solution of all its problems by discussion around the conference table.

The boundary with Mexico was also established before there was much settlement in the region. It ran up the course of the turbulent Rio Grande and across the southwestern desert to the Pacific Coast. It raised difficulties because the Rio Grande is a violent river, changing its course at each flood; there were problems also because this is desert country where water is scarcer and more valuable than cropland, and the arguments about water rights were longer and more acrimonious than any that arose along the Canadian border.

It is generally thought that a range of mountains like the Alps, the Pyrenees, the Andes, or the Himalayas make a good boundary. They are high enough to have a zone of uninhabitable territory, and wide enough to form a significant barrier. Yet it has sometimes proved to be extremely difficult to agree upon the line of a boundary even in such a region. The Alps and Pyrenees may present no great difficulty, but the precise line of the Chilean-Argentinian boundary in the Andes was the subject of a war, and Indian and Chinese boundary claims in the Himalayas are un-reconciled and probably irreconcilable.

It is also assumed such mountain ranges separate peoples and cultures. This, however, they never do with any degree of completeness. In the first place, all mountain ranges form a zone of territory, within which a mode of life has been evolved, adjusted to the climate and the terrain of the mountains. The mountaineers commonly meet on the summits in summer, when the snow retreats and they can graze their animals on the higher pastures for a few weeks before returning to the shelter of the valleys for winter. Boundaries drawn through such mountain areas commonly break up the economy that has developed.

Nor are mountains the impenetrable barriers which they are presumed to have been. Napoleon is said to have looked out from Milan, in northern Italy, at the wall-like barrier which the Alps present as they rise abruptly from the Italian plain, and to have condemned these "splendid traitors" for allowing so many invaders to pass. All mountains have done so. There are none without passes, through which, as if by some osmosis, peoples have filtered through to the other side. Only approximately do boundaries separate cultures.

If mountains have shortcomings as political boundaries, rivers—that other "natural" boundary so much favored in the past—have disadvantages that far outweigh their assets. In some parts of the world, the Mexican border, for example, the river is naturally changeable and its course uncertain. In many areas rivers are the highways of commerce; shipping links the opposite banks together and binds the river basin into a functional unit. Most rivers have to be controlled in order to prevent disastrous flooding, to facilitate navigation and land reclamation, and to assist in water supply and power generation. None of these can be done so effectively if political control over the river is divided.

Unsatisfactory as these natural barriers are in setting limits and giving protection to the nation, they are better than no barrier at all. Poland had no such physical barrier to protect it. The level plain in each direc-

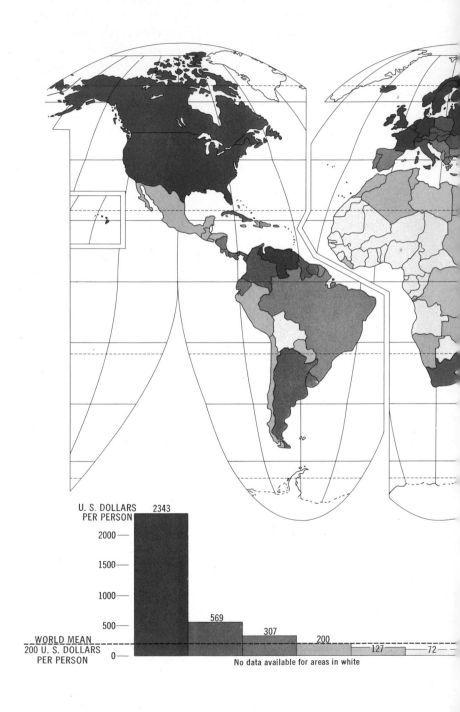

U. S. DOLLARS
PER PERSON   2343

2000 —

1500 —

1000 —

500 —   569

WORLD MEAN   307
200 U. S. DOLLARS   200
PER PERSON   0 —   127   72

No data available for areas in white

GROSS NATIONAL PRODUCT PER PERSON
(National averages)

VALUE IN UNITED STATES DOLLARS
MID.1950'S

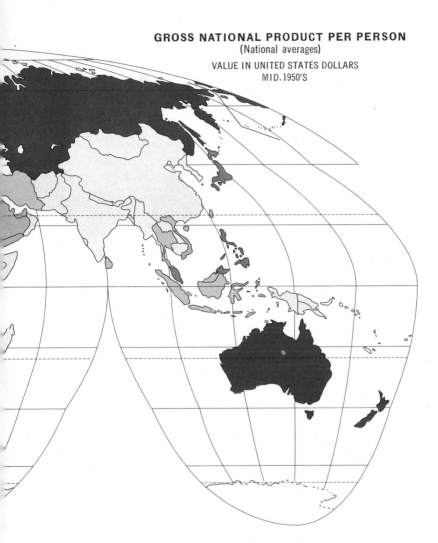

tion encouraged the mixing of peoples. It was hard to separate the Polish lands from the German on the one side and from the Russian on the other. The boundary toward each had neither precision nor clarity, and this encouraged aggression from both. The tragedy of Poland is written in her geography.

Many of the boundaries on the political map are drawn as straight lines. Such boundaries divide many of the states of the United States, the provinces of Canada, and the states which make up Australia. There are several such boundaries in Africa. Many of these run through empty lands where a few square miles of desert more or less make little difference. That such lines—like the 49th parallel—have come in many instances to be very successful boundaries is due either to the fact that they divided areas of little value or because they were established before the coming of settlers. Boundaries that are arbitrarily established through settled areas and across developed resources are more often than not the source of friction.

There are, lastly, the boundaries which wriggle across the land following no feature consistently, but merely separating field from field and village from village. These are the boundaries that have changed most frequently. Their origin is as diverse as the forms they assume, deriving in some places from ancient property lines, in others from legal jurisdictions, and in yet others from attempts to fit the boundaries to the will of the peoples. Many of the boundaries in Europe and Asia are of this nature, each the product of centuries of claim and counterclaim, of conquest and compromise, and of adjustment to popular desire and to technical considerations of military defense and land use.

As we noted at the beginning of this chapter boundaries between countries, drawn as thin lines on the political maps, do not conform with boundaries between the great climatic and physical divisions of the world. Small nations may be enclosed within a single region; large nations may spread across several. A single kind of environment is used or developed differently in one country from another. Compare the prairies of the United States of America, settled and developed with the Russian steppes, parts of which, without road or railroad, are still "virgin lands"; Malaya, its jungle cleared to make room for plantations, with the untouched forest of neighboring Borneo.

Thus countries differ, not merely in area and population, but also in the degree of efficiency and success with which they use their natural endowment, and even in their psychological attitudes toward their resources. There are rich countries and poor countries, and their wealth and their poverty depend in part on the ways in which they have been endowed by nature, but also in part on the variations in man's use and misuse of the gifts of nature.

Strangely enough, the richness and the poverty of a country are very difficult to measure, obvious though they may be to the casual eye of the traveler. But however measured, personal incomes are far higher in Anglo-America and in industrial Northern and Western Europe than in densely populated China, India, Egypt, or Java.

We have two measures of the distribution of the variations in human welfare: what people produce economically and what they eat. Of these, their production, expressed as gross national product, is the better measure of levels of development. It is defined as the total value of all goods manufactured and of all services performed in the course of a year. It is computed, at current prices, from the amount paid by individuals, companies, and the government for all the final goods and services they buy.

Any estimate that we may use of gross national product on a worldwide basis is approximate only, and for many countries we lack even the statistics upon which such an estimate should be based. If, however, we are going to have some kind of a picture of the geography of human welfare, we must use this data, crude as in many instances it is. Nothing else tells us as clearly where there is poverty and what are the degrees of poverty between one country and another. Usually, for purposes of comparison, we divide the gross national product of a country between the number of people in it, thus arriving at the gross national product per capita.

Now let us look at the comparison between countries. At the head of the list stands the United States, incomparably the richest country in the world, with a per capita gross national product of about $2,442 a year. Next comes Canada with about $2,018. Below this comes New Zealand, Switzerland, and Australia. The list continues with Belgium, France, The United Kingdom, West Germany, and the other developed countries of Western Europe. Then come the richer countries outside Western Europe and North America: Venezuela and Argentina, Finland, and Chile. Last come the mass of the underdeveloped countries, most of them with a per capita gross national product of less than $100 a year.

A bare table of gross national product is less meaningful than a map, which can be compared with maps of population density, of food supply, of climatic characteristics, and soil and mineral resources. On pages 144–45

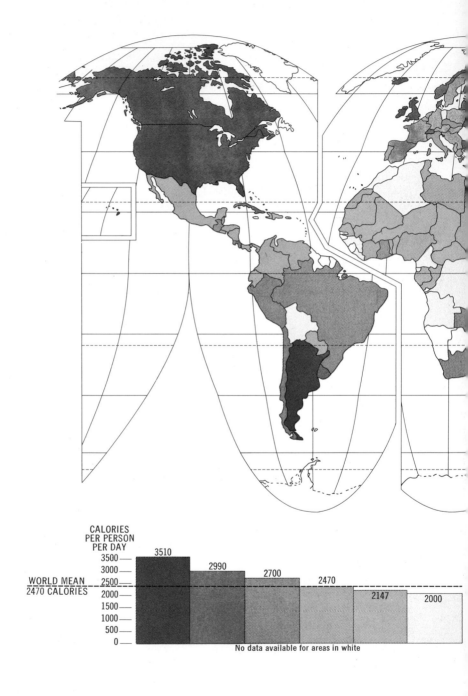

CALORIES
PER PERSON
PER DAY

3510

2990

2700

2470

2147

2000

WORLD MEAN
2470 CALORIES

3500 —
3000 —
2500 —
2000 —
1500 —
1000 —
500 —
0 —

No data available for areas in white

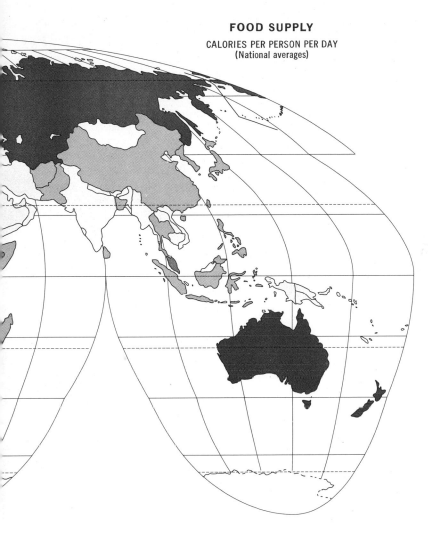

FOOD SUPPLY

CALORIES PER PERSON PER DAY
(National averages)

is such a map, which attempts by means of graduated shading to show the approximate gross national product per head of population. It is necessarily incomplete, for how can one figure out the per capita gross national product of the Bedouin of the Middle Eastern desert, or of tribesmen in New Guinea who rarely use money for the exchange of goods and whose products cannot easily be valued in monetary terms. For many areas the figures are little more than intelligent guesses. Yet, for all its errors and inadequacies, we have here a map of human wealth and poverty and of economic development and backwardness.

The map showing the average caloric intake or food supply, on pages 148-49, supplements that of gross national product. A comparison of the two shows that in general the poor countries are the ill-fed countries. All Southeast Asia, most of Africa, and much of Latin America have less—sometimes a great deal less—than the average caloric intake per person over the world as a whole.

The rich nations are the industrial nations, those with factories, developed means of transportation, and the mechanism for the exchange of goods. They are specialists; even their agriculture is specialized. In some instances the farming family itself may consume none of its own products. All are sold into the market, and the farmer buys his food and his fertilizer, his machines and his seed for sowing. Most of the countries which our map shows as enjoying a high national income are industrial, and the others, like Denmark and New Zealand, carry on an agriculture that is so specialized and so mechanized, that it seems to differ little from factory industry itself. Higher living standards and a bigger national income are associated with industrialization, and industrialization is the goal of many if not most of the poorer and more underdeveloped countries. The road to industrialization is not an easy one. It demands fuel, power, and raw materials, technical skills and investment capital; it requires also a market for the products of its industry. A poor people have no surplus to buy better clothes, tools, and equipment, and only after the income of the mass of the people has been raised through improvements in agriculture, will it be able to purchase the products of the factory.

The range of difference between rich and poor has been great within any society ever since the beginning of human history. But it is new for such differences to develop between societies. Formerly there were rich and poor individuals; now we have affluent and depressed societies.

Climate and resources alone do not suffice to explain the differences between the developed and the underdeveloped. It is not difficult to isolate areas comparable in terms of natural wealth and fundamentally different in terms of human welfare: perhaps France and some parts of India, Scandinavia and Japan, Switzerland and the Caucasus. It is easy, also, to point to areas which once flourished and supported what we have come to call a civilization, where now its ancient buildings lie in ruins and the sites of ancient cities are occupied only by a few squalid huts. Try as we may to explain these contrasts in terms of minor variations and changes in weather and climate, we are left wanting a basic explanation for the widely separated levels in wealth and welfare. Only man and human societies supply this.

It happened that in some areas human society was more fluid, more mobile, than in others; the entrepreneur was not only encouraged but rewarded when he proved successful. In more rigid caste-bound societies he was allowed less scope. Until recently China, India, and the tribal world of Africa belonged to the latter. Western Europe belonged to the former, at least after feudal society had begun to break down during the later Middle Ages. One cannot explain Europe's rise to pre-eminence altogether in terms of coal and iron; these were either unknown or little used when this rise first began. Least of all can it be explained in any biological or racial terms. The answer lies in social organization and attitudes, in the tolerance of skepticism, and in the encouragement given to innovation and experiment. That a people can change in these respects through the centuries is all too apparent from the most superficial examination of the societies which now live in the shadow of the Pyramids or on the site of the Hanging Gardens of Babylon.

Poverty and backwardness have no simple remedy; nor can industrialization and development be carried through easily and painlessly. They require careful planning, material aid, and ungrudging assistance from outside. A world free from want may not necessarily be a world at peace, but the removal of poverty would remove much of the cause of war and unrest. The now familiar quotation from John Donne comes again to mind when a political leader is murdered in Africa, or famine and catastrophe sweep an Indian village or an Andean community: No man is an island, and the bell is tolling for all of us.

6 THE LAND
RICHER THAN ANY:

Anglo-America

There was always the forest ahead of us opening on—
The blue ash in the coves of the Great Smokies:
The hickories staking the loam on the slow Ohio:
The homestead oaks along the Illinois:
The cypresses on the Arkansas to tie to:
The cottonwoods following water: the wild plums:
The lodgepole pines along the hill horizon.

ARCHIBALD MACLEISH—Land of the Free

America is a large continent, and Americans are a mobile people. Few remain all their lives in the town of their birth, and long vacation trips are the rule rather than the exception. Yet most Americans do not know this continent. Few have set foot in every one of the United States; even fewer in the provinces of Canada as well. The view from the windows of Americans embraces so small a part of the continent, and all the views that each one has ever had, added together, leave most of the continent unseen. They take it on trust, assuming that what they have not visited in some way is like what they have. But is it?

There are 185,200,000 Americans and a further 18,460,000 Canadians. Taken together they have 22 acres of land apiece. If there were a road all the way from northern Canada, where the Mackenzie River enters the Arctic Ocean, to the southern tip of Texas where the Rio Grande empties into the Gulf of Mexico, it would take about two weeks of driving, at three hundred miles a day, to cover the distance. Anglo-America covers no less than a sixth of the land surface of the globe.

153

We all know that this is new country; that the first permanent settlements by European peoples were made on it only three and a half centuries ago; human societies in Egypt can stretch their ancestry back more than ten times as far as this. And when European settlers did come they pushed their way only slowly over the land. It was not until 1890 that the Bureau of the Census could state officially that within the territorial United States the frontier existed no more, that there were no more empty lands calling out for settlers. But there is still a frontier in Alaska and across the whole enormous breadth of Canada. North America is still not a densely peopled continent, and much of it never will have many people because it has neither the soil, the climate, nor the minerals to attract and support them.

What was this land like, to which the ancestors of Americans or Canadians, or even they themselves, came during these past few hundred years?

The New World was discovered by accident, and accident determined that many of the early discoverers should strike its least promising parts. At the very end of the fifteenth century the English-sponsored explorer, John Cabot, reached Newfoundland. A generation later, in 1534, the Frenchman, Jacques Cartier, sighted the barren, treeless coast of Labrador, so sterile that he observed that this must have been the land that God gave Cain.

But Cartier persevered, and in the course of his second voyage the next year, he sailed up the St. Lawrence River, passing the future site of Quebec, where he found the land "as fine as it is possible to see, being fertile and covered with magnificent trees of the same varieties as in France." He sailed on and reached an island with a low hill, which he named Mont Réal. From its summit, he wrote, "We had a view of the land for more than thirty leagues around about. Toward the north there is a range of mountains . . . and another range to the south." These were the margin of the Laurentian Shield and the Adirondack Mountains of New York State. "Between," he continued, "lies the finest land it is possible to see, being arable, level, and flat. And in the midst of this flat region one saw the river extending beyond the spot where we left our longboats. At that point there is the most violent rapid it is possible to see, which we were unable to pass." It was, of course, the Lachine Rapids which thus set a limit to the explorations of Cartier, and they were to continue to restrict or impede navigation until 1959 when the St. Lawrence Seaway was opened around their southern flank.

Anglo-America includes Canada and the United States. Greenland was declared a part of North America during the Second World War.

But these voyagers did not then want vast land tracts which, however fertile, could yield a return only after much hard work. They wanted the Indies, where, as they supposed, wealth could be had for the taking. North America blocked their way; but there must be a way around, and they would find it. This had been Cartier's objective, and the search for the Northwest Passage exercised the boldest of navigators for almost a century. John Davis, Martin Frobisher, and Henry Hudson, and Button, Bylot, and Baffin, whose names decorate the map of the Canadian Arctic added greatly to geographical knowledge; but they never penetrated the maze of islands and twisting channels and the pack ice, which at this latitude covers the sea for much of the year. In fact, the Northwest Passage was never navigated from end to end until the Norwegian Amundsen did it in 1903–06.

Also in the early sixteenth century the Spaniards in Mexico sent expeditions northward into what later became the United States. These culminated in the great expedition of Coronado in 1540–42. Northward from Mexico he led his party into the deserts of Arizona and New

Mexico. A group of Coronado's men reached the Grand Canyon. "This country was elevated," one of them wrote, "and full of low twisted pines, very cold, and lying open toward the north." Here they "spent three days looking for a passage down to the river, which looked from above as if the water was six feet across, although the Indians said it was half a league wide." Eastward they went, across the mountains of New Mexico and down into the grassy plains of Kansas. This held little attraction to them. There was no gold to redeem the barrenness and aridity, and so they made their way back to Mexico.

Soon afterward Cabeza de Vaca journeyed across the South, from Florida to Mexico. De Soto in 1539–42 led an expedition into the southern Appalachians, then westward to the Ozarks, "a very rough country of hills," and then south to the impassable swamps which fringe the coast of Louisiana. There De Soto sickened and died, and was buried in the Mississippi.

It was an unpropitious continent that the French and Spaniards between them had revealed. It was left, in the main, for the English-speaking peoples to discover and settle an intermediate area, which avoided the extremes of both arctic cold and tropical desert and swamp; where the summers were long and warm enough for plant growth, and rainfall was sufficient without the need to irrigate.

From Massachusetts Bay to Tidewater Virginia and the Carolinas they settled, and here settlers from northwest Europe could feel as much at home as at any other point on this continent. They could recognize the wild plants and animals; they could use their familiar agricultural practices. But, in the words of Carl Sauer, this "was indeed a lustier land to which the settlers had come, a land of hotter summers and colder winters, of brighter and hotter sun and more tempestuous rain, a land suited to and provided with a greater variety of vegetation than the home-lands of Europe." This the Pilgrim Fathers learned during that first, rugged New England winter, and this too those other early settlers who came to the southern colonies discovered when they began to grow tobacco and indigo and cotton in the heat of the southern summer.

The North American continent presented a challenge, which the majority of the American settlers accepted. That they succeeded is evident from the fact that within two and a half centuries they had dotted the continent with settlements all the way from the muddy estuaries along the Atlantic Coast to the surge of the Pacific Ocean against the cliffs of California.

Let us set out with these pioneers, cross the Coastal Plain and the Piedmont, and see the Appalachians ahead. Then the hills fade into plateau which becomes plain, as gradually the Midwest stretches on to the Mississippi and then on again to the Missouri. The humid Midwest merges into the less humid Great Plains and these rise gradually, imperceptibly, until they end abruptly where the Rocky Mountains rise like a wall, with Pikes Peak set like a sentinel out in front. Routes were taken around and through the Rocky Mountains: the South Pass in Wyoming, which led on, below the fretted summits of the Tetons, into the plains of the Snake River, and on to Oregon and Washington; and routes which clustered around the southern end of the range and led on to Sante Fe and Albuquerque, running across the plateau and the desert of Arizona to the western Sierra of California and the Pacific Ocean.

Such was the view of this land which the pioneers gradually pieced together, as each moved out through the mountains and across the plains. Their social practices and their ways of using the soil were gradually changed. Architectural styles were adapted to the climate and to whatever building materials were available. They were functional for the most part, but always some little evidence showed that these styles had been brought in from the east. They built log cabins and covered bridges in the forest regions; sod houses on the plains; stone houses where building stone was easy to come by; adobe houses in the desert. The size and pattern of the great barns changed with the crop and the climate: big barns where the winters are long and cold; little barns and corn cribs where the animals can be left outdoors.

There developed an almost infinite variety of landscape and life in the mid continent between the Atlantic Ocean and the Pacific. It was as if the whole complex of culture, brought from Europe to the eastern seaboard, had been filtered as it spread west and man adapted it to the physical circumstances he found, the elements deriving from Europe one by one being strained out from it.

But not all the early North American settlers were English-speaking. Jacques Cartier's reports about the fair country which lay up the St. Lawrence, almost a thousand miles from the ocean, attracted other Frenchmen. There, in 1608, came Samuel de Champlain, looking for lands for French colonists to settle. During the following decades they established themselves along the banks of the great river, from below Quebec upstream to Montreal. They laid out their farms along the waterfront, each with a narrow strip of land reaching back through the culti-

vated fields into the forest beyond. They brought something besides their French language; they introduced an almost feudal social structure, so rigid that it suffered little change in the course of being transplanted to the New World. And for three hundred years it has altered little. The French-speaking Canadians provide the closest parallel which North America can offer to the self-sufficing, conservative peasant societies of Europe. Here, today, their now archaic French is spoken; the civil law of France is practiced and small, almost self-contained, conservative communities live much as they have always lived. The world passes them by, just as the liners do that sail along their river front on the voyage up to Montreal.

The French-speaking Canadians stayed close to home. They took little part in the westward movement. Only in recent years has mounting population pressure along the St. Lawrence Valley driven some of them westward into Ontario and the Prairie Provinces. The Canadian Midwest and West were settled mainly by English-speaking peoples. Some of them from the United States after the American War of Independence; others came directly from Europe. But whatever their origin, they brought a way of life, fundamentally European, and gradually modified it as they settled into their harsher environment on the farms of the prairies and the mining and lumber camps of the northern forest and the western mountains.

The exploration of the Canadian Northland was slower than that of the American West. Its wealth was not readily apparent; it had to be looked for in its rocks. The earliest explorers were the fur trappers, who followed the beaver and the muskrat through the forests and down the rivers that flowed to the Arctic Ocean. The rewards of their hunting were sold to the traders of the Hudson's Bay Company, who had established their trading points deep in the Northland. Late in the eighteenth century Alexander Mackenzie followed the river that now bears his name as far as the delta by which it enters the Arctic Ocean. During the following century, there can have been few parts of the Canadian North that remained unvisited by trapper or explorer. Many remained silent about their discoveries, but between them they put together a picture of this vast region of forest and lake which stretches from the St. Lawrence, the Great Lakes, and the Prairies northward to the limit of tree growth, and then on to the wild, bleak shores of the northern ocean.

The earliest human influences in North America, other than those of the North American Indians themselves, were Spanish, French, and English, and of these the English influence was for a couple of centuries preponderant. Before the end of the seventeenth century, however, other European peoples began to arrive: the so-called "Dutch" Germans who settled in eastern Pennsylvania; colonies of Swedes and Finns and Netherlanders, who sprinkled their names around the lower Hudson Valley, and in Delaware.

During the nineteenth century immigrants to both Canada and the United States increased in number and variety. The failure of each revolutionary movement in Central Europe brought with it the migration to America of thousands who saw no political hope in Europe. Sometimes economic hardships swelled the ranks. In Ireland, the potato famine, coupled with rapacious English landlords, reduced the population to less than half. As the century wore on, Italy, Poland, the Danubian countries, and the Balkans each sent their share of immigrants to help make the American people. In the twentieth century, the influx has not ceased. It has been added to by peoples of Chinese and Japanese stock, who came by way of the Philippines or Hawaii. And in recent years it has become more necessary and urgent as the stream of refugees sought haven, first from Nazism and Fascism, and then from Communism.

These diverse elements from Europe and from Asia have been merged in this great melting pot. Yet the cultural legacies which they each brought from their homelands beyond the Atlantic and Pacific oceans

ARCTIC OCEAN

N

ICELAND

Reykjavík

Cape Farewell

ICELAND

Ice Cap

GREENLAND

Ice Cap

Thule

DAVIS STRAIT

Godthaab

Baffin Bay

BAFFIN ISLAND

LABRADOR

NEWFOUNDLAND

St. John's

GULF OF ST. LAWRENCE

Gaspé

Trois-Rivières River

Québec

Halifax

Hudson Bay

NORTH POLE

ELLESMERE ISLAND

PARRY ISLANDS

VICTORIA ISLAND

ARCTIC CIRCLE

Churchill

CANADA

Lake Winnipeg

Winnipeg

ARCTIC OCEAN

Polar Ice Pack

Great Bear Lake

Great Slave Lake

River

Peace River

Mackenzie River

Saskatoon

Edmonton

Regina

Calgary

BEAUFORT SEA

ROCKY MO

Fraser River

Vancouver

Victoria

OLYMPIC MOUNTAINS

Point Barrow

ASIA

ALASKA

Yukon River

Fairbanks

Mount McKinley

Anchorage

Juneau

Ketchikan

Prince Rupert

Nome

BERING SEA

PACI

NORTH AMERICA

Scale of Miles

0   100   200   400   600

⊗ National Capitals   ☆ Colonial Capitals   ● Other Cities

COPYRIGHT 1962 BY RAND MC NALLY & CO.   MADE IN U.S.A.

have not been lost. All over this country there are echoes of Italy and Germany, Spain and England, Japan and the Philippines. They merge to produce the harmonic overtones of American civilization.

It is the method of the geographer to divide the lands which he studies into regions. Regions on the land are like the seasons of the year. They are distinct, but yet it is sometimes hard to draw a line between them. The long, slow awakening of spring from the winter sleep is like the gentle transition from the Appalachian Mountains to the Midwestern plains. The two regions—mountain and plain—could not be more distinctive, nor the transition from the one to the other more gradual.

In this chapter, and indeed in the rest of this book, we shall divide the larger land areas into regions for the convenience of describing and remembering; and on the maps we shall use, the transition from one region to another will be represented by a firm line. This is like saying that spring begins on March 21. Within each region we must generalize; this is the only way in which we can cope with its variety, for within each region there is variety, just as there is within the span of each season. The day to day changes in our weather do not prevent us generalizing about the long, hot summer or the cold, dry winter. We must generalize about the hills, valleys, and plains, or we cannot convey a general impression of what the land is like.

THE UNITED STATES

The Union, begun in 1776, now reaches from sea to shining sea and even beyond. Between the Atlantic seaboard settlements, which formed an integral part of the British Colonial Empire before the war for independence, and the shores of the Pacific Ocean there lie more than three thousand miles of country, as varied in its physical geography as were the peoples who settled it. A regional study of the United States will show best its physical variety and the immense resources that nature has bestowed upon it.

West from the Atlantic

All the way from New England to Florida there is a coastal plain, a hundred or more miles wide in the south, but in the north pinched out between the hills and the sea. It is low and flat, and when the earliest settlers came it was wet and swampy as well. Parts of it are still undrained: marshes along the New Jersey coastal rivers, and patches of swamp along the Virginia coast, becoming more extensive through the Carolinas and Georgia, merge into the vast swamps of Florida, with their cypress trees standing on root-stilts in the water, the Spanish moss swinging in the breeze, and a fetid smell of rotting vegetation.

The Coastal Plain is geologically the youngest region of the United States. It is the creation of the rivers that cross it to the sea, bearing their loads of silt and sand. Sandy areas give rise to the Pine Barrens of New Jersey, but much of this plain is good truck-farming land. Once it grew sugar and rice along the Tidewater; now each day the trucks carry produce to New York, Philadelphia, and the other great cities. Much of its coast is fringed by swamp and beyond the swamp is a narrow lagoon. Sandy bars, piled up by the waves of the Atlantic, cut off the lagoons from the ocean, and now provide hundreds of miles of bathing beaches all the way from Long Island to Miami Beach. Small craft sail in relative safety along this coastal waterway, and gaps in the bar allow ocean-going freighters to reach the ports which lie in the shelter and security of the river estuaries.

Immediately behind this low, coastal plain is the somewhat higher Piedmont which has an elevation of 500 to 1,000 feet. The Piedmont is built of older, harder rock; its edge is a low, almost inconspicuous, step. The rivers of the Piedmont drop over this step to the Coastal Plain in rapids that set a limit to navigation inland from the sea and once served to generate power through the water wheel. Cities grew up along this line, the so-called Fall Line, reaching from Montgomery in Alabama to New Brunswick in New Jersey. In the north the Fall Line draws close to the coast, as the Coastal Plain narrows and almost disappears. New York City spreads out over the solid rock of the Piedmont; you can see the rock in the Palisades along the banks of the Hudson. Long Island is a fragment of the Coastal Plain. Philadelphia, Baltimore, and Washington spread out over the junction of the Coastal Plain with the Piedmont, and in each it is possible to trace out the gentle gradient, lying to the west of the downtown area, which separates the one from the other. It is no accident that the great ports grew up where they did. Here the Coastal Plain is narrow; the rivers—the lower Hudson, the Delaware— and Chesapeake Bay are navigable, and the Piedmont immediately be- hind the ports offered good farm land and easy routes into the interior.

The Piedmont is rolling, undulating country. Here and there the hard rock of which it is built shows through, and its surface is occasion-

The pattern of the highlands and the lowlands of the United States conforms closely to its regions. Note the mountain barriers, the plains and basins.

ally interrupted by a ridge of hill, a wooded island rising above the gentle swell of the cropland around. Much of the Piedmont is cultivated, evidenced by the large, trim barns, the neat farmhouses, and well-kept fields of the Pennsylvania Dutch country, inland from Philadelphia; the farms in Virginia; the tobacco farms, their little drying barns dotted about the fields of the Carolinas; the peach orchards in Georgia.

The southern Piedmont was once cotton country, and today you will still see a field or two of cotton if ever you drive into the South through this region. The abundant cotton crop helped to attract cotton mills to the cities of Greensboro, Charlotte, Greenville, and Spartanburg. But cotton is hard on the soil, and the humid climate is kindly to the boll weevil. It is now easier to grow cotton farther west, in Texas and beyond, although it is still grown in the Deep South. Old cotton fields are grassed down, and beef cattle graze where once the cotton grew.

Behind the Piedmont lie the Appalachian Mountains. All the way from the White and Green Mountains of New England to where the ridges and valleys die out in the Alabama Piedmont, these mountains create a barrier between the coastal regions and the interior. Between its two extremities, the Appalachian chain provides a picturesque region of natural beauty. Because they lie well within a day's drive of any one of the great eastern cities, they are much frequented. The Catskill Mountains in New York State; the Blue Ridge of Virginia, with the scenic drive along its sharp ridge and the view out over the meanders of the Shenandoah; the Great Smoky Mountains of North Carolina and Tennessee, where the Appalachians reach their highest point—all these are a part of this eastern range.

To the early settlers these mountains seemed an almost insuperable barrier. It is not that they are high—they rarely rise above 4,000 feet—but that ridge rises behind ridge in almost endless sequence. No sooner had the traveler topped one ridge but he saw the next in front, and knew not when this sequence would end. Rivers—the Delaware, Schuylkill, Susquehanna, Potomac, and James—snake their way through the mountains, cutting "water gaps" across the ridges and opening up routes through the mountains. All these routes led up to the last ridge, through which the rivers had cut no route. This was the Allegheny Front, continued southward as the Cumberland Mountains. The passenger on the Pennsylvania Railroad who travels the Horseshoe Curve, west of Altoona, is crossing this barrier. The Pennsylvania Turnpike goes through it by means of the Allegheny Tunnel. The pioneers, farther to the south, journeyed between the Appalachian ridges until they were able to cross it by the Cumberland Gap, up through which their horses strained as they pulled their wagons over into Tennessee and Kentucky.

Beyond this mountain rim stretches a plateau, known as the Allegheny Plateau in the north, and the Cumberland Plateau in the south. At its eastern margin it lies at heights of over 3,000 feet, but it drops gently to the west. From any high point within it the surface appears to stretch away to a level horizon, but in detail it is very broken. Rivers are deeply etched into its surface, flowing in deep, narrow valleys. Most of these make their way to the Ohio River, or to the biggest tributary of the Ohio, the Tennessee. The city of Pittsburgh grew up where two of these entrenched rivers, the Allegheny and the Monongahela, join to form the Ohio.

Northward from New York City stretches the Hudson River Valley, the Catskill Mountains rising to the west and the Taconic Mountains and the Green Mountains of Vermont to the east. The river has made for itself a deep, flat-floored trough, and this extends beyond the source of the Hudson into the valley of the northward-flowing Richelieu River in Quebec. Thus nature has provided a depression, a natural routeway between New York City and the St. Lawrence River. Part way along this depression, approximately 150 miles up the Hudson, it is joined from the west by another, the Mohawk Valley, which opens up a route westward from Albany, past Syracuse and Rochester to Buffalo.

Neither of these great troughs was excavated merely by the rivers which now occupy them. They were carved out by the mighty torrents that rushed from the great ice sheet when it lay across Canada, slowly melting and liberating quantities of water beside which the Mississippi in flood might seem but a small stream. Thus was created the Waterlevel Route, by which the New York Central Railroad carries its passengers west through the northern end of the Appalachian Mountains; the New York Thruway also takes advantage of this route.

East of the Hudson Valley is New England, the major gateway through which the essentially European culture entered this continent, and where it was broadened and deepened by its contacts with the New World. New England, as it is viewed on the map, is an extension of the Appalachian Mountains proper. It is a hilly region. Two chains of smoothed and rounded mountains, the Green and White Mountains, stretch south from near the Canadian border. Between them flows the Connecticut River; to the south and east a narrow strip of plain separates the mountains from the sea. It is a land of cold winters and heavy snow, of thin, poor soil, from which the rain has leached away much of the goodness. Yet this was the land which those tough-minded, hard-working Puritan settlers tamed. In the words of one eighteenth-century settler, "there never was a people, situated as they are, who with so ungrateful a soil have done more in so short a time."

The face of the eastern seaboard and of the mountains and plateaus which border it has changed greatly since the early settlers staked out their farms and built their mills beside the tumbling rivers to process

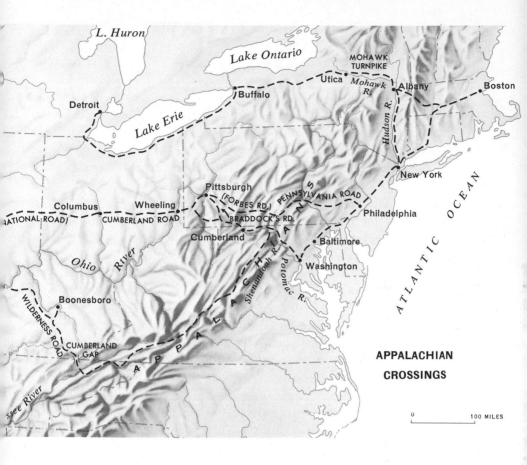

APPALACHIAN
CROSSINGS

0   100 MILES

the wool from sheep that grazed the nearby hills. New England blossomed into the first industrial heart of this country. Cotton mills in
Lowell and Fall River; leather and shoe factories in Lynn; shipyards
in Boston and Salem supplied a good part of this nation's needs. And
the wealth of the factory built the sedate, rather austere houses of the
towns that spread out around Boston and supported the first flowering
of American literary culture. Now, that New England spring of the
American spirit has passed through its summer and into its autumn.
Many of the mills are closed along the Merrimack River; cottons woven
in the Carolinas have replaced those from Lowell and Manchester, and
the old Yankee stock is scattered to the ends of the United States. But in
its place there came the no less hardy immigrants from Ireland and Italy
and the thrifty, hardworking French Canadians from across the border.

New England was well placed in the early days, when industry depended upon the power of its flowing streams. When steam power, and then electricity which derived from mightier rivers than those of New England, began to be used, the fate of the older industries was sealed. Much of the cotton industry has gone to the South, the metal industries to the Appalachians and Midwest, and of the original industries of this region only the manufacture of woolen cloth and leather footwear retains anything like their earlier importance.

Southwest of New England is the region commonly known as the Middle Atlantic Seaboard. It reaches from Connecticut to Virginia and extends inland for some fifty to one hundred miles, until it ends against the first of the ridges of the Appalachian Mountains. It is made up of the northern, tapering extension of the Coastal Plain and the Piedmont before these are snuffed out by the New England hills and the sea. To the early settlers its distinguishing feature was the long, branching inlets which penetrate it from the sea, carrying salt water and ocean shipping up a hundred miles and more from the coast.

On the shores of these sheltered inlets there grew up several of the oldest settlements of this continent: New York, Baltimore, and Philadelphia. These long estuaries had been formed in recent geological times by the sinking of the land—or rise of the sea level—and the drowning of the lower courses of rivers. The rivers, which thus provided harbors and outlets seaward, had eroded valleys back through the Appalachian Mountains. The Hudson, Delaware, and Susquehanna, with their tributaries, had dissected the mountain region, carving its ridges into short segments to facilitate transport and communications.

This region, lastly, had a climate intermediate between the cold, snowy winters and warm summers of New England, and the mild winters and hot, humid summers of the South. It was a region where the winters were not too cold, nor the summers too hot for continuous work in field and factory; where rainfall was sufficient for agriculture, and the New World offered perhaps one of its closest imitations of the climate of northwestern Europe.

Today about a sixth of the total United States population lives in this region between New Haven, Connecticut, and the mouth of the Chesapeake, and at least one-half of these live in metropolitan New York City. New York epitomizes the natural advantages of the Middle Atlantic Seaboard. Its harbor is deeper and more accessible than the others. To the north the valley of the Hudson River, especially now that new bridges across the river and the Thruway up the valley have been completed, gives it a naturally easier access across the mountains to the Great Lakes and the plains of the Middle West than the other port cities possessed. These facts account largely for the more rapid growth and the greater spread of New York City. Urban functions have accumulated in New York, each bringing others with it. The greatest port has become one of the most varied industrial cities. Commerce has helped to make New York City the greatest financial center in the country, and these functions of the city have attracted the world of entertainment and of learning. The majority of the immigrants to the United States have come in through New York and some groups have not spread far from the piers where they landed, so that New York remains the most cosmopolitan city in the United States.

Philadelphia and Baltimore had neither the landward nor seaward advantages of New York, and big as they are, they have never come to have the great size and the breadth of function of greater New York. Washington is the most specialized of all the cities of this region. It was founded as a governmental city, and it has attracted very few functions that are not related to the federal administration. It is as if bureaucracy had the effect of repelling, rather than of attracting, others of the functions performed by cities.

In the Appalachian Mountains and the plateaus there is coal, one of the richest reserves of fuel in the world. In eastern Pennsylvania, around Scranton and Wilkes-Barre, is hard coal, or anthracite. Beyond the ridge-and-valley country thick, level beds of bituminous coal underlie the Allegheny Plateau and come out to the light of day along the flanks of the valleys. What traveler in this region has not seen the tipples where the coal is brought out to the valley side and allowed to cascade down to the waiting barges and freight cars below. Scattered through these hills was iron ore. None of the deposits were large, and most of them are now exhausted, but together the coal and iron served to locate the iron industry near Bethlehem, Pittsburgh, and Youngstown. Now the ore has to be brought into the region.

Some ore comes by freighter from the Upper Great Lakes to the Lake Erie ports and on by rail. Some comes from overseas, from Newfoundland, to Baltimore and Philadelphia, and some is beginning to arrive from Labrador via the St. Lawrence Seaway and from Venezuela. This has led to a change in the pattern of the iron and steel industry. No longer is it found only in the valleys of the Appalachians; it has spread out also to Chicago, Detroit, Cleveland, and Buffalo on the one side of the mountains, and to Trenton and Baltimore on the other, places where the coal can be freighted down from the mountains to meet the ore coming in by ship.

Thus the pattern of life in the Appalachians has changed, just as it has in New England, as industry spread out more widely. Distress in the cotton towns of Massachusetts is matched by unemployment in the mining valleys of West Virginia, and business which once kept them active has moved off southward and westward. Industry thus moved through the New England and Appalachian regions, leaving in favorable locations a few prosperous cities, where better transportation facilities helped industry to become more diversified. In the Appalachians there are abandoned, grass-grown spoil heaps from the mines, and tumble-down, half-employed mining villages spread out over the valley sides. Yet in some Appalachian areas industry never came. Without coal, with no minerals to tempt the miner, they remained agricultural. As the pioneers moved through the Cumberland Plateau some dropped out of the westward trek, and in the remote valleys of North Carolina and eastern Tennessee they made their homes, perpetuating into the twentieth century the society of the eighteenth.

The Midwest

The Midwest begins where the Allegheny Plateau gets lower and its valleys wider and where its hills die away in low rounded hillocks on the margin of the plain. The Midwest is the creation of the Ice Age. Its level plains and deep soils would not have existed without the vast quantities of material which the ice sheets transported south from Canada, deposited, and then smoothed out with the flow of their melt water. The rivers Ohio and Missouri, together with the lower Mississippi, form a giant letter Y, spanning about a thousand miles of territory from west to east. The Ohio and Missouri mark very roughly the southern limit of the Midwest, because they are the line reached by the farthest extension of the ice. Indeed, they were created by the ice at this time, and carried its melt water away to the Mississippi. Between them they embrace most of the territory of eight states. A fan of rivers is gathered to the Mississippi from the expanse of the Midwest, between the extremes represented by the Missouri and Ohio: the Des Moines, the Upper Mississippi, Illinois, Wabash, Miami, Scioto. They are generally slow-flowing and muddied with the easily eroded soil of the plains.

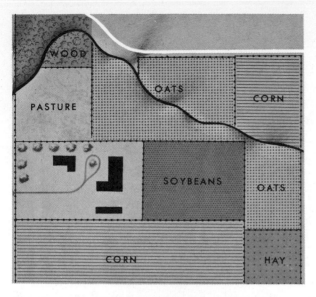

Iowa farms are rectangular in shape, and about 35 per cent of the land is devoted to corn. Traditionally a wood is planted to break the bitter winter winds.

Their valleys are merely shallow depressions in the almost level surface, and when they flood they spread out over it.

Winters are cold here; average temperatures in January range from near freezing in the south, to about 10° in the northern Midwest. Snow comes and goes to the south, but lies continuously in the northern parts of the Midwest, and the radio reports regularly on skiing conditions in Michigan, Wisconsin, and Minnesota. Spring is an interlude between winter and summer. Trees rush into leaf. For a period there is a sharp alternation between warm, humid air borne north from the Gulf, and colder, drier Canadian air. Tornadoes are spawned along their line of meeting. Then the warm winds take over and summer has come.

Agriculturally, the Midwest is a corn, wheat, and fodder growing region. Fall-sown wheat, germinating during the early winter and growing slowly during the first frost-free days of spring, makes a splash of vivid green beside the drab color of the sere, yellow pasture land and the brown-black of the newly plowed soil, waiting for the corn to be sown. The Corn Belt, stretching from Ohio to Iowa, forms the heart of the Midwest. Here a climate with hot, moist summers and a dark, rich chernozem soil provides the best physical conditions. To the west the climate is too dry for the best crops, and cornland passes gradually into wheatland. To the north summers are not hot enough or long enough, and the dairy farms of Wisconsin and Michigan take over from the corn and livestock farmer. To the south, beyond the limit of the ice sheets, the terrain is rougher, and the soil poorer. Crop farming is less important, and more of the land is under grass and fodder.

The Midwest focuses upon Chicago, which grew up where the Great Lakes extend deep into the heart of this country and where it is now possible via the St. Lawrence Seaway for ocean-going freighters to dock in the Corn Belt. The Great Lakes have been shaped by the action of the ice sheet. As it slowly retreated northward, lakes formed along its margin, fed by the melting ice and discharging southward across the Midwest toward the Ohio and the Mississippi. Today, marshy depressions mark the course of these earlier outlets, and along some of them canals have been cut to link the Great Lakes southward with the Mississippi system. In this way Chicago has itself been joined with the Illinois and thus with the Mississippi River, and water from Lake Michigan again flows, as it did during the withdrawal of the glacier, through the Chicago River and the ancient spillway linking it with the Mississippi Basin.

As the ice retreated yet farther to the north, it uncovered a lower outlet from the Great Lakes Region. The drainage foresook its old paths to the south, and began to flow to the northeast, creating the falls of Niagara and the rapids of the St. Lawrence River. The building of canals and the improvement of the waterway have made the St. Lawrence one of the world's great navigable rivers. The upper lakes have been thrown open to the ocean's shipping, and Chicago, seventeen hundred miles from the sea, has now become an important ocean port; at the head of the lake, in northern Indiana, a new port is being built.

The actual site of Chicago was determined by a small river, which created a harbor, and a patch of land high and dry enough to support a settlement. Its future was determined by its location. Here the pioneer stepped ashore after boats had carried him and his gear as far as the lakes allowed. Routes from the east, forced south around the head of Lake Michigan, converged on Chicago. The western trails started from here; and Chicago became also the beginning point of the western railroads. The convergence of routes from the west on Chicago made it the destination of the agricultural produce of the plains. Wheat came here for milling, and on Chicago's stockyards converged the cattle, first bred on the high plains, later fattened on the corn of Iowa and Illinois, and destined for the meat packer.

Chicago became the great intermediary between East and West, but it was not alone in playing this role. Detroit also was a meeting place of

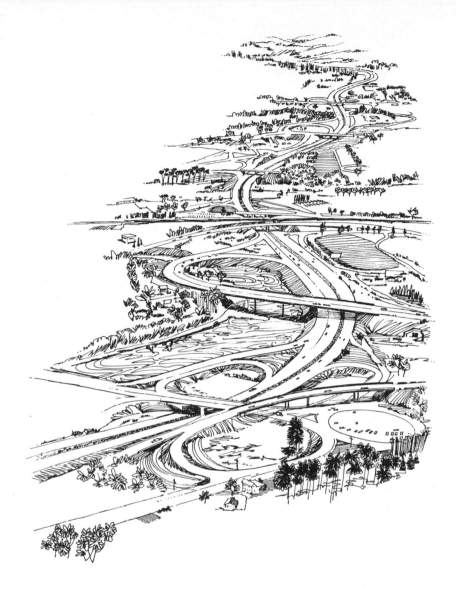

land and water routes, and those who would not face the long water voyage up around Michigan disembarked here and went on by road. Here developed a flourishing business of building wagons. Conestogas, built in Detroit, carried the pioneer families and their possessions westward. When the internal combustion engine began to replace the horse, Detroit, keeping up with technology, prepared to put a motor in its wagons. It is no accident that the automobile industry today belongs exclusively to the Middle West; here the need for wheeled vehicles was greatest, and here that need was met.

Pittsburgh, back within the hills that made up the Allegheny Plateau, and the cities of the Upper Ohio were also setting-out points for the westward journey; the only difference was that from here the traveler most often dropped down the river by barge or flatboat. Here he bought his hardware, tools, and equipment for building his future homestead and plowing his land. That was why Wheeling made nails. Downriver, Cincinnati and Louisville rose to importance as the westward movement passed through and the frontier was extended beyond. Those who went by land traced out the National Road, the future Route 40, through Columbus, and Indianapolis. River and road converged again in St. Louis, only to fan out and join up again in Kansas City.

Those who went up the Mississippi found their journey checked by the falls at Minneapolis, which constituted yet another starting point for the westward cavalcade. Wheat from the Red River Valley in North Dakota was freighted back to Minneapolis and St. Paul, where the grain elevators and flour mills sprang up. Yet others went by way of the Great Lakes, establishing lake ports at Cleveland, Toledo, and Milwaukee, points where they embarked or went ashore.

All these cities have something in common. All are route centers; all began as brash, brawling frontier towns, and then developed the industries that the frontier needed. All have changed as their frontier character gradually evaporated and as newer industries—lumber, meat and grain processing, steel, machinery, electronics—began to supplement or replace the older.

The Midwest is mainly a region of fields and farms, but in the north it merges into one of forests and mines. This is in part because the summers become cooler and shorter and winters longer and colder; in part because the deep rich soil of the plains thins out against the hard, old rocks of the north. These rocks extend south from Canada into Michigan, Wisconsin, and Minnesota. Their surface, thin-soiled, undulating, and forested, rises into low ridges of yet harder and more resistant rock—the iron ranges.

The pioneers discovered this immense reserve more than a century ago, and smelted the ore with charcoal made from the forests. Lake Superior at this time was remote and access to it was difficult. The Sault Ste. Marie—St. Marys Rapids—obstructed the river that joined Superior to Lake Huron, and only after the "Soo" Canal was opened in 1855 did ore from the upper lakes move eastward in quantity. It was a 750-mile journey from Duluth to Pittsburgh, but most of it was by water. Ore moved to the fuel, and thus rose the great smelting and steel industry of Pittsburgh and Youngstown. Then fuel and ore began to meet at some intermediate point, where the ore freighters were unloaded on the lake shore—at Buffalo, Cleveland, Detroit, Chicago, and Gary—and the iron and steel industry arose at these points too.

Even the largest mineral deposit is exhaustible. Those around Lake Superior have been worked now for over a century, and the best ore is gone. Immense quantities of low grade ore, known as taconite, remain, but before long the iron industries of the Great Lakes region will have to rely on the recently opened sources of high-grade ore in Canada.

The Great Plains

It is hard to draw a line between the Midwest and the Great Plains. From the Mississippi River, which even at St. Paul is only 828 feet above the level of the Gulf of Mexico, the land rises to the foot of the Rockies. Denver stands a mile above the sea; and Colorado Springs is even higher. This ascent is not quite regular; there is a series of broad steps which lift gradually to the plateau from which the Rocky Mountains rise suddenly in all their majesty.

The climate gets drier to the west. Chicago receives, on average, 34 inches of rain a year; at Omaha rainfall has dropped to under 30, and in eastern Colorado, to 15. In its more easterly parts the Midwest was basically a forested land; the Great Plains are grassland. Beyond the Mississippi River the forest ends very gradually, sending only long straggling fingers of woodland up along the rivers. Perhaps one may say that the Midwest ends where the forest ceases to grow.

Patches of prairie land occurred quite far to the east, in Illinois and even in Indiana, surrounded by the forest. But these probably arose from the activities of the Indians who burned the trees; and the repeated burning in late summer of the tall grass that took their place prevented the young seedling trees from growing. Thus the more easterly patches of prairie were manmade, for man has almost everywhere played a role in shaping what appears to be the natural condition of the landscape. To the west, in the Great Plains proper, the grasslands are natural; they are a response to the conditions of temperature and rainfall which exist there.

Beyond the Mississippi there is tall grass, passing westward into short grass, and then into arid scrubland. In the nineteenth century this was the open range, stretching from Texas to Montana. The cattle trails ran across it to the railhead at Abilene or Dodge City, back in Kansas. Into this region came the dirt farmer, running his barbed wire across the range, putting up steel windmills to pump water, and forcing the rancher ever deeper into the arid west.

Prairie grass forms a thick sod of tangled roots. It takes a good plow to cut through it, and not until manufacturers back in the Midwest came out with a better tool could this be done. The plow that broke the plains was of smooth, polished steel. Horse-drawn, then tractor-drawn, it cut through the tall and then the short-grass prairie, sparing only areas like the Sand Hills in Nebraska and the Flint Hills of Kansas, whose names tell us why. The newly turned prairie soil cropped well, and farmers pushed the frontier of settlement far out into the dry lands.

In such arid regions the annual rainfall is apt to vary greatly from one year to another. Wet years have abundant rainfall for wheat; in dry years, the grain burns up before its ear is formed. A series of moist seasons tempted farmers far out into the dry plains; then a sequence of dry years parched the soil and drove the farmers back off the land in clouds of dust which the wind blew up from the untilled fields. Farming on the high plains always faces this risk. It is not possible to increase the amount of rainfall, but greater quantities of water can be drawn from the rivers. A few rivers like the Missouri, the Platte, and the Arkansas have their source back within the Rocky Mountains, where they are fed by melting snows. They are large rivers bringing vast quantities of water down onto the plains. A greater number of rivers rise out on the plain in front of the Rockies. They are smaller, but even they deliver their quota of water.

Today the valleys of the rivers stand out as long, green oases straggling across the plains, green not with cottonwoods, but with cropland permanently irrigated by the waters of the prairie rivers. The program of building dams and constructing reservoirs on the dozens of rivers that flow down to join the Missouri or Mississippi is forging ahead, and the strips of green drawn out across the plains will gradually lengthen, as more water is made available for irrigation, until they reach right across the high plains, from the mountains to the Mississippi.

What are now the cities of the plains were formerly the stopping places of the pioneers or the shipping points for cattle at the end of their long march. The biggest lie back on the Missouri River: the two Kansas Cities, each on its bluff overlooking the Missouri, separated from one another by the Kansas River; Omaha and Council Bluffs, facing one

another across the Missouri. Then, just west of this line, Lincoln, To-
peka, Wichita, and beyond only the small prairie towns until the Rocky
Mountains are reached.

The Great Plains are perhaps in the imagination of the nation and
also in that of outsiders, the typically American region. For long this was
the frontier, the area of expanding settlement, where a new world was
won from reluctant nature by work, tenacity, and endurance. The frontier has shaped American life and institutions more than we sometimes
think; its culture and its folklore are with us still. If there is a specifically
American epic, it is that of the conquest of the plains. The folk songs of
the cowboy lie back of much of the native American music. The lawlessness of the expanding frontier, where law-enforcement had not fully
caught up with the advanced wave of settlers, the saga of the open range
and of the long journey of the pioneers in the covered wagons from the
Missouri River, through Indian territory, to the relative safety and security of the mountains, all are an essential part of the American heritage.

The landscape of the prairie is unique. It is made up of rolling grassland, long or short according to the rainfall; with tabular, flat-topped
hills rising a few hundred feet above it, such as Scotts Bluff, that served
as beacons shining out across the plains; of the wire fences and tumble-
weed, and the straight, empty road rising and falling like a ship on a
gentle swell. It is a landscape made up of horizontal lines, with few vertical lines to break its regularity. Around the isolated farmhouse some
trees have been carefully planted and tend to give it shelter from the
wind. More rarely, the tall, white tower of the grain elevator rises above
the plain as if to command a more distant view.

And the climate of the prairies deals in extremes: the savage winter,
when the snow is driven by blizzard winds and cattle are lost under the
drifts; the spring, when a violent rush of warm air comes to drive out
the cool, strewing tornadoes along its path; and summer, when the sun
burns down from a cloudless sky, day after day, as the wheat harvesters
work northward with the harvest all the way from the Texas Panhandle
to North Dakota.

Such are the Great Plains. In the east, a European people took an
American environment and shaped it to their needs; here on the plains
an immigrant people were shaped, toughened, and tempered by their
environment. This was, indeed, more than ever "a lustier land to which
the settlers had come."

The South

No contrast could be greater than that between the Great Plains and the South, not so much in the landscape itself as in the ways in which these lands have shaped and conditioned man and his institutions of society and government. Around the southern margin of the Midwest, where bedrock emerges from beneath its cover of boulder clay, there is a rougher, poorer terrain. This is not a mountainous area; at most it is hilly. From the Cumberland Plateau, back in eastern Tennessee and Kentucky, these Southern Highlands stretch west to the Mississippi. Here it is interrupted by the flat bottom lands which the river has created. Then, beyond the river, a similar landscape runs through the Ozark Highlands of Missouri and Arkansas, and ends in the Ouachita Mountains on the border of Oklahoma.

The rocks of which this rough plateau is made, yield only a poor soil. But in places it has been interrupted. Imagine a giant window cut through these rocks to expose those lower in the geological scale. That is how the Nashville Basin of Tennessee, lying across the valley of the Cumberland River, and the Blue Grass country of Kentucky, just south from Cincinnati, originated. These lower rocks are kinder to man; they are predominantly limestone, and yield a good soil; they are islands of fertility set in a rocky frame of infertile sandstone. The Blue Grass and the Nashville basins are good farmland, and the Blue Grass in particular is known for its trim farms, with their white fences and large barns, and the raising and training of race horses.

The surrounding hills which rise steeply from most sides of these two basins, walling them in as it were, are poor land. The bottom lands along the winding valleys are cultivated, and attempts were made to cultivate the slopes. Like the Midwest itself, this is a land of fierce summer rains. The soil, once disturbed by the cutting of the trees and the plowing of its surface, is easily and quickly washed away. Gullies were etched into the valley sides; they were cut right down to bedrock; they headed back up the slopes to the crest of the hills, and they widened until they coalesced; and then over vast areas the soils had gone. They were only soils of indifferent quality, but their loss was felt by the farmer, and the silt they formed helped to choke the creeks and to turn the Tennessee, the Cumberland, and the Ohio into muddy streams.

This was once a sick land, and the gullies were like sores which festered and spread. The sickness has been cured. The gullying is now checked, and new forests have been planted to bind the soil with their roots. The creeks have been cleaned out, and the bigger rivers run smoothly and steadily down over dams, ever down to the Ohio. They are deep enough to navigate, powerful enough to generate electric current, numerous enough to power a whole new industry. Cheap power is attracting industry to the valley of the Tennessee. Knoxville, Huntsville, Nashville are changing character; they are now a part of the new industrial South. At Oak Ridge in Tennessee is the national laboratory for nuclear physics and the chief source of radioactive materials. But the old sickness, though cured, can always recur. The price of cultivating these hills is eternal watchfulness, for soil erosion is an ever present danger.

Beyond the Mississippi, in the Ozarks and Ouachitas, the danger is less pressing because the denudation of the hills was less drastic. But the basic problems here are the same as back in the Cumberland Plateau or up in the Knobs of Kentucky. Here, too, as in the valley of the Tennessee, "poor land makes poor people, poor people make poor land."

Just as this region of plateau and low hills fades northward into the glaciated plain of the Midwest, so on the south it merges into the Gulf Coastal Plain of the South. Near the Gulf the land is defended from the sea by the belt of swamps where De Soto died. These swamps help to explain why the Spaniards made so small an impact on this region; they just could not get to it. On the north is the line of higher, rougher country from the Appalachians west to the Ozarks; in the south the swamplands. Between the two lies Dixie, the Old South.

The Coastal Plain that we have traced southward from New Jersey through the Carolinas and Georgia swings west and broadens as it approaches the Mississippi River, and extends until it abuts the high plain of Texas. It is crossed by a multitude of rivers with strange, familiar-sounding names—the Suwanee, Chattahoochee, Tombigbee. The Piedmont narrows as it wraps around the southern end of the Appalachians, and most of Dixie is made up mainly of the rich alluvial plain, of silt and sand, the creation of the rivers that flow south toward the Gulf.

Settlers came in from the northeast, extending the cotton crop gradually west to the Mississippi and beyond. Except for the desert of the southwest, the Old South had the least familiar climate to the European immigrants. Its mild winters, with only an occasional touch of northern austerity, and its long, hot, humid summers were new to them. So too was the opportunity to grow tropical crops: indigo and rice in the tide-

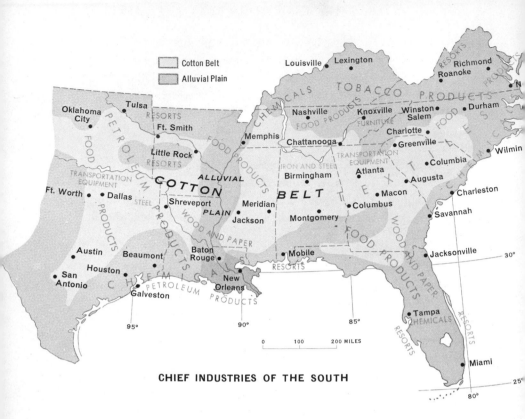

CHIEF INDUSTRIES OF THE SOUTH

water swamps; tobacco over the plain; and cotton everywhere. These conditions bred an aristocratic, almost a feudal society, based upon the plantation, slave labor, and white supremacy.

A century ago this social order was defeated in the most bitter war this continent has known. It was founded upon cotton, which formerly ruled the Old South, but King Cotton has been dethroned, and the old economy, along with the old social order, has changed.

Cotton is an exhausting crop, and the fields deteriorate rapidly under it; inevitably the frontier of cotton growing moves forward, leaving a worked-out soil behind it. And in its wake come sown grasses and beef cattle, fruit orchards and softwood plantations. Agricultural change makes the unskilled plantation worker less necessary than he once was. Only in a few especially favored areas, like the rich bottom lands along the Mississippi from Memphis south, and in Alabama, is cotton still the king, and even here his throne is endangered. Cotton has gone west, where irrigation can be used and the climate is too dry for the boll weevil to flourish, where larger fields can be plowed with a tractor and the cotton can be sucked off the plants by a giant vacuum cleaner. A cotton-picking machine is a wonderfully democratic machine; it abolishes the hard manual labor of the cotton picker, trailing his long sack behind him through the fields; it elevates cotton picking to the status of a skilled job.

The Old South is often regarded as the most romantic, nostalgic, and backward-looking region of the United States. In the words of the *Economist,* "One of the South's principal exports is its past. The raw materials inherent in romantic memories and the nostalgia that comes with defeat have been exploited by southern writers and music-makers so brilliantly that today they dominate the American literary and theatrical scene." As the South has long ceased to be the land of cotton, it is ceasing now to be a curiosity of history and folklore; it is one of the fastest growing, fastest changing regions of the United States.

Back in the Old South industry has come in. This is not altogether new. There has long been some industry along the Fall Line. Birmingham, Alabama, has been smelting iron and making cast-iron pipes for almost a century. But that is up on the northern hilly margin of the South. Now industry is coming across the old cotton fields, and the *Economist* reports, "What was once a cotton patch near Baton Rouge . . . is now the site of the largest oil refinery in America. On the bayous and cypress swamps bordering the Mississippi River now stands an industrial complex of oil and chemical enterprises, paper mills and aluminum plants, synthetic rubber and fertilizer factories." Add to these the cotton mills that have spread down through the Piedmont and into Georgia, and the lumber mills which process the South's newest crop, the vast tracts of softwood lumber, and the extraction of sulfur and salt from beneath the Gulf Coast to supply the new chemical industries.

The South has large resources for industry; the vast reserves of oil in Louisiana, Arkansas, Oklahoma, and Texas; the coal and iron ore of Alabama; the potash deposits of Florida; the salt and sulfur which underlie the Gulf coast. Many navigable rivers flow south to the Gulf, and are being improved and interconnected. Ports have grown up where they cut their way through the coastal swamps and the offshore bars to the sea: Newport News and Norfolk, the chief coal ports; Charleston and Savannah, which once shipped out much of the cotton crop; Mobile and New Orleans, which took their place; and Port Arthur, Galveston, Houston, and Corpus Christi, the ports of Texas.

Before Alaska entered the Union, Texas was the largest state. It is the only state that has ever known a sovereign existence, independent of the other states, for however short a period. Texas began as a ranching state, from which the cattle trails led back to the advancing railhead in the Great Plains, and the ranching tradition remains very strong in Texas. Then came the dirt farmer, extending wheat, corn, and cotton through the moister and more easterly parts of the state. But Texas never really belonged to the Old South; it was opened up too late for the old-style plantation ever to have been really important.

Then came the discovery of oil, on which is founded both the current prosperity of Texas and also the fortunes of its millionaires. Oil underlies the Texas coast and stretches back into the interior. Oil refineries and the chemical industries that are based upon oil have sprung up, bringing with them construction and consumers' goods industries.

The industrial city and port of Houston, lying fifty miles inland from the Gulf coast, with which it is linked across Galveston Bay by a deep ship channel, has now over a million inhabitants. Away from its downtown area lies the new space-craft center which will direct the Apollo project, the United States' moon shot. Dallas, Fort Worth, and San Antonio are cities of over half a million, and ten other cities have each more than a hundred thousand. Southern Texas stretches almost as far south as southern Florida. Like Florida, it has a climate of subtropical warmth, occasionally touched by the cold arctic winds of winter. But despite these hazards, southern Texas has developed into a major citrus-growing region.

Modern developments have been superimposed on the Old South. It has ceased to live in the past, but it can still to some extent live on its past—its old plantation homes; its mansions opening on to the Mississippi, with their parks and shade trees; the warmth of winters, the flowers of spring; and the strange, exotic fascination of the Spanish moss swinging slowly from the branches of the trees, and of the swamps, their dark pools, their tangled cypress roots, and their strange, exuberant waterlife.

New Orleans, lying a foot or two above the water level, the river Mississippi on one side, and its lake, Pontchartrain, on the other, epitomizes the Old South. In origin it is French; and it is still in part French in culture. Its old city, the Vieux Carré, with its iron balconies overlooking the streets, and the courtyards behind shaded by the trailing wisteria, its good food and feeling of gaiety, belongs culturally to southern Europe as much as to Louisiana. At night the city is pervaded by the sound of jazz. Along the waterfront they still load cotton, but nearby are chemical factories, an oil driller's rig rises above the reeds of the swamp, and on a nearby damp island one of the bayou dwellers continues his strange amphibious life undisturbed.

The long, flat, marshy promontory that the Coastal Plain sends out to the southeast, Florida, also belongs to the South. But it is a part of the South to which the cotton plantation never came, partly because it was under Spanish control, partly because it was too damp and low. Florida is one of the fastest growing states of all, yet its resources are few. It has a climate which all must envy: abundant sunshine, a near freedom from frost, and mile after mile of golden, sandy beach; sheltered coastal lagoons, good sailing and good fishing; and the added charm that today one might perhaps see a rocket go up.

Florida has become America's resort par excellence. Around its shores from Jacksonville to Pensacola is a succession of resorts, some quiet and unassuming, others garish and strident. But all yield to Miami Beach in size and sophistication. Yet only a few miles back from the gilded splendor, the cabarets, and the heated and illuminated swimming pools lie the fetid swamps on which man has left no mark.

The heavy traffic on the airlines to Miami brings not only vacationers. Florida is booming in other ways. It is the chief citrus-growing state, and all down through the middle of the state are orange and grapefruit groves, always at the mercy of the slight winter frost that can wreck the fruit growers' prospects for the year. The climate and the amenities are attracting also business undertakings which, with modern communications, are no longer tied to the great cities of the north, and also those industries that can use the South's timber, potash, and salt.

From the Rockies to the Pacific

Population and industry have moved west as well as south from the earlier centers of settlement in the northeast of the United States. Florida and the Old South have long been settled, but manufacturing industry has come to them only in the last generation or two. The West, that region beyond the low plains of the Midwest and the higher and more rolling prairies, belongs also to the movement of expanding industry, intensive agriculture, and settlement. The West begins with the chain of the Rocky Mountains and stretches on across the plateaus and ranges and the Great Basin, to the western mountains which border the Pacific.

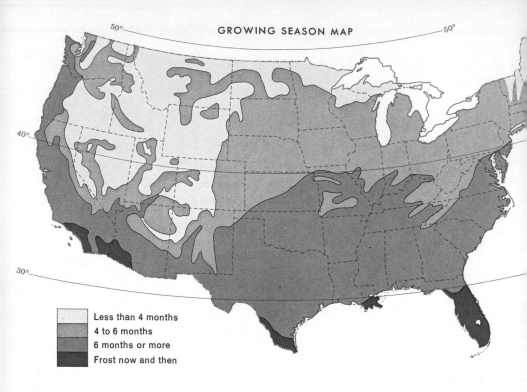

50°   50°

40°

30°

Less than 4 months
4 to 6 months
6 months or more
Frost now and then

From Denver the line of the Rocky Mountains shuts in the western horizon. They look like the jagged, blunted teeth of an old saw. They lie continuously for three hundred miles at over ten thousand feet, and their summits, sharply etched against the clear, western sky, are permanently snow-capped. To the south they continue as the Sangre de Cristo Mountains, and these are prolonged in the lower ranges which terminate in giant cliffs by the Rio Grande or are continued into Mexico. Eight hundred miles west is another and similar range, the Sierra Nevada, which is also continued north to Canada and south to Mexico. Between is the dry, empty Great Basin.

To the north the Colorado Rockies fade out, and there is a depression drained east to the Platte and Missouri and west, by way of the Green River, to the Colorado—for from north to south through the Rocky Mountains there winds the Continental Divide, separating the rivers which flow to the Atlantic from those which drain to the Pacific. Through this gap go main roads and railroads to the west. But north of it the Rocky Mountains again line up all their powers, and continue, range overlapping range, the jagged teeth of the Tetons, the splendor of Yellowstone Park, the long sinuous ridge of the Bitterroot Mountains, which separate Idaho from Montana, until they have crossed the 49th parallel and run on into Canada.

It makes the world seem small just to think that these mountains that rise above Denver are part of a mountain system—the whole of it formed at one single geological time—which runs southward through the Sierra Madre of Mexico to the mountains of Central America, which are in turn linked with the Andes of South America. The Andes are continued through island groups of the Antarctic Ocean to mountain ranges which are deeply buried beneath the ice of Antarctica.

In the opposite direction, the Rocky Mountains are continued through the Bitterroot, the Lewis, the Absaroka, and other ranges of Wyoming, Montana, and Idaho, into the Rocky Mountains of Canada. They rise, wall-like, on the border of Alberta and British Columbia; they continue through the Yukon territory and into Alaska. From Alaska the loop of the Aleutian Islands marks their continuation across the Bering Sea into Asia. They twist and curve across Asia, until at last they join the mountain knot of the Pamir, from which other ranges reach south into Southeast Asia, and westward through the Middle East and into Europe. This mountain system serves as a kind of skeleton for the continents, and around it are grouped the hills, plateaus, and plains, like the softer organs of the body.

Beyond the Rocky Mountains of the United States are the basins and plateaus of the West, and these are enclosed on their far western side by fresh ranges of high snow-capped mountains, the Sierra Nevadas and the Cascades, the Olympics and the Coast Ranges. Most of this intermediary region is a high plateau, but above it rise mountain ranges, most of them short, steep-sided, overlapping one another, so that roads must zigzag to get around them.

The plateau itself was fractured and split into a thousand parts in the course of the earth movements that created the Rockies themselves. Some of these blocks were raised by subterranean forces; some tilted, and others even depressed. Big ranges like the Wasatch, which looks down on Salt Lake City, and the dozens of little ranges that are dotted about the desert of Nevada, Utah, and Arizona were formed. Depressions were cut off from the sea by the mountains, and one, Death Valley, was lowered almost three hundred feet below the level of the sea. Volcanic activity accompanied these violent movements of the earth's crust; lava flows, volcanic peaks and craters were formed. Some of these remain to add a bizarre attraction to the western landscape.

Many of the more striking of these natural phenomena are protected and preserved in National Parks or as National Monuments, both from the destructive hand of man, and also from the eroding hand of nature itself. The Grand Canyon is the most spectacular and most visited of these. But to the list should also be added Bryce Canyon, Mesa Verde, Zion Canyon, and Death Valley, in each of which are exhibited the striking land forms produced by the work of erosion. In other parks and monuments, such as the Craters of the Moon in southern Idaho, and Crater Lake in the Cascade Range of Oregon, and Lassen in California, fantastic forms produced by volcanic action are preserved; and in the Glacier National Park in Montana, and Yosemite in California, can be seen the work of the glaciers which were formed in these mountains during the Ice Age.

In a climate moister than the present great rivers were formed, flowing down from the mountains which enclose the Great Basin onto the plateau. Some, trapped by the mountains, formed lakes which later slowly evaporated, leaving sheets of smooth hard salt for racing motorists to establish their records on. Some, on the plateaus of Oregon, Nevada, and Utah, have not yet evaporated, but remain, slowly becoming more saline, like the Great Salt Lake itself. Some rivers disappear into the rock without ever forming lakes. Yet others have cut deep valleys into the plateau, narrow and gorgelike where the rocks are hard, wider and more gentle where they erode more easily. Almost a third of this region of mountain and plateau drains to the Colorado River, and from almost as great an area the drainage makes its way to the Columbia.

Today the western plateau is a region of little rainfall. Though the winds come in from the west, they lose much of their moisture as they rise to cross the Sierra Nevada and the Cascade Mountains. The western slopes, in California, Oregon, and Washington, are moist and green. Clouds are piled up against them much of the time, but beyond their summits, the clouds break up, thin out, and disappear. Rain clouds are rare to the east of the mountains.

On the high ground of the western ranges the air is cold. It then sweeps down to the basin and plateau region, dropping maybe five or six thousand feet. Down there it is hotter. The air is heated in its descent, and becomes hot and dry. It does not bring moisture; it takes up and absorbs it, drying up the land, withering plants, and causing the few rivers to disappear into nothing. This is the chinook wind, and it explains why the land is often so parched and arid in the lee of the mountain ranges of Washington and Oregon, of Montana, Wyoming, and Colorado.

But the dozens of ridgelike mountains of the Great Basin, tilted blocks and upthrust masses of the crust, reach high enough for the air again to be cooled, for moisture to be condensed and to be precipitated as rain. Around Flagstaff, Arizona, through which the tourists stream along Route 66 on their way to Los Angeles, is coniferous woodland, which reaches out to the lip of the Grand Canyon. Fifty miles west and five thousand feet lower is the bare, burned surface of the desert where no rain may have fallen for years. North of the great gash which the Colorado River has cut across the plateaus, patches of woodland, which cover the highest ground, become more numerous and more extensive as the climate becomes imperceptibly cooler and the exposure to the rain-bearing westerly winds greater. In Oregon the scrub desert gives way to poor grazing land, and this along the Snake and Columbia river valleys passes into dry cropland.

But most of the region between the Rocky Mountains and the Sierra Nevada and Cascades is scrub desert. It is made up of bare rock, drifting sand, with sage and creosote bush growing in the drier parts wherever they can establish their roots and gain a little sustenance from the dry soil, and thin grass ranging over the rest.

Indian tribes lived in the semidesert, sometimes practicing a nomadic agriculture and going wherever the needs of their sheep and goats took them; sometimes more settled, building tight villages of adobe houses and growing corn by irrigation. These Indian societies, their cultures adjusted both to their physical conditions and to the modest level of the technology which they knew, still live amid the canyons of New Mexico and Arizona. But today a different kind of culture has been imposed upon the desert with the aid of modern technology. Over large areas the soil is potentially fertile, but a limit to the cropland is set by the amount of moisture that falls as rain and makes its way to the rivers. Agriculture can be carried on only with irrigation. Hence, little of this water is ever allowed to reach the sea; much is evaporated, and the rest is made to irrigate the cultivated fields and orchards.

The greatest river of the region, the Colorado, lies for much of its course too deep in its canyon for its waters to be available for irrigation on the nearby plateau. The mile-deep canyon does, however, form a magnificent reservoir. The Hoover Dam, built between the red-brown walls of the lower gorge, impounds water when the river level is high and liberates it for the cultivated cotton fields and fruit orchards of the Imperial Valley. It also supplies water to Los Angeles and irrigated cropland along the Pacific Coast. Phoenix lies in the midst of a fertile oasis of citrus groves, watered by the Gila River, which flows down from the mountains of Arizona and New Mexico. Along the foot of the Wasatch Mountains, where dozens of little rivers, fed by the rains and snows of the mountains, flow out onto the plateau, is a long, narrow oasis, with Salt Lake City in its midst, set here to trap and use the water before it can be lost in the sands and the shallow salt lakes of the desert. The Snake River Plain of Idaho relies heavily on irrigation, and farther north, where rainfall is greater, the aid and the assurance which irrigation can give are not rejected. Dams on the Columbia River and its tributaries are accumulating water to supplement the modest and not wholly reliable natural rainfall.

The organization of these irrigation projects along the Columbia River in the north, and the Colorado, Gila, and Rio Grande in the south is not only a matter of concern for the United States. It touches both neighbors, for the Columbia comes in from Canada, and most of its water fell as rain or snow on Canadian soil. What is left of the Colorado, after water has been taken to irrigate the Imperial Valley and to supply Los Angeles, flows on into Mexico. Careful negotiations are necessary both to secure the maximum flow from Canada and in order not to deprive or offend the Mexicans. This has not been an easy problem, but is of a kind that we shall run into again—in Egypt, Israel, Pakistan, and India—wherever, in fact, a river flows through a dry land, or is needed for water power, and is shared by two or more countries which compete to use its water.

In the desert water is gold, but in the western deserts of the United States there is an alternative source of wealth. The West has an abundance of minerals. These in all their variety are accumulated deep beneath the crust. As was noted in an earlier chapter, if the crust is twisted and weakened as it was when the mountain ranges were folded, or shattered by thousands of cracks as happened in the Great Basin, these minerals are able to rise upward toward the surface. They rise as fluids, filling the cracks, then cool, solidify, and form crystalline masses. These are the mineral lodes of the geologist and miner. They thread their way through the rocks, sometimes many feet across, sometimes only a fraction of an inch, like the nervous system running through the human body. In time, erosion removes the upper parts of the lodes; the less stable minerals are oxidized and carried away in the rivers. The more stable, like gold, remain as fine bright grains and particles, hidden in the sand of the river bed, awaiting the pan of a gold prospector.

It was the mineral wealth of the West that did more than anything to bring settlers to it. The lure of gold took them up into the Rockies of Colorado, Montana, and Idaho. At the mention of gold, they trudged across the desert of Nevada to the rough, raw mining camps along the foot of the Sierra Nevada. When they had exhausted the alluvial deposits, some returned home; some turned to farming; a few traced the minerals back to their lodes, and pursued them deep into the crust of the earth. Even deep mines do not last forever. The West is strewn with their remains—Cripple Creek, Virginia City, Central City—and dozens of other ghost towns, which once hit it rich and for a few years lived high on the profits of their bonanzas, and are now almost abandoned and in ruins.

The West is still mining country, but the mining is now concentrated on a few resources of great size and is carried on with the aid of the largest and most complex equipment. The vast open pits, where the ore-bearing rock is blasted, crushed to a powder, and the metal extracted, are indeed a far cry from the shovel, pan, and water of those who opened up the mineral wealth of this region. Today the West contributes about a quarter of the world's copper from Butte, Montana, Bingham Canyon, Utah, Coeur d'Alene, Idaho, Globe, Miami, and Morenci, Arizona. Copper is the most important mineral in the West, but one must not omit the silver, lead and zinc, iron, and, perhaps for the future the most important of them all, the small scattered deposits of uranium.

No one who has read *Grapes of Wrath* ever can forget, even if he has never seen, the road across the desert and down into the Great Valley of California:

". . . Over the red lands and the gray lands, twisting up into the mountains, crossing the Divide and down into the bright and terrible desert, and across the desert to the mountains again. . . . And now the high mountains. Holbrook and Winslow and Flagstaff in the high mountains of Arizona. Then the great plateau rolling like a ground swell. Ashfork and Kingman and stone mountains again, where water must be hauled and sold. Then out of the broken sun-rotted mountains of Arizona to the Colorado, with green reeds on its banks. . . . Up from Needles and over a burned range, and there's the desert. And 66 goes on over the terrible desert, where the distance shimmers and the black center mountains hang unbearably in the distance. At last there's Barstow, and more desert until at last the mountains rise up again, the good mountains, and 66 winds through them. Then suddenly a pass, and below the beautiful valley, below orchards and vineyards and little houses, and in the distance a city. And, oh, my God, it's over."

The "good mountains" shut off the plateaus and ranges of the West from the ocean. They form in fact a double line; the Sierra Nevada and the Cascade Mountains to the east and the Olympic and the Coast ranges to the west. There are few gaps in either. There is Tehachapi Pass, around the southern end of the Sierra Nevada, a mere cleft in the mountains, down through which the "Okies" in the novel traveled to their promised land and the modern traveler follows Route 466; and Donner Pass across the central Sierra, the way the transcontinental railroad and Route 40 goes. Farther north the Columbia River has slashed a great gash across the Cascades between Mount Hood and Mount Adams. The Coast Ranges are interrupted at the Golden Gate, where the Pacific Ocean reaches in behind its spurs to broaden into San Francisco Bay. They are interrupted again north of Portland, Oregon, where the Columbia River broadens into its estuary, and also west of Seattle.

Between these two ranges which make up John Steinbeck's good mountains is the even better land of the Great Valley, or Central Valley. The Great Valley of California, the Willamette Valley of Oregon, the Puget Sound Lowlands of Washington are not quite continuous with one another, but they lie end to end, and road and railroad join them together like elongated beads on a string. All are made of flat, rich, alluvial lowlands. In the Great Valley the climate is hot and dry; in the Willamette Valley and Puget Sound Lowlands, it is cooler and moister.

In the southern part of the Great Valley water is fed down from the nearby high Sierras and from the distant mountains of northern California, where the winter rains begin to lengthen until they last almost all the year. This is expensive land to cultivate; water channels run through the fields, sprinklers simulate rainfall, and the crops of lettuce and artichokes, cabbages, cotton and corn look bright green against the gray and brown of the distant hills. The Great Valley is a gigantic oasis, whose growth is checked only by the shortage of water. Sacramento, Fresno, Stockton, and Bakersfield are the chief business and manufacturing centers for this rich farmland.

All around are the sharp, clear mountains, dry and sun-parched through their long Mediterranean summer; bright with flowering shrubs, vineyards, and fruit groves during the short-lived winter rains. The Coast Range drops steeply to the rugged California coast, drawing back from it at intervals to reveal patches of Coastal Plain where again a good soil, helped by irrigation and the hot sun, yields abundant crops. These too are little green oases, set between the brown hills and the blue sea.

Through this country from Mexico came the Franciscan missionaries in the eighteenth century, converting the Indians, introducing their crops and building their missions which still stand amid their gardens and shrubberies. On one of the small plains is San Diego; on another is Los Angeles, its fast growing suburbs spreading up to the base of the canyons that drop down from the mountain ranges and the desert. To the northwest, 350 miles away, is San Francisco, the second city in size of California. With its suburbs and its neighbors, like Oakland and Berkeley, it spreads out around the shores of the bay, linked by vast suspension bridges, over which commuters drive from their homes up in the hills to the city-center of San Francisco. The city spreads out over the steep, rounded hills in which the Coast Range subsides. Docks line the water's edge; old-fashioned cable cars climb up Nob Hill, up through Chinatown, to the homes of the well-to-do that stand silhouetted against the western sky.

San Diego and Los Angeles have the hot, dry climate of the Mediterranean. At Monterey the climate begins to change. By the time we reach San Francisco a decided change is in the air. It is cooler and the rains last longer. Offshore the sea is cool; cool enough to chill the warm, damp air from the ocean so that moisture begins to condense as fog. Banks of fog often lie off the coast, sullen and gray, and sometimes the wind blows them onshore. Fog pours in through the twin headlands of the Golden Gate, like an enormous flood breaking through a sluice; it spreads out over the bay and the city, and dissipates inland as the air warms up over the heated surface.

In Oregon and Washington there is no really dry season, and rain occurs in every month. The effect of this upon the vegetation is obvious. The Pacific Northwest is a region of forests and green fields, of frequent cloud and rain, and of more temperate crops than those which grow so well in the almost tropical heat of California. The apple orchard replaces the vineyard and citrus grove, and wheat, grass, and fodder crops are grown instead of the more demanding and more remunerative crops of irrigated lands.

Water is the life-blood of the dry West. Water, impounded behind

THE PACIFIC COAST REGION

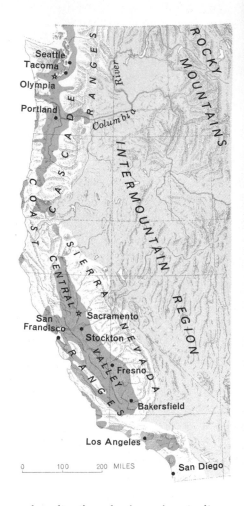

Areas of irrigated land

Areas farmed
without irrigation

huge dams, flowing through canals, distributed through pipelines, pumped from beneath the soil until salt seawater seeps in from the sea to take its place, supplies city and farm. Local governments press their competing claims for water all the way up to the Supreme Court. The sawmills of the Cascades, the aircraft and engineering industries from Seattle to San Diego use power generated from the force of falling water. Water from Canada and from the faraway Rockies of Colorado is being used for all these purposes, and agriculture and industry will continue to expand until not a drop of water runs unused to the sea.

Such are the main regions of the United States, with the exception of the noncontiguous states of Alaska and Hawaii. These were the most recently acquired and the last to be admitted to the Union. That a discussion of their geography has been deferred to a later point in this chapter in no way detracts from their position as integral and highly important parts of the United States; it merely suggests that, in a geographical account, they do not logically follow immediately after that of the conterminous United States.

The regions that have been examined each offers its peculiar combination of opportunities, each demands for their realization the input of different knowledge, skills, and equipment. We have the climate setting limits to agriculture, but limits that can be overstepped with the use of technology; deserts that can be made to grow crops, swamps that can be reclaimed, dry prairies that can be irrigated. Where there is no mineral fuel there is hydroelectric power, and when the last drop of moisture that falls on this land has been used to the full to turn wheels and grow crops, then perhaps future generations will be able to levy their toll on the radioactive elements in the rocks and the waters of the sea, purifying them for their use.

That these resources are immense is shown by the ranking of the United States in the production of many of them. The United States is the largest producer of wheat, corn, and cotton; more petroleum is pumped from the earth, more copper extracted than in any other country. The amount of coal mined is exceeded only by the output of Red China. The capacity of the American iron and steel industry is larger than that of any other, and almost twice as large as that of the second ranked Soviet Union. The machinery and chemical industries are more far ranging and, even if in individual lines of production they are exceeded in some other countries, the total output far exceeds that of any rival.

But the United States makes up only half the total area of Anglo-America. The Canadian half is less populous and less developed. It lies to the north, and for this reason alone it is less well endowed with agricultural resources. It has little coal, but in other resources—the ferrous and nonferrous minerals, petroleum, hydroelectric power, and lumber—it cannot be said that Canada is in any way less well off than the United States. It is, in fact, one of the great frontier regions of the modern world, and in terms of development, stands where the United States stood a half-century or more ago.

CANADA

In 1783 a boundary was drawn by a group of statesmen meeting in Paris between the United States and Canada. They knew little about either land, and their maps were incomplete and inaccurate. But haltingly they traced a line southwest and west through the hills of northern Maine across to the St. Lawrence River and through the Great Lakes. They subsequently had a little trouble around the Lake of the Woods, which we can see for ourselves today, in making their boundary description agree with the facts of geography. Later agreements righted the many little errors in this treaty and continued the line west along the 49th parallel until it ran out into the salt water, and so through the Strait of Juan de Fuca to the ocean.

North of this line the land remained British. It was one of the strangest quirks of history that the provinces which today make up the Canadian Maritimes took no part in the American Revolution which began in 1776. Perhaps it was the roadless wilderness of Maine which made contact difficult between New England and the provinces of New Brunswick and Nova Scotia; perhaps the thinly settled character of the latter made collective action on such an issue difficult. There was considerable sympathy in the Canadian provinces for the American Revolution. For a short time, American forces occupied Canadian soil; but Canada as a whole remained aloof from the struggle and offered refuge to the United Empire Loyalists, whose effect was to strengthen the ties linking Canada with Great Britain.

Nevertheless, the British were quick to give some limited degree of autonomy to what remained of their North American empire. A problem arose from the start, however, from the dual character of the Canadian people. At this date the French-speaking population of Quebec—that close-knit feudal society pioneered by Champlain—was in a majority, and was prepared to fight to retain its customs, legal systems, language, and religion. In 1791 two legislative councils, in part elected by the local people, were established, one for French-speaking Lower Canada and the other for English-speaking Upper Canada, where many of the Loyalists had settled.

Canada at this time consisted of a thinly populated strip of land lying along the St. Lawrence River, and broadening at its extremities in the Maritime Provinces and Ontario. The rest of this country, larger than the United States, was little known and almost empty of settlers. Its size, combined with the dual origin of its population, made administration difficult. The ideal solution would have been some form of federalism, but this the British authorities were for a long time reluctant to allow. They were afraid that this would give too much freedom to the independent-minded, French-speaking Canadians.

After many changes of policy, Canada emerged in 1867 as a federal state, though one in which the balance of power between the provinces and the federal government had been greatly modified over the American system. In the United States the southern states had only recently tried to break away from the Union, and in doing so had precipitated a savage and costly war. Due to the example of its neighbor, the Canadian constitution was drawn on federal lines in order to accommodate the variety within its vast territory, but so much power was to reside at the center, in the federal government, that there could be no possibility that the French-speaking province of Quebec should ever be able to secede.

At first there were only five provinces; Ontario and Quebec and the three Maritime Provinces—New Brunswick, Nova Scotia, and Prince Edward Island. Settlement spread across the Canadian Midwest just as it did across the American. One by one the Canadian Prairie and Mountain provinces—Manitoba (1870), British Columbia (1871), Saskatchewan (1905), and Alberta (1905)—came into being and were admitted as Provinces of the Dominion of Canada. In 1949, they were joined by Newfoundland, which had hitherto been a separate member of the British Commonwealth. Today Canada has ten provinces and two "territories," the Northwest Territory and the Yukon, which together span the Canadian Arctic from Hudson Bay to Alaska and extend northward to within 10° of the North Pole.

The hills of New England, the Great Plains, and the Rocky Mountains are each continued northward, beyond the border and into Canada. But in Canada there is a distinctive region, which makes only a small and grudging appearance in the United States. Between the Maritime Provinces and the Prairies, which cover much of Manitoba, Saskatchewan and Alberta, there intrudes the Laurentian Shield. This is by far the largest physical region of Canada, and occupies more than half its total area. The Shield is a vast area made up of rocks of great age and hardness. Unlike such young mountains as the Rockies, the rocks of the Shield have been folded and refolded, worn down and worn down again, and lastly, scraped and scratched by the ice sheets of the last Ice Age.

This region sends spurs into the United States, to form the Adirondack Mountains of New York State and to support the iron ranges of northern Wisconsin and Minnesota. It forms the rugged northern shore of Lakes Huron and Superior, and the St. Marys River cascades over it between the two lakes; it wraps around the western end of Lake Superior and reaches into northern Wisconsin. Then its western margin sweeps away to the northwest, along Lake Winnipeg and the Great Slave and Great Bear lakes, to the Arctic Ocean. On the map, the Canadian Shield appears as a huge, rounded mass, shaped somewhat like a shield.

The long, tapering estuary of the St. Lawrence blazes a route, between the Maritimes and the Shield, into the heart of the continent. It was by this route that the earliest explorer of Canada, Jacques Cartier, came in the sixteenth century, and the French settlers followed in the seventeenth.

These French-speaking Canadians have spread back into the Maritime Provinces, and over the hills and into New England. They are a robust, frugal, hard-working people, and when the older New Englanders moved out in search of greater opportunities farther west, the Canadians moved in. New Brunswick, Nova Scotia, and Prince Edward Island sound British, and they *were*. Many English and Scotch came here and farmed the cool, damp hills and fished off the rocky coasts; but many of them also joined the westward movement. The Maritimes are today not growing much in population in spite of the drift of French-speaking Canadians into the area.

Even cooler, damper, and more bleak and inhospitable is the island of Newfoundland, in reality a continuation of the Maritimes beyond the Cabot Strait. Rough and forested, its wealth lies in its lumber, its mines, and its fisheries. It supplies pulpwood to Europe. Fish caught in the area of shallow sea known as the Grand Banks are dried and canned for export. Iron ore from Bell Island (Wabana) is shipped to smelters in North America and in Europe. The most important part of Newfoundland is the Avalon Peninsula in the extreme southeast. This has the least severe climate and is closed by ice for a shorter period than other parts of the island, and here, in the port of St. John's, is based much of the Newfoundland fishing fleet.

In summer ships on the run from northwest Europe to Montreal may save a few hundred miles by sailing to the north of Newfoundland and through the Strait of Belle Isle. There is a chill in the wind as the ship approaches that long northern peninsula of Newfoundland that a bright sun seems to do nothing to abate. The water is cold, almost ice-cold, against the hull of the ship, and all through summer a few icebergs are to be seen, drifting slowly south from their birthplace in the glaciers of Greenland and Labrador, iridescent and beautiful in the sunshine and carrying nine-tenths of their menacing bulk beneath the water. In early fall ice begins to form over the sea. It is broken up by the swell, freezes together, breaks and refreezes, until the surface is impassable with piled-up masses of ice. The Strait of Belle Isle is navigable only for a month or two, and the Cabot Strait, to the south of Newfoundland, is closed for almost half the year. During this period no ships can sail up the St. Lawrence, and Canada's seaborne traffic goes in and out of Halifax, Nova Scotia, whose harbor, in spite of the bitter cold, manages to get enough of the warm, northward-drifting ocean current to remain clear of ice.

The coast of Labrador, along the northwestern shore of Belle Isle Strait, is barren and rockbound. Not a tree or habitation is in sight, though inland, where the land is flatter, the winds less violent, and a little soil has been able to form, there begins a forest of stunted conifers. Part of Labrador is included in the Province of Newfoundland, and part in Quebec.

As the ship moves into the Gulf of St. Lawrence and then into the estuary, its southwesterly course takes it into more temperate as well as more sheltered areas. Forests drop down to the water's edge, interrupted by farm clearings. Villages of little white-frame houses appear, each dominated by the tall, fingerlike spire of the church. They become more numerous, until the ship reaches Quebec, and docks at the foot of the steep Heights of Abraham, which the British troops under Wolfe scaled in the night, back in 1759. The heights are dominated by the soaring Château Frontenac Hotel. Below it lies the quaint old French city, still in parts enclosed by its seventeenth-century walls.

From Quebec to Montreal, a distance of 165 miles, the river is more difficult to navigate. The ship sails through farm land which improves as its latitude diminishes. There are small industrial towns set between the river and the distant hills. For most large ships Montreal is the end of the voyage. The city lies at the foot of an isolated hill—Mount Royal, or *Mont Réal,* surrounded by branches and tributaries of the river. Here a limit was formerly set to navigation by the Lachine Rapids. These were first circumvented by a canal which allowed small craft to sail on up to the Great Lakes. The canal has now been replaced by the Seaway, by means of which large freighters are enabled to reach the Lakes. For an increasing number of ships the terminal point is no longer Montreal, but Toronto, Cleveland, Detroit, or Chicago.

As Cartier observed, from the summit of Mount Royal the low, rounded hills of the Canadian Shield are visible on the northern horizon. To the south, beyond the river plain and faint in the distance, are the Green Mountains of the Vermont border and the Adirondacks of upper New York State. To the northeast, the way we have come, is the river, island-strewn, broadening slowly toward the sea between the embrace of the hills. In the opposite direction, to the southwest, the St. Lawrence valley continues; in the foreground the Lachine Rapids, the great bridges across the river, and the end of the straight, clean-cut seaway. Beyond, the lowlands continue, through the dim blue distance, widening as the hills retreat on each side, into the plains that enclose on the north the lower Great Lakes.

This is the industrial hub of Canada, an irregular peninsula of land, reaching from Montreal to Windsor, which lies opposite Detroit, with Lake Erie and Ontario to the south, Lake Huron to the north and west, and to the northeast the gentle rise from the farm lands of this Ontario Peninsula to the forests of the Shield. Here in the Lakes Peninsula are some of Canada's most important industrial cities: Toronto, Montreal, Hamilton, London. There are immense sources of hydroelectric power in Niagara Falls and in the rivers dropping from the Shield. Here is some of Canada's best farm land; fruit grows well along the sunny, sheltered shores of Lake Erie; dairying flourishes on the damp, glaciated plain behind. Here also is the political center of Canada, the federal capital of Ottawa, built roughly on the boundary of the two great language communities of Canada.

Almost directly to the north of Ottawa lies the Shield, vast, untraveled, and still little known. Except here and there, where the ice has left a patch of clay, there is not enough soil for agriculture. The climate is too severe for any except the hardiest of vegetables and fodder crops. Over much of its surface is the bare rock, rounded, smoothed, scratched by the passage of the ice. Large areas are covered by water—thousands of lakes, large and small, some held up by a small dam of glacial debris, others filling hollows from which the ice has plucked and removed the rock. Small rivers join these lakes together, forming a net of waterways through which once circulated the canoes of the trappers. The forest cover of coniferous trees—the taiga—thins out toward the north. They

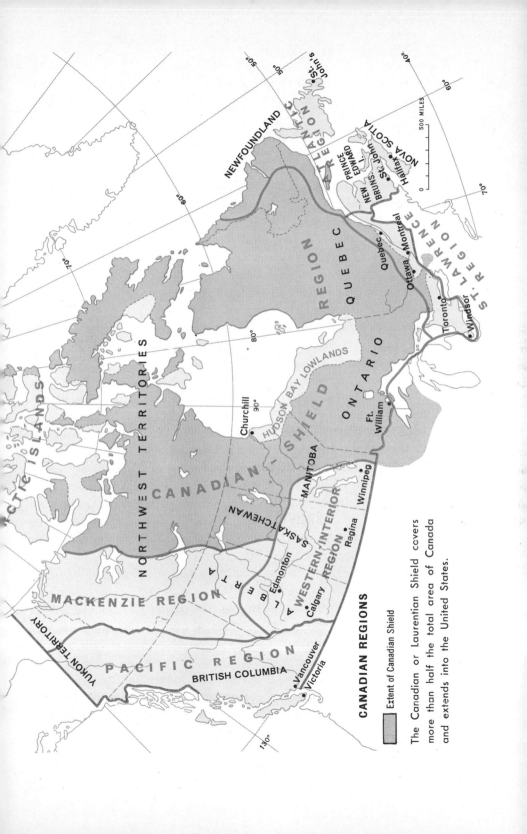

ATLANTIC
REGION

NEWFOUNDLAND

PRINCE
EDWARD I.

NEW
BRUNS.

St. JOHN

NOVA SCOTIA

Halifax

500 MILES

60°

70°

QUEBEC

REGION

Quebec

Montreal

Ottawa

ST. LAWRENCE REGION

Toronto

Windsor

ONTARIO

CANADIAN SHIELD

HUDSON BAY LOWLANDS

80°

Churchill

90°

Ft.
William

ARCTIC ISLANDS

NORTHWEST TERRITORIES

70°

MANITOBA

Winnipeg

SASKATCHEWAN

Regina

WESTERN-INTERIOR REGION

Edmonton

ALBERTA

Calgary

MACKENZIE REGION

YUKON TERRITORY

PACIFIC REGION

BRITISH COLUMBIA

Vancouver

Victoria

130°

CANADIAN REGIONS

Extent of Canadian Shield

The Canadian or Laurentian Shield covers
more than half the total area of Canada
and extends into the United States.

grow shorter, more gnarled and stunted, until they disappear completely. Moss, lichens, muskeg, and rock take over and reach to the shores of the Arctic Ocean itself.

The resources of the Shield are limited, but none the less real and important. Lumber is floated down to mills along the Ottawa and St. Lawrence rivers, and scattered over the Shield are mines. Severe though the climate may be, prospecting is made easier here, as it is in the western deserts of the United States, because the rocks show through without the camouflage of soil. Here is copper in abundance, lead and zinc, the world's largest deposit of nickel at Sudbury, and in the last few years iron ore has been discovered near Schefferville, in the eastern section of the Shield. A railroad now ships this ore down to the port of Seven Islands on the St. Lawrence River, from which much of it goes upstream to the iron and steel centers around the Great Lakes. Ores from Labrador are now beginning to replace those from Wisconsin and Minnesota, where many of the ore bodies are becoming exhausted.

Between the Shield and the Rocky Mountains are the Canadian Prairies, an extension of the Great Plains of the United States. The land forms of North Dakota and Montana continue beyond the border. There is no change in landscape, and one has to look hard to see the markers that show the line of the boundary. The wheatlands of the Red River Valley in North Dakota continue into the wheatlands of Manitoba and Saskatchewan. The grazing lands of Montana are continued in the ranches of Saskatchewan and Alberta. Only climate sets a northern limit to these activities. The summer days grow longer toward the north, but the sunshine gets feebler and the growing period between the last severe frost of spring and the first in the succeeding fall grows shorter.

The Canadian Prairies are shaped like a wedge, pointing eastward between the United States boundary and the Shield. Over them were spread glacial deposits, which have been cut into gentle corrugations by the rivers that flow out of the Rocky Mountains and across the plains and the Shield to Hudson Bay. The Canadian Prairies have the greatest rainfall toward the east. At Winnipeg it rains around 20 inches per year, enough for most cereal crops, for roots and fodder. In Saskatchewan it tapers off, and the prairies of Alberta are generally too dry for crop farming unless irrigation is used. The western part of the Prairie remains ranching country; over the rest, wheat farming has spread from the east and is being followed by a wave of more diversified agriculture.

On the eastern margin of the Canadian Prairies, at the very point of the wedge, is the city of Winnipeg. It lies in a kind of gap; to the south, about sixty-five miles away is the United States border; to the north is Lake Winnipeg, which extends three hundred fifty miles into the Shield. The east-west routes across Canada are obliged to pass between the boundary and the lake. Here they converge from the east as if a giant hand had gripped the parallel routeways and held them firmly together, and from here they fan out across the Prairies to the west. Winnipeg, by virtue of its focal position, is the biggest city of the Prairies, and now has nearly half a million people. There are few cities to the west in this region; the largest are Edmonton and Calgary, on the dry grassland of Alberta, close to the Rocky Mountains, and Saskatoon and Regina, amid the wheat fields of Saskatchewan. The growth of these cities has been phenomenally rapid in recent years as industry and the production of petroleum have moved into the Canadian Prairies.

The spring-sown wheat in North Dakota takes over four months to grow, mature, and be harvested. In Manitoba the growing period is cut below this. The plant breeders' reply to this challenge of nature was to evolve quicker growing and quicker maturing species of wheat. The growing period was reduced first to a hundred and then to ninety days, and with the shortening of the period of growth the frontier of cultivation was extended ever farther to the north. Today the limit has been reached in the valley of the Peace River, five hundred miles north of the 49th parallel, and close to the foothills of the Canadian Rockies. Here there is a chinook effect as the westerly winds rise to cross the Rocky Mountains, lose their moisture, and drop as dry but relatively warm winds for their latitude into the plains of Alberta.

A combination of warm winds, the long summer days that occur this far north, and the careful breeding of quick maturing strains of wheat has carried grain farming this far toward the Canadian Arctic. Will the frontier of farming be pushed yet farther to the north? The answer lies partly with the plant breeder, whose skill so far has produced species suited to these harsh conditions, but in part also it rests with transportation and the demand for wheat. It costs a lot to grow food this far north and to haul it to the market. But the population of Canada is growing fast; industry is coming into the Rocky Mountain and Prairie regions, and in the Northlands themselves mines are opening up. Local circumstances may tempt the farmer to open up a new northern frontier, whatever the difficulties and the cost.

Among the mineral resources of this western part of the Canadian Prairies is petroleum. The oil fields extend from Wyoming and Montana northward into Alberta and British Columbia. Their exploitation in Canada came later than in the United States, and has had to await the development of means of transportation. But in the last ten years petroleum production from this region has expanded very rapidly, and it now produces as much as Oklahoma.

Three hundred miles beyond the Peace River settlement and north of the 60th parallel are the Yukon and the Northwest territories, which span the taiga and the tundra and reach to the Arctic Ocean. These harsh, forbidding, and thinly peopled regions are not yet provinces of Canada. Their combined population is only about 35,000, and they have a status similar to that of their neighbor Alaska, before it was admitted to the Union.

The Canadian Rockies consist of range after range of high mountains, separated from one another by narrow valleys, drained by the Columbia and Fraser rivers and their tributaries. These valleys, protected by the ranges to the west of them, are dry, but in the mountains themselves there is a heavy rainfall. The continental severity of winter is moderated toward the ocean; the rain comes at all seasons, and the mountainsides stream water down to the sea. Here is one of the largest reserves of hydroelectric power on the continent. Like the American Rockies, the Canadian are endowed with minerals: copper, lead, zinc, and others. There is a little coal, and petroleum occurs along their eastern foothills. Smelting industries have been established in the mountains, and recently a huge aluminum smelter has been built on a coastal channel, at Kitimat, to take advantage of the electric power of the mountains. Its ore is brought in by sea from the West Indies and Central America, for so great is the consumption of electric power in the smelting process that it pays to ship the ore all the way to this wild British Columbian coast where power is cheap and abundant and to distribute the refined metal from here.

The rivers which occupy the trenchlike valleys between the ranges of the Canadian Rockies break through by narrow defiles from one valley to the other. Although the valleys and plateaus which separate the mountains are fairly dry, the rivers provide water for irrigation. To the south the intermontane valleys become drier, until they merge into the arid plains of the interior of the state of Washington. The Columbia River, with many of its tributaries, flows southward from the moist Canadian

Rockies into these dry plains, bringing water from Canada, where it is abundant, to the state of Washington east of the Cascades, where it is scarce. For many years this water has been conserved by the Grand Coulee Dam, and used to irrigate lands along the lower course of the river. Now, the Canadian and United States governments have agreed upon a joint use of the water of the Columbia system, so that little, or none, will flow unused to the sea. Rain which falls on mountains in Canada will be used to the full for power and irrigation purposes in both countries. Dams, built on the United States sections of the rivers, will force the water to back up far into Canada. Only a quite unusual degree of international good will could make such a proposal possible.

As one moves toward the north along the coast of the Pacific Ocean, the coast line becomes more rugged, more deeply indented by fjords, and more frayed out. The action of the glaciers during the Ice Age was more profound here than farther to the south. The ice gouged out the valleys, turning them into deep, steep-walled trenches, and after the ice had melted away from the lower ground, the sea flowed in, turning valleys into fjords. What farther to the south had been mountain ranges, rising up behind the coast, are here reduced to chains of islands by the work of the Ice Age and by the rise in the level of the sea which followed. The change was not wholly disadvantageous. The precipitous mountains of the British Columbian coast receive heavy rainfall—well over 100 inches in many areas—and this, as it cascades down to the sea, is beginning to provide the motive force of industry. The smelter at Kitimat is only one of many giant plants that are planned or being built.

Manufacturing and smelting are already the most important activities in British Columbia. Lumbering is second in importance. The mountains are clothed with spruce and fir, and timber is floated down the rivers to the sawmills which lie along their lower courses, to be made into pulp and paper, or cut into sawn lumber for building. Up the rivers of this rugged coast the salmon run to lay their eggs, and the young salmon swim back down them to their life in the ocean. Fish "ladders" circumvent the dams of the hydroelectric stations. The salmon fishermen put out their nets in the estuaries, and take their share of the salmon run for the canneries built along the coast.

The most important cities lie where the railroads, using the easiest passes across the mountains, come down to the Pacific coast. Vancouver, near the mouth of the Fraser River, is the most important of them. It is Canada's chief Pacific port, and her link with Asia and Australia. About six hundred miles north along the coast is Prince Rupert, a port for the lumbering and mining country of northern British Columbia. At the southern tip of Vancouver Island, largest of the offshore islands, is Victoria, capital of British Columbia.

Railroads are the key to Canada's development. Canada is a very little larger than the United States. It has a much longer coast line and many rivers, but most of these are locked in ice for so long a period each year that they are almost useless for navigation. The longest of them, the Mackenzie, flows into the Arctic Ocean, and its mouth is free of ice for too short a period in the year for it to be reached regularly by shipping. Many of the rivers that flow into Hudson Bay are navigable, but they discharge to an almost land-locked sea, icebound for much of the year, and almost inaccessible to ocean shipping.

The population of Canada is strung out across a narrow belt in the south of the country. It lies in four major clusters: in the Maritime Provinces, in the Lakes Peninsula of Ontario stretching into Quebec, in the Prairies, and in British Columbia. Between each of these there protrudes southward an extension from the empty lands of the north, either the margin of the Shield, or the higher ranges of the Rocky Mountains. The wilderness thus breaks settled Canada up into compartments, between which the railroads provide the chief bond of union. Canada is held together by its railroads; in fact, British Columbia only entered the Canadian federation on the condition that such a link was built across the mountains to link it with the east. Canada is well equipped with railroads. Look at the Canadian Prairies on the railroad map, and compare the dense net of lines with the emptiness of neighboring Montana and North Dakota.

The railroads have been inching slowly north into the northern forests. Spurs from Edmonton run north to the Peace River; from Regina up to Hudson Bay, and from Seven Islands, on the St. Lawrence, to the iron ore fields of Labrador. But it requires a powerful magnet to draw the railroads toward the Arctic, to the Northwest Territory, where agriculture is difficult and population scarce. So far, only minerals have done this. During the Second World War the urgent need to establish communications by land with Alaska led to the building of the Alaska Highway, which was made to run from the railhead in Alberta, across northern British Columbia and Yukon, to Fairbanks, Alaska. Surveys made so far indicate that the mineral resources of the northern Rocky Mountains and of the Shield are immense, and that they include such strategically important materials as uranium and high-grade iron ore. Whether these resources will be opened up with the aid of railways or of all-weather roads is yet to be seen.

Canada has one of the fastest growing populations in the world. In recent years the population of Canada, aided by immigration, has been increasing as rapidly as that of any other country within the Americas. This population growth has been matched by the expansion of industry, by the volume of capital investment, and by the exploration and utilization of the resources of this huge country. In this the United States has played an important role by the investments of its financiers in Canadian development. A former rivalry between the two has deepened into a partnership, a partnership that has now been cemented by the agreements for the joint use of the St. Lawrence Seaway and the shipping facilities of the Great Lakes and for the joint development of the resources of the Columbia River, as well as co-operation in continental defense through the DEW (Distant Early Warning) Line and BMEWS (Ballistic Missile Early Warning System).

Continental early warning systems provided an opportunity for United States and Canadian co-operation.

NORTHWEST TO ASIA

The Soviet Union is very close to the United States. Only about fifty miles separate Alaska from eastern Siberia. The ancestors of the Indians and Eskimos entered North America by this route thousands of years ago, and by this same route Russian fur trappers came more recently. They pushed their way across southern Alaska and into its long pan-handle. South to 54° 40′ of north latitude they came and built a few Russian churches, established a settlement or two, and traded for a lot of beaver. In fact, the Russian fur trader ranged as far as California. Then in 1867, Secretary of State Seward bought this huge, little-known area from the Russians. It graduated slowly to the rank of territory and was admitted to the Union as a state in 1959. Its remoteness from the rest of the United States; the severity of much of its climate, and the difficulty over much of its area of establishing agricultural settlements discouraged immigrants. Alaska now ranks as the largest state in the Union, having no less than 16 per cent of the total area of the United States.

The Rocky Mountains, whose chains we have followed through British Columbia and the Yukon Territory, swing around to the west in Alaska, and end in the chain of the Aleutian Islands, thrust out toward Asia. The state is built of a series of more or less parallel mountain ranges—among them the Brooks Range in the north, the Alaska Range in the south, and between them valleys, marshy plains, and the lower ranges of the Kuskokwim, Ray, and other mountains. Across one of the largest of these flows the Yukon River to enter the Bering Sea. The most southerly mountains, the so-called Alaska Range, is the highest, and in Mount McKinley, rises to 20,320 feet, the highest point in the North American continent.

Seward was wiser than he knew when he purchased what, at the time, was called "Seward's Ice-box." The severity of the climate is in fact moderated by the sea and by the ocean current that drifts from Japan along its southern shore. Alluvial gold was found below the swamps that filled many of the valleys of the interior; as always, it attracted settlers, and many who came to mine stayed on to tap the added attractions in the lumber, fish, and fur-bearing animals. Agriculture was established along parts of the south coast, and in the Matanuska Valley giant fruits and vegetables are produced. A railroad was built inland from the port of Anchorage to the city of Fairbanks, in the center of the state.

The northern half of Alaska, where winter lasts for most of the year and the climate is too severe even for good stands of lumber to grow, remains almost unpeopled and undeveloped. But even here the location of the territory, only a few hundred miles from Soviet Siberia, gives it a strategic importance. In the southwest, the Alaska Mountains are continued into the Pacific Ocean by the thin, tapering Alaska Peninsula and its prolongation, the Aleutian Islands. These storm-swept islands, many of them little more than bare rocks rising from the ocean, are the extreme outpost of the New World toward Asia. The last islands in the chain, notably Attu, were occupied by the Japanese in the Second World War. They lie only 1,500 miles from Japan, and only 2,200 miles from the Soviet port of Vladivostok.

WEST TO THE PACIFIC

Hawaii is no less a frontier state than Alaska and is the only part of the United States to have experienced a large-scale hostile attack in recent years. Climatically the Hawaiian Islands are the opposite of Alaska. They lie within the tropics; the temperatures range from warm to hot, though moderated by the trade winds which bring rain at most seasons. The Hawaiian group is volcanic, and the largest of them, the island of Hawaii itself, has the active craters of Mauna Loa, Kilauea, and Kilauea-Iki, which at intervals disgorge streams of molten lava, and the quiescent Mauna Kea, which rises more than 13,000 feet above the sea.

The volcanic soils add to the fertility of the islands. Most of the land that is not too steep and rugged is under cultivation. Sugar cane has long been the most important crop, and refined sugar the chief export, but in the popular imagination Hawaii can never be dissociated from pineapples. The island of Hawaii is the largest, but its altitude and the ruggedness of much of its terrain have restricted settlement. Oahu, on which lie both Honolulu and Pearl Harbor, is lower and flatter, but also very much smaller. It is the focus of Hawaiian agriculture and with about 700 people to the square mile, one of the most densely populated areas in the world.

Three others among the more populous Hawaiian Islands are Maui, where the Haleakala Crater and the Iao Valley lie, and Kauai and Molokai. Along with agriculture, the chief occupation is tourism, which also contributes to the economy of Oahu and Hawaii.

Hawaii is, in its population, the least European and the most cosmopolitan state in the Union. Its original people were Polynesian. To these have been added yellow-skinned groups from all over eastern Asia who have mixed, on terms of complete equality, with pink-colored people from the Western World.

NORTHEAST TO EUROPE

The first Europeans to visit the New World came by way of Greenland. They sailed from Norway in the ninth century, reached Iceland, and sailed on to Greenland—and thence to some unknown spot on the coast of Labrador or the Maritime Provinces. Little is known of this early Norse discovery, and the Norse settlement in Greenland itself failed to survive the deterioration of the climate which marked the closing centuries of the Middle Ages. Greenland has long been a possession of Denmark, but it took a political act to determine whether Greenland was part of Europe or of America. During the Second World War President Roosevelt decided that it was American, and thus within the scope of hemisphere defense.

Greenland has none of the attractions of Alaska. It is much larger, and instead of the warm current of the Pacific has the cold Labrador and Greenland currents running along its coast. Greenland is a region where the Ice Age has lasted until the present. This huge land mass is almost covered by a vast sheet of ice, whose weight depresses the land surface like a saucer. The rocks peep out from under this burden around the margin and form high, rugged cliffs. Glaciers protrude between them, calving great icebergs which drift south in summer to the danger of shipping in the North Atlantic. There is no plant life except mosses and lichens. Aside from military personnel at Thule Air Base, its population is limited to a handful of Eskimos, and a few miners, administrators, and doctors. There may be great mineral wealth hidden beneath the ice, but only a deposit of cryolite, used in smelting aluminum, is worked near the west coast. For the rest, the wealth of Greenland is in its fisheries and its importance lies in its location on the exposed far northern frontier of the North American continent.

Canada and the United States divide almost equally between them the vast expanse of Anglo-America. Apart from their similarity in area, the two countries have much in common. They both stretch from ocean to ocean; both were settled mainly by peoples from western and central

Europe; both span the same types of physical environment, and both adopted a federal constitution as a means of coping with the physical as well as the human variety in their respective sectors. The fundamental difference between the two is that the one occupies the northern half; the other, the southern half, with consequent results upon climate and crops, soil and natural vegetation.

The peoples who originally settled these two divisions were broadly similar in cultural background. That they did not, in the late eighteenth century, join to build a common state, is the result of historical accident. Yet the international boundary of 1783 once it had been established, proved to be increasingly divisive. The peoples on each side of it diverged slowly; each had its own frontier into which to expand; each had its own peculiar problems deriving from climate, crops, and the lesser facets of its social organization. Two nations took shape to divide the greater portion of the North American continent between them. A century or so of growing divergence, marked by periods of hostility, even of violence, ended and they have come closer to one another.

This rapprochement, which is typified in the unguarded boundary which separates them, is the product of two important factors—the one technological, the other ideological. The growing complexities of life necessitate understanding and co-operation. Each has given to the other rights to traverse its territory and use its railroads and ports. Rivers are used and waterpower is produced jointly, and an unpublicized and highly effective International Joint Commission takes care of all the technical problems that arise.

The threat to the freedom of the institutions of Anglo-America, which was vaguely hinted in the First World War, and openly made by Nazi Germany in the Second, has in the years following the war's end become a terrible danger from yet a third world power. Not only do the United States and Canada co-operate in the defense of this hemisphere with early warning systems and strategic bases, but they combine to present a united front to the political dangers which face it. Between them, technology and ideology are restoring a certain functional unity to a continent which man, in his unwisdom, had divided politically.

7

BEYOND
THE MEXIQUE BAY:

Latin America

A revolution-broken landscape, with lingering, tall,
handsome churches whose domes are like inflations that
are going to burst, and whose pinnacles and towers are like
the trembling pagodas of an unreal race. Gorgeous churches
waiting, above the huts and straw hovels of the natives,
like ghosts to be dismissed.

D. H. LAWRENCE—The Plumed Serpent

The Rio Grande is a shallow, muddy river. For much of
the year it has little water in it, and the wetbacks can swim or wade
across, emerging on the northern bank with the opportunities of the
United States before them and only a wet shirt behind. It is a more
powerful boundary than the 49th parallel, and it separates bigger differences.

Beyond the Canadian border of the United States most features of the
landscape are familiar; the language generally is the same, and institutions are similar. At the southern border the plains of Texas and the
savage, black cliffs where the Rockies run down to the river do continue
on the other bank of the Rio Grande, but all else changes. The language
is different, Spanish instead of English. Building styles are different;
houses have pantiled roofs and churches are plastered with baroque or-
nament; locally these styles appear in the American Southwest, but
south of the border they become general. The people are differently clad.
An open market, with food piled upon the ground, replaces the super-
market. And it becomes apparent that not everybody rates cleanliness

211

next to godliness. The outward signs of poverty are more conspicuous than ever they had been in the United States.

North of the Rio Grande customs, culture, and institutions sprang mainly from Western Europe, and were later shaped by the environment and modified by the successive strains of subsequent immigrants. The civilization of Latin America was created by a different people, drawn from the Iberian, or Spanish, Peninsula of Europe, with a different social and political philosophy, and settled in an environment more tropical and more demanding than that of North America.

Latin America was discovered by Spanish ships and explored and conquered by Spanish soldiers. Christopher Columbus, who first landed on a lush West Indian island on October 12, 1492, explored in the course of his four voyages only the coasts of the Caribbean. It was for his successors to penetrate to the continental interior.

Columbus lived in the illusion that he had reached the eastern coast and the islands of Asia, or at least was concerned that it should not be thought that he hadn't. But his dream was soon to be shattered. From the day in 1513 when Nuñez de Balboa from a hill top in Panama looked upon the Pacific and then, wading into the sea, waved his sword above his head and took possession of the waters in the name of his royal master, it was known that an ocean separated America from Asia.

Already the Portuguese, trying to use the northeast trade winds to help them on their long voyage round the Cape of Good Hope to India, had stood out too far from the coast of Africa and in 1500 had touched Brazil. In 1519 Magellan, setting out to complete the unfinished task of Columbus, sailed through the rugged, tortuous, rock-strewn strait that bears his name at the southern tip of the continent, and so into the Pacific Ocean. Though he was killed in the Philippines, his ship sailed on to the Orient and home.

About the same time, Hernando Cortés landed on the coast of Mexico. With a gesture of desperation and defiance, he burned his boats and with his small army advanced to the overthrow of the empire of the Aztecs in Mexico. A few years later, in 1535, Francisco Pizarro invaded Peru and defeated the Incas. Valdivia marched south into Chile; Orellana crossed the Andes, reached the headwaters of the Amazon, and sailed down it to the Atlantic.

These conquistadors of Spain were a very different people from the French and English who settled in North America. They were soldiers and adventurers, trained and toughened in the military campaigns of

Latin America includes Mexico in the southern portion of the North American continent, the West Indies, and the countries of Central and South America.

Europe. Many had recently been fighting the Moors, and had driven them out of Spain. They thought of themselves as crusaders, though less spiritual crusaders there never were. The society from which they came in Europe was feudal, and this form of social organization they transplanted to the New World, with themselves as the land-owning nobility and the unheeded Indians as the serfs. The social system of the Indian tribes who already lived here was rigid and not disposed to change. Upon this native society was superimposed the no less rigid society of the Spanish and Portuguese immigrants. Latin American society began as a feudal society; most of it has never escaped from this heritage.

The Spanish settlers in the New World had been conditioned by their experiences in the Old to despise manual labor and to regard commerce —beyond the selling of the products of their own estates—as something beneath their dignity. More to the Spaniards' liking was the search for hoards of bullion, in which they believed true wealth existed. Their attitudes and those of the New England settlers could not have been farther removed from one another. In the nature of the Spanish society, as much as in the influences of the physical environment, we must look for the roots of that lack of development, that reluctance to change, coupled with a certain distrust of those who have made material progress, that we find in many Latin American countries today.

Nevertheless the Latin American environment set very obvious limitations to human societies. In discussing the Europeans' settlement in North America, we have emphasized the similarities between their new home and their old. In Latin America it is more the dissimilarities that are conspicuous. Latin America is also composed of mountain, plain, and plateau, but here these take on a harsher form, and their adverse qualities are immensely magnified. The mountains are higher and more difficult to cross; the deserts are drier and more barren; the plains more marshy and intractable. Settlers from Western Europe could never have marched with their wagons across the South American continent as they did across the North.

The early European settlers in Latin America were mainly from Southern Europe, from the Iberian Peninsula. Accustomed as they were to hotter suns and more arid lands than those who came from Western Europe, they nevertheless found that the jungle, the mountains, and the deserts presented environments to which their European home had not accustomed them. Most of them moved up into the hills, above the mosquitoes and the malaria, and there their descendants have remained.

Most came in the sixteenth and seventeenth centuries. There followed a lull, when migration from Europe was much reduced, only to revive and increase in the nineteenth century with the rapid expansion of Europe's population that characterized that period. This migration from the countries of Germany, Italy, and the rest of Southern Europe was chiefly to Argentina, Uruguay, and Brazil. These were environments more like those of North America, regions suited to producing meat, skins, and hides, the grains and other food crops.

With the prospect of producing commodities already in demand at home, Europeans were more prepared to invest in these countries than in other parts of Latin America. Here they built railroads and docks; they equipped packing stations and factories to process the food products. It is paradoxical that the areas most recently opened up have become the most progressive. The paradox is explained by the fact that this opening up took place at the very time when the countries of Western Europe were looking for opportunities for foreign investment.

A continuous belt of settled and developed territory spans at least half the United States; and neighboring Canada has large population concentrations. The Spaniards did extend their authority into the southwest and south of what is now the United States; St. Augustine, Florida, Santa Fe, New Mexico, and the Missions of California all are witness to the extent and also to the depth of this colonization. But Florida, Louisiana, and the Gadsden strip were purchased by the United States; Texas was absorbed, and the western desert conquered. Through unavoidable contact, society in Anglo-America has developed a mutuality and a cohesiveness which give it social and political unity. But Latin American society remains fragmented.

Latin America was born united, or at least shared by two great powers. The fine lines which appear to have separated province from province, were never marked on the land. They ran through forest and desert and were imprecise, because precision seemed to be totally unnecessary. The settlers from Europe lived in islands of population scattered through this continent, separated from one another by mountain, desert, and forest. Their contacts with one another were minimal, and they each developed a local allegiance, which in many instances was never superseded by any feeling for the Spanish or Portuguese empires as such, and very little for the states that grew out of its provincial divisions.

At the end of the eighteenth century, Latin America was made up of two empires, those of Portugal and of Spain, and it has broken up into seventeen separate independent states. In North America the United States began divided, as did Canada, and each has since grown together, and their cohesiveness has been intensified through the years.

Let us look briefly at the lineaments of this continent and a half, South America and the connecting link to North America called Central America, together with Mexico which is traditionally considered part of North America. All these make up Latin America. The dominant feature is the series of mountain chains which extend southward from the Rocky Mountains; they unite, spread apart, and reunite and terminate only at Cape Horn, which, though on a small island, is generally reckoned to be the most southerly point of the continent. For most of this distance—no less than six thousand miles—the mountains are high and rise steeply from the plains on each side. Only two small breaks occur in their con-

SOUTH AMERICA

Scale of Miles

0   100   200   400   600

COPYRIGHT 1962 BY RAND MC NALLY & CO. MADE IN U.S.A.

⊗ National Capitals   ☆ Other Capitals   ● Other Cities

TROPIC OF CANCER

West Longitude

Gulf of Mexico

Yucatan Peninsula

CUBA

⊗ Havana

JAMAICA

HAITI

DOMINICAN REPUBLIC

Puerto Rico

Leeward Islands

Windward Islands

Barbados (W.I.F.)

Port-of-Spain

Trinidad

C A R I B B E A N   S E A

W E S T   I N D I E S

CENTRAL

AMERICA

Panama Canal

Colón

Barranquilla

Point Gallinas

Maracaibo

Lake Maracaibo

Cúcuta

Bucaramanga

Medellín

Cauca River

Magdalena River

Buenaventura

Cali

Bogotá ⊗

COLOMBIA

Caracas ⊗

Ciudad Bolívar

Orinoco River

VENEZUELA

Georgetown

Paramaribo

Cayenne

GUIANA

(BR.) (NETH.) (FR.)

SURINAM

G U Y A N A   H I G H L A N D S

GUIANA HIGHLANDS

Rio Negro

Rio Caquetá

Iquitos

ORIENTE

Quito ⊗

Cotopaxi

Chimborazo

ECUADOR

Guayaquil

Point Aguja

Trujillo

Cerro de Pasco

Lima ⊗

La Oroya

Callao

Cusco

P E R U

Amazon River

Rio Madeira

Manaus

Rio Negro

Rio Tapajós

S E L V A S

B R A Z I L

Belém

Rio Tocantins

Fortaleza

Recife

Maceió

Salvador

Cape São Roque

Rio São Francisco

EQUATOR

North Latitude   0°   South Latitude

P A C I F I C

20°

10°

0°

10°

80°   70°   60°   50°   40°

TROPIC OF CAPRICORN

Rio de Janeiro

Belo
Horizonte

Volta Redonda

São Paulo

Santos

Curitiba

Pôrto Alegre

Rio Paraná

Rio Paraguay

GRAN
CHACO

PARAGUAY

Asunción

Rio Uruguay

Paraná

URUGUAY

Montevideo

Río de la Plata

Buenos Aires

PAMPAS

Bahía Blanca

Santa
Fé

Rosario

Salta

Córdoba

Tucumán

ARGENTINA

Mendoza

Mount
Aconcagua

MOUNTAINS

Comodoro
Rivadavia

PATAGONIA

STRAIT OF MAGELLAN

Tierra del Fuego

Ushuaia

Cape Horn

Punta Arenas

ama Desert

Antofagasta

CHILE

Coquimbo

Viña del Mar
Valparaíso

Santiago

Concepción

Puerto Montt

Falkland Islands

South
Georgia

ATLANTIC

OCEAN

TROPIC OF CAPRICORN

A T L A N T I C   O C E A N

tinuity, both in Central America. One is in the Isthmus of Panama, where they are low enough for a canal to have been cut across them from ocean to ocean. The other is in Nicaragua, where another canal has been considered. At their highest point, Aconcagua, on the border of Chile and Argentina, the Andean chain rises to 22,834 feet, more than 2,500 feet higher than Mt. McKinley in Alaska.

Between the mountains and the Pacific Ocean is only a narrow shelf of land. Most of the plains lie on the eastern side, toward the Atlantic: the forested and generally marshy peninsula of Yucatán, the river plains of the Orinoco and Amazon, and the lowlands that are drained by the cluster of rivers that feed the Plata River, the Río de la Plata. Between these river systems are areas of highland, much lower than the Andean mountains—they rarely rise to more than three thousand feet above the intervening plain—but yet high enough to be lifted up above the steaming heat of the low plains. These are the so-called Guiana Highlands and Brazilian Highlands, regions of promise amid the inhospitable forest and mountain that make up much of Latin America.

All the large and important rivers of South America, and most also of the smaller and less important, rise within the western mountain wall and flow eastward to the ocean, gathering tributaries from the plateau regions that separate their basins. The headwaters of the Orinoco are in the Andes of Colombia. From here they flow across the almost inaccessible plains of eastern Colombia, and through Venezuela to the sea. The Amazon, commonly regarded as the second largest river in the world, has its source in the Andes of Peru and from here it flows for an estimated 3,900 miles almost due eastward to the sea, keeping for almost all of this immense distance within 5° of the equator. The rivers that converge on the Río de la Plata—the Pilcomayo, the Paraguay, the Paraná, and the Uruguay—are drawn from the Andes of Bolivia and Chile as well as from the plateau of Brazil.

The immense plains across which these rivers flow insure that for much of their courses they are broad and slow-flowing. All are navigable. Ocean-going freighters can ascend the Amazon to Iquitos, in Peru, which by river is more than two thousand miles from the ocean, with not a single obstacle to navigation in all this distance. Ships can sail up the Orinoco into Colombia, and via the Plata up the Paraguay River well into the state of that name. Even in their natural condition, these are good, navigable rivers. They guided the early explorers into the interior, yet now they are unused over much of their lengths.

Climate has been unkind to Latin America. The beaches of Acapulco and the islands that lie in the West Indian sun, central Chile, the coast of southern Brazil, and the lowlands around Río de la Plata, are the exception. More typical are the extremes of the hot, humid selvas—the marshy silt plain of the Amazon—the cold, high Andean plateaus, and the deserts which border the Pacific.

This continent and a half extends from 32° north of the equator to 55° south, through nearly 90° of latitude, a distance of about 6,000 miles. It spans the whole region of the tropics which lie on both sides of the equator, and reaches far into the southern mid-latitudes, as far into the Southern Hemisphere, in fact, as Hudson Bay is to the north. Its mountain backbone, if one follows the twisting line of the Andes, is about 8,000 miles in length.

Along its eastern coast, from Mexico to Brazil, the trade winds blow onshore throughout the year, shifting their track with the seasons, to the north during the northern summer, to the south during the northern winter. They bring heavy rain—remember Belém (Pará) at the Amazon mouth has 80 inches a year—and for much of this distance the coast is backed by swamp and forest. This damp forest extends up the Amazon Valley right to the foothills of the Andes, and smaller expanses of swamp and forest run up the valleys of most other rivers.

The west coast in these tropic latitudes lies in the rain shadow of the Andes which protect it from the trade winds. It is drier than its latitude would suggest, and only a few degrees away from the equator it passes into desert. The desert which borders the Pacific Ocean in southern Peru and northern Chile—the Atacama—is the driest, barest, and most formidable that the world has to show, and that which lies along the west coast of Mexico and covers the peninsula of Baja California—the Vizcaíno—is barren enough.

The southern part of South America's west coast lies permanently in the belt of the westerly winds. It is like the Pacific Northwest and British Columbia. Rain clouds come in from the Pacific Ocean at all seasons and empty their moisture on the sodden mountains of southern Chile. But here, just as in the western United States, the wind belt shifts with the seasons, blowing farther to the north around Christmastime and to the south about July. Central Chile gets the winds in its own winter season, but in summer they pass to the south.

The Andes, which here cause the west winds to drop their moisture so liberally over their western slopes, shield the plains of Argentina.

The Viceroyalty of Peru later was broken down into three divisions, the Viceroyalty of La Plata in the south, Peru in the center, and Granada in the north.

These are dry, with rainfall of 10 inches or less in many parts. Large areas are too dry for crop farming and provide only rough grazing for sheep.

This then is a continent of harsh and violent contrasts, one in which a European society could take root only with difficulty; where the physical labor needed to overcome the obstacles of physical geography was often so great as to deter man from making the effort, especially man whose colonial policy was based on a feudal philosophy and a demand for quick economic returns.

Latin America begins today at the Rio Grande and stretches to Cape Horn. It is planned to build a motor road over much of this distance, and part of the road has already been built. The Spaniards who ruled most of this territory from the sixteenth to the early nineteenth centuries did not have an unfinished Pan-American Highway, and obviously did not have automobiles to drive. Indeed, they had nothing even as fast and as efficient as the Pony Express. The fastest means of communicating between the headquarters of one Viceroyalty and another, and one Captaincy-General, or *Audiencia,* and another was by sailing ship along the coast. And although the Spanish Empire was divided into administrative provinces, there were no really agreed boundaries between them because the mountain, forest, and swamp through which such boundaries ran were unknown and almost inaccessible.

From the earliest days of European settlement this continent was divided between the Spaniards and the Portuguese, a division springing originally from a Papal Bull of 1493 which drew an imaginary line from north to south, one hundred leagues to the west of the Azores, and declared that lands to be discovered to the west of this line were to become the sphere of Spain, and those to the east, of Portugal. In fact, the Portuguese were thus enabled to settle along the great eastern bulge of South America, which jutted across the Pope's line. The Spaniards settled around much of the remaining coast.

The Spanish government in Madrid always tried to control its colonies closely. Orders were sent to the Spanish governors in the New World, and after the lapse of months or even years, would be relayed to the outlying Spanish settlements. But control was so remote as to be almost ineffective.

Between 1810 and 1830 the Spanish Empire revolted against its European master, and the Portuguese Empire in Brazil severed its connection with Portugal. The fighting in the Spanish empire was very local. It all took place in a few scattered areas where the European population was less sparse and more articulate and cohesive than elsewhere. The greater part of the continent had no knowledge of what was going on. There was a kinship in the language and religion and in the imported culture of Spain between the rebels in Mexico and Colombia, in Chile and Argentina. They had plans for a political union. But these, alas, were never realized.

The leaders of the local rebel groups themselves were too ambitious to subordinate their role to that of a Bolívar, a San Martín, or an O'Higgins. And if they could have been far-seeing enough to unite, the environment itself would probably have pulled them apart, for, under the conditions of transportation and communication which existed a century ago, Latin America was of necessity fragmented into a number of political units.

When the new states of Latin America came onto the political map, they conformed as closely as they could to the boundaries of the administrative divisions of the empire which they replaced. The only political ties which most Latin Americans had ever known were those with their own local or provincial governor. Their feelings of cohesion were limited to their immediate surroundings. They knew little and cared not at all about what lay beyond the barrier of mountain, forest, or desert which cut them off from the next community.

From the ruins of the Spanish Empire there emerged a group of republics which for many years fused, divided, and rejoined in a kaleidoscopic pattern. Only three small territories in South America, lying just north of the equator on the northeast coast, passed into the hands of three other European powers. These are today British and French Guiana and the Dutch dependency of Surinam. In Central America there is the small area under the United Kingdom, known as British Honduras.

Today, after a century and a half of independent existence and development, most of Latin America remains poor. Of its total area of nearly 7,800,000 square miles, only about 110,000 square miles, roughly equal in area to Arizona or New Mexico, has what may be called improved or modernized agriculture. The rest is rough grazing land, dense, uncleared forest, desert, or uncultivable mountain.

All over the world we find that nature proposes and man disposes. Is the plight of Latin America the fault of man or of nature? Does it spring from man's neglect or abuse of his resources; does its cause lie in political and social organization and attitudes; or are the resources so niggardly that he must remain poor? In our journey through Latin America we will seek answers to these questions.

SOUTH AMERICA

South America is a large, compact, and almost impenetrable land mass. The European societies that came here have clung perilously to the coastlands, pressing into the interior only where physical conditions were unusually favorable, as in the grasslands of Argentina and Uruguay, or the rewards great, as in the mining camps of Bolivia. The population of South America when the Spaniards and Portuguese came was small, widely scattered, primitive and poor, with here and there evidences of a higher degree of civilization. Over large parts of the continent the descendants of these early inhabitants of the continent remain little if at all influenced by Europeans, and are practicing still a way of life that Pizarro would have recognized.

Here, in a continent twice the size of the United States, with a population only two-thirds as large, we find a host of social and economic problems: the evils of great estates and landless, poverty-stricken peasants; the dangers of excessive dependence upon export of one or two crops, or a single mineral; the lack of capital for investment; the lack of political experience to establish an orderly system of government; and a small, ambitious elite, much of it made up of students, which thinks it knows what is wrong, but has neither the power nor the ability to put it right. Everywhere there is poverty and the frustration that comes from rising expectations left unfulfilled. And in Central America, Mexico, and the West Indies these same problems exist, sometimes more, sometimes less intense than in South America.

Latin America has a more complex racial situation than is to be found in other parts of the New World. There are the native Indians, in varying stages of intellectual and social advancement; the immigrant Europeans; and the Negroes, brought in as slaves and retained as laborers. Miscegenation has produced an almost endless variety of human types.

Argentina and Uruguay are predominantly European in racial stock. In Brazil and Chile there is a managing, ruling, and land-owning class of Europeans, deriving mainly from Spain, Portugal, and Italy, with many of mixed blood, while in the remote forests of the one and the mountains of the other, live native tribes that have neither been corrupted nor improved by contact with the European. In Paraguay and Bolivia population is almost wholly mestizo, a variable and indiscernible mixture of Indian with European. In Ecuador and the northwestern states a clear-cut European aristocracy has maintained itself, with only a trace of Indian or Negro blood, amid the mass of half-castes.

The official languages are Portuguese in Brazil and Spanish in the remaining republics, but the native Indian languages and dialects remain important in proportion as the Indian communities remain intact. This is a fiercely plural society. Groups of different ethnic origins, speaking different languages and belonging to different cultures, live side by side. Sometimes—indeed, usually—the cultural and ethnic differences are underscored by contrasts in standards of living and levels of welfare that intensify the rift between the ethnic groups.

In the city of Manaus, in the heart of the Amazon jungle, there is an opera house. Only a few miles away are forest Indians whose way of life has not changed for centuries. This contrast points up the problem of South America: its wealth is localized geographically and concentrated socially into the hands of a narrow ruling caste.

In the Amazon basin the wealth was wild rubber until the plantations in Southeast Asia destroyed this business. Elsewhere on this vast continent it is oil, or tin, or iron ore, or nitrates, or coffee. The wealth derived from such enterprises has rarely been used for the benefit of the countries as a whole. It has gone into the hands of the privileged few, who built the opera house in the jungle, and created the garish social life of Caracas or Rio de Janeiro. It has not gone to alleviate the misery of the South American masses or to develop utilities and public services for the benefit of all. Amid luxury and extravagance, the majority of the people are illiterate, unskilled, and poor.

Brazil

Brazil is the largest, richest, and most powerful of the South American republics. It is the fifth largest state in the world in area and eighth largest in its population of 73,400,000; but its over-all density of population is only nineteen persons per square mile, which would make it comparable to Nebraska or Oregon in the United States except that immense areas of it are nearly uninhabited and almost unknown.

The northern half of Brazil is made up of the flat plain of the river Amazon. Imagine a vast jungle, without road or railroad, stretching all the way from New York City to the Grand Canyon and away on each side to north and south to embrace Wisconsin and Alabama, Idaho, and New Mexico. That is the size of the selvas of the Amazon. Into this plain come rivers from the Andes to the west, from the highlands along the border of the Guianas and Venezuela, and from the great plateau that makes up the southern half of Brazil. They add their quota of water to that which is contributed almost daily by the violent equatorial rains.

The whole of this vast area has been created during recent geological time by the rivers that traverse it; it is the largest alluvial plain in the world. Each day, each of the hundreds of rivers that flow down from the surrounding hills adds its contribution of fine silt, either to its own banks or to the thousands of growing islands which make up the delta of the Amazon. Two hundred miles out in the Atlantic from the mouth of the Amazon, the sea is still brown with the silt transported from the Andes.

The ground is always wet. The rivers break up into interlacing channels, between which are only low, flat, marshy islands. Below the surface of the ground this silt extends downward and ever downward. There is nothing solid here; no stone for building or road-making, no soil for firm foundations. Back a few miles from the river the surface may rise a few feet, just enough for moisture to drain a little from around the roots of the trees. Here are the few settlements of the Amazon, where a handful of merchants can be found who will buy wild rubber or some other forest product from the Indians.

The climate changes as little as the relief. It is hot and wet at all seasons, and on average the hottest month is 83°, and the coolest 81°; plants grow continuously and profusely throughout the year, arching over the rivers, and holding boatmen back from the slimy banks. And when a settlement is abandoned, the plants march in, spread through it, and reabsorb it into the damp soil from which its materials grew. The ground beneath the everlasting shade is damp and fetid, but up in the tree tops there is a rich bird and insect life.

In North America the northern forests of Canada are uniform, homogeneous; the stands of spruce or pine stretch on with never an intruder from a different family of trees. But in the rain forest of South America the trees are individualists. Species are hopelessly mixed up. The number of different species is almost infinite. Most have no value for commerce or building, but a few are more useful; those which yield rubber or valuable hardwoods like mahogany. The cost of extracting either product, however, is immeasurably complicated by the way in which the trees grow—intermixed with every other tropical species.

The Amazon forest had its brief era of prosperity; that was when its opera house was built. The discovery of the wild rubber trees, and, at about the same time, of innumerable uses for rubber, brought a rush to the Amazon. The natives were exploited and the rubber trees were ruined in the haste to extract the latex from them. The boom ended when, at the very beginning of the twentieth century, rubber plantations, propagated from seeds gathered in Brazil, began to produce in Malaya. Thus was the Amazon's most valuable resource squandered and lost.

More recently attempts have been made to grow rubber in plantations like those in Southeast Asia, but this has not succeeded. The dangers of soil erosion and plant disease, the difficulties of transportation, the high cost of supplies and services, and the lack of a labor force intelligent enough to tend the trees and tap the rubber and at the same time acclimatized to the rigors of Amazonian heat and humidity—these together have defeated experimental attempts to develop the world's largest expanse of tropical forest. One is left wondering whether the Chinese and the Malays could have done better than the native labor of these parts; perhaps with their greater capacity for organized work and their commercial instincts they would have done so.

South of the selvas the land rolls up gradually into the great plateau, called the Brazilian Highlands, which makes up most of the southern half of the country. It lies at from 1,000 to 3,000 feet. Its surface is trenched by the wide, shallow valleys of the rivers which flow north to the Amazon and those which flow west and south to the Paraná. Along the valleys, fingers of forest point to the south, and between them the swelling upland rises above the jungle into the drier, cooler savanna. This plateau rises gradually, unevenly southward, strewn with ridges and ranges, all that remain of mountains long ago eroded, until it culminates in the high mountains that look down on Santos and Rio de Janeiro and the Atlantic Ocean.

This plateau lies well to the south of the equator, and it stretches south of the Tropic of Capricorn. The alternation of the seasons, which is absent from the selvas, begins to show itself as we move southward. The dry winter begins to emerge; rainfall is increasingly concentrated in the summer months. Trees become more sparse, and begin to lose their leaves in winter, until the vegetation passes into savanna.

This is an easier country in which to move about. Except during the summer rains, the land is dry and the stream beds can be forded. But over much of its surface the old hard rocks of the highlands have yielded only a poor soil which becomes a sticky clay during the rains, and is hard, dry, and dusty at other times. Only the more favored parts are cultivated with corn, tobacco, cotton, and the beans which enter so prominently into the Latin American diet. Large areas are covered with dry savanna—the campos—or are grazed by half-wild cattle, sheep, and goats.

This is also the pioneer fringe of Brazil. It is as if the Brazilians had said to themselves: The selvas are beyond our capabilities to domesticate and use, but the savanna we can do something about. Railroads push out into it; roads of a sort have been built; and at Brasília, nearly six hundred miles inland from Rio, a brash, new capital city is arising amid the raw savanna, symbolizing the Brazilians' will to make this undeveloped but unquestionably Brazilian hinterland the core of their state and the focus of their life.

But this hinterland presents problems as well as opportunities, and nowhere are these greater than in the northeast where Brazil approaches closest to the Old World. Here the rainfall is smaller and less predictable than in other parts of the Brazilian savanna. In relation to its limited resources, the population is dense, farm-holdings small, and the absentee landlords greedy. Here is a region boiling with social and political discontent, where only foreign aid, generously and tactfully given and wisely administered, can avert a crisis.

Coffee is to Brazil what sugar is to Cuba and cotton was to the Old South. It is by far the most important export and is cultivated on 40 per cent of the total crop area. It is the crop of the damper, more southeasterly parts of the plateau. Here rivers have dissected the surface, cutting great valleys through it as they flow to the Atlantic. On the slopes of the valleys lie the coffee fazendas, or plantations; the coffee tree is sensitive, and in these hills the valley bottoms become quite chilly on winter nights, so they are avoided by the planters.

A coffee fazenda is large, covering usually many square miles. The native brush is cleared and the seedling coffee trees set out in straight, regular rows across the rolling hills. The beans are gathered by hand from the trees late in the Brazilian fall, dried, cleaned of their husks, and put in bags for shipment. São Paulo, forty miles inland from the ocean and about three thousand feet above the level of the sea, is Brazil's greatest industrial center. It rivals Rio in population and is the chief city of the coffee-growing region. On the coast below it is Santos, the chief port for the shipment of Brazil's coffee.

Harvesting coffee beans requires a great deal of labor as does preparing them for market. The climate of these highlands was found suitable for European settlement, and here came many Europeans during the nineteenth century, especially Italians. Labor, thus, has not been a problem to the coffee grower as it has to the rubber planter.

Along the southeast coast of Brazil, where a narrow coastal plain is overlooked by the high crest of the Brazilian Highlands, the trade winds blow onshore. They bring rainfall at all seasons, but most comes in their summer. Along this tropical coast the earliest Portuguese colonies were made, and the colonists used slave labor to grow sugar and rice and cotton for export. These are still grown, though their importance as export crops has declined.

Rio de Janeiro, the oldest city of Brazil and its former capital, ranks also as its most important port. Everyone who has ever studied the posters and pictures in the tourist agents' windows and traveled in his mind will remember Rio: the Bay of Guanabara, its narrow entrance from the ocean between towering cliffs, the white, shining buildings stretched out around its shores, and backed by the towering façade of the Brazilian Highlands, of which Sugarloaf Mountain and the other abrupt, scattered hills of the city are but detached fragments. There are few harbors more spacious and more sheltered than that of Rio and none more beautiful. Outside the headlands at its entrance is the resort of Copacabana Beach. Rio is on the tourist route, but it is a great industrial and commercial city in its own right. The nationalistically minded Brazilians of today find Rio too cosmopolitan, and that is why they have replaced it as the capital with Brasília. But it will remain the commercial capital of Latin America's richest and fastest growing country.

Although Rio is the largest and most important port, it is far from being the only one. As Brazil was developed and commercial agriculture was extended over the coastal plain, a number of port cities grew up, well spaced along the coast between the Amazon basin and the boundary of Uruguay. Fortaleza, Recife, Maceió, Salvador, Santos, and Pôrto Alegre are all large cities.

The Brazilian Highlands, where agricultural resources are somewhat restricted, are well endowed with minerals. Gold is mined; there are deposits of chrome ore, of mica, titanium, and magnesite as well as such unfamiliar minerals as beryllium, zirconium, and thorium. But the most important is the large reserve of iron ore. Production, however, is still small—about an eighth of the output of the United States. Iron ore is exported, and is also being used on an increasing scale in the iron and steel industry at Volta Redonda.

Brazil is, and is likely to remain for a very long time, a predominantly agricultural country, but manufacturing industries are steadily growing in importance. Foremost among these is cotton spinning and weaving, which draws its raw materials from the tropical lowlands north of Rio de Janeiro. The manufacture of textiles is always one of the first to be adopted by the underdeveloped countries as they try to rise on the scale of economic growth. All of them try first to clothe their own people. Brazil is the most advanced in this respect of the Latin American countries, and it has greater resources than most. But it is short, like the others, of fuel. There is very little coal, and not much is known about the possible reserves of petroleum. But the potential hydroelectric power from the rivers that descend from the plateau is almost unlimited.

To the southwest the savanna of Brazil merges into the gran chaco of Bolivia and Paraguay, and in the south it dries out in the grasslands of Uruguay and Argentina. In the northwest the forests of the Amazon reach on into Venezuela, Colombia, and Peru; and beyond the forests, suddenly and abruptly, rises the wall-like barrier of the Andes, extending from Colombia in the north through Ecuador and Peru to Bolivia and Chile. These are all Spanish-speaking countries. They are individually smaller and weaker than Brazil, but in each of them, with the possible exceptions of Venezuela, Argentina, and Uruguay, we meet with some phase of the same problem of meager resources poorly utilized.

Venezuela

"Little Venice" is somewhat incongruously named. The modern traveler is at a loss to detect the similarity between the Venetian lagoons and this swampy coast which so impressed itself upon a sixteenth-century Spanish explorer that he gave it this name. But when Ojeda sailed into Lake Maracaibo, there he saw natives living in stilt houses, and from this the name comes. Today Venezuela is one of the richest and flashiest of South American countries.

A spur of the Andes Mountains enters Venezuela from Colombia and runs northeastward, somewhat parallel to Venezuela's coast. In its foothills is oil. South of this region are the humid lowlands across which the Orinoco flows to the sea. And south of the forested Orinoco lowlands is an area of highland, or plateau, rather like that of Brazil, but lower and smaller and less accessible. It stretches eastward into the Guianas, and is called the Guiana Highlands; it is covered with savanna —the llanos—and offers the possibility of grazing land. But access to it is impeded by the surrounding forest through which there are no means of transportation—not even by the rivers which are too obstructed by rapids to be navigable.

The life of Venezuela centers in the most northerly of these three divisions of the country. Between the mountains and the coast are the petroleum lands, the source of much of Venezuela's wealth. Oil wells

		PETROLEUM EXPORTS VENEZUELA
1.7%	West Germany	
2.5%	Canada	
2.9%	Brazil	
3.1%	Trinidad	
3.2%	Puerto Rico	
3.4%	Cuba	
3.7%	Argentina	
5.5%	United Kingdom	
29.9%	United States	
35.7%	Neth. Antilles (Aruba and Curaçao)	

United States takes a large portion of Venezuelan oil and also a large portion of that refined in the Dutch islands of Aruba and Curaçao.

lie along the foot of the Andes and spread out into shallow Lake Maracaibo. The petroleum is largely processed at the Dutch-owned refineries on the nearby islands of Aruba and Curaçao, but the wealth obtained from it shows in the glitter and sparkle of Caracas, the Venezuelan capital, up in the hills, three thousand feet above the sea and ten miles inland. In these hills are most of the larger cities—Barquisimeto, center of the sugar-growing region, Valencia, and Maracay—and much of the crop farming. Here coffee, cacao, and sugar are grown for export, and corn and beans for local consumption.

The population of Venezuela, about 7,600,000, is typical of that of Latin America, in both its distribution and its composition. It is concentrated in the hills which border the Caribbean Sea, whereas the vast interior is almost empty of people. In this latter area dwell the small groups of South American Indians, remote, primitive, and quite untouched by the gilded splendor of Venezuela's city life. They make up less than 2 per cent of the population, and peoples of wholly European descent are probably no more numerous. There is also a small number of Negroes, but up to 90 per cent of the Venezuelan people are of mixed descent, most of them some undiscoverable blend of European and Indian.

In relation to her population, Venezuela is the richest of the Latin American republics, and this wealth derives chiefly from the fact that about 15 per cent of the world's petroleum production is obtained here. But this does not preclude the abject poverty of many of the people, for extremes of wealth are also a characteristic of Latin American society.

Only the coastal fringe of Venezuela can be described as developed.

Inland, cattle raising is carried on where the land slopes down toward the Orinoco Valley, and from here on to the Brazilian border the European has made no impact at all on most of the land. Yet in this distant and almost inaccessible interior is the second string in Venezuela's resource base; her iron ore. Ore from mines in the interior highlands is now being freighted down to the Orinoco River, where it is loaded for export; the iron industry of eastern United States is using Venezuelan ore. Now Venezuela plans to use some of the ore herself in the iron and steel industry which she plans to create beside the Orinoco, both to supply much needed metal goods and to advertise to the world that Venezuela is, relative to her size, the richest state in Latin America.

The Guianas

East of Venezuela are the three Guianas, the only colonial territories on the mainland of South America. They were occupied respectively by the British, the Dutch, and the French in the seventeenth and eighteenth centuries. Each is a belt of territory stretching from the plateau of the Guiana Highlands across the swampy coastal plain to the coast itself. Each is thinly peopled and underdeveloped. Their combined population is less than a million, and that of French Guiana is only 32,000. Together they have only 250 miles of railroad. Although plantations producing sugar, coffee, cacao, and bananas are being developed, all three are overwhelmingly dependent on the export of a very narrow range of products. Sugar and bauxite make up 75 per cent of the exports of British Guiana, and bauxite comprises 80 per cent of that of Surinam, as Dutch Guiana is usually known. The trade of French Guiana is quite negligible. In each of the Guianas there is only one significant city and chief or only port: Georgetown in British Guiana, Paramaribo in Surinam, and Cayenne in French Guiana. Together they have only a handful of Europeans, and their population is a discordant mixture of native Indian and immigrant Negro and East Indian.

Colombia

To the southwest of Venezuela is Colombia, stretching like its neighbor from a narrow strip of coastal plain on the Pacific side across the mountains to the almost unknown interior. The coastal lowlands are hot, humid, and forested. Then the mountains rise steeply and sharply from the coastal plain to some of the highest peaks in the New World. Clearings along the banks of the Magdalena and Cauca rivers, in upland areas at about 2,000 feet, produce coffee—the chief export of Colombia—cacao, bananas, and sugar. Nowhere else in the New World is there so great a variety in so small an area; steep forested slopes; high, cool upland basins where the Spanish settlers laid out their farms in the sixteenth century; and above them the towering, snow-capped peaks.

The population of Colombia presents the same ingredients as that of Venezuela; only the proportions are different. There is a minority—larger than in Venezuela—of tribal Indians, and a similar minority of unmixed European descent. The Negro element is larger and the rest is mestizo.

Bogotá, the capital of Colombia lies up in the mountains at a height of 8,700 feet, and here too are most of the cities and settlements of Colombia. Bogotá lies only three hundred miles from the equator, yet its school of agriculture teaches cold-climate farming. East of the city one of the branches of the Andes rears its crest to over 10,000 feet, forming a continuous, unbroken barrier to movement.

Medellín and Cali, both cities of 400,000 people, as well as Bucaramanga and Cúcuta, also lie high up in the Andes, amid the coffee and sugar plantations. The only important cities in the lowlands are the ports of Barranquilla and Cartagena on the Caribbean coast and of Buenaventura on the Pacific.

On the other side of the mountain barrier the land drops steeply, almost precipitously, to the plains of the Orinoco and Amazon. No roads and railroads penetrate this forested wilderness which covers almost two-thirds of the whole country. Colombia got possession of a narrow corridor running down to the navigable Amazon in 1922. The idea was to establish a river port here at Leticia, and to export through it some of the products of Colombia's farms and mines. This, however, lies in the distant future. Between the mountains around Bogotá and the river frontage on the Amazon are almost seven hundred miles of unknown, unexplored forest.

In the Andes of Colombia, as throughout the Andean range, there are rich deposits of minerals. Colombia has gold, iron ore, many of the non-ferrous metals, as well as coal and petroleum. Many of these deposits are large, but their output is pathetically small. Coal resources, estimated to be 40,000,000,000 tons, yield only about 100,000 tons a year. Here as everywhere in Latin America, is the spectacle of resources wasted and neglected through lack of capital and of technical skills, and of a poverty-stricken people not knowing how to move to improve their lot.

Ecuador

Geographically Ecuador is a Colombia in miniature. It is at present only a quarter of Colombia's size and has about a quarter of its population, but formerly Ecuador covered a wider area. It claims to derive from the Audiencia of Quito, but the boundaries of this administrative division of the Spanish Empire were never very clear, even to those who administered it. To pursue them now is to try to catch a will-o'-the-wisp. On the basis of ancient Spanish pretensions both Peru and Ecuador have laid claim to the Oriente territory, which to judge from the map would seem to be the hinterland of Ecuador. But here might proved to be right, and Peru has occupied about half of the territory which once belonged to Ecuador. Ecuador is embittered; the regaining of the vast, undeveloped Oriente remains one of its primary objectives.

Ecuador is, as its name suggests, an equatorial country. Indeed, its capital Quito lies almost on the equator, but at a height of over 9,000 feet. Its climate is idyllic: bright sunshine at all seasons and a cool, crystal-clear air that gives it the feeling of eternal spring. Down in the swampy coastal lowlands, cacao, the chief export, and bananas are grown. The railroad which climbs up from the coastal port of Guayaquil to Quito at 9,350 feet, rises through coffee plantations. The forest thins away and passes into the savanna and the grassland of the upland basins; the railroad winds along the foot of Chimborazo and the volcano Cotopaxi, which are among the highest mountains in the New World. Up here only hardy plants, like the temperate grain crops and potatoes can be grown. The majority of Ecuador's people engage in agricultural pursuits, some of them specialized, but most of a subsistence nature. Only a small number of the population take part in commercial activities.

Very few Ecuadorians can trace an unmixed descent from the Spanish settlers; but many have Spanish blood in their veins. Over a third of the population is descended directly from the Indians who were conquered by Pizarro and the conquistadors, and many of these still practice their self-sufficing agriculture, just as they did before the Spaniards came. The rest of the population shows every possible combination of white, Indian, and Negro.

Peru

Peru is compounded of the same ingredients as Colombia and Ecuador: the coastal plain, the mountains, and the forests of the remote

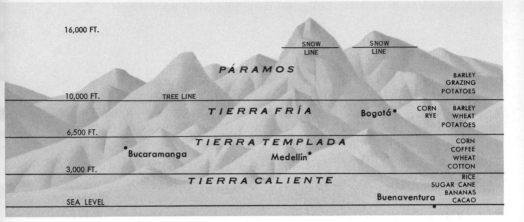

The vertical agriculture of the Andes in Colombia shows how the land near the equator passes through four temperature zones, and four types of farming.

interior. But in Peru everything is drawn upon a larger scale. Although Ecuador contains two of the highest peaks in the New World, the Andes of Peru are in general higher and constitute a much more formidable barrier to movement and communication. The ranges diverge to enclose high, cold, barren plateaus and basins, and to the east Peru reaches five hundred miles out into the forests of the Amazon.

Peru lies entirely to the south of the equator; it has a stronger contrast between the seasons than is found in Ecuador. Winters are cooler, but the winds—the trade winds coming off the Atlantic Ocean and across Brazil—bring heavy rains to the east-facing mountains and leave the plain along the Pacific coast almost dry.

When the Spanish conquerors reached Peru in the sixteenth century, they found a numerous, well-organized and, technically, a relatively advanced people living in the high valleys of the Andes and on the high plateaus between the Andean ranges. These were the Incas. The center of their power was at Cusco, on the Andean plateau itself. On the east their empire extended to the edge of the forest land, and on the west it reached down the valleys toward the desert lowlands. The Incas had learned to extract and refine metals. Above a deep mountain valley in one of the more easterly ranges of the Andes, overlooked by the high, cloud-capped mountains, is Machu Picchu, a city of the Incas, whose masonry even in its present ruinous condition is testimony to their extraordinary technical skill. Agriculture was difficult because of the low rainfall in much of the Inca country, but they developed irrigation works that have not been improved upon by modern societies. Steep hillsides were terraced and watered, and they used their control over the streams flowing down from the mountains as a means of controlling politically the settlements at lower levels near the desert edge.

This Inca civilization was blighted by the coming of the Spaniards. Many of the irrigation works have never been used since, and this region, the scene of one of the most advanced civilizations in the Americas, is now one of the most backward. Agriculture is practiced; corn, the traditional food of the Indian, is grown, and the more accessible lands are occupied as great estates, owned by absentee landlords and cultivated by a poverty-stricken Indian peasantry. In remote areas, where the great landowners have not penetrated, the Indians live their primitive, self-sufficing lives, growing corn, grazing their alpacas on the dry grassland, and transporting their merchandise on the backs of their gentle, stubborn, soft-eyed llamas.

Today a railway runs inland from the Pacific coast port of Callao, which the Spanish conquerors established here where a small island gave some protection to their ships, to nearby Lima, which they established as their capital. For a capital of an Andean state, Lima is remarkably low-lying; it lies at only 500 feet above the sea, and only ten miles inland. It is a center of elegance and good living amid the poverty which characterizes much of Peru. Indeed, to a large degree it is supported by the labor of the peasant of the altiplano, the high plateau, and the irrigated oases of the coastlands. The railway then climbs higher inland until, high above the tree line, it reaches the copper mines of La Oroya and those of Cerro de Pasco, which lies at 15,665 feet and claims the distinction of being the highest important town on this earth. In the days of the Incas silver was mined here; now it is copper; and other metals, like vanadium, are growing in importance.

Like that of all other Latin American countries, the trade of Peru is dominated by just a few agricultural and mineral products. Cotton, sugar, and coffee make up almost half of the exports, and minerals—copper, lead, and iron ores—about a quarter.

Bolivia

To the Spaniards the coastal desert of southern Peru had no value. It was merely an obstacle and they felt no compulsion to trace their provincial boundaries across it. Thus there was no certainty regarding the boundaries between Chile, Peru, and Bolivia when these states came into existence. At first none of them wanted the desert. Then its wealth of nitrates was discovered, and they all wanted it. Chile won the so-called War of the Pacific (1879-1883), and today Bolivia is cut off from the sea. Because of this Bolivia embraces only two of the three physical divisions which have characterized the Andean states so far; the high plateau, or altiplano, with its bordering ranges, and the lower, forested country to the east, drained in part to the Amazon, in part by the Paraná to the Río de la Plata.

Peru is poor; Bolivia is even poorer. The most reliable calculations make it the poorest country in the Americas, and one of the poorest in the world. On the altiplano, lying between Bolivia and Peru, is a large lake, Lake Titicaca. Like water bodies generally, it moderates the cold, and makes it possible to grow hardy grain crops near it. This must be one of the most elevated areas of cultivation in the world. But most of the altiplano is too high and too cold for agriculture. At best it is grazing land for sheep and goats, llama and alpaca. But beyond the eastern ranges there is wetter and warmer country where the mountains slope down to the forested lowlands, regions too remote to carry on much commerce.

After Bolivia lost her outlet to the sea in the War of the Pacific, she then tried to open up routes through the eastern forest toward rivers flowing to the Atlantic. This was blocked by Paraguay, which in the Chaco War of 1928-35 occupied a part of Bolivia's eastern lowlands. Hence, Bolivia is land locked. All of her small commerce must pass through the territory of one or other of her neighbors, whose transportation has never been developed to suit Bolivia's needs.

The population of Bolivia is mostly Indian, with only a minority of mestizo, and there are very few persons of pure European descent. In addition to the wheat, barley, and potatoes, grown in the cooler areas near Lake Titicaca, corn, sugar, and rice crops are produced in the hotter lowlands. Farming is carried on both by estates run on the old Spanish model, and also by remote, self-sufficing, and primitive Indian communities. Little material progress has been made since the Spanish Empire ended.

There is, however, one Bolivian resource that has been developed. The Andean plateau is highly mineralized, and like Peru, Bolivia has many minerals of economic importance. Among these is tin. The Bolivian mines are the only important source of tin in the New World; they produce up to a fifth of the world's supply of this metal, and tin makes

CHIEF MINERAL RESOURCES
OF LATIN AMERICA

B Bauxite
C Coal
C Copper
D Diamonds
G Gold
I Iron
L Lead
M Manganese
N Nitrates
P Petroleum
S Silver
S Sulphur
T Tin
T Tungsten
U Uranium
V Vanadium
Z Zinc

up the major part of Bolivia's exports. But all is not well with the tin industry. The mines lie at very great altitudes, over 12,000 feet; transport is costly; deep mining requires a heavy investment; the atmosphere is so rarefied that only the native Indians who are accustomed to it, are able to live and work here, and the world market for tin has for several years been contracting.

The titular capital of Bolivia is the town of Sucre, but the actual seat of the government is La Paz, the chief commercial and industrial center and, with its 350,000 inhabitants, the only large city in the state. Most other cities are primarily mining centers, such as Potosí, where the Spaniards opened up silver mines in the sixteenth century; and Oruro, the present center of tin mining.

In Bolivia again we find that phenomenon of the underdeveloped Latin American republics, excessive dependence upon a single export, and that a commodity with an uncertain future.

Chile

One of the countries that profited by the defeat of Bolivia was Chile, and the ports of northern Chile still provide the most convenient access to the sea for land-locked Bolivia. We all can recognize Chile, a long, thin, ribbon of a country, 2,600 miles from north to south and at most 250 miles across. One asks whatever planner could have devised a shape so strange and so difficult to administer.

It is the Andes that give Chile this shape. From the Bolivia border the range narrows as it continues southward, like a great wall of rock, barring movement across it. Chile is what lies to the west of this mountain wall. It is made up of the hills that rise between the rocky coast and the high mountains which rear their snowy crestline scarcely more than a hundred miles away. In the northern two-thirds of Chile valleys lie between the hills, but to the south it looks as if some great weight had pressed the land downward, allowing the sea to penetrate the valleys and turn hills into islands. Southern Chile is all coast, and resembles the fjords and islands of British Columbia and the panhandle of Alaska.

A journey from northern Chile to the extreme south is like a trip from Baja California to Alaska, passing through each type of climate. First comes the desert, though the desert of northern Chile is altogether drier and more barren than that of the Vizcaíno of Mexico; then comes the mild, sunny climate of California; this corresponds with central Chile for about 200 miles to north and south of Santiago. Lastly, southern Chile resembles not only in its fjords and islands but in its climate too the Pacific Northwest and the British Columbia and Alaska coast. It lies throughout the year in the zone of the westerly winds which come off the Pacific Ocean laden with moisture and cover the mountains with cloud and drench their lower slopes with rain.

The heart of Chile is the middle section of the country, with its California-like climate. Here lies Santiago, the capital, in a mountain basin sixty miles in from the coast. On the coast is its port of Valparaíso. The valley of Santiago resembles the Great Valley of California. Summers are warm, and in winter frost is rare and snow unknown. Farms are large and well cultivated. Just as in California, water is brought down from the mountains to irrigate the crops during the dry summer. Wheat, barley, and corn are grown; vineyards and fruit orchards cover large areas, and where the land has not been brought under cultivation there are cattle ranches. Yet this rich, smiling land has the same social evils as the grim, rugged altiplano of Bolivia and the humid jungle: a few rich persons own the land and a multitude of poor ones do the work.

It is the desert of northern Chile, the Atacama, that in the late nineteenth century became the most important part of the country. It is so dry that soluble salts, deposited on the desert surface, are never dissolved and removed by rain. They lie there, to be blasted, loaded on trucks, and removed to purifying stations, and then sold to the farmers of the world. It was nitrate rock that gave value and importance to the desert, and led ultimately to a war for its possession. Despite the world-wide use of synthetic nitrates, the Chilean product still is the country's second largest export.

The largest export also comes from this area. It is copper, which makes up almost 71 per cent of Chile's exports. Iron ore is also mined in northern Chile. Many years ago the Bethlehem Steel Corporation acquired possession of some of these deposits, and ore from northern Chile today makes its way to the company's furnaces in Baltimore.

Southern Chile is much less developed. There are no railroads in the far southern third of the country; the population is small and only the lumber resources are much used. The land is too mountainous and too wet to attract settlers, and transportation is too underdeveloped for them easily to market whatever they might produce.

The railroad to Buenos Aires climbs out of Santiago, up into the Andes. In a straight line it is only forty miles to the summit of the pass, but the railroad covers more than twice this distance as it winds and climbs. The Uspallata Pass lies at a height of 12,650 feet. There is an ever-present danger from snow, and the railroad in fact tunnels under the summit, while the road goes over the top. The crest of the pass forms the boundary, and here is an immense statue, the Christ of the Andes. This was erected by Chile and Argentina to commemorate the peace which ended a long struggle between them.

The dispute had been about their mutual boundary. It might seem that there was little to dispute in a boundary that followed one of the highest and least interrupted mountain ranges in the world. But when the boundary was first adopted by the two republics, the mountains were still almost unexplored. As they became better known, there was seen to be in the complexities of the range abundant room for disagreement. Did the boundary join up the highest peaks; was it to follow the drainage divide? With the possibility of discovering minerals, it was clearly desirable to settle these points, and the statue by the roadside witnesses that the two countries have no longer any territorial disputes. It is good to have at least one boundary settled, apparently for all time, in a continent which abounds in territorial disputes.

Paraguay

The most easterly ranges of the Andes drop steeply to the plains. In Bolivia they drop to a rolling, forested region called the gran chaco. This is really a savanna region. Winters are warm and dry, summers hot and very wet. Over much of it the vegetation is open woodland, which thickens along the rivers into swampy forest. In winter there may be a shortage of water; in summer the swamps and flooded rivers may make movement difficult. This is the "Green Hell" for which Bolivia and Paraguay fought. Most of it now lies in Paraguay, and it is drained by the Paraguay River and its tributaries, which flow south to join the Paraná and to cross Argentina to the sea.

The same kind of rolling savanna country stretches across Paraguay to the Brazilian border. This is a land that has promise of riches and prosperity. Rice, corn, sugar, and subtropical fruits grow well, yet in reality the population of Paraguay is one of the smallest and poorest in any of the Latin America republics. Generations of misrule, the ownership of the land by a handful of rich families, the lack of capital for investment and skills for its use, all tend to produce apathy and unwillingness to change. The volume of trade is small. The chief exports are from the flocks and herds which graze the savanna: hides, skins, and meat products.

The population of Paraguay, like that of Bolivia, is mainly Indian and mestizo. In recent years there have been a few immigrants from Europe who have settled in and around Asunción, the capital and only important city. But, though nature offers abundant opportunities, the social order discourages would-be immigrants.

The rivers of Paraguay join to make the Paraná, a broad navigable river which flows southward into Argentina and then broadens into the estuary known as the Plata River, or Río de la Plata. It ought to provide a more important highway for shipping—like the St. Lawrence or the Mississippi or the Rhine—into the heart of the continent. Although there is some river traffic from Asunción into Argentina, this is another of the many wasted opportunities with which this underdeveloped continent is strewn.

Uruguay

The northern shore of the Plata River forms the southern boundary of Uruguay. It is a small country, the smallest in South America. Like Paraguay, it is also made up of rolling plains and low hills; then it sinks to a flat coastal plain. It is the "purple land" of W. H. Hudson. And it is a land with only one large city, the capital Montevideo. But unlike Paraguay, Uruguay has a population that is more European than Indian, for it was mainly settled by nineteenth-century immigrants from Europe; it has a political and social order more stable than that in most Latin American republics; and it has developed a specialized agriculture and attracted the capital necessary for the building of railroads and factories. There was a time when in Europe one would ask in the store for a can of Fray Bentos. Fray Bentos is a small shipping point on the Uruguay River, and it became the trade name of a brand of Uruguayan beef.

Uruguay remains predominantly a pastoral country. Much of its lightly wooded grasslands are grazed by cattle and sheep. Wool is its most valuable export, and wool is followed by meat—canned, frozen, or processed—and leather and hides. Other agricultural products make up the remainder. The small Uruguayan cities are packing centers, which in the range of their operations and the varied uses to which they put everything that enters their doors, in no way yield place to Chicago, Omaha, or Kansas City.

Uruguay has a greater variety in its list of exports than many of the Latin American republics that have been examined. It is to this extent less vulnerable than the others, but it is more dependent on trade than they are; its income is greater and poverty is less apparent. In its modest way, Uruguay points to the direction in which many other Latin American republics could and should develop.

Argentina

Across the Plata River from Montevideo, too far away to be visible, is the flat coast of Argentina, and a hundred miles up the estuary is its capital, Buenos Aires.

Argentina is a large country. It is one of the ten largest in the world, and in Latin America is exceeded only by Brazil. The first area to be settled was along the lower course of the river Paraná and the southern

shore of the Plata River. This is so far south that the trade winds are beginning to die out. Summer rains are less heavy, and the natural vegetation, which the Spaniards found here, was rich grassland, lightly wooded along the valleys and in moister areas. This area of rich grassland came to be known as the pampas.

But away from the coast the rainfall diminishes. Westward toward the Andes and southward toward the hilly region of Patagonia the grasslands become drier and merge into dry scrub. Distances are shorter than in the Great Plains of North America, but the changes in vegetation are similar. Yet across this region, even the driest parts of it, there flow rivers from the eastern slopes of the Andes. Here and there this water is taken and used for irrigation. Oases, founded by the Spaniards who came down from the northwest, from beyond the Andes, have grown up along the foothills of the Andes, where fruit, sugar, and cotton are grown. The cities of Salta, Tucumán, and Mendoza nestle amid their irrigated fields and orchards along the foot of the mountains, like Phoenix and Tucson in the American Southwest. Northwestward the pampas merge, with increasing rainfall, into the gran chaco.

The earliest settlers in Argentina, like those in Uruguay, were ranchers, and skins and hides were the first exports. But as settlements grew in number along the lower Paraná, crop growing was introduced. Wheat gradually displaced cattle from the wetter areas close to the river, forcing them out into the drier interior. Wheat has in its turn been forced out by the need for dairy produce and fresh vegetables.

The gaucho, the South American cowboy, still rounds up his cattle and drives them to the railhead or to the packing stations, but his open range is increasingly restricted by the encroachment of the dirt farmer. That struggle which we know so well from the stories of cattlemen and farmer in the American West, has also been enacted on the pampas of Argentina. There, too, the farmer is winning, as he must do. The farmer makes the more intensive use of the land, and in a world threatened with food shortage, the more intensive use of the land must triumph over the more wasteful, if also more colorful ways of living.

Crop farming has spread over only a part of Argentina. In the north, the west, and the south, apart from the small irrigated areas, the cattleman or the sheep farmer still reigns, though the land over which he rules is not very good and the number of cattle or sheep he can keep to the acre is everywhere small, and extremely small in the cold, semidesert lands of Patagonia. The flocks and herds, with their meat, wool, skins, and hides, make up just about half the exports of Argentina. The rest is the product of the forests and farms, grain and oil-bearing seeds like sunflower and flaxseed.

Argentina differs from all South American republics except Uruguay, in one important respect: its population is almost entirely of European origin. There are practically no Indians or mestizos; there is no primitive, subsistence farming, surviving from the period before European settlement. Most of the European immigrants came during the past century; they never knew Spanish rule. Many of them became hired hands on large farms, but the worst excesses, the extremes of wealth and poverty, that generally characterize the great estates of Latin America, were avoided.

It is, in part, this higher level of human welfare, and the resulting demand for factory-made goods, that produces the second contrast between Argentina and most of the remainder of Latin America. It is a country in which factory industry in textiles, iron and steel, and machinery are making progress. The manufacture of cement, always an index of progress in this direction, is large.

The urban population is growing fast. Greater Buenos Aires, with over 6,000,000 people, is the largest city in the Southern Hemisphere. It has grown from a small settlement established here, on the southern shore of the Río de la Plata, near the mouth of the Paraná. It is a spacious city of wide streets, regularly planned, broad parks and squares, and impressive public buildings. It has become the chief port of Argentina; from it railways radiate over the pampas, and in recent years heavy industry has grown up here. Around it is a ring of smaller cities, and up the Paraná, to the northwest, are the large and growing cities of Rosario, Santa Fé, and Paraná—all of them shipping points at one time for the livestock products of the pampas, now diversified industrial cities. Two hundred miles west of the river, where the mountains begin to rise from the plains and the rainfall tapers off, is the city of Córdoba, regional capital of the province of Córdoba. Beyond at the foot of the Andes lies the most western of the great cities of Argentina, Mendoza.

There is a marked contrast between the countries which border the Atlantic Ocean and those which occupy the Andes. The former have been more accessible from Europe, and their physical environment, with the exception of parts of Chile, more inviting. Their resources are greater, or at least more easily used, and they have developed a higher level of economy and welfare.

Cape Horn and the Offshore Islands

Any traveler into the far south of South America is halted at last at the Strait of Magellan. It was through this narrow, winding, and rock-studded waterway that the explorer Magellan sailed in 1520. He supposed that the cliffs which arose to the south and merged in the distance into the cloud-enshrouded mountains belonged to a great southern continent. Later in the century he was proved to be wrong by the English navigator, Francis Drake, who discovered that this was only the island which now bears the name of Tierra del Fuego, the Land of Fire.

This group of mountainous islands terminates in Cape Horn, named by the Dutch sailor Le Maire, who first saw it, for his home town of Hoorn. The passage around Cape Horn is a very stormy one and many a ship in the days of sail piled up on its rock-bound coast. The direction of the Andes here curves round toward the east. Beyond the eastern headland of Tierra del Fuego they are continued in a few islands and then by a submarine ridge which breaks the surface of the sea only in a few small islands which include South Georgia, visited occasionally by the whaling ships which work this southern ocean. Then curving back toward the west and south, this ridge, crowned by the South Sandwich and South Orkney Islands, passes into the Palmer Peninsula before merging into ice-covered, uninhabited Antarctica.

About three hundred miles east of the Strait of Magellan is a small group of islands, ruled by Great Britain and called the Falkland Islands. They are bleak and windswept. Agriculture is almost confined to raising sheep and wool, and the products of whaling are the only important exports. The population is only about 2,000. Yet these were once one of Britain's prized possessions: from them, the British could control the shipping around Cape Horn. Their importance was suddenly extinguished when the Panama Canal was opened and the long, dangerous sea voyage around Cape Horn ceased to be regularly used. They are now just an outpost of European colonialism, forgotten except by Britain which still exercises sovereignty over them, and by Argentina which presses her claims to them.

MEXICO AND CENTRAL AMERICA

We customarily divide Latin America into Mexico, Central, and South America. The Spaniards never made this distinction. To them the area now contained within the republics of Panama, Colombia, Venezuela, and Ecuador made up the Viceroyalty of New Granada; while the rest of Central America, Mexico and the parts of North America then under Spanish rule—St. Augustine in Florida, Santa Fe in New Mexico, and the Missions of California—made up the Viceroyalty of New Spain. After the revolt from Spain a short-lived Central American federation emerged in the area which lies between Colombia and Mexico. But a people so politically immature that they could not operate a small feudal state, could certainly not run a federation. In 1842 it collapsed, and from its ruins emerged the five republics that lie between Mexico and Panama: Guatemala, Honduras, El Salvador, Nicaragua, and Costa Rica. These Central American republics are alike in their physical geography, their small size, their underdevelopment, and their blend of Spanish and Indian cultures. From the time the attempt to merge them into a republic failed, they have remained aloof from one another. Only today are there the beginnings of a free trade area among them.

These republics, with Mexico and the British colony of Honduras to the north and east, and Panama to the south, make up the area we will now examine. The group is dominated by Mexico, the largest in terms of area and population, the most developed economically, and the most powerful of them politically.

Mexico

Mexico is a large country with 758,000 square miles, three times the size of Texas, but it is made up mainly of semidesert. The mountain ranges of Arizona and New Mexico spread apart as they continue southward from the Rio Grande, to form the Western and Eastern Sierra Madre. These "terrible blue-ribbed mountains of Mexico," with their thin cover of drought-resisting, heat-resisting shrubs, converge about seven hundred miles south to produce a mountainous region of extraordinary complexity.

Between the Western and the Eastern Sierras is a plateau, like the plateaus of the western United States, but hotter, drier, and even more barren and desolate. In the north, where its surface lies at less than two thousand feet above the sea, the temperatures may average over 90° in July and at least 70° in the coolest month. The level of the plateau rises toward the south; its temperatures become lower at all seasons, and forest begins to cover the higher ground.

The modern traveler who drives to Mexico City from Laredo, Texas, along a completed stretch of the Pan-American Highway, misses the plateau and desert. His road keeps to the higher land of the Eastern Sierra Madre, where it is cooler and a little less arid. The road winds between the ranges which border the plateau, crosses deep, narrow valleys where the vegetation thickens and up again over bald, rock-strewn mountains, until a final climb leads up into the high mountains of southern Mexico. This is Mexico.

The Eastern Sierra Madre is a barrier between the coast and the plateau, but it is not an insuperable barrier. Roads and railroads take their winding courses through the mountains, between the hot, steaming coastlands, where Mexico's ports and oil fields are found, up to the plateau.

The Western Sierra Madre is less simple and less easy to negotiate. Imagine a range of mountains as high as the Rockies and as steep and barren as the walls of the Grand Canyon. Only a couple of modern roads cross this range, snaking through its defiles to the small ports of Mazatlán and Guaymas, and only a single railroad, which crosses it from Chihuahua to the coast. It is one of the most formidable natural barriers in the New World, and beyond it, down by the Pacific Ocean, there is only a narrow strip of desert, with a rare oasis watered by streams that flow from mountain springs.

But toward the south, along both the west and the east coasts, rainfall increases as one passes into the zone of the trade winds. The Yucatán Peninsula has in places more than 60 inches of rainfall a year, and the coastal lowlands of southern Mexico, hot at all seasons, have a natural vegetation of tropical rain forest.

It is the highlands, however, where the Eastern and the Western Sierra Madre come together, that constitute the heart of Mexico. Here the land is high enough to be cool in summer, with a summer average of about 64°, and far enough south for winters to be mild. December, the coldest month, averages 54° in Mexico City. The rains are heavy in the summer months, when the trade winds blow more strongly, but the rest of the year is dry and sunny.

Here, in this almost idyllic climate, is Mexico City. The original settlement, established by the Aztecs, was on an island in a natural lake. The lake, with its surrounding marshy land, has been drained, and the modern city spreads out, but at the expense of considerable difficulties with the weight of its buildings on the yielding subsoil over the former lake bed. The "mile-and-a-half high city" lies at a height of 7,349 feet. It is overlooked on the south by an arc of high mountains, from among which the extinct volcanoes of Popocatepetl and Ixtacihuatl rear their snow-capped summits to nearly 18,000 feet. Beyond them to the east, hidden by their own great bulk, is the highest of them all, Citlaltepetl, which reaches 18,696 feet.

Beyond these mountains, to the south and west, the land drops steeply through some of the most rugged and the most wildly picturesque country in the continent to the tropical lowlands. Vegetation changes from moss and lichen in the higher mountains, through coniferous forest, grassland, savanna, to jungle-covered lowland. Here on the Pacific Coast, amid its luxuriant vegetation, the high mountains behind and the long white breakers rolling in from the Pacific in front, is the resort of Acapulco.

Not merely geographically but also geologically, Mexico is a southward continuation of the American West, and like the West, its rocks are richly endowed with minerals. It was minerals that attracted the Spanish conquerors, and mining today constitutes the most important industry of Mexico. The oil fields which lie close to the coast of Texas are continued, as it were, beyond the Rio Grande, and petroleum is obtained from many points on the eastern coastal plain. Tampico is the chief city of the oil-field region, the chief center of oil refining, and the chief oil port of Mexico. Exploration for oil still goes on, and in the past few years several more oil fields have been found.

Mexico's silver production today amounts to about a quarter of the world's production. Mexico produces also about a tenth of both the world's lead and zinc and important amounts of manganese, copper, and other metals. Many of the cities of Mexico began as mining centers, and some of them, Zacatecas, Durango, Guadalajara, San Luis Potosí, and Chihuahua, are still important for their mining and smelting industries.

Despite this wealth of mineral ores, iron is scarcely to be found among them. Mexico's production of iron ore is small and insufficient to supply a modern steel industry, and Mexico has to import part of the materials needed at her thriving new iron and steel manufacturing center of Monterrey.

About a seventh of the population of Mexico lives in Mexico City, which with its 5,000,000 people, rivals Chicago. In most of the Latin American republics the capital is not only the largest city, but is often larger than all the others put together. These states are dominated and overshadowed by their capitals.

Mexico, like most every other Latin American country, is predominantly agricultural. Considerably over half the population of 36,650,000 lives and works on the land. Most carry on a rather primitive form of cultivation; and over half the cultivated land grows corn. Yet the country is not self-sufficing even in the ordinary foodstuffs like grain. There are plans for a great expansion of the area under irrigation, and for improving the quality of farming in nonirrigated areas, where there is urgent need for better seed and better tools and equipment, and for more modern methods of soil conservation.

The chief port of Mexico is Veracruz, down on the gulf coast about two hundred miles to the east of Mexico City. At its docks freighters are loaded with minerals, petroleum, and certain special agricultural products, especially coffee and cotton, grown on irrigated fields like those in California and Arizona. But in the trade balance of Mexico, however, we must include tourism, the largest single dollar-earner.

South of Mexico to Colombia

South and east of Mexico are six small republics, which together with the dependency of British Honduras, make up Central America. Their total area is only a little more than that of California, and a great deal less than that of Texas, and their combined population of about 12,-600,000 is about equal to that of Pennsylvania. All are mountainous; all lie within the tropics; all have heavy rainfall brought by the northeast trade winds, with a heavier rainfall in summer than in winter.

In Central America the land rises steeply from a coastal plain, very narrow on the west; not so narrow on the east, through slopes that become gradually cooler, up to the cool, high summits and upland basins. The native peoples regularly distinguish three zones according to their own reaction to the climatic conditions.

The lowlands are the *tierra caliente,* or hot lands, where the banana palm and rice can be grown in the forest clearings; where the climate is enervating and malaria endemic; and where the sparse population lives generally at a low economic level.

Above this are the temperate regions, *tierra templada,* warm at all seasons, unduly hot at none, where labor in the fields is not exhausting and malaria is rare. Here are the coffee groves, and fields of corn, beans, and other vegetables, which provide the chief food of the native people. And here, above the mosquitoes and the steamy heat, are to be found the chief cities and most of the population.

The mountains themselves rise higher, and in Guatemala and Costa Rica many peaks reach heights over ten thousand feet. This is the *tierra fria,* the cold land, where few people live and the soil is either given over to rough grazing or left under forest.

The Spanish conquerors in the sixteenth century found a native Indian population throughout the region, but one which had not evolved a civilization as refined as that of the Aztecs. Among these people came the Spanish conquerors, here too occupying the congenial upland areas, where they created estates and reduced the native Indians to peonage. Lastly, Negroes have spread across to the mainland of Central America from the islands of the West Indies. They are now chiefly found in plantations along the tropical coastlands of British Honduras, Honduras, and Nicaragua. Pure Indian tribes are to be found in Guatemala, where they make up more than half of the total population, and also in Honduras and Nicaragua. People wholly of European descent are few, except in Costa Rica and over most of Central America the population is predominantly mestizo.

Guatemala, Mexico's neighbor to the southeast, is one of the most mountainous of the Central American republics. Its postage stamps formerly depicted a row of volcanoes, all in active eruption. This over-stated the hazards of living in Guatemala, though both volcanic activity and earthquakes are not uncommon. Guatemala is predominantly Indian —more so than the other republics—and the majority of its population lives in small, self-sufficing village communities.

Although Guatemala is the most populous of these countries, with about 3,900,000 people, it is far from being overpopulated and its re-sources from being fully used. Its chief exports are coffee and bananas, which are the most important commercial crops of the country. Its cap-ital, Guatemala City, lies at a height of about 5,000 feet, overlooked by volcanoes and not infrequently ravaged by earthquakes.

British Honduras, in reality a small enclave in the Guatemalan coast, was occupied in the seventeenth century by British sailors who came here only to extract tropical hardwoods from the forests. It is small— smaller than Vermont or New Hampshire—and its population is less than 100,000 and its capital city and chief port of Belize has less than 35,000 people. Over its jungle-covered region grow the mahogany and other hardwoods which first attracted Europeans to the area and which still constitute the most important product.

El Salvador, which stretches along the western coast, is a smaller and more homogeneous state than most of the others, with a population that is almost wholly mestizo. Through El Salvador runs the continuation of the volcanic mountains of Guatemala, and beneath the shadow of the volcanoes themselves lies the capital city of Salvador and most of the country's population of 2,550,000. The people of El Salvador have shown more initiative and have achieved a greater success than their neighbors in using their resources. In upland basins, fertilized by volcanic dust, corn and vegetables form the chief food crops. But coffee, the basis of

El Salvador's prosperity, provides the money crop and makes up about 75 per cent of the country's exports.

Honduras, one of the larger but less developed of the Central American republics, nowhere rises as high as its neighbor to the west. Instead it is made up of a complex pattern of steep-sided ranges, narrow valleys, and small basins, floored with alluvium, in which are found most of the settlements. In such a basin near the center of the country is the capital city of Tegucigalpa. The whole is naturally forested, but clearings made in the coastal plain in the east are planted with bananas, and West Indian Negroes have moved in to tend the plantations.

Nicaragua very nearly became a Panama. It lies where the isthmus of Central America begins to narrow, and here for the first time, we find a gap in the mountain ranges, now occupied by lakes, through which it was once planned to cut a canal from the Caribbean Sea to the Pacific. Nicaragua has, in fact, a much greater area of low-lying, forested land than any other Central American republic, and this helps to account for the fact that it is one of the most sparsely populated and one of the least developed. Most of the population of 1,550,000 lives in the western part of the country, where the hills rise a few thousand feet above the lowlands and provide a more healthful environment. The capital city of Managua, however, lies in the lowlands, beside the Lake of Managua. If ever the route were opened up across Nicaragua from the Atlantic to the Pacific, Managua would find itself in a very strategic location.

Nicaragua has shown a degree of political instability unusual even in Latin America. This has discouraged economic development, and, combined with the government's restrictions on Negro immigration from the West Indies, has prevented the development of plantation crops on the scale found in most of the other republics.

Costa Rica is in marked contrast with Nicaragua, but the differences lie more in the field of human development of resources than in the physical geography of the countries themselves. Costa Rica is smaller and much more densely peopled; in fact, the basins and plains around its capital city of San José are among the most densely settled areas in the New World. In its population of 1,250,000 the European element is larger, the Indian smaller, than in other republics. Up in the hills, which make up the whole center of the state, the land is mostly held in peasant farms; down below, on the coastal plains, are large plantations, chiefly for bananas and cacao, worked in part by Negro labor. Both area and population are small enough to be unified and cohesive, and in the stability and orderliness of its government it is a refreshing change from the conditions that prevail in some of Costa Rica's neighbors. But Costa Rica also demonstrates the Latin American tendency to rely on a single dominant crop; coffee makes up over half the total exports.

The isthmus of Central America narrows in Nicaragua; in Costa Rica it has become little more than eighty miles across. The complex mountains straighten themselves out and merge into a single chain which becomes narrower and lower until, at the Isthmus of Panama, it is represented by only a few low hills. At this point it is only forty miles from ocean to ocean, and here it was decided, early in the present century, to cut the canal.

Panama came into existence as an independent state because of the need for the canal. Until 1903 its territory was only an outlying and unimportant province of Colombia. In that year, not without some external support, it revolted, became an independent state, and granted a lease to the United States government to construct a canal from ocean to ocean. The canal was opened in 1914, and soon brought about a change in the pattern of transport. No less than about 10,000 miles were shaved off the sea voyage from New York City to San Francisco, and at least a month off its duration. So important did this forty miles of canal, locks, and manmade lake become that the United States government began at once to consider what it should do if the locks were closed by accident or war, and the canal made unusable. Hence, in 1916, it acquired from Nicaragua an option to cut a canal along the San Juan Valley into Lake Nicaragua, and from the lake through to the Pacific.

Panama is the smallest of the Central American republics in population, with only a little more than a million people. It is made up of forested hills and plains. Its population was very small at the time when it was established as a state, and even today most of its area remains un-cultivated and unused, and a large part of its food supply is imported. Over a quarter of its population lives in the capital, Panama City. Panama focuses on the canal which is its mainstay. A slowly emerging sense of nationalism among the Panamanian population may object to the occupation of the Canal Zone by the United States, but the republic is overwhelmingly dependent upon the canal, the traffic that passes through it, and the spending of the tourists, the military, and others who come to the zone.

THE WEST INDIAN ISLANDS

In Guatemala and in Honduras the mountain chain, which forms the hard, spiny backbone of Central America, sends off spurs eastward toward the Caribbean Sea. Mountains lying in the same direction, but to the north, run through parts of Cuba, through Jamaica, and continue into Haiti and the Dominican Republic. From here the line continues eastward, then curving to the south toward the mainland of South America through the Leeward and the Windward Islands, it joins the mountains of Venezuela.

The islands which are strung out along this gently, gracefully curving arc are of all sizes, from Cuba, the size of Pennsylvania, to the smallest rock that can support a yellow, sandy beach and tuft of palm trees. Most of these islands are high, even rugged and mountainous. Some are volcanic, like the French islands of Martinique and Guadeloupe, which as recently as 1902 suffered violent and destructive eruptions. Only Cuba and the Dominican Republic have extensive areas of flat land.

The West Indian islands lie in the track of the trade winds throughout the year. These blow continuously and steadily off the Atlantic Ocean, piling up great white clouds which rise up over the mountainous little islands. The windward slopes are drenched with rain; the leeward may remain almost dry. The flat islands, over which there is little turbulence in the air, are sometimes too dry even for agriculture. The rains, when they come, are generally short-lived, and the West Indian islands are bright, sunny, and warm, the extremes of heat moderated by the steady flow of the trade winds.

The West Indian islands are small and accessible, and in their soil could grow all the crops that Central America could produce. Europeans greatly preferred the idyllic climate of the West Indies, and thus they were prepared to fight for these small islands, but not for the Central American mountain and jungle.

It was the Europeans' liking for sugar that attracted them. The West Indies have the climate for sugar cane, a crop which acquired immense importance in the eighteenth and nineteenth century economy. Since Europeans first occupied these islands, they have grown sugar, and for this reason, Great Britain and France always set a very high value on their West Indian possessions. And for most of them—Barbados, Jamaica, Trinidad, and many of the Leeward Islands and Windward Islands— sugar remains the dominant crop and the chief export. In Cuba sugar assumes an even greater importance, covers over half the cultivated area, and in former years has made up nearly 90 per cent of Cuba's exports. Some of the West Indian islands—Jamaica, Barbados, and Cuba, for example—rely as much on their sugar crop as the Central American republics rely on their coffee. But some islands have succeeded in diversifying their agricultural patterns: cacao and rice in Trinidad, coffee and citrus fruits in Jamaica, limes in Montserrat, mace and nutmeg in Grenada, tobacco in Puerto Rico and Cuba, and bananas and coconuts almost everywhere.

Politically and culturally there is great diversity in the West Indies. The largest islands formed part of the Spanish Empire, and then shook off Spanish rule and became independent. Cuba, the largest and richest of them, has had little more than half a century of somewhat anarchic independence and now is ruled by an admitted Communist dictatorship. The neighboring republic of Haiti, which occupies the western third of the island of Hispaniola, was formerly French, and has developed as a French-speaking Negro republic. The Dominican Republic, which makes up the remaining two-thirds of Hispaniola, secured its independence by revolt from Spain. It then became a model of political instability, subsequently order was restored at the price of a dictatorship, oppressive even by Latin American standards, until Trujillo succumbed to the common fate of dictators, that of being murdered.

Puerto Rico, smaller in area and incomparably more densely peopled than Cuba, Haiti, or the Dominican Republic, passed from the feeble grasp of Spain to a more vigorous United States control in 1898. It remains a dependency of the United States, and its citizens are free to enter and leave the United States at will. Since 1952 it has had complete internal autonomy, and is free at any time to sever its connection with the United States, and at the same time to lose the benefits which this connection confers. Among these benefits has been investment capital for industrial development. This has made the Puerto Rican one of the fastest growing of all the Middle American economies.

Jamaica and most of the smaller West Indian islands were gathered up at odd times by Great Britain, and were chiefly valued because they could produce the subtropical goods that the British Isles could not. The British West Indies are made up of over a dozen islands, spread in a great arc of nearly two thousand miles from Jamaica to Trinidad. Formerly, when communication was less easy than it is today, the islands were governed separately from one another, and this bred a kind of isolation in many of them. In 1958 the islands were merged in the federation of The British West Indies, and it was intended that it should gain independence within a year or two. But the political situation is proving to be difficult. A strong enough sense of unity within the federation has not yet emerged. The two large members, Jamaica and Trinidad, have pulled out, and the small islands by themselves are too weak and poor to constitute a viable state. In the summer of 1962 Jamaica celebrated its emergence as a dominion in the Commonwealth of Nations.

Guadeloupe and Martinique are now so intimately associated with France that they are represented in the French Chamber of Deputies and thus are regarded by the French as integral parts of France itself. The Dutch have a small group, including Curaçao and Aruba, lying close to the coast of Venezuela, important today for their oil refineries which refine much of the Venezuelan oil. The United States is responsible for the administration of the American portion of the Virgin Islands, purchased from Denmark, which lie nearby Puerto Rico.

All over the world we find poverty and distress in places of almost idyllic beauty, with climates as generous as nature can provide. Most of the people of the West Indian islands are poor, and most of the islands are dangerously overcrowded. When Columbus sailed among them, they had a thinly scattered native population, either too feeble to satisfy the Spaniards' labor needs or too savage to be controlled. The Spaniards, followed by the British and the French, brought in West African Negroes to provide labor on their plantations.

The proportions in which these elements are combined in the total population differs from island to island. Haiti is 95 per cent Negro; many of the British islands are heavily Negro in their population. On the other hand, Cuba and the Dominican Republic are predominantly white or mulatto. In Trinidad and neighboring Tobago, where the sugar plan-

VENEZUELA	PETROLEUM 92%	HAITI	COFFEE 70%
CUBA	SUGAR 79%	BRAZIL	COFFEE 62%
COLOMBIA	COFFEE 78%	PANAMA	BANANAS 59%
EL SALVADOR	COFFEE 77%	BOLIVIA	TIN 58%
GUATEMALA	COFFEE 71%	HONDURAS	BANANAS 57%
CHILE	COPPER 71%	URUGUAY	WOOL 56%

Latin American economies are dependent on a single, predominant export.

tations were late in developing, the labor was supplied not by Africans but by Indians from British India. Over a third of the population of Trinidad is East Indian, and they have spilled over into other islands of the British West Indies. Today Hindu temples are evidence of the cultural diversity of the West Indies.

All the islands were formerly distinguished by their large plantations, devoted to sugar or some other tropical crop, owned by the Europeans and cultivated by the Negroes. Most of these plantations have now gone: those of Cuba were among the last, broken up into small farms, or taken over and operated by the state. The market for sugar is not as easy as it once was. The number of states producing it has increased, and in the European market the competition of beet sugar is acute.

On the other hand, the population of the West Indian islands has continued to increase. Population pressure is the great problem facing the West Indies today. Haiti is bursting at the seams, and for years the pent-up crowds of Haitian Negroes have threatened to flood the less densely peopled Dominican Republic. Puerto Ricans crowd into New York City, and from there spread into other parts of the United States in search of employment; Jamaicans and others go to London, where they get jobs on the railroads, buses and streetcars, and frequently contract chest illnesses in this damp and chilly climate so different from their own islands in the sun.

From the Rio Grande south to Cape Horn, the face of most of the country bears the stamp of poverty, backwardness, and ignorance. The land we have seen is not particularly rich in resources nor unusually well favored by climate over much of its extent, but nowhere is it as poor as the conditions found here would suggest. We have already asked the question: What would have happened if the Western European had come to Central and South America, and the Spanish and Portuguese had gone to North? The question is unanswerable, as are all the "ifs" of history. The land and its resources would have been the same, but the immigrants would have brought a different political and social structure, and this would have encouraged a different attitude to the resources and a different development of this continent.

The immigrants came, in fact, in two waves, separated by a period of time when there was relatively little migration from Europe. The first wave came mainly in the sixteenth century; its organization was feudal and military; it was obsessed with the desire to gain possession of the precious metals, which are only the symbol of wealth, not wealth itself. It was the essence of this perverse and structured society that it discouraged initiative, invention, and change, and it fastened upon some parts of Latin America a legacy of fatalism and a control of the state by landed interests.

The second wave came mainly in the nineteenth century, and it came in search of the truer wealth that lies in the soil and in industries. In part it was drawn from the peasant masses of Europe, which like all peasantry, was conservative and averse to everything new, though able to yield at times to the need for violent and revolutionary change in political structure and social organization. These peoples were more adaptable, more progressive than those who came three centuries earlier.

Yet it is impossible, merely by comparing the achievement of each, to form some assessment of the variable role of man in shaping this continent to his will. They came to different parts of it; the first wave primarily to Central America and the Andean states; the later, to Argentina, Uruguay, and parts of Brazil. But so great is the contrast in political maturity, in economic welfare today between those areas settled mainly in the sixteenth century and those which had to wait till more recent times, that one is forced to believe that the difference does not lie wholly, or even mainly, in what nature offers. In those southeastern republics to which immigrants came in the nineteenth century and later, man has organized and used nature more skillfully and more effectively.

There lies hope in this conclusion, hope that by means of better social organization and education, by changed attitudes to experimentation and the entrepreneur, progress can be made in material things. The Latin American continent-and-a-half is no treasure house of good soil and valuable minerals, but it is far richer than it seems. Well might an Indian of the altiplano say to the gaucho of the pampas, the fault lies not in our stars, but in ourselves, that we are underlings.

8 EUROPE—

WEST BY NORTH:

Western and Northern Europe

This noble continent, comprising on the whole the
fairest and the most cultivated regions of the
earth, enjoying a temperate and equable climate,
is the home of all the great parent races of the
western world.

WINSTON CHURCHILL

To North Americans the countries of Northern and Western and Southern Europe have a special attraction. It is the foreign area, aside from Mexico and the Caribbean, they visit most frequently. It was from these countries most of their first ancestors came; these countries were the source of their law and social institutions and nourished the roots of their society.

The European continent which today draws as a magnet hordes of American tourists is the most irregularly shaped of all the major land areas of the globe. Europe is, in truth, a bundle of peninsulas joined together and thrust westward from Asia. Off the coast are islands and island groups, of which the British Isles are the most extensive and the islands of the Mediterranean the most numerous. Although this bundle of peninsulas covers less than 4 per cent of the land area of the earth, so complex is its geography that in this book we will visit it in three stages: the first, this chapter, will be the northern and western sections, in which we find the strongest kinship to American culture; the next stop in Chapter 9, will be those smiling lands south of the Alps, which with portions of two other continents form another geographical entity; the

259

The bundles of peninsulas jutting from the heartland of Eurasia are so diverse in terrain and climate that they are commonly separated into four divisions. This chapter will consider Western and Northern Europe.

last stop will be later on, in Chapter 11, in the eastern section where those countries which lie for the most part in the shadow of Communism will be considered along with their political brothers.

The European peninsula projects almost two thousand miles to the west from its base in the Soviet Union. To the north of it is the smaller peninsula that comprises Norway and Sweden; to the south, the peninsula that makes up European Turkey. The peninsula of Europe narrows to the west, until, in southwestern France, it is little more than three hundred miles across. It then expands into the Iberian Peninsula, and suddenly contracts and terminates in the southwestern headlands of Cape St. Vincent in Portugal and Point Marroqui at the Strait of Gibraltar. From its north coast the European peninsula sends out the lesser peninsulas of Denmark and Brittany; from its southern, those of Italy, Greece, and the Balkans.

In Northern and Western Europe, between the peninsulas, long arms of the sea carry maritime influences deep into the land. No place is more than three hundred miles from the ocean or from one of its bordering seas. Salt water runs far up its estuaries with the tide; rain-laden winds from the Atlantic cover every inch of it; and maritime influences permeate it through and through. Offshore, especially to the northwest, the continental shelf is wide and shallow, trenched only by the deeper channels scoured at a remote time when the rivers of the continent were continued seaward across its surface. This shelf is a rich fishing ground, and most of the countries of northwestern Europe have fishing fleets.

For the latitude, these seas are warm; the steady drift of water from the Caribbean Sea, the North Atlantic Drift or Gulf Stream as it is called, raises their temperature in winter and keeps the coasts ice-free. Shipping is assisted and the climate moderated right into the heart of the European continent. Only in the Baltic Sea, where the water is less salty and freezes more readily, and at the heads of some of the longer fjords on the Norwegian coast, does ice form on the sea in winter. The drift of warm water from the West Indies creeps around the North Cape, the most northerly point of Norway, but beyond this it is gradually extinguished by the cold arctic waters. Norway is ice-free along its coast, but ice increases and thickens eastward along the northern shore of the Soviet Union; only the most westerly of the Soviet ports are ice-free.

Europe contains an immense variety in structure and relief within a small area. Its rocks range in age from the oldest on the earth's surface—laid down perhaps a thousand million years ago—to the very newest deposits of the last Ice Age, which was witnessed by the earliest human beings. And this range in age and hardness is reflected in the richness of the forms of its surface features. Within the area covered by this chapter five distinct regions can be distinguished.

The first comprises the mountains and hills of the north and west, and embraces Finland, Norway, and most of Sweden, as well as the highlands of the British Isles, the peninsula of Brittany, and the islands of the North Atlantic. It is made up of rock of great age and hardness, and it has gone through many cycles of erosion, and now is one of subdued, even monotonous relief, which we shall call the Scandinavian Hills. Only along its western margin does it culminate in high, rounded mountains—the Dovrefjell and Hardangervidda—bounded by the angular, deeply gouged fjords of the Norwegian coast. The whole bears today the imprint of the Ice Age, when sheets of ice covered the region, scraped it clean of soil, and rounded and polished its surfaces.

To the south and southeast is the second of these broad divisions of Europe, the Great Plain of Northern Europe. Its surface is uneven. Marshy hollows alternate with sandy ridges, but all of it is lowland, and much of it is agricultural land. Such is the land which stretches over southern Sweden and Denmark, across northern Germany and south-eastward into Poland and the Soviet Union. It is deep-soiled and more fertile, but like the lands farther to the north, its forms too were created and shaped by the ice: to the north the present land surface was created by glacial erosion; here by glacial deposition. The contrast is the same as that between the rocky surface of the Canadian Shield and the plains of the Midwest. The rock, stone, and soil, scoured out by the glacier in the one, were laid down in the other.

In relief the third region differs little from the second. The ice sheets which rounded the hills of Scandinavia and laid down a thick cover of boulder clay over the lower ground to the south, never spread into north-ern France and Belgium and their imprint on southern England was light. Here is a land of gentle ridge and valley, carved out of rocks younger and softer than those of Scandinavia. Soil is deeper and richer, and agriculture more profitable. Such is the region which extends over western and northern France, the Low Countries, and southern England, and extends eastward through West Germany as a narrow belt between the glaciated plain and the Central Uplands which constitute the fourth region. The line which divides the glaciated from the unglaciated plain— barely perceptible on the ground—runs across the Netherlands and Ger-many and so into Poland and the Soviet Union.

A band of hills stretches from central France through Belgium and Germany and so into Czechoslovakia. Though varied in detail, these Uplands have much in common. They are plateaulike, rising to an undu-lating surface that lies from one to two thousand feet above the level of the sea. The rivers that cross them are generally entrenched in deep val-leys, of which the most familiar is the Rhine Gorge with its castle-crowned rocks. In general the rocks of the Central Uplands have yielded only a poor and rather thin soil. The heavy rainfall tends to leach it, and although there are numerous sheltered and fertile basins and depressions in the plateau, the region as a whole is not one of great fertility.

The fifth and last of the major physical divisions of Western Europe, which also provides the northern boundary of Southern Europe, is made up of the mountains of the Alpine system. These mountains were up-thrust in the most recent of the great earth movements that have, at long intervals, disturbed the earth's crust. Their forms are relatively new and fresh; they are high and constitute by far the greatest natural barrier to movement in Europe.

On the map the Alpine mountain system assumes a complex pattern. It begins in the west, in Spain, with the Cantabrians, the Pyrenees, and the Sierra Nevada, which enclose the Iberian Peninsula on north and south. It is continued beyond an arm of the Mediterranean by the Alps of France, Italy, and Switzerland, where the system attains its greatest height and complexity. It is continued eastward into Austria, and then eastward into Czechoslovakia and southeastward into Yugoslavia, and so beyond the limits of this chapter. The Alpine system also extends from the Alps of southeastern France through the Italian peninsula as the Apennines. Beyond the narrow Strait of Messina the system continues into Sicily, and then on through the Atlas Mountains of North Africa until the mountains fade out on the borders of the Sahara Desert.

There are few gaps in the Alpine system, and most of the mountain passes are open only in the summer months; but the roads are often steep and winding and occasionally hazardous. Commerce, which once crossed the passes, now generally uses the few tunnels that have been cut through the mountains, or goes by sea from the Mediterranean to the ports of northwest Europe.

South of the Alps there is an abrupt change. Summers become hot and dry; water, of which there had been a superfluity in Western Europe, here becomes a scarce commodity. The pattern of settlement, the organization of agriculture, the whole texture of economic life changes. For this reason, the examination of the lands on the Mediterranean side of the Alps is postponed until the next chapter; here we are concerned only with the lands which lie to the north of the Alps.

This region of Northern and Western Europe is made up of the British Isles, France, the Low Countries, West Germany, the Alpine states of Switzerland and Austria, and Norway, Sweden, Denmark, Iceland, and Finland. Together they cover about 988,000 square miles, more than a quarter of the continent, and have a population of about 213,000,-000. They make up one of the most densely populated areas of the world; one of the most richly endowed with agricultural and mineral resources, and one of the most advanced in all the technical and material aspects of civilization.

Temperature and rainfall in Northern and Western Europe are influenced by the sea. Summer temperatures are cooled by it and the winters warmed; but away from the coast, the moderate temperatures gradually give way to greater extremes. Yet intense summer heat is rare, and it is unusual for more than a few days or a week to pass without rain.

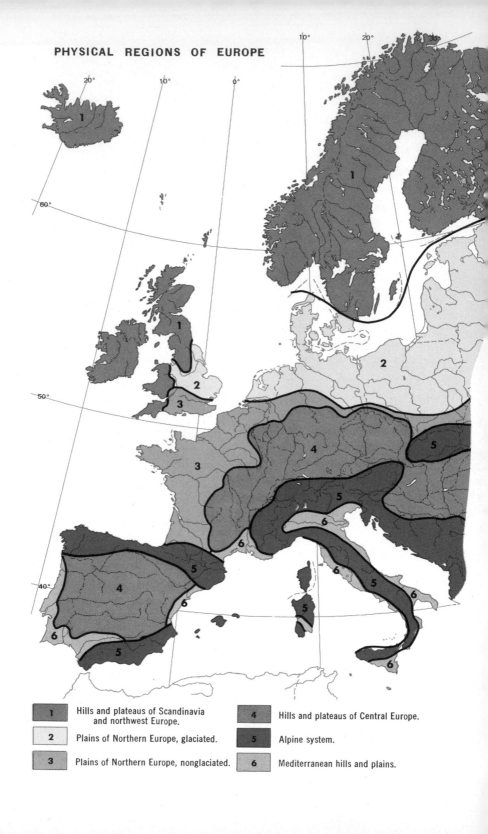

PHYSICAL REGIONS OF EUROPE

1	Hills and plateaus of Scandinavia and northwest Europe.	**4**	Hills and plateaus of Central Europe.
2	Plains of Northern Europe, glaciated.	**5**	Alpine system.
3	Plains of Northern Europe, nonglaciated.	**6**	Mediterranean hills and plains.

The west winds, eddying eastward in giant spirals, bring heavy rain to the hills at all seasons. The mountains of Britain and Norway may have more than 100 inches a year. The air is humid and the cloud cover heavy.

In western France and the British Isles—even in Scotland—winters are mild, with the mildness of Seattle or Portland on the west coast of the United States; the January average may be as high as 40° on the coast, and frost is not common and never severe. Summers are cool; July temperature averages are often no more than 65° on the coast and only a degree or two higher inland. On many a summer's day the sandy beaches around the coast can be as dank and cheerless as if it were winter. But toward the interior of the continent as a whole this gradually changes.

Summers are warm and often sultry in Paris. In the Rhineland they are hotter. In Germany the city streets of Munich or Berlin are sometimes like a hothouse, and rising temperatures and humidity often culminate in a violent thunderstorm. In winter the opposite takes place. Ice may appear on the Seine at Paris, and on the Rhine it may occasionally be thick enough to dislocate shipping. There is skating much of the winter in Berlin where the January temperature averages about 30°, and Warsaw is locked in frost. Winters are typically those of the Midwestern United States, though with the higher latitude, summers are less hot. In Northern Europe the transition from the moderate contrasts of the Norwegian coast to the continental extremes of Sweden or eastern Germany is abrupt, and ice covers the more sheltered gulfs and bays of the Baltic Sea in winter.

Both natural vegetation and cultivated plants respond to the changes in climate. Spring and summer are the seasons of growth, not winter, as in the Mediterranean. Over most of Western Europe, the natural vegetation, before man began to clear it and to make farms and homes for himself, was of broad-leaved trees. The autumn leaf fall enriched the soil, producing the good brown earth which covers much of the lower land But on the high ground in Central Europe and over much of Scandinavia, summers are too short and winters too severe for broad-leaved trees to flourish. There conifers take over, covering the Alpine slopes, the plateaus and hills of Central Europe, and much of Scandinavia with spreading stands of softwood pines and firs. Their irregular leaf fall contributes little to the soil; the heavier rains of the hills leach its minerals and reduce it to a gray podsol, an ash-colored soil of low fertility.

The broad-leaved forests which once covered most of the plain of Western and Central Europe, by contrast, provided a more generous

COAL AND IRON IN EUROPE

● △ Coal deposits
● □ Iron-ore deposits

environment for man. Soils were deeper and more easily tilled; the forest cover was more easily cleared; and the climate better suited to agriculture. This region, from France to Poland, is well suited to wheat, fodder, and root crops and has long been the most important agricultural region of Europe and has supported the densest farming population.

The density of population in Europe does not, however, depend only, or even mainly, on the fertility of the soil. Most of Europe is industrial, and the western portion is the most highly urbanized and industrialized area of the world. This industrial development is based upon generous natural resources.

From west to east, from northern France into eastern Germany, there stretches a line of coal basins. Most lie near the meeting of the Northern Plain and the Central Uplands, and include the well-known fields of northern France, Belgium, and the German Ruhr. In Great Britain also, coal fields are similarly located near the junction of the western hills and the eastern plains, on the flanks of the Pennine Hills and the margin of the Midland Plain. There are also widely distributed resources in iron and other metalliferous ores. Great Britain, France, Germany, and Sweden are especially rich in iron. Petroleum is obtained in only very small quantities; Europe as a whole, excluding the U.S.S.R., contributes only 5 per cent of the world's production. But tin, copper, lead, and zinc are also found.

Industrial growth in Western Europe began in the eighteenth century when coal was first used to power machines and to smelt metals. The feudal system had broken down, labor was more mobile than elsewhere, and people freer to experiment and innovate. Industry was attracted to the coal fields and population to the growing industries. The cities mushroomed rapidly in the nineteenth century; factories, railway yards, and homes fused together into giant complexes, gradually blackening under the spreading pall of industrial smoke. The factories of Birmingham and the "Black Country," the Ruhr, Lorraine, the Saar, central Belgium, and several other such industrial regions, became the source of much of Western Europe's wealth and of its power in the world.

Coal is no longer quite so important; power can be transmitted by cable and more efficient systems of transportation make it easy to scatter industry more widely. But the past cannot be wiped out; the greatest concentrations of people and of industry are still near the coal fields.

The distribution of coal and of good soil have together determined the basic pattern of population distribution in Western Europe. The dominant feature is a belt of dense population which begins in the northwest, in England, continues across northern France, Belgium, and the Netherlands to the Rhineland and from there stretches across central Germany to the regions of Saxony and Silesia. It shows no regard to political boundaries, only to the distribution of resources. It suggests a kind of functional unit in Western Europe, but superimposed on this unit is a political pattern of states. Their boundaries break up the geographical continuum. Before we examine more closely what each of these boundaries encloses, it would be well to look at the attempts that are now being made to diminish their importance and to build a

EUROPE

Scale of Miles

0 50 100   200   300   400

⊗ National Capitals ☆ Other Capitals ● Other Cities

COPYRIGHT 1962 BY RAND MC NALLY & CO. MADE IN U.S.A.

ARCTIC CIRCLE

30°   20°   10°   0°   10°

Reykjavik
ICELAND

NORWEGIAN SEA

Bodø

Faeroe Islands

Trondheim

60°

Shetland Islands

Bergen

Oslo

Stockh

Glasgow

Göteborg

50°

IRELAND

Edinburgh

NORTH

DENMARK

Copenhage

Dublin   Belfast

UNITED

SEA

Hamburg

Berlin

Liverpool

Elbe

Oder

ATLANTIC

KINGDOM

NETHERLANDS

Amsterdam

Essen

GERMANY

P

London

Antwerp   Cologne
BELGIUM   Bonn

Rhine

River

OCEAN

ENGLISH CHANNEL

Brussels

Prague

CZECHO

Nantes

Paris

Seine

River

Danube

Munich

River

Vienna

40°

Bay of
Biscay

Loire

FRANCE

SWITZERLAND

Bern

AUSTRIA

Drava

YUG

Santiago   Gijon

Bordeaux

Lyon

Milan

ALPS

Trieste

ASTURIAS

PYRENEES

Rhone

River

Turin

Po River

Venice

Oporto

Bilbao

Genoa

APENNINES

ADRIATIC

Lisbon

Valladolid

Douro River

SPAIN

Marseille

Florence

ITALY

Dubro

PORTUGAL

Tagus River

Madrid

Siena

Rome

Guadiana River

Barcelona

CORSICA

Guadalquiver
River   Córdoba   Murcia

Balearic

Islands

Naples

SIERRA NEVADA
MTS.

Valencia

Seville   Granada

Cartagena

SARDINIA

M E D I T

Tangier

STRAIT OF GIBRALTAR

Algiers

E

Palermo

SICILY

Casablanca   Rabat

R

R

MALTA

A

MOROCCO

A

ATLAS   MOUNTAINS

ALGERIA

TUNISIA

Tunis

A

30°

Tripoli

R

LIBYA

C

10°   West Longitude   0°   East Longitude

functioning unity amongst at least the countries of Western Europe, including the industrial north of Italy.

Much the greater part of the trade of the countries of Western and Northern Europe is with one another. Each has so great a degree of specialization in its agriculture and industry, that this commerce is essential to them. Their prosperity is founded on trade, and any obstacle to trade injures their well-being.

In 1950 the French Foreign Minister proposed that the countries of Western Europe should abolish all restrictions on trade between themselves in all materials that entered into the manufacture of iron and steel—coal and coke, iron ore and scrap metal, pig iron, and part-finished steel. The Coal and Steel Community came into being two years later. The liberalizing of trade brought prosperity and progress in six countries —France, West Germany, Belgium, the Netherlands, Luxembourg, and Italy—and encouraged plans for an even wider application of the principle of free trade.

The United States constitutes a market of about 185,000,000 people. The "Six" together have about 173,000,000. If there were no barriers to trade and migration, they would have the kind of advantage that has made the United States pre-eminent in industrial growth and human welfare. In 1958 the European Economic Community came into being. By degrees the Six undertook to abolish all obstacles to every kind of trade among their nations. Henceforward, the industrialist would establish his plant where the advantages were greatest, irrespective of which of the six countries it might be in. Agricultural produce would be grown wherever in the territory of the Six it could be grown most cheaply. The utilization of resources would be pressed to the farthest extent; the price of commodities would drop, and each man's dollar would be worth more.

To revert to the old pattern of import duties, quotas, and obstacles to trade would be like erecting customs barriers between each of the fifty United States. And as there is virtue in size, the Economic Community is growing and welcoming new members.

The "Outer Seven"—made up of the United Kingdom, the Scandinavian countries, Austria, Switzerland, and Portugal—had reservations, and did not feel at the time that they should accept all the obligations of membership in the Community. Their reservations arose, in some instances from the sheltered position of their agriculture; in others from overseas commitments; and in others from the political implications of economic union. They formed, in 1960, their own, less rigorous trading group, the European Free Trade Association. Its success was less assured, and in 1961, its leading member, the United Kingdom asked to be admitted to the Common Market of the European Economic Community. The United Kingdom may be followed by Norway and Denmark, and then much of the productive and commercial power of Europe will be absorbed into a single economic community, with a far greater population and, in many respects, a larger productive power than the United States.

To many the economic unity of Europe which is slowly being forged is merely a prelude to a political unity, and Europe—or at least Western Europe—is conceived as becoming a federation of states, from which strife and conflict will be banished. But until this happy day dawns, we have still to deal with separate, sovereign states. These still constitute the most significant divisions of Europe, and to these we must devote the rest of this chapter and part of the next.

THE BRITISH ISLES

The British Isles lie, at their nearest point, barely twenty miles from the coast of continental Europe. On clear days, watchers on the French coast can see the chalk cliffs, crowned by the medieval castle of Dover. In no other part of the world has so narrow a stretch of water been of as great an importance. It has given the British Isles a degree of security and of freedom from invasion unknown on the continent. Britain's early political maturity, the adoption of mechanical power and its application to manufacturing processes, the rise of a middle class are all related to the relative freedom which these islands have enjoyed from invasion and war. Shakespeare's words were perhaps more prophetic than he knew:

> *This fortress built by Nature for herself*
> *Against infection and the hand of war,*
> *This precious stone set in the silver sea,*
> *Which serves it in the office of a wall,*
> *Or as a moat defensive to a house,*
> *Against the envy of less happier lands, . . .*

Small as they are, the British Isles are packed with geographical variety. First there is the political division into two sovereign states, the United Kingdom of Great Britain and Northern Ireland, and the Republic of Ireland, or Eire. Then there are the intensely local patriotisms of the Scots and the Welsh, peoples who formerly enjoyed political independence and, though they admit to being British, resent being called English.

The land itself should be divided into two parts. To the west is the Highland Zone, made up of Ireland, the Isle of Man, Scotland and its Western Isles, Wales and, in England, the Pennine and Lake District hills and the southwestern peninsula of Cornwall and Devon. This region is not really mountainous, and its greatest altitudes reach little more than four thousand feet, but these hills have the proportions of high mountains, and rising as they do straight from sea level, they look higher than in fact they are. To the east is the Lowland Zone.

The softer rocks of the Highland Zone have long since been carried away to the sea. During the Ice Age it was covered by ice, which plucked away at the bared rock, excavating corries—small, armchairlike depressions—on the higher slopes of the mountains, gouging out long, narrow lake basins and fjordlike estuaries along the coast. But the ice never covered Wales completely, and it did not reach the southwestern peninsula at all. In these latter areas the harder rocks, here mainly granite and resistant sandstone, stand out as rounded areas of hill; they lack the roughness, the sharp ridges, and conical peaks that characterize areas subjected to fierce erosion by ice.

These hills of western Britain rise straight from the stormy North Atlantic, in the path of the westerly winds. All parts have a very heavy rainfall, heaviest on the west-facing slopes of the mountains of Ireland, Scotland, the Lake District, and North Wales, where the average precipitation may be over 100 inches. One can stand near the coast and watch the gray clouds pile up against the mountain sides, deliver their rainfall, and then break up as they drop down over the English plain beyond. Heavy rain, cool temperatures, and strong winds greatly limit the growth of plants.

The higher ground throughout most of the Highland Zone is moorland; it is covered with a short, wiry growth of plants, including wild ferns and heather. In summer the moorlands are a blaze of color with the yellow flowers of the prickly gorse bush and the purple of the heather. A few sheep may graze, but from a strictly agricultural point of view the moorlands have little value.

The lower land around their margins and in the valleys that cross them has better soil, a smaller rainfall, and is less exposed to wind and weather. The cool summers and the dampness at all times make it difficult to grow wheat, but grass and fodder crops do well, and this western fringe of the British Isles is predominantly a cattle and dairy-farming country. Fresh milk is sent daily by train to the industrial cities of the Lowland Zone, and the southwestern peninsula and South Wales grow early potatoes and vegetables for the London market. During the short summer the inhabitants of the industrial cities crowd to the beaches and the resorts that lie along the west coast.

England, Scotland, and Wales

Leaving aside for a moment the island of Ireland, which stands apart in so many ways, we find that the Highland Zone is broken up into six separate and distinct areas by long arms of the sea. In the north are the Scottish Highlands, the largest and perhaps the most familiar part. The moorland surface is interrupted here and there by the reforestation plantations established by the government. The beauty of the glens sloping down to the sea, the long sea lochs flanked by steep mountain slopes, and, offshore, the shapely islands of the Hebrides, all combine with the romantic glamor of the vanished clans to give the Highlands a special place in the hearts of Americans.

In reality the Highlands are a depressed area: agriculture has collapsed, except on the sheltered regions along the east coast, and the crofts—the small fields and roughly built homes—lie ruined and abandoned in the glens; the fisheries have declined; so far industry has not moved in to use the hydroelectric power that is available, and the tourist season is too short to bring much wealth to the Highlands. Yet their beauty continues to attract the traveler who puts up with days of cloud and rain for the rare moments when the sun illumines the heather-clad slopes, lights up the distant purple mountains, and turns to an opalescent blue the sea that leads to Skye and the Western Isles.

Between the Highlands and the Southern Uplands lie the so-called Lowlands of Scotland. They lie where the estuaries of the Clyde and the Forth have narrowed Scotland to less than sixty miles. They are a gently waving plain, much of it underlain by coal deposits, and all of it industrialized. Glasgow is its largest city and, with the smaller satellite cities of Motherwell, Paisley, Hamilton, and others, makes up a metropolitan area of nearly two million people. Shipbuilding and the manufacture of textiles and of iron and steel goods are the most important of the industries carried on here. Loch Lomond lies only fifteen miles northwest from the grimy, smoking factories and shipyards of Glasgow.

Only forty miles to the east of Glasgow is Edinburgh, titular capital of Scotland, center of art and culture, and epitome of Scotland's history. It is a dark city, spread out over the plain between its castle-crowned rock and the misty shore of the Firth of Forth. Beyond the Forth one sees the smoking chimneys of Kirkcaldy, backed by the hills of Fife. The lowlands taper away to the northeast and here are the cities of Perth, the gateway to the Highlands, Dundee with its jute mills, and Aberdeen, fishing port and commercial capital of northeast Scotland.

The Highlands rise suddenly and abruptly, like a wall, from the plain, but the rise to the Southern Uplands from the Scottish Lowlands is more gentle, and the hills themselves are lower and more rounded than the Highlands. Sheep graze the short grass which covers much of the hills, and their fleece contributed to the growth of little woolen mills along the valley of the Tweed. Farther south the Southern Uplands merge into the Cheviot Hills, through which the Romans built Hadrian's Wall to mark the northern limit of their jurisdiction. The hills have since constituted the historic "border" between England and Scotland.

The backbone of northern England is formed by the Pennine Hills which, with the neighboring Lake District hills, makes up the third division of the Highland Zone. The Pennines form a ridge with a rounded, moorland summit, and agriculture and factories push their way up the valleys. To the west of it lies the Lake District, a mountain region in miniature. It is so small that a vigorous person can walk across it in a few hours, the mountains so low that a climber can ascend the three highest peaks in a day, their proportions so perfect that one has the illusion of being amid high mountains—and the combination of lake and mountain so beautiful that this region is second only to the Scottish Highlands in attracting visitors.

Wales is the fourth division of the Highland Zone. In the north, the mountains are rugged and fretted by the ice. To the south, they are more rounded and broken up by lowland areas where agriculture is important. And in the extreme south, there is a coal basin, which, like that of the Scottish Lowlands, has given rise to heavy industry.

Wales, like Scotland, is a land apart. Along its eastern border are the Marches, the zone which in the popular imagination separates Wales from England. The Welsh language is spoken in many parts of Wales, and in the mountains of the north one still finds occasionally a Welshman who knows no English. In the south, between the mountains and the sea, is industrial Wales. There, on the margin of the outcropping coal field, were built the industrial cities of Swansea, Cardiff, and Newport and those with more obviously Welsh names like Llanelly, Rhondda, and Ebbw Vale. Coal, especially anthracite, is mined for export. Iron, steel, and tinplate manufacture are the most important branches of industry, and today the steel industry is being very greatly expanded.

The southwestern peninsula of Britain, beyond the Bristol Channel and made up of the counties of Devon and Cornwall, has in all respects a more congenial climate than the rest of the Highland Zone. Its summers are longer, warmer, and more sunny, and for about three months in the year its beaches are strewn with the sun-tanned bodies of Londoners. The climate favors agriculture more than in other parts of the hilly west. Spring flowers and vegetables are shipped to the markets of the big cities, the year-round growth of grass favors dairy farming, and each night the milk trains rumble north to the industrial Midlands. But in some ways even this is a depressed area. Its former dependence on mining has been terminated by the exhaustion of many of the tin and copper lodes and the opening up of more cheaply worked deposits in other parts of the world. Over large areas of Cornwall and Devon today one comes across the ruined engine houses of once flourishing mines. The miners themselves are gone; in the words of A. L. Rowse,

> . . . For a day came in the late seventies when the
> mines were ruined and the men driven forth
> To earn their bread across three continents,
> In Johannesburg, and Kimberley, in Butte
> (Montana), in Michigan and California,
> In West Australia, Victoria and New South Wales
> The cottages in neighboring Mount Charles
> Where my miners lived were emptied of their Men.

Look through the telephone directory of any American mining community and you will see where some of the Cornish miners went. The prefixes of Cornish surnames, the "Tre," "Pol," and "Pen," in such names as Trewartha, Polglaze, and Penwarn, are almost as widespread as the Scottish "Mac" and the Irish "Mc" and "O."

If the Highland Zone has in recent years been an area of decline and of changing values, the Lowland Zone has been one of growth. It covers all of midland, eastern, and southeastern England. It is a region of low, rolling hills and level plains. It is built of younger and softer rocks. Beds

of harder limestone and chalk rock give rise to low ridges, between which the clay has been eroded away to form lowlands. Over much of this English landscape low vales, eroded in the soft clay, alternate with the chalk rock of "blunt, bald-headed, bull-nosed downs," which lift their summits only a few hundred feet above the vale, giving the area such little topographical variety as it possesses.

The Cotswold Hills rear their limestone escarpment five or six hundred feet above the plain of the Avon and the Severn. To the east, they slope gently down toward the vale where Oxford lies on the sluggish river Thames. Beyond, the downs of the Chiltern Hills, composed of white chalk rock which here and there shines through where the short grass has been removed, rise above the vales of Oxford and Aylesbury and then sink southeast, toward London. In the southeast of England the North Downs and South Downs continue the pattern of ridge and vale until they end in the cliffs of Dover and Beachy Head, where the whiteness of the chalk is stained by the smoke of the passing steamers.

Much of this is agricultural land; the clay soils are mostly under grass; the thin, light soils of the downs and other uplands are mostly used for grazing; the drier east is mostly cropland. But agriculture has everywhere to be adjusted to soil and climate. The farmer employs usually a crop rotation. In the wetter areas two or three years under crops alternate with several under grass; in the drier, the farmer rotates grain crops, such as wheat, barley, or oats with root crops, like potatoes and sugar beets.

Some areas have their specialties. Kent, the driest and sunniest part of this damp and cloudy land, grows fruit and hops for brewing. The rich soils of the reclaimed Fens of Cambridgeshire yield heavy crops of wheat, and near London there is an intensive cultivation of vegetables and of hothouse fruits, like tomatoes. But, with it all, Great Britain is a heavy importer of food, the heaviest, in fact, in the world. Only one-half of the food that is consumed can be produced within these islands.

Coal is the foundation of Britain's industrial prosperity. Coal powered the earliest factories, and industries were attracted to the coal fields. As we have seen, coal occurs on the border of the highland and lowland zones, in South Wales, in the Scottish Lowlands, and along the western and eastern flanks of the Pennines. From here the coal seams dip down and extend away beneath the plain, too deep in most places to be worth mining, but rising here and there through the cover of younger rocks to reach the surface, like islands rising from the floor of a shallow sea. Birmingham, in the heart of the Midlands, lies on such an island, its industries fed by coal seams which here come close to the surface.

Industrial England is mostly in the Midlands and the north. Factory industries began to establish themselves here in the eighteenth century. Through the nineteenth century they continued to grow with the opening up of export markets in every continent of the world; and as coal provided the motive force for most of the industries, they gathered close to the coal fields.

A regional specialization developed. Yorkshire emphasized the manufacture of woolen and worsted cloth in its mill towns of Leeds, Bradford,

Halifax, and Huddersfield. To the south, around Sheffield and Doncaster, the local specialization came to be the manufacture and fabrication of steel, and Sheffield itself acquired a world-wide reputation for high-quality metal. Yet farther to the south there grew up the hosiery and knit-wear industries of Nottingham, the automobile and aero-engineering of Derby, home of Rolls-Royce.

To the north, in Durham and Northumberland, the coal field comes down to the coast. Newcastle-on-Tyne became a byword for the shipment of coal, and London came to rely on "sea coal." The iron ore of Yorkshire combined with the coal of Durham to supply the iron and steel industry of Middlesbrough along the lower Tees Valley.

West of the Pennines is Lancashire, as noted for its cottons as Yorkshire is for woolens; a ring of mill towns grew up around Manchester—Oldham, Rochdale, Bolton, Bury. And out on the plain to the west are chemical and machinery industries. There too is Liverpool, the chief port of Lancashire and of all the industrial north.

In the heart of the Midlands, around Birmingham and Wolverhampton, is the Black Country, a region of closely concentrated mine and factory, where every variety of metal goods, from nuts and bolts to anchor chains and armor plate, is made. The most important branch of these metal industries is automobile manufacture at Birmingham and its neighboring cities, such as Coventry.

In the past, factory industry has belonged mainly to northern England, where most of the coal resources are found. In our earlier discussion of the northern industrial city, we saw that it bears the imprint of its nineteenth century industrial growth. It is not surprising then that modern industries try to escape this grim legacy of the past. New factories, many of which use electric power, gravitate toward the south, where modern factories are being grafted onto sleepy cathedral towns. The most vigorous of this industrial growth is near London and the southern ports. There it has more space; conditions of work are cleaner, and industrial growth is not inhibited by the abandoned hardware of an earlier industrial age.

To avoid having southern England turn into a twentieth-century version of a Pennine mill town, the government has intervened, and industrial growth is now planned. London may not grow any larger, and industrialists in search of sites in southern England are encouraged to build their factories in the so-called "new" towns which are arising in the countryside of southeastern England. Many of the older cities also have industries; the ports of Southampton and Bristol, the manufacturing cities of Swindon, Reading, Oxford, and many others.

The planning of new towns and the limitation of industrial growth in the old is one example of the control exercised by the government over many aspects of economic life. This is relatively new, and dates only from the period immediately following the end of the Second World War. Most aspects of transportation have been nationalized; coal mines are operated by the government. The steel industry is no longer publicly owned, but it continues to be strictly controlled. A limited degree of socialism has come to stay and the country has fared well under it. In a country as small as Britain, with so many competing claims on the available land, with so great a public dependence on the fuel and manufacturing industries, production and price could not be left to the simple operation of the market. Some degree of state control was essential. Britain considers that this degree has, on the whole, been achieved and there are few who would willingly relinquish public control of the use of land and the development of industry.

Every city is dwarfed by London. In the London metropolitan area lives a fifth of the population of Britain, 10,900,000 people. It is the largest and most varied industrial center, by far the most important port and center of culture and education. The city grew up on the north bank of the Thames, within reach of seagoing ships and at a point where the river could be crossed. There, close to the northern end of London Bridge, were built in the eleventh century the chief castle of the English kings, the Tower of London, and the Cathedral of St. Paul's. Later, in the thirteenth century, Parliament began to meet here, and government buildings were built in what was once the suburb of Westminster, about three miles to the west. In the opposite direction docks have spread for miles along the flat, muddy banks of the Thames. Government and commerce have attracted industry and banking, the world of entertainment and the arts, and the whole towering structure of British bureaucracy. From London there radiates an excellent net of railroads and a system of narrow and tortuous roads that no longer suffice for modern needs.

The sight of London Docks brings home Britain's dependence on trade. Not only does about half the food consumed have to be imported, but also most of the raw materials of the textile industries. This has to be paid for by exports, or by the services in shipping, banking, and commerce which the United Kingdom performs for the rest of the world.

Periodically foreign sales and services fail to suffice, and there is an economic crisis until the two can be brought again into better balance.

It is easy to explain these recurrent crises by the loss of Britain's overseas empire. This, however, would not be wholly correct. The Empire had, it is true, supplied Britain with a variety of foodstuffs and industrial raw materials, and there was a tendency to value imperial possessions in proportion to their ability to supply what Britain herself lacked. To some extent these imports were not fully paid for by exports to the colonies, and to this extent there was exploitation. But after the early years of the empire it would probably be true to say that almost everything which Britain obtained from her overseas possessions she paid for by exports and services. But she was able to control the markets of her colonies; she could give her own products a preference and in some degree restrict the competition with them of the products of other countries. She could, in general, secure as large a share as she needed of the surplus products of the colonies.

This would have been true only of colonies—and it was not, in fact, true of all of them—because some were covered by international agreements not to discriminate in trade in favor of the mother country. Beginning with Canada in 1867, and followed by Australia, New Zealand, South Africa, and other territories, the former colonies gained a large degree of independence, and in matters of trade and commerce, they acted like other sovereign and independent states. If Britain acquired commercial concessions in any one of them, these were negotiated like any other international agreement.

Nevertheless, the ghost of the former empire lives on in the Commonwealth of Nations. The Commonwealth defies any simple definition. It is a procession of states; some have crossed the divide that separates dependence from independence; some are crossing now, and others hope to reach that barrier only in the distant future. All are held together by ties more of sentiment than of interest. They are not obliged—at least the independent members are not—to assist one another in war. They grant commercial concessions to one another, but they are not obliged to do so. About 85 per cent of the area and 93 per cent of the population of the Commonwealth enjoy this degree of independence, and much of the remainder—territories like the Federation of Rhodesia and Nyasaland, Singapore, the West Indian federation—are almost as free. The few territories which it would still be within the power of Britain to exploit, are, in fact, not worth exploiting; they have almost nothing to offer.

Ireland

Ireland is separated from Great Britain by something more than the few miles of the Irish Sea. The regular nightly crossings by the ferry boat fail to bridge the gap in culture and sympathy. Whereas the other Celtic lands of Scotland, Wales, and Cornwall have to varying degrees been drawn into the stream of English cultural life, Ireland—or at least most of it—has stubbornly resisted and has gone its own way. Two islands, which one might be tempted to say were destined by nature to be partners, have been turned by the force of circumstance into enemies, and for this British policy must bear a large share of the blame.

Ireland remained a Catholic country at the Reformation. England attempted to subdue it, to parcel it up into English-owned estates, and to dilute the Irish by bringing in Protestant Scots to settle in the northern province of Ulster. But all to no effect. Ireland only remained the more obstinately Irish. Its frequent rebellions culminated in 1921 in the creation of the Irish Free State, which in 1949 became the Republic of Ireland, or Eire. But it does not embrace the whole island. The six northern counties, most of the ancient province of Ulster, where the Scots settled in the seventeenth century, remains part of the United Kingdom; in fact, it is the inclusion of Northern Ireland which entitles the Kingdom to call itself "United." Eire has never ceased to claim the northern counties as part of historic Ireland; the United Kingdom has consistently rejected the claim, and the question of "partition" is the most significant political issue between the two countries.

Ireland is more compact in shape than Britain. It is made up of a central plain across which the river Shannon meanders from lake to lake. Around the margin, like the rim of a plate, is a series of mountains and hills, none of them high, but many of them steep, isolated, and highly picturesque. Ireland is wetter even than England, and the grass grows greener. Much of the island is grazing land, and Irish butter and bacon, and occasionally even milk, are sold in the English market. The Irish Republic is one of the less densely populated areas of the British Isles. The population is in the main agricultural and, apart from Dublin, the cities are small, serving chiefly as market centers for the surrounding countryside. Dublin itself has manufacturing industries, such as brewing and the making of cookies, based in the main on the local agricultural production.

Only Northern Ireland, tied politically with the United Kingdom and mainly Protestant, is to any large degree industrialized. Irish linen is woven in Belfast and in a number of small mill towns in the vicinity. And at Belfast there is also an important shipbuilding industry.

FRANCE

The gray cliffs of Dover look across to the gray cliffs of France. The sea which separates them, known by the English in a certain proprietary fashion as the English Channel, is of quite recent geological origin; similar land forms are to be found over northern France and in southern England. Dry, dusty limestone ridges and plateaus alternate with valleys floored with clay, the former usually cultivated, the latter mainly under grass. Yet the landscape is different.

The English scene is made, like a patchwork quilt, of little fields, each surrounded by a tall hedge with a few trees scattered along it, and in Normandy and Brittany we also find compact fields separated by hedgerows. Yet the landscape of most of France lies open. Avenues of trees line the main roads of France, the excellent *routes nationales*, as they rise and fall over hill and vale, and the trees stand silhouetted against the distant horizon. But between the trees the fields lie bare except for their growing crops, field against field, with only an unplowed strip to separate them. The village on the distant horizon is a close huddle of cottages grouped around a small open square. A church in the corner of the square raises its tower and spire above the village, and through the streets lurch farm wagons, for most of the village houses are also farmsteads from which the cattle make their daily pilgrimage to the fields. If we, the travelers, could look more closely, we should find that each farm is made up, not of a compact piece of land, but of several fragments or parcels, scattered through the unending open fields which enclose the village.

And so, the organization of the land is found to contrast strongly with that in Britain. Apart from the greater importance of grain crops, which makes France almost self-sufficient in this respect, and the importance of the vine, one notes the great strength of tradition. In the scattered fields and the concentration of the farms in the village, the whole structure of agriculture belongs more to the past. There is less scope for innovation and experiment than in Great Britain, and this traditionalism in agriculture is reflected in the organization of French industry.

The average size of much of the French factory undertaking, like that of the French farm, remains small. It is organized on a family basis, and is a craft more than an industry. The heavy hand of the past lies over France; it diminishes the efficiency and increases the cost of production, but is not without its advantages. It emphasizes quality, refinement, and taste. The excellence of French wines, the French *cuisine*, the *haute couture* of Paris could never be maintained with mass production methods.

Since the Second World War, however, a revolution has overtaken French industry. In 1946, a plan was put forward by the government for its modernization. The plan has been implemented, and within the space of a decade France has been turned into one of the fastest growing industrial countries of the world. Coal mining, iron and steel production, chemicals, automobile and other forms of manufacturing have all been greatly expanded—and this without altogether abandoning the older branches of industry for which France is famous.

France spreads across four of the major physical divisions of Europe that were discussed earlier in this chapter. In the extreme northwest Brittany and much of Normandy belong, like Cornwall and Devon on the opposite side of the Channel, to Northern Europe. They are built of old rocks, worn down through the cycles of geological time to gentle rolling hills. This is a greener land than the rest of France. There is more rain, the soil is less suited to crop farming, and a larger proportion of it is under grass. Spring vegetables and flowers are grown around the coast, and are shipped to the Paris market, but over the region as a whole dairy farming is more important than crops. The coast is long, rugged, and deeply indented by winding estuaries. On some of these fishing ports have grown up, and on one is the French naval base of Brest.

Stretching diagonally across France from the Belgian border in the northeast to the foot of the Pyrenees, is the second region, part of the unglaciated plain of Northern Europe which covers much of the country. The northern half of it is drained by the river Seine and its radiating network of tributaries. Across the middle flows the Loire, and in the south many small rivers are gathered together to the Garonne, close to the city and port of Bordeaux, and delivered to the sea through the long estuary of the Gironde. The region is one of gentle relief; large areas of it are level plain, rising almost imperceptibly to an escarpment, beyond which is a steeper drop to a clay vale and a slow ascent to the next plateau. This alternation of scarp and vale is most conspicuous to the east of Paris, but over the whole of northern France is spread a series of outward-facing escarpments, set concentrically one inside the other, with Paris itself lying at their center. They form, as it were, a series of ramparts guarding in a loose ring the approaches to the capital. The rivers converge on the Paris area, cutting deep, wide valleys through the limestone escarpments and plateaus that encircle it.

To the geographer the chief contrast here is not that between hill and vale, but between the qualities of soil. The clays mostly support grass; the light sandy soils have remained forested, and the rest is cultivated. South-facing slopes are often under vineyards. Paris is near the northern limit of the grapevine, but in France it is the marginal vineyards that are often the most valuable. Those which produce Champagne lie over the south-facing slopes of the escarpment which overlooks the city of Rheims. Farther to the south near Bordeaux and in the lower Rhône Valley,

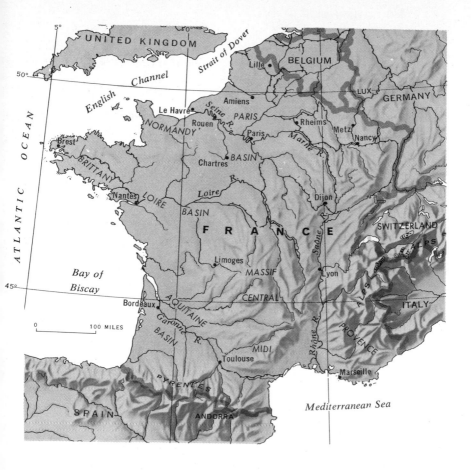

much of the land is also under the vine. Everywhere wine is made in wineries near the city, which have for storerooms the caves in the rock beneath the scarp on which the grapes have been grown.

Paris dominates France as London does England. The city lies near the convergence of several rivers—the Seine, the Marne, the Oise—and grew up on a small defensible island in the Seine, where a royal castle and the Cathedral of Notre Dame were built. The buildings spread beyond the island to the river's banks. The Louvre, the seventeenth-century palace of the French kings, was built close to the right bank of the river, and public buildings spread outward, up the slopes that enclose the Seine Valley. But the Paris which the tourist knows, apart from a few old buildings, is the creation of the nineteenth century, when the civil prefect Haussmann pulled down much of ancient Paris, obliterated its narrow winding streets, and laid out the avenues and the squares of modern Paris. The presence of the king and his court attracted luxury industries to Paris—clothing, jewelry, precious metal work. These have remained, though supplemented more recently by modern factory industries, among which automobile manufacture is one of the foremost. One must always remember that behind the elegance of the Champs-Elysées are the factories and workers' housing of Billancourt and St. Cloud.

The plain of northern France is dotted with small cities; some dominated by the soaring spires and traceries of the medieval cathedrals for which France is so justly famous—Chartres, Rouen, Laon, Rheims, Beauvais, Amiens; others bursting with modern industry, like Lille, Metz, and Nancy. In the extreme north, close to the Belgian border, is the industrial region of Lille and Valenciennes, with its textile and metal industries; to the southeast, in Lorraine, is one of Europe's largest reserves of iron ore, and France's most important steel-making center, near the cities of Metz and Thionville.

South of Paris the rolling wheatlands of Beauce stretch to the river Loire. The Loire Valley was long the playground of French kings and their courtiers. Along the valley from Orléans westward they built their glorious *châteaux,* really renaissance palaces set amid the gentle slopes of the warm, smiling countryside, where the vineyards mingle with the wheat fields. And at the mouth of the Loire are the shipyards of St. Nazaire.

From the Loire Valley, the plain reaches on, past Poitiers and Cognac, where the wine is distilled to make the finest of brandies, into Aquitaine. Bordeaux centers the life of Aquitaine and handles the trade in the wines Barsac, Sauternes, Medoc—all of them named for the vineyards where they are made.

South of Bordeaux the strong west winds off the Bay of Biscay have blown sand inland, covering a large area known as the Landes. Conifers, planted to hold the sand, now yield lumber and turpentine. To the south the land rises gently toward the Pyrenees and to the east toward the so-called Massif Central. Between these two hilly regions is an opening, the Gate of Carcassonne, named for the fortified medieval city which lies in it, and through the gap runs the road to the yellow shores and blue waters of the Mediterranean.

The Massif Central is part of the upland belt of Central Europe, the third of the geographical regions of France. It is built of old hard rocks, which here rise to a high plateau. Mountain ridges and isolated peaks rise above this level. Some of them are volcanic and have become extinct only in recent years. This is a poor land; the soil is thin and those parts exposed to the west have a heavy rainfall. Like many other such highland areas in Europe, its fortunes have decayed; people have moved out, and its agriculture and its few industries are in decline. But a little coal is mined within the Massif, and this has encouraged the growth of industries, especially steel-making and metal manufacturing, at St. Etienne and Le Creusot.

This belt of highland is continued toward the northwest. The forested Morvan hills and the limestone escarpment of the Côte d'Or, beneath which nestle the snug, protected, sun-washed vineyards of Burgundy, connect with the Vosges hills, and the Vosges look down on Strasbourg and the Rhine.

To the east of the Massif is the deep valley of the Rhône and its chief tributary, the Saône. The Rhône itself rises in Switzerland, and at Lyon is joined by the Saône which rises in the wine-growing country of Burgundy. From Lyon to the sea, the Rhône flows between the Massif Central and the Alps. The climate becomes increasingly Mediterranean. The summer rains diminish; winters become warmer; the green of northern France gradually gives way to the tan-colored hills of the Mediterranean, and as the sea is approached, olive groves make their appearance. This is Provence, where the climate becomes that of Southern Europe; France is the only country of Western Europe that reaches into the Mediterranean basin. It was through the Rhône Valley that the civilization of Rome reached France; in its very name Provence goes back to the word *Provincia* of the Romans, meaning "province," and the river banks are dotted with remains of the monuments which the Romans raised.

The Rhône is not naturally a navigable river, though dams are now being built to regulate and improve its flow. At its mouth is an extensive delta, through which silt is carried into the Mediterranean Sea; it was necessary to establish France's Mediterranean port, Marseille, on the rocky coast to the east. East of Marseille is the Riveria, the most famous section of Europe's coast, where resorts—Cannes, Antibes, Nice, and Menton, not to mention the independent Principality of Monaco and its casinos at Monte Carlo—lie strung out between the gray-green hills and the blue sea. This is one of Europe's favorite playgrounds. The color and the sunshine, the hills, the sea, and the islands, the flowers and fruits, combined with judicious publicity, have made this both the Miami Beach and the Palm Beach of Europe.

The French Alps which are part of the southernmost geographic region of Western Europe, lie along the border with Italy, as the Pyrenees do along that with Spain. Both are high, snow-capped ranges, and their ice-fretted summits interpose a formidable barrier to human movement. The mountains have long been regions of poverty and backwardness, but they possess an inexhaustible reserve of water power. Industrial development, based on hydroelectric power, is gradually changing the situation. Mountain valleys which only a generation ago were little known and almost uninhabited, are now becoming filled with factories, and the fumes from smelters and chemical plants are killing the vegetation.

This juxtaposition of ancient crafts and modern industry is typical of France. The plan for economic development calls for the extension of manufacturing in areas best suited for it, like the north, Lorraine, greater Paris, and the leading ports, while small-scale industries slowly wither in the little towns of France.

THE BENELUX COUNTRIES

No countries show more clearly than the three which make up Benelux—Belgium, Netherlands, and Luxembourg—the importance of accident in history. It could all so easily have happened differently. These three states have grown from a cluster of medieval principalities. They were mostly united under the Duke of Burgundy, then split apart by the revolt of the Dutch against Spanish rule, and now they are again being slowly knit together in an economic community.

Together these three cover an area a little more than a tenth of that of France; but within this small area is included a remarkable geographical variety. Luxembourg, in the south, shares the scarp and vale and the iron-ore deposits of eastern France. To the north and west of this country lies the plateau of the Ardennes; a level or rolling surface dissected by the deep, gorgelike valleys of the Belgian rivers. This then drops to the plains of central Belgium. Northern Belgium and much of the Netherlands are, in reality, the highly complex delta of the rivers Schelde, Meuse, and Rhine. The land, as we see it today, is the creation of man, who has diked the fields, laid island to island, and made a land out of them.

Lying north of France and east of England, the Benelux countries have a climate wetter than the one and more extreme than the other.

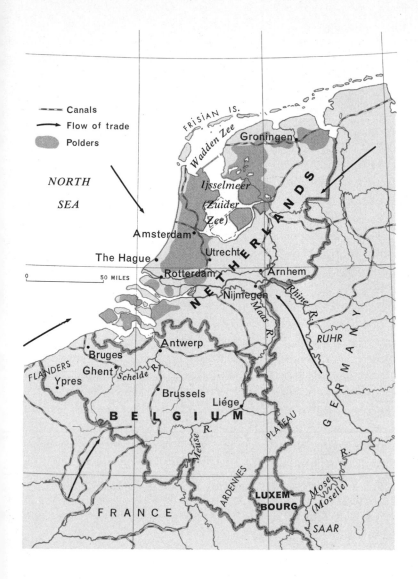

Canals

Over the Ardennes, snow may lie for much of the winter. Ice may lock up the still waters of the Dutch canals, as we see it so often portrayed in the paintings of the Flemish master Brueghel. Grain crops grow well in the rolling country of central Belgium, but in the plains of Flanders and of much of the Netherlands the soil is too damp and the water level too high for crops to be widely grown. This is meadowland, grazed by dairy cattle; several of the well-known cheeses, like Gouda and Edam, take their names from small Dutch cities.

The Benelux countries owe much to their location north of France, northwest of Germany, and almost opposite the port of London. It has been part of Britain's traditional foreign policy to see to it that no great continental power gained control of the country around the mouths of the Rhine and Meuse, and she has given much to maintain the independence of the so-called Low Countries. Indeed, it was her guarantee to preserve Belgium that took her into the First World War in 1914.

On the other hand, these countries have always provided the most useful outlet to the sea for western Germany, the Rhineland, and eastern France. The ports of Belgium and the Netherlands compete with one another for the business of transshipping to river barges the goods destined to Düsseldorf, Cologne, or the Ruhr.

Barges bring coal from the Ruhr down to Rotterdam, where specially constructed docks and cranes transfer it to the ocean-going freighters. At the same time, much of Germany's imported iron ore is taken out of seagoing vessels and transferred to barges for the upriver journey. Amsterdam and Antwerp share to a smaller degree in this business because their waterway connections with the Rhine are less easy and less direct. Thus Belgium and the Netherlands together serve as middlemen in the commerce of northwest Europe.

The Benelux countries are, however, important industrial nations in their own right. Across central Belgium stretches a coal field, which has been worked since the middle ages, and on it have grown up such important industrial centers as Liège and Charleroi, with their iron and steel works. The Netherlands also has a small coal field, a continuation of the Belgian, and has too its industrial cities, though their fields of specialization are the lighter industries, such as electrical machinery, ceramics, and textile manufacture.

Luxembourg

With an area of only 998 square miles, this is the smallest and simplest of the three Benelux countries. It is a survivor in the modern age of an earlier feudal period, and, but for its steel industry, it might have retained the feudal atmosphere of Liechtenstein or Monaco. But the occurrence of iron ore led to the rise of a smelting and steel-making industry, which relative to the size of the country is large and dominates the economy of this little nation. Luxembourg depends on imports for part of its food supply and also for all its fuel needs, and on foreign markets for the sale of its steel goods.

Belgium

From the high, forested, and unprofitable Ardennes Plateau, this country slopes northwest through the fine, rolling farm land of central Belgium to the damp Flanders plain. It was in this last region, close to the coast and within reach of sailing ships, that the earliest of Belgium's great cities grew up. Bruges (Brugge), Ypres (Ieper), Ghent (Gent), and Antwerp (Antwerpen) were centers of medieval industry and trade. They were the cloth towns par excellence of northwestern Europe, and some of the wealth acquired in commerce was used to build the market halls, churches, and merchants' houses which still today give these cities an air of solidity and dignity.

Now Bruges' river has silted and the city is inaccessible to shipping; Ghent has kept its port open by cutting a canal across the plain, and only Antwerp, on the bank of the navigable Schelde, remains a great ocean port.

Flanders is no longer the leading industrial region of Belgium. The use of mechanical power has attracted it to the region of the Belgian coal field, stretching across the country from Mons to Liège, roughly along the valleys of the Sambre and Meuse. Here is now to be found much of the Belgian textile industry, as well as all of its important manufacture of iron and steel. Brussels, the capital, lies between the industrialized coal-field region and Flanders, centrally placed with good communications to all parts of Belgium.

The growth in importance of this more southerly industrial region has been reflected in that of Antwerp. The Meuse is a navigable river, much used for the transport of fuel and iron ore; north of Liège, a large modern canal—the Albert Canal—joins it to the port of Antwerp, which thus serves the needs of the industrial region.

Belgium lies astride the most important language divide in Western Europe, that between the French and the Germanic languages. In southern Belgium, French, known here as Walloon, is the language generally spoken. In northern Belgium, the language is Flemish, which is almost the same as Dutch. The language boundary is sharp and precise, running across the country from west to east and passing just to the south of Brussels, and dividing the country's population into almost equal parts.

Rivalry between Walloon and Fleming has split Belgium ever since it emerged as an independent state in 1830-31. It is a difference which outsiders, like the Germans, have always been able to use to divide and weaken the Belgian people. It seemed in recent years that this difference had diminished, and that both Fleming and Walloon were beginning to show a greater loyalty to a common Belgian state. Now old wounds have been reopened, and suggestions made that the more industrialized Walloon country of the south might be separated in some way from the more conservative Flemish north. From this running feud the Dutch, to their credit, have never sought to make capital, nor to take over any part of Flemish Belgium, which is in so many ways indistinguishable from their own country.

Netherlands

Despite their many similarities, the Netherlands forms, in fact, an interesting contrast with Belgium. It is lower and flatter; there is more agricultural land and farming is more important. In fact agriculture employs more people than industry, while the reverse is the case in Belgium.

The agricultural land of the Netherlands is man-made. Most of the western half of the country lies below sea level and can be used only because pumps are ceaselessly at work, lifting water from the drainage ditches that crisscross the fields up to the canals, and from the canals to the rivers. This is reclaimed land, or polder, formed by building an enclosing dike around an area of very shallow sea, pumping out the water, and bringing the soil gradually under cultivation. This task was originally performed with the help of windmills, but the hundreds that remain today beside the Dutch canals are mainly decorative. The work now is done by less obtrusive, but more dependable, gas and oil engines which are not dependent on the wind and the weather.

This process of reclamation is continuing. The shallow gulf which used to be called the Zuider Zee has been closed by a dike and converted into a lake, called the IJsselmeer, and is now being reclaimed for agriculture. About a third of its former extent has now been turned into rather damp farm land. The islands around the Rhine mouth also are gradually being extended and reclaimed, and it is now proposed to join up these islands by a dike and to reclaim all the shallow waterways between them. These reclaimed fields remain too damp for most crops, but they make excellent grazing for dairy cattle.

The largest cities are Amsterdam, Rotterdam, and The Hague. Amsterdam is the titular capital of the Netherlands and the residence of the queen, though the seat of the government and the meeting place of the Dutch Parliament are in The Hague, twenty-five miles away. Amsterdam is also the chief port in the trade of the Netherlands, though Rotterdam handles a much greater volume of commerce, much of it in transit to and from West Germany. Formerly Amsterdam was reached from the Zuider Zee, but modern ships have grown too large for this shallow waterway, and the building of a dike across its entrance has cut it off from the sea. Now a ship canal, extending across the polders from Amsterdam to the sea at IJmuiden, links it with the sea.

Amsterdam is a city of great charm. Along its streets the old, red-brick merchants' houses look out over the canals which intersect the city and still carry much of its merchandise. Rotterdam, on one of the branches by which the Rhine reaches the sea, was largely destroyed by the Germans in 1940 and has been rebuilt in modern style, which contrasts with the quaintness of Amsterdam.

The Hague, the ancient seat of the Counts of Holland, is the place where government and parliament meet. It is dominated by the ancient palace, the Binnenhof, which is the focus of Dutch politics. Here also is the Peace Palace which houses the International Court of Justice. Scattered over the Dutch countryside are dozens of little cities, neat, trim, colorful, and exceptionally clean, filled with red-brick, gabled houses that the Dutch masters of the seventeenth century liked to paint. Some of them have had modern factories added, like the great electrical equipment works at Eindhoven and the metal goods and textile factories at Utrecht, Arnhem, and Nijmegen. Others remain small, serving the business needs of the dairy lands around them.

The Dutch landscape is one of the most distinctive in Europe: the level polders, with the quiet canals reflecting the willows and poplars; a village grouped on a patch of higher ground with a tall, red-brick belfry rising above its cluster of red-tiled roofs. Above it all is the great sweep of the sky, which here seems more expansive than in more hilly lands, its deep blue dappled with tufts of white, carried in on the west wind to show that, however fair the day, rain cannot be far away.

WEST GERMANY

The river Rhine rises in Switzerland, where it flows through Lake Constance, and for part of its course it forms the eastern boundary of France; then it enters the sea through the Netherlands—yet it is regarded as an essentially German river. In the Rhineland cities of Frankfurt, Mainz, Worms, and Speyer the medieval diets of the German Empire

held their meetings, and along the Rhine and its tributaries has been conducted much of the trade of Germany since the Middle Ages. Although Germany did not really know political unity until the foundation of the German Empire in 1871, the German people and the states which formerly made up Germany, expanded eastward from their original core in the Rhineland, and at their greatest extent included Warsaw, Vienna, and Prague. But these eastern provinces have been lopped off in the course of centuries, and as a result of defeat in the Second World War, Germany itself has come to be divided into separate states, West and East Germany. Once again the basin of the river Rhine is essentially the core of a nation—the German Federal Republic, or West Germany. In this chapter we will deal only with this section, leaving East Germany to a later discussion.

As one moves inland from the Rhine mouth the climate becomes somewhat more continental, the winters somewhat colder and summers just a little hotter. But the climate, even at the farthest point from the sea, is not really extreme. July rarely averages more than 65°, or January below 28° This is neither hot enough for corn, nor cold enough for ice to remain long on the rivers. Rainfall varies with the relief. As is usual away from the coast, most comes in summer, but in the hills it seldom amounts to over 40 inches a year, or in the plains to less than 30.

Today powerful tugs pull lines of barges, loaded with coal, iron ore, or lumber, along the Rhine. Upstream their limit is the Swiss river port of Basel. Above Basel the Rhine, here a swift and turbulent stream, for fifty miles divides Switzerland from Germany. At Basel the Rhine turns sharply to the north and toward the sea. For 160 miles it flows across a plain, framed by the mountains of the Vosges on the west and the Black Forest on the east, both clearly visible beyond the willow trees, the poplars, and the meadows that line the river's banks.

The Rhine is joined from the east by the Neckar at Mannheim. The Neckar rises on the other side of the Black Forest and flows past Stuttgart and Heilbronn, cuts across the Black Forest by a deep, wooded valley, flows beneath the ruins of the old castle of Heidelberg, past the walls of the quaint old city, and so to the Rhine.

Along the Rhine, or linked with it by canal, are the river ports and industrial cities of Karlsruhe, Mannheim, and Ludwigshafen. Then, near Mainz, the Rhine is joined by the river Main. The Main rises in the mountains along the Czechoslovak boundary. It flows in giant meanders through the hills and across the small plains of central Germany. It passes by Bamberg, Würzburg, and Frankfurt.

A few miles to the south of the Main's course is Nürnberg, once one of the most glorious of all German cities, now rebuilt after the Second World War and restored as nearly as possible to its ancient beauty. The Main is being regulated and canalized and a modern canal—about eighty miles long—is projected, across the limestone ridge of the Swabian Alps, to join it with the Danube. Coal barges may in a few years supply the needs of Vienna with coal brought by water all the way from northwest Germany.

A few miles below Mainz, the plain ends, and the Rhine enters the gorge by which it crosses the uplands of Central Europe; this is the part of the Rhine which typifies the river to the tourist. The river is narrowed; steep cliffs rise from the water and conditions of upstream navigation become more difficult. In summer, when the water level is high, the tugboats with their trains of loaded barges from Rotterdam seem scarcely to make progress at all against the speed of the current. Above the steep banks are the ruins of the castles, built here centuries ago for the purpose of exacting toll from the passing vessels. Now signal stations control the movement of barges as if they were freight trains on a railroad. This is the busiest waterway in Europe; perhaps in the world.

At Koblenz the Rhine is joined by the Mosel (Moselle) which, by its winding course etched deeply into the Uplands, comes in from eastern France. This river is as deserted as the Rhine is busy, and yet it links two of the more important industrial regions in Western Europe, Lorraine and the Rhineland. Political reasons have in the past restricted its use, but with the improved relations between France and Germany, there is promise that the Mosel will be made navigable, and that an exchange of ore and iron products from Lorraine for the coal and chemicals of the Rhineland will develop. Today this is wine country. The steep slopes of the Rhine Gorge and of the Mosel Valley are terraced for the vine, and the wines from this area, in their tall, tapering bottles, are sold all over the world.

Near the capital, Bonn, seventy miles below Mainz, the Rhine emerges from its gorge; the hills draw away to west and east, and the plain stretches to the Dutch border. This is the industrial heart of modern Germany; here, on the northern flanks of the Central Uplands, coal beds come to the surface west of the river near Aachen and to the east in the Ruhr coal field, the largest and most important in Europe, perhaps in the world. Downstream from Bonn is Cologne (Köln), with the lofty spires of its cathedral rising over 500 feet above the ground. It is now rebuilt after its wartime destruction, and supports a wide variety of industries. Next is Düsseldorf, industrial city and business headquarters for much of this region. Then comes the Ruhr itself.

The river Ruhr from which this area is named, is a small, unimportant, and almost inconspicuous river. Its chief function today is to provide water for industrial use. But to the north of the river is a line of smoking industrial towns, from Duisburg on the Rhine in the west, through Essen to Dortmund. This is a coal-mining and iron-and-steel-making region. There are almost no industries that are not connected with these dominant pursuits. Coal there is in abundance and of the highest quality for smelting purposes. Iron ore is brought in from Sweden, Newfoundland, or elsewhere; it moves by barges up the Rhine or through the canalized river Ems and the Dortmund-Ems canal from the North Sea port of Emden. Steel sheet, plate, strip, and wire, structural steel, and steel castings are sent to every part of the world. German technicians are today erecting machines and buildings of German steel in India, Egypt, and Brazil.

The Ruhr is an immense concentration of economic power. It was bombed during the war; dismantled after it, and its great "concerns" broken up into smaller and presumably more controllable units. But with typically German resilience it has grown again. The factories and furnaces have been rebuilt and Alfred Krupp sits again in the seat of his ancestors. From the Ruhr mouth the busy Rhine, crowded with barges, flows on to the Dutch border, to Rotterdam, and to the sea.

The Rhine basin does not make up all of present-day West Germany. The southeast belongs to the Danube basin, and the northeast is drained by the Weser and Elbe. North Germany, north of the Central Uplands, is part of that plain which begins at the Pyrenees and ends only in the wastes of Soviet Siberia. The hills end abruptly along the southern margin of this north German plain; the Harz Mountains rise like a wall from the lowland. Spread out in front of them is a belt of open fertile country. Its soil is light and dry and from the earliest times it lent itself to agriculture and to a pathway for human movement.

There grew up along this belt a succession of cities, as German settlement and civilization pushed eastward: Münster, Osnabrück, Hannover, Braunschweig and, beyond the steel and wire which marks the boundary of East Germany, Magdeburg, Leipzig, and Dresden. North of this, where the imprint of the Ice Age was more strongly felt, the quality of the land deteriorates; much is covered with sand and gravel; the valleys are damp and poorly drained. Settlement is less dense and cities are less frequent, until the great ports of north Germany are reached.

Hamburg is the biggest city in West Germany, unless we include West Berlin. Despite the fact that much of its hinterland is cut off by the Iron Curtain, it remains one of the greatest ports of the continent. It lies on the north bank of the Elbe, and its docks line the river for many miles downstream toward the North Sea.

Bremen, the second port of Germany lies at the head of the estuary of the Weser, a smaller and less easily navigated river. At the mouth of the Weser is the outport of Bremerhaven, used by ships which for one reason or another cannot make the voyage up to Bremen itself. Over on the short stretch of Baltic coast which belongs to West Germany are the decayed ports of Lübeck and Kiel, their former commerce with East Germany and Eastern Europe blocked by the Iron Curtain.

Southeastern Germany belongs to the basin of the river Danube, here called the Donau. The Danube itself rises in the Black Forest, only twenty miles from the source of the Neckar, but its course is eastward toward the Black Sea. The Swabian Alps, a limestone ridge, separate the Danube basin from that of the Rhine and Main. The Danube flows through Württemberg and Bavaria and into Austria. It has always directed the attention of Germans toward the east and southeast, opening up vistas of commerce and conquest in the lower Danube Valley and the Balkan Peninsula.

This German section of the Danube is fed by tributaries from the Alps. Among these is the Isar, a swift, torrentlike river on whose banks stands Munich, capital of Bavaria. To the west is the Lech, with the ancient city of Augsburg, once the commercial and banking metropolis of south Germany and home of the Fuggers, merchant princes of the sixteenth century.

West Germany's recovery since the Second World War is almost legendary. Today one has to look hard for any trace of the ruins. The system of superhighways is being rapidly extended. Old factories are rebuilt; new industrial plants and power stations are being erected; navigation of the rivers is being improved. To some extent this can be explained by the generous natural resources—the soil, coal, and other minerals—with which Germany is endowed; to some extent also by the Germans' capacity for hard work, and by the influx of refugees from the east, who have provided a supply of labor. But these alone would not have sufficed if the Allied powers had not carried through the currency reform in 1948, thus giving the Germans an incentive to work and save; if they had not abandoned their foolish policy of dismantling and dismembering; and if the American government had not given generous aid to Germany and the German Federal Government itself placed a premium on economic growth.

The city of Berlin today is valuable to the West Germans chiefly for the lessons which it teaches them. It lies 120 miles east of the zonal boundary, surrounded by Communist East Germany, and access to it is always at the mercy and the whim of the East Germans. Divided Berlin is one of the concessions which the Western Allies made for Soviet friendship in 1945, and, looked at from a 1962 point of view, it was a costly mistake. The city is divided into western and eastern sectors; the western sector, supported financially by West Germany, is bright, rebuilt, and prosperous; the eastern, only partly rebuilt, is drab and dull. This contrast, which West Germans never cease to emphasize, reinforces the ties which bind West Germany with its Western Allies.

Although the fiction of quadripartite city government had long been abandoned, superseded by the east and west division, Berlin remained, in a sense, one city until August, 1961. For sixteen years it had been a kind of escape hatch for the Eastern Zone, because here there was no physical barrier between west and east. From East Berlin refugees streamed into West, and from West Berlin, they were flown to West Germany. Well over two million people made their escape in this way.

In the summer of 1961 it seemed as if East Germany would lose all the younger and more enterprising elements of its population by this route. Therefore the East German authorities built a wall to separate East Berlin from West, and escape has since become difficult and hazardous. The East German authorities have closed the only safety valve which the Democratic Republic possessed; perhaps mounting pressures in East Germany may yet lead to an explosion more violent than that area has ever known.

THE ALPINE STATES

The Alps belong to France, Italy, Germany, Yugoslavia, but more than to these countries, they belong to Switzerland and Austria. The greater part of each is made up of mountains, and everything in them bears the stamp of their mountain environment. After forming the boundary between France and Italy, the Alps swing round toward the east, and in two, and sometimes three, parallel ranges they stretch eastward until they die away in low rounded hills on the margin of the Hungarian Plain. At their greatest heights they reach more than 15,000 feet, and for great distances they are continuously above 9,000 feet. There are numerous passes, but few of them are easy to cross. Most are closed by snow in winter; all are steep and for travelers of another age, on foot or on horseback, they must have been exhausting in the extreme. Yet without the passes and the travelers across them, there might never have been a Switzerland.

There are certain features common to life throughout the mountain zone. The valleys are deep and narrow. In summer they may be quite hot and oppressive; in winter pools of cold air lie in them, filling them with fog or mist. Here lie the permanent villages, and along the floors of the valleys stretch cultivated fields. Commonly the mountains rise

Grazing patterns in the Alps show that cattle seek higher ground as summer approaches. In the fall the herds return to warmer valleys.

steeply from the valleys, then flatten off, producing shoulders of gently sloping or almost level ground above which the land rises more steeply through forest to the bare rock and snow. These shoulders are the "alps," which provide summer grazing for the cattle which make the journey up to them each spring and return from them in the fall to their winter homes in the valleys.

This is the traditional pattern of life in the mountains. To some extent it has been eroded by modern tourism and industry, but over much of the mountain belt the pattern continues. Crop farming is unimportant; in general, the soil is too poor and the climate too severe throughout the mountain zone; most foodstuffs that are not of pastoral origin have to be imported from other parts of Europe. Both Switzerland and Austria have, in fact, substantial imports of food.

Another feature which the mountains share is water. Rivers cascade over falls or rush down in torrents toward the lower ground. This energy is being harnessed, and the power generated from it is used to work the railroads, to drive machinery, and to operate the smelting plants. High tension cables, now to be seen throughout the Alps, carry electric power to cities in the neighboring lowlands, but much is consumed within the Alps themselves as modern industry penetrates its valleys.

Lastly, the Alps are one of the foremost tourist resorts of Europe. The Swiss have been described, with only a little exaggeration, as a nation of inn-keepers, and they have certainly learned how to attract and to entertain tourists. In terms of both industry and tourism, Austria is rather less developed than Switzerland and the simple life of the mountains is more traditional; but in the Austrian Alps, though more slowly than in Switzerland, change is taking place.

It would be a mistake to assume that these two countries consist only of mountains. Both have extensive areas of lower land, though it would be wrong to call this plain. On the lower land are most of the cities and industries and here lives the majority of the population.

Switzerland

This country consists of a confederation, a union of cantons, which are in most respects self-governing. Switzerland grew up this way, and the earliest Swiss state was a group of three small units—the so-called Forest Cantons—which lay at the northern approaches to the St. Gotthard Pass. Travelers and merchants from Italy began to take this route to Germany in the thirteenth century. They brought with them from Italy ideas of political freedom, which they passed on to the Swiss.

The Swiss also saw profit for themselves in the developing traffic across the mountains and were eager to control it themselves. But Swiss independence would probably have been impossible without the protection of their mountains, because on a different terrain they probably could have been overwhelmed by the Germans. As it was, their independence was infectious. Other territories joined, and, though some of these were later lost, the confederation came ultimately to consist of twenty-two cantons, three of which are consolidations.

Switzerland is at once one of the most united and one of the most divided of states. The Swiss are bound together by their political traditions and their economic policy, which has been so strikingly successful. But they are divided culturally, and have no less than four officially recognized languages. The majority speak German, a large minority French, and smaller groups Italian and the related language of Romansh.

Most of Switzerland lies within the Alps, but about a quarter of its area is a great deal less mountainous. Along the northwestern boundary is the Jura, a series of limestone ridges, mostly forested, and between them and the Alps lies the Swiss Plateau. This is the heart of modern Switzerland. It is a hilly region. Rivers from the mountains flow across it to join the Rhine, and their valleys, dammed up by glacial deposits, contain the lakes to which Switzerland owes much of its beauty. Here lie most of the cities of Switzerland: Bern, the federal capital, a lovely buff-colored city with arcades over its sidewalks and ancient sculptured fountains down the middle of its streets; Zürich, modern and spacious, the business center of Switzerland; Basel, a busy industrialized river port on the Rhine and financial center; Geneva, the headquarters of several international organizations; and many others.

Switzerland is also a commercial and banking center of world-wide importance. This is a continuation of the commercial functions developed by the Swiss during the Middle Ages, but the international financial role of Switzerland has been reinforced by her peace and stability, the strength of her currency, and the neutral political path of her government during the past century or more.

Switzerland is an industrial country, but its industries are highly specialized. Switzerland lacks almost all industrial raw materials, except hydroelectric power, and this it has in abundance. Swiss industries are of the kind which lavishes great skill upon small amounts of imported materials. This is how the Swiss overcome the obstacle of distance. The watch industry and the manufacture of turbines, generators, and other complex machines is typical of Swiss industry. Almost all factories are clean; their setting is rural, and their power brought from the mountain streams. Even the food industries share these characteristics; they are quality industries, and the country which cannot feed itself, nevertheless, exports its cheese and its chocolate.

Switzerland is a small and vulnerable country. The mountains may have given shelter to the original Forest Cantons during the Middle Ages, but the Swiss Plateau lies open to invasion; the mountains shelter it only on the southeast. By adopting a policy of neutrality, of making no political alliances, Switzerland hopes to remain free from involvement. This policy has been conspicuously successful, and for more than a century it has remained an island of peace in the stormy European sea.

Austria

About twice the size of Switzerland, Austria has only half again as many people. Like Switzerland, it lies mostly within the Alps, but to the northeast and east, along the Danube Valley and on the borders of the Hungarian Plain, is lower land where lives the bulk of the Austrian people. Austria was once both heart and head of a vast empire, which embraced Czechoslovakia, Hungary, and part of Poland, and reached far down the Danube Valley to Romania. In 1918 the Austro-Hungarian Empire broke up, and all that was left of Austria was the state we have today, with its overgrown capital, the city of Vienna, containing more than a quarter of its total population. There are good reasons why

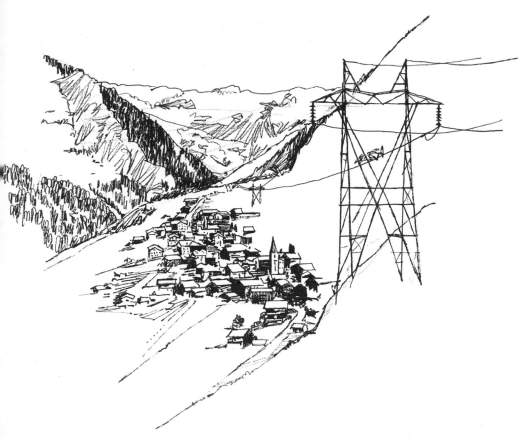

Vienna should be so large; it grew up as the capital of a great empire. The city lies on the south bank of the muddy, brown Danube, a very unromantic-appearing river, overlooked from the west by a low wooded ridge, the so-called Vienna Woods. In the eighteenth century Vienna began to acquire the appearance of a great capital and during the nineteenth much of the city was rebuilt. The Vienna of Beethoven was a very different city from that which danced to the waltzes of Johann Strauss.

Austria has greater resources than Switzerland, including high-quality iron ore and some petroleum. But in the days of the Hapsburgs, Austrians encouraged industrial development in other parts of their Empire, especially in the Czech lands, rather than in the Alps. Vienna itself has a wide range of industries, among which the manufacture of furniture is one of the more important. There is a small but progressive iron and steel industry; but on the whole Austria is only now beginning to take full advantage of its great resources in water power to build up a sophisticated industrial structure such as we find in Switzerland.

Most of Austria's agricultural land lies along the Danube Valley and the margin of the Hungarian Plain. It is insufficient for Austria's needs, and, like Switzerland, Austria has to import foodstuffs.

After Vienna, the most important industrial cities are Graz, in the eastern province of Styria, and Linz, on the Danube. More familiar, however, are Salzburg, Innsbruck, and Klagenfurt; these are smaller, and are given over more completely to tourism and the arts. Salzburg capitalizes on its beauty and on its association with Mozart to establish one of the most visited music and drama festivals in Europe today.

Austria is the victim of its own past. It has been punished for having been the center of the Hapsburg Empire, and, after the First World War, was deprived of so much territory and left with so many liabilities that it was scarcely viable. Its problems received a solution at the hands of Hitler, who incorporated Austria into his Reich, though this was certainly not a solution desired by most Austrians. The country was occupied by the Allies after the Second World War until agreement was at last reached, in 1955, to restore Austrian independence for the price of Austrian neutrality.

Since political independence, Austria has faced up to her problems in the only way possible: by a fuller exploitation of resources and by the extension of manufacturing industries to employ the population. And the signs are that she has been unusually successful. Austria has capitalized on her scenery, and the tourist industry has expanded rapidly. Hydroelectric plants—in the mountains and along the Danube—are coming into production; the total value of manufacturing industries has almost doubled in the past ten years; steel production has increased four-fold since the end of the Second World War. Austria is making strides toward becoming another Switzerland.

THE SCANDINAVIAN COUNTRIES

Something more than the Baltic Sea separates the Scandinavian countries from the rest of Europe. There is a different atmosphere, a fresh sense of values in these small, efficient, and nonaggressive countries. They serve collectively as a restraint on the ambitions of their neighbors, and they are respected and trusted because it is recognized that they have no

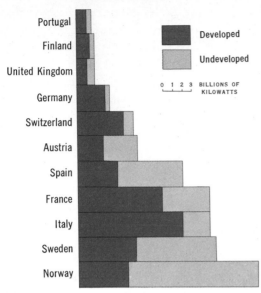

WATER POWER

Portugal
Finland
United Kingdom
Germany
Switzerland
Austria
Spain
France
Italy
Sweden
Norway

Developed

Undeveloped

0 1 2 3 BILLIONS OF
KILOWATTS

Water power is well developed in Sweden and Norway, with a reserve potential. When the coal of Europe gives out, hydroelectric power resources are waiting.

territorial aims. Their stormy past is forgotten, and they attract the respect due to elder statesmen among the nations.

The Scandinavian countries, strictly considered, are Denmark, Sweden, and Norway, but along with these three it is usual to associate also Finland and Iceland. Geographically they have so much in common that it is natural to treat them as a unit, and their tendency to act together politically intensifies the features which they have in common. They have come to use the term Norden as a collective name for themselves.

All have damp climates, cool in summer and cold in winter. Only in Denmark are there extensive areas of good farm land, and in all of them, the range of agricultural production is greatly restricted by the cool, damp, northern climate. In Denmark, the most southerly of them, grass and green fodder crops grow well, but in the extreme north of Scandinavia the climate is in general too severe for any agriculture to be practicable at all.

None of the Scandinavian countries possess coal or petroleum, and this has hindered their industrial growth. All, however, except Denmark, are rich in hydroelectric power, and this is now the basis of a vigorous economic growth, encouraged by the iron, lead, zinc, copper, and other ores to be found in the old rocks which make up most of Scandinavia.

An important distinction within the Scandinavian countries is that between those from which the soil and the rocks have been stripped by the action of the ice, and those over which some of this material was laid down. As we saw at the beginning of this chapter, Denmark lay at the receiving end. Its surface is composed almost wholly of materials borne southward by the ice sheets. Southern Sweden resembles Denmark, but elsewhere areas of glacial deposition, where the ice sheet has left materials to build up a soil, are small and scattered.

Over much of Scandinavia, bare rock, smoothed by the passage of the ice, breaks through the soil. Smooth, rounded masses of rock protrude through the grassy fields and parks, and, in the cities, provide a firm foundation for the daring creations of the modern architects.

Denmark

The peninsula of Jutland thrusts northward from Germany to shelter a maze of small islands which almost close the entrance to the Baltic Sea; this peninsula and these islands comprise the country of Denmark. The backbone of the Danish peninsula is a ridge of coarse sand and gravel. This has been spread out by the rivers toward the west, so that the western half of Jutland is a region of poor, sandy soils. It is also a chill, damp, and windswept region; winds off the North Sea have bent over the few trees that have been brave enough to grow near the coast, so that they appear to slope against the land. Most of the land is under grass, and is grazed by cattle. Eastern Jutland and the islands are more fertile, a little drier, and considerably less exposed, but most of this land is also under grass or fodder crops to support the herds of dairy cattle for which Denmark is famous.

The farms of Denmark are small and very efficient. Most are grouped around a co-operative dairy, which receives the milk, processes it, makes butter and cheese, and markets the products. The farmer receives back the waste products which he uses to fatten his hogs. All is carefully organized, and the government itself supervises the quality of the products.

Dairy and farm products make up by far the largest part of Denmark's exports, but the country is a long way from being without manufacturing industries. Electrical and mechanical engineering goods, the construction of small, specialized ships, and the manufacture of leather goods and ceramics are all important.

Situated on the Sound, the waterway which separates Denmark from

Sweden, is Copenhagen, the largest city, with more than a quarter of the total population. A city of great charm, it owes its importance in part to its controlling position at the entrance to the Baltic Sea, and it is one of the most important ports of Northern Europe. The Danish islands are linked by bridge and by ferry boats which carry passengers, cars, and freight from one to another and bind this fragmented country into a functioning unit.

Sweden

Sweden is one of the largest European countries, stretching a thousand miles from Skåne in the south to its most northerly limit in Lappland. Southern Sweden resembles Denmark with its low, rolling country of small dairy farms. But this aspect changes toward the north. Almost within view of the Sound, or Oresuna, the old, hard rocks of Scandinavia come to the surface and, though they are in places mantled by softer and more fertile sediments, they make up most of the country. In the north, and toward the Norwegian border, the rocks lift up into high, bare mountains on which the snow lies for much of the summer and where the arctic reindeer graze on the mosses and lichens of the northern tundra.

Most of Sweden is hilly and forested. Rivers cascade down from the mountains along its western border toward the Baltic, sweeping timber down to the sawmills and generating the electric power to operate them. The natural wealth of Sweden is in its forests and mines.

Copper and iron ore are the most important minerals to be found in the old rocks of Sweden, and the early wealth and prosperity of the country was based on its copper mines. These have now become very largely worked out, and the copper that remains cannot compete with that produced more cheaply in Africa and America. Iron ore, however, has grown steadily in importance. In central Sweden there are deposits of a very high-grade ore, free of phosphorous, now used in the production of Sweden's high-grade steel.

In the far north of Sweden are larger iron-ore reserves, at Kiruna and Gällivare, which are mined to supply the iron industry of Western Europe. The mines lie within the Arctic Circle, and are operated under conditions of great difficulty. The severe frost, and the long darkness of the arctic winter, increase the problems of mining. The Gulf of Bothnia, the most northerly arm of the Baltic Sea, is closed to shipping for a large part of the year, and ore is shipped out by a railroad which crosses the mountains to the Norwegian port of Narvik. Here the warmth of the North Atlantic Drift is still just sufficient to prevent sea-ice from forming and to keep the port open through the winter months.

In the life of Sweden, however, the most important region is one of relatively low-lying land which extends across the country from the Skagerrak to the Baltic. Much of this area consisted formerly of the bed of a vast lake, and its soils are derived from former lake deposits. Lakes Vänern, Vättern, and Hjälmaren are among those that remain today from the formerly more extensive lake. Much of this lowland is cultivated; rye, oats, potatoes, and fodder crops are grown. Between the port city of Göteborg in the west and Stockholm in the east are a number of small industrial cities, with metallurgical, machine, glass-making, and woodworking industries.

Stockholm is the largest city in Sweden. It lies on Lake Mälaren, in reality a narrow, island-studded branch of the Baltic Sea. It is accessible to large ships and yet protected from the sea. Its factories and docks spread over the islands in the lake and over the rising ground on each side; waterways penetrate its innermost recesses, and its public buildings gain in dignity from the fact that many of them rise from the water-front. It is not without good reason that Stockholm has come to be called the Venice of the North. Its factories turn out chemicals, paper, textile, and rubber products; and in its port lumber and the manufactured goods pass by the imports of fuel and raw materials.

In many ways, northern Sweden has the appearance of a frontier country. The scattered farmsteads, with small windows and good insulation against the cold; the woodpile; the large barns, often painted red like those in Wisconsin, in which the cattle are gathered for protection in winter; and the dark green of the ever present forest—all remind one of the settlements that are today being pushed into the Canadian forests. Yet Sweden does not really belong to the pioneer fringe; its cities are too sophisticated; its art and its architecture are too modern; and its industries too specialized and refined.

Finland

This land bears even more strongly than Sweden the stamp of the frontier. The woods are more dense; patches of cultivated land are smaller and more scattered. The little farmsteads, mostly groups of small, wooden, red-painted buildings set in the forest clearings, look as if they had been established only yesterday. The landscape looks newer and more raw than that of Sweden, as Wisconsin or Minnesota must have looked a century or more ago.

Finland is a low plateau. Its surface is strewn with the debris of the Ice Age, whose evidence here is newer and fresher than in Denmark or Germany. Of the multitude of lakes which give Finland its distinctive character, some occupy hollows gouged out of the rock by the ice; some are held up by banks of earth and stone, or moraines, left by the retreating ice and lying parallel with the coast. These lakes form a fantastic interconnected pattern over the southern half of Finland, providing waterways for commerce and the distribution of supplies to remote settlements.

Around the coast of southwest and southern Finland, the climate is moderated by the sea; the winters are less severe, and ships are able to break through the thin ice to the ports of Helsinki and Turku. This coastal belt is the most densely settled and intensively cultivated part of Finland. But even here only hardy crops—rye, oats, barley, potatoes, and fodder crops—are grown. North, in the lake country of central Finland, these gradually fade out as the winters lengthen and summers become cooler.

Most of the cities of Finland lie in the milder region of the southwest. Here is Helsinki, the capital, a city of almost half a million people, spread out over a bundle of peninsulas and islands in the Gulf of Finland. In the extreme southwest is Turku, an ancient center of Swedish culture in Finland. Inland, at the southern end of the great lake systems of Finland are Tampere, center of Finnish textile manufacture, and Lahti, a focus of the lumber industry.

The forest dominates the economic as it does the artistic life of Finland. It forms the background of the Kalevala, the Finnish national epic; much of the music of Sibelius is a tone picture of the forest. The forests are the greatest resource of Finland. Forest products—cut lumber, wood pulp and paper—make up over 70 per cent of the total exports. Much of the remainder is made up of the products of Finland's highly specialized manufacturing industries. Imports include mineral fuel—none is obtained in Finland—machinery, chemicals, textiles, and foodstuffs to supplement the restricted output of Finland itself. Finland's prosperity is narrowly based on the world market for her small range of exports. She has been fortunate; sales of lumber products have held up well, and Finland has paid her way, discharging both her earlier debts to the United States and also her war indemnity to the Soviet Union.

Finland did not become an independent nation until 1918; its territory had previously been part of Russia or of Sweden. The new state was mainly Finnish, but in the southwest there was—and still is—a Swedish-speaking minority. By the treaty which established her independence, Finland got a corridor to the Arctic Ocean where the small port of Petsamo, now Pechenga, grew up. But in the course of two wars with the Soviet Union, between 1939 and 1945, this arctic corridor was lost together with much more valuable territories along the Soviet border. These included the isthmus separating Lake Ladoga and the Gulf of Finland—Karelia—with its industrial city of Viipuri, now the Soviet city of Vyborg. The loss of this territory, which to many Finns represents the homeland of their race, sent almost a half million refugees westward into the territory that remained Finnish. Their settlement and assimilation presented the Finnish government with one of its most acute problems, solved only at the expense of greater congestion on the better soil and the pushing out of the frontier of agricultural settlement in central Finland.

Norway

This sliver of territory along the western edge of the Scandinavian peninsula curves around to the north of Sweden, beyond the North Cape, and into the Barents Sea. In the south, it expands into the high fjeld or plateau, of southern Norway. The coast is high and rugged for most of its length, and offshore lie a multitude of small and generally barren, storm-washed islands, the skerry guard. The coast is cut up by countless fjords. These narrow arms of the sea, set in deep, rock-walled valleys, were cut by glaciers as they pushed their way down to the ocean from the mountains a short distance inland. The longest of these fjords such as the Sognefjord north of Bergen, penetrate up to a hundred miles inland. They interrupt communications, and although a railroad now runs from Oslo to Bodö, beyond the Arctic Circle, communications are still maintained chiefly by boats which sail from village to village along the coast and among the offshore islands.

There is very little farm land along the fjord coast. At the very most there is a narrow shelf along the side of the fjord and a little flat land at its head, permitting the growing of hardy grains and fodder crops. Farm animals which graze in summer on the fjeld are brought down to these lower levels in winter. Most of the coast settlements engage mainly in fishing and the largest of them, Bergen and Trondheim, have large fishing fleets.

In the extreme south, the mountains draw back from the coast, and a narrow strip of lowland runs up toward Oslo. The Norwegian capital lies at the head of a winding estuary, misnamed the Oslo Fjord. A few miles from the city the land rises, through farm land to the forested hills, and on to the bare upland plateau. Oslo is the largest city of Norway, and the country's most important center of industry. Its manufactures are based mostly upon the local Norwegian products—lumber and hydroelectric power. Its chief imports are fuel, manufactured goods, and foodstuffs to make up the deficiencies of Norway; its exports, lumber and wood products and the products of Norwegian farms, fisheries, and mines.

Norway is not, by European standards, a small country. In extent it is half the size of Texas. Yet its area of cropland is smaller than that of almost any other European country, and about three-quarters of its surface is made up of mountain and waste. So inhospitable a land has driven Norwegians to the sea. Since the days, a thousand years ago, of the Norse voyagers, many of them have sought their fortunes beyond the seas. They settled Iceland and raided the richer shores of Western Europe. Today, Norway's merchant fleet, one of the largest in the world, provides an occupation outside the limits of this sparsely populated and yet crowded land.

Modern technology, however, is revealing resources that were unknown only a generation or two ago. The heavy rainfall along Norway's western coast gives rise to torrents which cascade down the mountainside to the fjord below. These are now being harnessed to produce electric power, and the abundance and cheapness of power has attracted such industries as electric-smelting and electrochemical industries, which are heavy consumers of power. Along the shores of the fjords one now finds generating stations; the fumes from industrial plants fill the valleys and across the high fjeld run high-tension cables. Hydroelectric power is the basis of industrial development in all the Scandinavian countries; it is "exported" from Sweden to Denmark. In Norway power is almost the only important industrial resource, but its consumption per head of the population is among the very highest in the world.

Iceland and North to the Arctic

From the Norwegian coast, during the eighth and ninth centuries, the Vikings made the hazardous voyage across the North Atlantic to Iceland. Such was their land hunger that they settled even this bleak and inhospitable land. Their descendants are there still, though the Icelanders have now severed their political connection with the Scandinavia from which their ancestors came.

Iceland is reckoned to be a part of Europe, though it is the most sparsely populated of all European countries. The Icelanders number only about 182,000, nearly half of them live in Reykjavik, the capital, largest city, and only port. The density of the population is only about five to the square mile. Their land has short, cool summers and long, cold winters. Only about one two-hundredths of its area is cultivated, and only hay and hardy root crops will grow. The Icelanders depend rather upon the harvest of the sea. Over 90 per cent of their export trade is made up of fish and fish products. Any danger to their fisheries is a threat to their livelihood. Overfishing and the competition of other fishermen in the Icelandic waters constituted such a danger. Thus the Icelandic government in 1958 claimed exclusive fishing rights over the surrounding seas up to a distance of twelve miles offshore, an extreme measure justified only by the exceptional circumstances of Iceland's economy.

If Iceland is on Europe's northern frontier of settlement and agriculture, Svalbard, or Spitsbergen, lies beyond it. It lies between 15° and 10° from the Pole, and but for the slight moderating influence of the Gulf Stream the islands which make up Svalbard would be covered with ice, like Greenland. There is no agriculture, and the only resource that is exploited is the coal which is regularly mined, and exported in summer. Svalbard is part of Norway, as is also Jan Mayen Island, a small island lying between Iceland and Greenland, chiefly useful as a meteorological station.

It is a far cry from the lands around the Baltic Sea to those which encircle the Mediterranean. It is a change from a region of modern, technological civilization to one of ancient civilization, of early promise left unfulfilled; from one of political stability and social equality to one of instability and inequality; from poor soil and harsh climate to the sunny land of the grape and olive; and yet, paradoxically, also a change from wealth to poverty. The central character in Ibsen's *Ghosts,* a play set in a small Norwegian town, curses the gloomy, cloudy, climate of the north, and longs for the sunshine of the Mediterranean, and to the Mediterranean we must now turn.

9

AROUND
THE INLAND SEA:

Southern Europe, North Africa,
and the Middle East

*Rough, but the mother of men, and the sweetest
of lands to me.*

HOMER—The Odyssey

The Mediterranean, as its name suggests lies in the midst of the land. It is the meeting place of Europe, Asia, and Africa. Across its waters in the early days of human history, cultural contacts were established between these three continents, and around its shores influences from each fertilized the culture of the others.

No sea has played a more important role in human destinies than the Mediterranean. All the early civilizations from which the Western tradition has been derived grew up on its shores, or very near to them. Its calm surface was one of the earliest schools of seamanship. Its gentle climate, without either the harsh alternation of summer and winter which characterizes Northern and Western Europe or the continuous, sultry heat of the tropical region of Africa, encouraged the early steps in agricultural progress. Deserts and mountains framed the Mediterranean region, gave it protection, and allowed Western civilization, like a fragile plant, to grow with a minimum of interference.

This Mediterranean region is marked off from all other regions by both history and geography. Climatically no region is more distinctive. It has mild, moist winters and hot and generally dry summers. This characteristic, which it shares with California and central Chile, and

315

with parts of Australia and South Africa, is dependent upon the seasonal shift of the westerly winds. Here the climate is carried deep into the body of the land by the large extent of the sea itself. The Mediterranean Sea extends no less than 2,500 miles inland from its western boundary, the Atlantic Ocean, and it spreads the area of Mediterranean climate over a vastly larger area than the Mediterranean regions of either California or Chile.

On the south, the Mediterranean region is bounded by the great desert which covers most of North Africa, the Sahara. To the north is the region of humid West European climate, and, toward the east, the moist winters become drier and the summers hotter, until the Mediterranean climate is lost in the Arabian Desert of the Middle East.

Mediterranean rivers are short and torrentlike. They quickly fill with water after the winter rains. In spring they shrink away, and through the summer their beds are dry and boulder-strewn. The rivers which the summer tourist sees in southern Spain or Italy, in Greece or Cyprus, or in Morocco are merely dried-out torrent beds. There is little water except where a dam has been built to store the surplus from the winter rains. The landscape is red, yellow, or brown, except where the water, held back from the previous rainy season, has been used to irrigate a field of corn or rice or some other crop that needs only moisture for luxuriant growth in the heat of the Mediterranean summer.

If the Mediterranean region as a whole had been obliged to rely throughout the year upon the accumulation of its winter rains, our civilization might have developed in a very different way, focused, like the Egyptian and the Babylonian, on irrigation works. Fortunately this reliance was not wholly necessary. Several Mediterranean rivers rise outside the region of Mediterranean climate, and are fed by the rains of a different climatic regime. They carry water through the Mediterranean region to the sea, not only in winter when it is needed less, but also in the summer when the need is greatest.

Foremost among these extra-regional rivers is the Nile. Its two most important branches rise one, the Blue Nile, in the highlands of Ethiopia, the other, the White Nile, on the equator in Lake Victoria. The latter supplies a steady flow of water throughout the year, and is joined by the Blue at Khartoum. The Blue is fed by the torrential rains of summer which are carried through the Sudan and Egypt to the sea. Egypt, as Herodotus remarked in the fifth century B.C., is the "gift of the Nile." Without its water for irrigation there would be no crops in the land that

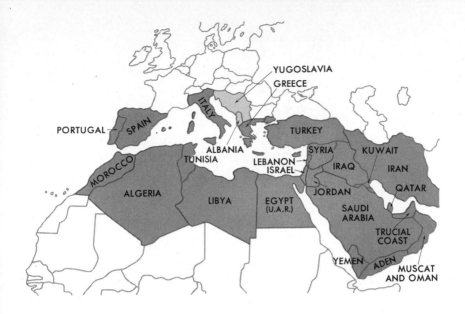

Southern Europe, North Africa, and the Middle East share the Mediterranean Sea.
Yugoslavia and Albania will be considered again in Chapter 11.

we now unofficially call Egypt and more correctly the United Arab Republic; without the fine silt which it carries down from the mountains where it rises, there would be no soil in which to grow the crops.

The Tigris and Euphrates, which bring water to Syria and Iraq, must also be classed as rivers of the Mediterranean region, though like the Nile they rise outside the strict limits of the Mediterranean climate. The Po in northern Italy is fed by the melting snows of the Alps; the Ebro in northern Spain, by those of the Pyrenees.

It is no accident that the two related civilizations, those of the Nile and of the Tigris and Euphrates valleys, whose achievement laid the foundation of the classical civilization of the Mediterranean, grew up where the heat of the summer was balanced by flood waters and good soil. Nor is it surprising that the legacy of these civilizations in art, architecture, literature, and law was spread by ship across the Mediterranean Sea from the cities of the Levant—the eastern shore of the Mediterranean —to those of Greece, and from Greece to Rome, and from Rome to Western Europe.

The desert sets a limit to the Mediterranean region to the south and east, but to the north the mountain ranges of the Alpine system are its sentinels. From the northwest of Spain, through France, Italy, Yugoslavia, Bulgaria, Turkey, and the mountains of Kurdistan, this mountain system stretches for four thousand miles with scarcely a break in its continuity. Like a wall it shuts in the Mediterranean region. There are many passes across the Alps, but it was not so much the case with which the Alps could be crossed, as the attractiveness of the lands which lay to the south which continually attracted tribes, conquerors, and adventurers down to the plains of Italy. That was the undoing of this region.

The pattern formed by the Alpine ranges is complex. From the central mountain knot of Switzerland and Austria, the mountains, as the Apennines, extend through Italy, then are continued through Sicily and, beyond the breach which the Mediterranean has created, are continued into the Atlas Mountains of North Africa. These stretch westward and at the Strait of Gibraltar curve to the north and are continued in the Sierra Nevada of southern Spain. The Pyrenees and Cantabrian Mountains of northern Spain are part of the same system.

Eastward from Austria, the Alpine mountains sweep through Yugoslavia as the Dinaric Alps and on to the bold headlands of southern Greece as the Pindus Mountains. From here chains of islands mark the continuity of the mountains, through Crete and Rhodes to the Taurus Mountains of the mainland of Turkey. More northerly ranges, the Carpathian Mountains, the Transylvanian Alps, and the Balkan Mountains curve south through Romania and Bulgaria, and are continued beyond the Black Sea in the mountains of northern Turkey, until all are joined up again in the mountain knot of Armenia, where Turkey, Iran, and the Soviet Union meet. A spur from these mountains stretches south through Syria and Lebanon, to die out in the deserts of southern Israel, and higher and more rugged ranges loop eastward to enclose the plateau of Persia, and to coalesce again in the mountains of Central Asia.

The Mediterranean can be visualized as made up of two basins, a western and an eastern. The more westerly is encircled by mountains, except where the sea has worn a narrow breach through them between Tunisia and Siciliy. The eastern basin has mountains along its northern and northeastern margins, and to the south and southeast lies the lower, flatter plateau which covers most of North Africa and the Middle East. Both basins are studded with islands; both communicate by narrow straits with other seas. The western basin is joined by the Strait of Gibraltar with the Atlantic Ocean; the eastern, by way of the Turkish Straits—the Dardanelles, the Sea of Marmara, and the Bosporus—with the Black Sea. Almost a century ago the cutting of the Suez Canal established yet another routeway into the Mediterranean Sea, this one from the Red Sea and the Indian Ocean.

In ancient times the Mediterranean was quite literally in the "middle of the land"; it was the focus of commercial and cultural life, around which the states of the ancient world lived like frogs around a pond. Its role today is different. It no longer focuses; it canalizes trade. It is a short cut between West and East. The long, narrow gulf of the Adriatic Sea reaches to within fifty miles of the Hungarian Plain and the Danubian basin. By way of the Turkish Straits and the Black Sea, the Mediterranean gives access to the southern coast of the Soviet Union, and the Suez Canal places it right on the trade route from India, Eastern Asia, and Australia to Northwest Europe and North America. The importance of the Mediterranean has not diminished; only its role has changed. It is now a great commercial highway, and nations have fought to gain access to it, to protect their commerce and to maintain control over strategic sites within it.

There is a kind of symmetry in the Mediterranean basins. In both west and east the Alpine ranges spread apart to enclose, as between the jaws of giant pincers, the plateaus of Spain and Turkey; in the west the Pyrenees and Sierra Nevada perform this function, in the east the Pontic Mountains which border the Black Sea and the Taurus Mountains. These two plateau regions are in some respects non-Mediterranean. They are cut off by the enclosing mountains from marine influences. Their climate is drier; winter temperatures are more extreme and, though reduced by altitude, summer temperatures are high. Madrid has a July average of 77°, and the interior of Turkey is even hotter. Crop farming is of less importance than animal husbandry. It is no accident that both the Meseta, or high plateau, of Spain and the Anatolian Plateau of Turkey are known for their flocks of sheep and goats, and for the quality of their wool and mohair.

In the times of the Roman Empire the Mediterranean Sea was a unit. A broadly uniform civilization existed around the whole of its shore line; Rome was provisioned by the grain of Egypt and Algeria, and travel was easy—perhaps easier than today—between its ports. Now the Mediterranean Sea forms a cultural divide. Its northern and northwestern shores belong to the Western tradition of culture and civilization. In varying degrees the social order and the spoken languages look back to ancient Rome. On the opposite or southern shore is a different world, the world of Islam.

An old ferry boat wallows across the few miles of sea that separate Gibraltar from the opposite shore of Morocco. In the clean, clear Mediterranean air it is possible almost to distinguish the houses on the opposite shore, so near to one another do the opposite coasts seem to be. Yet culturally they are poles apart. Gibraltar is a blend of the British and the Spanish, and in all its essentials Western. Tangier, on the opposite shore, is Eastern: the mosque replaces the church; the streets are narrow, winding alleys; dress is different and many of the women are veiled. This is the land of the Mohammedan, which extends eastward along the southern shore of the Mediterranean Sea, all the way from Morocco, which is itself a name derived from the Arabic for "the West," to the borders of India.

This cleavage was created in the seventh century. Islam, the religion of the prophet Mohammed, arose some six centuries later than Christianity. It originated in the desert of Arabia, and was spread by the arms of the Arabs. Arab leaders carried it to Egypt, and then through North Africa, between the desert and the sea, to Morocco. From here the Arabs crossed to Spain, and the farthest point of their advance was in central France, where they were checked in the Battle of Tours in 732. They were quickly driven out of France, but they maintained a foothold in Spain for over seven centuries longer, and there they left an indelible stamp upon landscape and life.

At the other end of the Mediterranean Sea in the later Middle Ages, the Arabs, reinforced by Turkish invaders from Central Asia, carried their conquests through the Plateau of Anatolia to the Turkish Straits. From here the Turks advanced up through the Balkan Peninsula, and, at the farthest extent of their advance, first attacked Vienna in 1529. Only about eight hundred miles separate the limits of the Moslems' advances in France and Austria. This is how near Islam came to turning the Mediterranean Sea into a Moslem lake.

But the Turks failed to maintain their hold on southeastern Europe. The tide of Turkish advance broke on the resistance of Vienna, and from that point it ebbed slowly back. Today only the small area of Turkey which lies to the northwest of the Straits remains of the once great Islamic empire in Europe. But the Turks and Islam together have left their imprint on the Balkans as they have also on Spain. There remain in Yugoslavia, Albania, and Bulgaria islands of the Moslem religion; and Turkish architectural styles, with mosque and minaret and secluded shuttered homes, continue to lend an oriental flavor.

The boundary between Christendom and Islam has not now changed for many years; the African and Asiatic shores are Moslem; the European are Christian. But there are islands of Christianity to the south and east of this line—in Cyprus, Lebanon, and Egypt especially—just as there are Moslems in the Balkans to the north and west of it.

The nineteenth and twentieth centuries have seen an attempt on the part of the European nations to reassert the classical unity of the Mediterranean basin. None pursued this objective as deliberately as the Italian government of Mussolini in the twenties and thirties. With its slogan of *mare nostrum,* "our sea," borrowed from the ancient Romans, it strove to make the Mediterranean an Italian lake, again focused upon the city of Rome.

Britain, France, and Spain had more modest ambitions. Great Britain was the first in the act. In 1704 she seized the Rock of Gibraltar from Spain; for a few years at the beginning of the nineteenth century she occupied Malta, and in 1878 Cyprus. She acquired a dominant position in the operation of the Suez Canal; and after the First World War she was given the mandate to administer the territory of Palestine, and began to develop it as a national home for the Jewish people.

The ambitions of France and Spain were limited to acquiring control of the Mediterranean shore line lying opposite their own coast. Beginning in 1830 the French conquered and settled Algeria, across the sea from their port of Marseille, and later assumed a protectorate over Tunisia and most of Morocco. Despite Spanish hopes for wider territorial gains, she managed to acquire and hold only the zone of Morocco that lay opposite her southern shore.

France's ambitions outran her resources. She claimed, and obtained from the League of Nations, the mandate to administer the former Turkish provinces of Syria and Lebanon, in which a French cultural influence had long been present. An uneasy French rule lasted for twenty years, constantly opposed by the unassimilable forces of Islam, and then collapsed during the Second World War. From the ruins of the French mandate emerged the Republics of Syria and Lebanon.

A generation and more ago it seemed that the European grip on the sea was complete. It is so no longer. The former French holdings in North Africa and the Middle East are now independent. Italy's former colony of Libya has become an independent monarchy. The Arab states of the Middle East and North Africa, independent, brash, and strong-willed, are in no mood to brook any interference from Europe.

They are drawn together as members of the Arab League, and the political division of the Mediterranean basin along sectarian lines is as firmly established today as it ever was. This fact has to be borne in mind in discussing the basin's geography.

THE EUROPEAN MEDITERRANEAN LANDS

We shall consider first the peninsulas and lands which lie along the sea's northwestern and northern shores which in a general sense may be described as Western in civilization and Christian in religion. Then we will turn to the remaining lands—from Morocco to Turkey—which, whatever their political orientation, are, with the exception of Israel, today basically Moslem.

The Iberian Peninsula

The Iberian or Spanish Peninsula is a tableland—the so-called Meseta, or "little table"—framed by mountain ranges which form part of the Alpine system. Most of the Meseta lies at two thousand or more feet above the level of the sea. It is tilted slightly downward toward the west, so that most of its rivers—the Douro, Tagus, Guadiana, and Guadalquivir—flow in this direction to the Atlantic Ocean. The rivers are, for the greater part of their courses, deeply sunk in narrow valleys below the surface of the Meseta. Between them there rises from the level or rolling Meseta surface a series of mountain ridges, most of them short, rugged, and barren, which divide the Meseta into a series of west to east strips. Most conspicuous of these Meseta ranges are the Sierra de Gredos and de Guadarrama, lying to the west and north of Madrid, and the Montes de Toledo to the south. Along its southern margin, the Meseta rises to the rounded hills of the Sierra Morena, which curve over and drop steeply to the valley of the Guadalquivir, beyond which are the Betic Mountains, culminating in the perpetually snow-capped peaks of the Sierra Nevada.

Forming the northern rim of the Meseta are the Pyrenees and their westward continuation, the Cantabrian Mountains. Along the Mediterranean coast, the Meseta drops steeply to a narrow, interrupted strip of coastal plain. In the northeast this broadens out where the Ebro, the only important Spanish river that flows to the Mediterranean, enters the sea. But the only extensive areas of lowland in the whole Iberian Peninsula are in the west, along the coast of the Atlantic Ocean and the lower

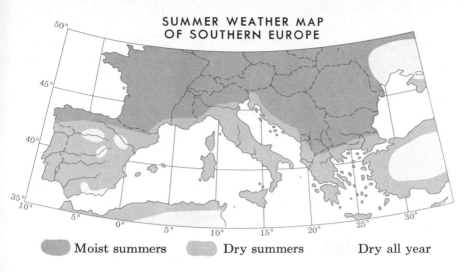

Moist summers   Dry summers   Dry all year

courses of the westward-flowing rivers, where they make up most of Portugal.

The peninsula lies in the path of the westerly winds. In the north they blow onshore for most of the year; in the south in winter only. The climatic range of the peninsula is that found between Oregon and southern California. A journey across Spain from the Pyrenees to Gibraltar in summer is one from green, rain-soaked mountains, where trees are in leaf, the grass is lush in the meadows, and dairy cattle graze, to a desert landscape, where the harvest has long since been gathered, the earth is burned almost brick-red, and the few evergreen trees are brown with dust. At Santiago, in the green northwest of Spain, the hottest month rarely exceeds 65°, and rain comes at all seasons and generally abundantly. At Seville, in the south, the warmest month is a full 20° hotter, and the summer months are almost rainless. But a more careful examination of the landscape would reveal here, as in most other parts of this sun-scorched region, small patches of green, where irrigation can be practiced with water either brought down from the higher mountains or carefully preserved from last winter's rains. There are many small dams in the rivers of the Meseta and in the northern mountains. But few major works have been attempted, or even contemplated. Spain is the first European country we meet that has characteristics similar to those of the underdeveloped lands of North Africa and the Middle East.

In winter all is different. The first rains of autumn wash the dust from the trees; grass grows, and arid Spain begins its short season of growth.

Such is the peninsula which Spain and Portugal share. These two states are all that remain of the many that existed here during the Middle Ages. When the Arabs, or Moors as they are more often called in Spain, overran the country in the eighth century, many of the Christian communities fled to the mountains in the north. Here they maintained a precarious independence, isolated from one another by the rough terrain. With the decline and retreat of Moorish power, these states expanded southward across the Meseta, and as they met geographically on the high plains of northern Spain, so they began to merge politically to form larger and more powerful units. The last such merger was between Castile, which occupied the high plains, and Aragon, down in the Ebro Valley between the Pyrenees and the Mediterranean Sea.

Portugal has for most of its history remained separate from Spain. The Portuguese speak a language that is distinct from Spanish, though closely related to it. There are physical barriers, deep river valleys and rough hill country, between Portugal and Spain. But these facts alone do not explain the separateness of Portugal.

In Spain, Aragon, which includes the present province of Catalonia, is also distinct from Castile in language and cut off from it by mountains, but it has not been really independent since the sixteenth century. Marriage and inheritance were the means whereby Aragon and several other of the states of the Spanish Peninsula came to be joined together. This accident of history never happened to join Portugal permanently with its eastern neighbors. Spain many times has cast envious eyes on Portugal, and from 1580 to 1640 actually annexed and ruled Portugal. But Portugal, generally secure in her alliance with Great Britain, which has on more than one occasion come to her defense, was usually able to resist the threat of conquest by Spain.

Spain is more than five times the size of Portugal and has almost four times as many people. Its environment is more varied; its climates more extreme. It includes, besides the mountains of the north and northwest with their heavy rainfall, the grain-growing plains of Castile which spread out around the cities of Valladolid and Salamanca; the drier plains to the south of La Mancha, in New Castile, whence Don Quixote came; and the deep, almost tropical valley of the river Guadalquivir which spreads across Andalusia. Here are the cities of Seville and Córdoba, where Moorish influence has lingered longest. Here too grapes are grown for the sherry wine which takes its name from Jerez de la Frontera; nearby is the port of Cádiz, which lies on a spit of land between a coastal lagoon and the ocean, and carries on much of the trade of southern Spain. In the Sierra Nevada is the fairy-tale city of Granada, perched high in the mountains with the Moorish palace of the Alhambra on its hilltop.

Along the east coast, between the mountains and the sea are numerous plains, large and small; all of them irrigated and cultivated with the utmost care. These *huertas,* or gardens, are another of the legacies left by the Moors. On some of the largest plains lie the cities of Valencia, Murcia, Cartagena, and Málaga. At the southernmost end of this coast is Gibraltar, the barren limestone rock which Great Britain captured from Spain in 1704, and has since occupied as a means of controlling the western entrance to the Mediterranean Sea. Spain resents its continued occupation by the British, but is powerless to take it back.

But most of Spain is made up of the Meseta, the harsh, dry land which the Spanish kingdoms of the Middle Ages won back from the Moors. In fact, Spain embraces all of the Meseta except the bite which Portugal takes out of it along the western margin. The Spanish flag is red and gold, and these are the colors of Spain; they are the colors that predominate over the Meseta. The villages are yellow; their pantiled roofs are brown; their surrounding fields, green during the short growing season, turning to yellow and gold when the wheat and barley are ripe, and to red when the crop has been harvested and the earth exposed.

Over much of Spain the soil is too thin and the rainfall too small for crops; in the driest parts of the Meseta it is less than 10 inches a year. Here sheep were grazed, but it was too dry almost for sheep, and they were obliged to migrate northward in summer into the moister mountains that enclose the Meseta. It was a huge flock of sheep on their annual pilgrimage to or from the northern mountains that Don Quixote, in Cervantes' novel, mistook for the armies of the infidel and valiantly attacked. Yet it was also from the dry sheep runs of the Meseta that the merino sheep, long the mainstay of the Australian economy, originally came.

Most of Spain is a poor agricultural country, and over much of it the people practice a form of agriculture that is of another century and at best only self-sufficing. Wheat and barley are the chief crops, and large areas, especially in the south, are planted with the olive tree and grapevine. Yet the Spaniards do not even make the most of their own natural endowment. The reasons for this are, in part at least, to be found in history.

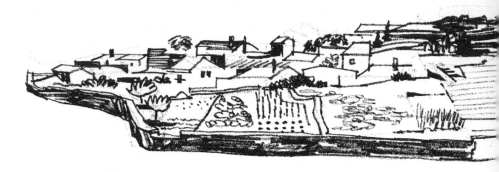

Much of the peninsula was overrun and conquered by the Moors. These people came from the Middle East and North Africa; they were familiar with the practice of irrigation, and skilled in the construction of dams and irrigation canals, and they were able to develop large parts of arid Spain. But they were conquered and driven out by the farmers from the humid north, quite unfamiliar with irrigation and with the problems of cultivating dry lands. Irrigation works, neglected or destroyed during decades of fighting, were never rebuilt, and southern Spain relapsed into the semidesert that much of it remains today.

Centuries of warfare between Christian and Moor bred an intolerance and a fanaticism in the former, that were exemplified in Cervantes' famous picture of the knight from La Mancha, and have remained with the Spaniard until today. Every internal dispute brings them again to the fore. They showed up in the revolutionary risings and the Carlist Wars of the nineteenth century, and above all in the savagery and the dedication shown in the Spanish Civil War of 1936-39. Here we have some of the reasons why the Meseta is no better, and in some parts a very great deal worse, than when the Moors were driven out in the later Middle Ages.

The city of Madrid, lying in the midst of the Meseta, with its population of about 2,000,000 is almost a paradox; its varied industrial development and its progressive attitudes are in sharp contrast with those of the surrounding Meseta. It is the youngest city of the Meseta. It was founded in the sixteenth century, and its site was deliberately chosen because it seemed to be as near as possible the center of the peninsula. The problem facing the Spanish government then—as today—was how to weld the provinces into a whole. A centrally located capital, it was

hoped, would help to do this. Spain became a highly centralized state, but any real cohesion and unity has eluded it. The Basques, the Asturians, and the Galicians of the north coast, the Catalans, the Valencians along the Mediterranean, and the Andalusians in the Guadalquivir valley, are all very far from seeing eye to eye with the Castilians. The Spanish Republic (1931-36) wisely gave autonomy to some of these peoples, but the heavy hand of General Franco has brought them back to an absolute dependence upon the central government in Madrid and upon himself.

Yet we should be making a serious error if we assumed that Spain is all agricultural and all backward. Northern Spain has long been deeply influenced by neighboring France. Even the Gothic cathedrals at Burgos and Santiago reflect a French style transmuted by Spanish culture. But above all, this influence of Western Europe is reflected in the industrial development of, in particular, the Basque country and Catalonia. The Basque city of Bilbao is the center of an important iron and steel industry. Farther west in the Asturias, Gijón and Oviedo are industrial centers. In Catalonia, the city of Barcelona, deriving from an important medieval center of Mediterranean commerce, has in modern times become a center of textile industries. In the hills behind the port is a ring of mill towns, where modern industry is pushing deeper into Spain. Spain is the fifth largest producer in Europe of cotton yarn. Along the Mediterranean coast, in Valencia, Murcia, Cartagena, is a more energetic, forward-looking spirit than is to be found in the Meseta which has never escaped from its past.

The rocks of the Meseta are old, and old rocks are commonly mineralized. And here again a geological law proves itself. There are numerous deposits of copper, zinc, wolfram, tin, mercury, and other metals.

These were formerly of very great importance, but today many deposits are small and nearing exhaustion. Iron ore and potash salts are mined, and Spain is the largest producer of mercury and the fourth largest producer of iron ore in Europe, but of the once important production of copper, manganese, wolfram, and tin, there is now only a trace.

Spain is today an underdeveloped country; much of its area stands in desperate need of the kind of technical aid that is given to Egypt or India. Yet Spain is too proud to admit its backwardness and to solicit help on the scale that is needed. Spain is held prisoner by its past greatness, and ideas and attitudes developed then prevent it from escaping into the present.

Yet Spain remains an imperial country, though its empire is largely one of rock and sand. Its possessions are entirely African: Spanish Sahara, Rio Muni, and Fernando Póo; several minute possessions on the coast of Morocco, the Canary Islands, and some small islands in the Gulf of Guinea.

Portugal is made up of a belt of lowland, moist in the north, very dry in the south, which rises inland toward the Meseta. It is a small, densely populated country, in area about the size of Maine in the United States, but in population more like Ohio. Across Portugal flow three of the great Spanish rivers, the Douro (the Duero of Spain), the Tagus, (the Tejo in Portugal, the Tajo in Spain), and the Guadiana. They are not navigable, and in summer they contain very little water. As it nears the sea the river Tagus widens into a broad, sheltered estuary which forms the harbor of Lisbon. This, one of the finest harbors on the whole coast of Europe, is one reason why Great Britain has always been attracted to Portugal.

British shipping formerly made very great use of this harbor. The political alliance, founded upon Britain's need for a harbor and Portugal's need for Britain's support against Spain, came later to be consecrated by the trade in "port" wine. Portuguese wine comes from the north. It is grown along the steep slopes of the Douro Valley, and gathered into the city of Oporto, which serves the Portuguese wine-growing region as Rheims does that of Champagne. Oporto is accessible to seagoing ships, which sail up the river to carry away the port, much of it to Great Britain, where it constitutes the traditional after-dinner drink.

Lisbon itself is the capital and largest port. It lies on the northwestern shore of the Lisbon Harbor, and stretches back over the low hills toward the more rocky coast that fronts on the Atlantic. The city was destroyed by a disastrous earthquake in 1755, and its center was rebuilt to a lavish classical design of large squares and wide avenues, so contrary to the usual plan of a Mediterranean city. The chief export is cork, obtained from the bark which the cork oak puts on to protect itself from the hot, desiccating air. Wine is second in importance, and is followed by sardines which are caught off the Portuguese coast and canned for export.

Portugal is even more an agricultural country than Spain, and the exports are largely made up of the products of the farms, the forests, and the fisheries. Wheat is the chief crop, and is followed by corn, though only in the north is the climate really moist enough for it. Manufacturing industries, most of them carried on in Lisbon, are much less developed than in northern Spain. They are light industries like textile manufacture, canning, and the preparation of local agricultural and fisheries products. Portugal shares the mineral wealth of Spain. Mining is still important, though Portuguese deposits of most of the minerals that occur are too small to give much hope for the future.

The Portuguese, like the Spaniards, are an imperial people, whose territorial empire, twenty-two times as large as Portugal itself, is scattered over Africa and East and Southeast Asia. It includes the large African territories of Angola and Mozambique, the smaller African outposts— mere staging points on the old sea route to the Indies—of Portuguese Guinea, the eastern part of Timor, all that remains of the former empire of the East Indies, and Macao, the last relic of the China trade. To these must be added four very small island groups in the Atlantic: the Azores, nine hundred miles due west of Portugal itself, and an important stopping point on the transatlantic air route; Madeira and the Cape Verde Islands, off the northwest coast of Africa; and the Portuguese islands of St. Thomas and Prince in the Gulf of Guinea.

But the Portuguese Empire has lagged more than most in its political and economic development. In fact, until recent years, it had been almost ignored by its mother country. It had given little trouble, because the revolution of rising expectations had not yet reached it; it had afforded very little profit because Portuguese investment in it had been negligible. Now, suddenly, all this has changed. The breath of change has blown across Portuguese Angola and Mozambique; the Africans are restless; the Portuguese know now that in their empire they must get on or get out, and the backlog of underdevelopment is so great that Portugal cannot possibly have the resources to bring her dependencies up to the levels demanded now in the New Africa.

The Mediterranean lands of the Iberian Peninsula are separated from those of Italy by southern France. It is over three hundred miles from the eastern extremity of the Pyrenees to the Italian border. The first half is flat, built of silt, brought down by the Rhône and other rivers, and fringed with lagoons; the second is backed by hills and lined with resorts. This is the French Riviera, which merges without perceptible change into the Italian.

The Italian Peninsula

Italy is in striking contrast with Spain. It is an irregular, spreading peninsula, whereas Spain is compact; it is made up of mountain and plain, whereas Spain is mostly plateau; it has fewer and smaller mineral resources than Spain, yet has developed a very much more extensive industrial system.

Italy is, like Spain, cut off from the rest of Europe by the Alpine mountain system. To the south of the mountains a long, narrow, mountainous peninsula stretches southward, shaped somewhat like a human leg, with a well-marked toe, heel, and instep. Just off the "toe" of Italy is the island of Sicily, and still farther out in the Mediterranean is Sardinia. North of Sardinia is Corsica, Italian in language and part of Italy until France took it in 1768, just in time for Napoleon to be born there, a year later, a citizen of France.

Italy contains only the southern flanks of the Alps. Generally the boundary follows the crest of the range. Toward the northeast, the area of foothills lying to the south of the main range of the Alps expands into a tangled mass of mountains, known as the Dolomites. But the relief is usually simpler than this.

During the Ice Age glaciers moved out from the Alps on to the plain of northern Italy, deepening the mountain valleys, spreading out an apron of gravels along the foot of the mountains, building moraines, or dams of stone, gravel, and sand transported from the mountains across the valleys, and ponding back the rivers and forming lakes. The Italian lakes —Maggiore, Como, Garda and the others—are the counterpart of the Swiss, and from the point of view of the tourist, have the immense advantage of the warm, dry Mediterranean climate rather than the damp, chilly climate of Western Europe, and, indeed, they seem to lie in an almost fairy-tale setting.

Spread out at the foot of the Alps, across the base of the Italian Peninsula, and bounded on the south by the Apennines, is the Plain of

Lombardy, the most extensive and most valuable area of lowland in Italy. Across it flows the Po, gathering tributaries from the Alps and Apennines, carrying silt from the mountains to lay it down in the Adriatic Sea, where the plain is slowly extending itself at the expense of the water. Already soil from the plain has engulfed the harbors of the ancient ports of Adria and Ravenna, and the lagoons of Venice are slowly growing shallower. The plain of the Po is made up of what the river has brought down from the mountains, and most of this is fine-grained, fertile silt.

The Po is a turbulent river. Its tributaries which come down from the Alps flood in late spring as the snows melt; those from the Apennines flood in winter when the Mediterranean rains are heaviest. Floods may be serious along the Po; its lower course is marshy, avoided by cities and settlements, and the river itself flows between levees. Most of the cities lie around the margin of the plain, raised a little above its damp surface, and opposite the routes which cross the enclosing mountains. Milan, Bergamo, Brescia, Verona, and Padua lie along the northern edge of the plain, within sight of the Alps. Milan is the largest of these north Italian cities. It grew up as a great center of commerce from which the routes radiated to the passes across the Alps and southward to the ports of the Italian Peninsula. It was a Roman city; it became an important ecclesiastical center, and now, with the help of hydroelectric power from the Alps, and a little oil and natural gas from the plain itself, it has become the most important center of Italian industry, with its products ranging from textiles to steel, and from chemicals to printing. And each of these phases has left its imprint on the face of Milan: evidences of the Roman city, the medieval castle, the Gothic cathedral, the Renaissance palaces, and the modern factories gathered around the city's periphery.

To the west, opposite the Mont Cenis Pass and railroad tunnel, which lead to France, is Turin, capital of the ancient province of Piedmont, smaller and more specialized than Milan, concentrating on its single great industry, the manufacture of Fiat automobiles. At the foot of the Apennines, along the southern edge of the plain, is a similar line of cities: Piacenza, Parma, Reggio, Modena, Bologna, Forli, and Rimini where it ends against the Adriatic coast. Like the northern line of cities, these too lie between the hill and the plain, where routes from peninsular Italy opened out upon the northern lowland. Bologna, at the end of a road across the mountains to Florence, became the largest, a golden city of medieval and Renaissance architecture, of fortified homes and baroque churches, thinning out through nineteenth-century suburbs and factories, into the neat, trim fields of the Lombardy Plain.

This northern plain, in which is most of Italy's industry, and a large part of the population, is served by ports at the west and east. Genoa is the more important. It grew up as one of the greatest centers of medieval commerce, and despite the barrier of the Apennines, it has become the chief port of northern Italy. To the east is Venice, now silted and commercially but a ghost of its former self; its place in Italy's commerce has been taken by nearby Mestre and the more distant but incomparably superior port of Trieste, close to the border with Yugoslavia. Yet it is the decline of Venice that has preserved for us in its pristine beauty this city which rides the islands on its lagoon, in all the splendor of its vivid color and architectural glory the noblest fossil in the world.

The Lombardy Plain is a rich farm land. Summers are hot—over 70° in July—and there is water, sometimes too much, for irrigation. There are corn, sorghum, and wheat; fields of bright yellow sunflowers; vineyards and orchards of peach and apricot; and rice fields in the wet soil beside the rivers. The village is a tight cluster of white houses with red pantiled roofs, as if huddled together to occupy as little of the valuable soil as possible. Above it rises the tall slender bell-tower, or *campanile,* visible like a lighthouse far out across the plain. Along the roads go the slow lumbering farm wagons, drawn by cream-colored, soft-eyed Lombardy oxen, and piled high with the produce of the fields.

The Italian Peninsula proper is different. Its central mountainous backbone is rugged, but it is not high, and it is flanked, especially on the west by rolling hills, interrupted here and there by a flat-floored valley or the basin of an ancient lake, long since drained away. The plains of the river Po are green throughout the year, but the peninsula is dry in summer. Its landscape becomes yellow or brown, splashed with the sage-green of the olive groves, the bright and dark green of the vines, and lighted by the dark cypress trees, shaped like candle flames. And villages and cities are always in view. For safety they have been built on the hilltops, and their towers—they all have towers—stand out sharply against the blue Italian sky. The farmer goes downhill to his work in the morning and in the evening, when he is tired, he has the long climb back again.

This is the landscape of the Italian masters; this is Tuscany or Umbria, with Siena, Perugia, and Assisi on their hilltops, and Florence itself spread out along the muddy little Arno, the marble dome of its cathedral

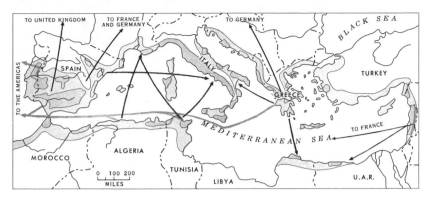

The olive tree flourishes in the summer-dry Mediterranean. Darkest tinted areas indicate highest production, and arrows the olives' route of export.

and the brown towers of the fortified homes of its medieval burgesses outlined against the gray-green hills of Fiesole, where the artists and writers live.

Italy turns its back on the Adriatic Sea. The coast is straight and almost harborless, and the strip of lowland between the mountains and the sea is narrow and unimportant. Between Rimini in the north and Bari and Brindisi on the "heel" of Italy, there are few cities, and only the small port of Ancona has much importance.

In Italy all roads lead to Rome. The city grew up more than twenty-five centuries ago on a group of very low hills beside the Tiber, which just served to lift it above flood level. These are the "Seven Hills of Rome," now scarcely distinguishable beneath the spreading streets and buildings of the city. The surrounding plain is more extensive than most that fringe the Italian Peninsula, and it yielded a larger food base. Onto this plain, the Roman Campagna, opened valley routes from most parts of the peninsula.

Rome grew to be the capital of the Roman Empire; roads radiated from it to the ends of the empire, and when travel to and from the city was interrupted and trade ceased, then Rome "fell." An extraordinary feature of classical Rome is the extent to which it has survived sieges, wanton destruction, and the neglect of fifteen centuries. The nondescript ruins that cover the Palatine Hill; the pillars that once surrounded the Forum; the triumphal arches raised by the emperors to commemorate themselves; the Colosseum, that stadium of ancient Rome, with seating for forty to fifty thousand; and the Baths of Caracalla, which they built for the entertainment of the masses—all these, and many others have come through nearly two thousand years to witness to the "grandeur that was Rome."

In the early days of Christianity, its headquarters were moved to Rome, and the Bishop of Rome came in time to be spiritual leader of the Western Church, as the Roman emperor had once been its temporal ruler. The empire, weakened internally and assaulted from without, decayed and disappeared, but the Papacy lived on, the "ghost of the Roman Empire, sitting," as Thomas Hobbes expressed it, "crowned on the ruins of the same."

Just west of the river is the Vatican City, the minute sovereign state at whose head is the Pope. The Papal States had once covered all central Italy. They disappeared in 1870, with the creation of the modern Italian State. In 1929 the Pope again became a temporal ruler when the city-state of the Vatican was created by an agreement between the Catholic Church and the government of Italy.

The Vatican covers less than a quarter of a square mile, and most of it is a triumph of Renaissance architecture, from the Cathedral of St. Peter, crowned by the dome designed by Bramante, to the sculpture of Michaelangelo and his paintings in the Sistine Chapel, and those of the Vatican by Leonardo da Vinci. But the artists of the Renaissance did not expend all their genius in the Vatican and St. Peter's. Among the ruins and remains of classical Rome are the palaces of the Renaissance princes and the baroque churches and monuments, which took and transmuted the styles of the classical world. And around and between these are spread the streets and homes, offices and factories of modern Rome. These three ages of Rome are clearly separable in the buildings of the city.

South of Rome, summers become longer, hotter, and drier; winters shorter and their rainfall less certain. Southern Italy has long been neglected. Its people are poor; its agricultural skills of another age, and its industries and communications underdeveloped. Into its cities have crowded the surplus population that the villages cannot support. Largest and most crowded and congested of these is Naples, spread out along the shores of its bay, and backed by the cone of Vesuvius, with, maybe, a slight plume of smoke curling upward from its crater.

The view of the Bay of Naples is justly regarded as one of the supreme sights of Europe: the curving shore of the bay itself, the shapely volcano that dominates it, and the long serrated ridge of Sorrento, pointing out to sea toward the almost legendary isle of Capri; in the other direction the pale blue of the Apennines, their relief emphasized by a darker blue in the valleys and hollows; and over the plain of Naples, enriched for thousands of years by the gentle, downward sifting dust from the volcano's innumerable eruptions, the deep green of corn and vine, the paler green of wheat, and the little clusters of red-roofed homes that make up the villages. Then look close under the shadow of the mountains at the ruins of Pompeii and Herculaneum, the one destroyed by ash, the other by the mud produced by the torrential rains that accompanied the great eruption of A.D. 79. Look closer at the villages and the back streets of Naples, at the crowding and the squalor, at the underemployed masses in the city. In few places can one see such extremes of luxury and sophistication on the one hand, and of human misery on the other as around the Bay of Naples.

The Italian government is now bringing help to the neglected region of *Il Mezzogiorno,* the South. Irrigation is being expanded and agriculture developed. Surplus population is encouraged to migrate to the more industrialized north, and industry—mainly the processing of local products like the olive—has been established. As in the TVA of the American South, the rich and developed areas are being called upon to assist the poor and backward parts of the same country.

Sicily is like the south of Italy, only hotter, drier, poorer, and more neglected. Its cities are more crowded, and its agriculture more backward. It is a mountainous island, which reaches its highest point in the smoking volcano of Etna. It grows lemons and oranges for the world market; it mines the sulfur that has accumulated from past volcanic action, but mostly it is poor, very poor. Its cities, like Palermo, Catania, and Messina, are huge, overcrowded, and poverty-stricken. And yet nearby the traveler finds the graceful temples built by the classical Greeks who established their colonies here. Between the Greeks and ourselves are nearly three thousand years of history, of invasion and conquest, of exploitation and destruction. It began under the Romans, and the orator Cicero delivered a violent attack on the rapacity, the cruelty, and the greed of Verres, the Roman governor of Sicily in his day. And since then there have been Arab, Norman, and French invaders, each taking their cut and leaving the land the poorer.

The contrast between the south and the north of Italy is not easy to explain. Northern Italy lies closer to the industrial hub of Western Europe; it has a wealth of hydroelectric power, but these alone do not explain its relatively advanced condition. Mediterranean piracy, a corrupt government, and a defective social system, which allowed such institutions as the *Maffia* to flourish, do most to explain why today we find misery and degradation beside the ruins of classical greatness.

The Yugoslav Coast

As if to make up for the western or Italian shore of the Adriatic Sea which is straight and harborless, the opposite shore is rugged, steep, indented by numerous bays, and fringed with islands. The branch of the Alpine system, known as the Dinaric Alps, runs close behind this coast. It is made up mainly of limestone, a porous and slightly soluble rock. Over much of the surface the bare limestone shows through, and elsewhere it is covered by only a thin layer of poor soil.

The mountains have formed a series of ranges, lying one behind the other and cutting the coast off from its hinterland. Rainfall is absorbed by the rock; there is little surface drainage and water flows deep underground to the sea. Locally the limestone has been dissolved, leaving shallow, rounded or elongated depressions, known as *polja,* and producing the type of terrain known as karst. The floors of these *polja* are covered with a layer of clay, left behind when the limestone was dissolved and removed, and in these depressions are to be found most of the human settlements and their small, cultivated fields of corn. The surrounding slopes, clothed in part with grapevines and olive groves, rise to the barren limestone surface which affords only rough grazing for sheep and goats.

Such is the barrier which separates the Danubian basin from the Adriatic Sea. This barrier is a climatic divide. Its seaward slopes have a Mediterranean climate, but only a few miles inland this gives way to a climate of continental extremes. Seaward the olive, peach, and apricot are grown wherever there is space enough. The warmth of the winters, where January rarely averages less than $45°$, attracts the tourist to Dubrovnik and many other resorts along this beautiful Dalmatian coast. But the hot dry summer parches the small fields.

The Dinaric Alps are a barrier to human movement. There are few roads and even fewer railroads across them from the Danubian basin to the sea, and the occasional gaps in the continuity of the mountains assume a very great importance. The most important of them is at the head of the Adriatic Sea. Here the mountains become low and narrow, and they can be crossed with ease. Opposite this opening, on a sheltered stretch of coast, are the ports of Trieste and Rijeka (Fiume). The role of these cities has been to handle the trade of the Danubian region; and for this reason they were claimed by Italy, while Yugoslavia, arguing that they were the natural outlet for the Danubian Plain, also laid claim to them. Today Trieste is in Italian hands; Rijeka, in Yugoslav.

The Dinaric Alps make up only a small fraction of the area of Yugoslavia, and an even smaller part of this region has a Mediterranean climate, and thus belongs to the Mediterranean world. The rest of Yugoslavia is continental in its climate, and belongs, with Hungary and Romania, to the drainage basin of the Danube. We shall return to it when we visit the Danubian lands.

Albania

This country also owes its importance to a gap through the mountains. The river Drin and its tributaries have cut back into the mountains and have opened up several routes between the Vardar Valley of southern Yugoslavia and the Adriatic Sea. The land through which these routes run is rugged in the extreme, and since early times has provided a refuge for the Albanian tribes. The Yugoslavs looked upon these routes as providentially designed to give access to the sea for themselves, but this was prevented by their enemies. The jealousies and suspicions between the powers, each of which wanted to control this vital area, were such that the only solution was to establish, in 1912, the independent state of Albania.

Albania is one of the most mountainous countries in Europe, but along the Adriatic coast is a strip of plain with Lake Scutari at its northern end, which can be cultivated with the help of irrigation. The Albanian people, with their language which belongs to a different branch of the Indo-European group, their folk customs, and their family and tribal feuds, are among the less developed in Europe.

At the end of the Second World War Albania passed into the hands of Communists, who have ever since maintained their grip on the country. It remains a small, poor, and predominantly agricultural country, and such importance as it has it derives from its location opposite the "heel" of Italy, at the entrance to the Adriatic Sea and only a few minutes flight from the Mediterranean shipping lanes. How diminutive Albania fits into the Communist scheme we shall inquire later.

Greece

The land we call Greece is a ragged bundle of peninsulas and islands, gathered together and cast into the Mediterranean Sea. It is made up of the southerly prolongation of the Dinaric Alps, the Pindus, frequently interrupted by deep arms of the sea, and terminating in the great cliffs of Greece's southern headlands. The Isles of Greece, whose beauty has been celebrated in poetry from the days of Homer until the present, continue seaward the line of the mountain ranges. Between the mountains and the sea are patches of flat land, all of them small, watered by small streams from the mountains, and cut off from one another by the bald, barren mountain ranges. It was on such sites as these that the Greek city-states of classical times—Athens, Argos, Sparta, Corinth, and the others—grew up. Greece was created divided; its small areas suitable for human settlement were held apart from one another by mountain ranges.

Greece is in the latitude of southern Italy, and, like southern Italy, most of it has mild winters and long, hot, dry summers. It is an outdoor climate, as the most superficial acquaintance with classical Greek literature will show. Water is scarce in Greece. That is why the mountain springs were so important in Greek literature and mythology. Only in the Pindus Mountains in the north of the peninsula, and in Macedonia and Thrace, which lie around the northern margin of the Aegean Sea, are continental influences felt. Here the winters are cold, frost is common, and snow lies over the higher ground. Bitter winds blow out from Eastern Europe and the Soviet Union. Summers are hot, but the typical Mediterranean drought is broken by heavy rainstorms.

Plato in one of his dialogues described the land of Greece as "like the skeleton of a body, emaciated by disease. . . . All the rich, soft soil has molted away, leaving a country of skin and bones." So it remains. Only about a quarter of the whole area of Greece is considered fit to grow crops, and even on this fraction of the total, agriculture is hindered by the lack of water for irrigation. Although wheat and other grain crops are grown, farming concentrates on the crops that grow best in the hot, dry climate, grapes, olives, and, in the northern plains, tobacco.

These crops provide the basis for most of Greece's exports. Foremost are the products of the grapevine: fresh grapes, wine and spirits and, above all, those dried grapes or raisins which we call currants. Indeed, the name "currant" comes from Greece, where they were known to the French merchants who handled them as *raisins de Corinthe,* "grapes of Corinth."

Greece is heavily dependent upon trade; she has to sell her specialized farm products in order to be able to import foodstuffs. A very large part of the food consumed in Greece is imported, just as, in classical times, the food supply of Athens was brought in by ship from the region of the Black Sea. During the Second World War, when trade was cut off, the Greeks found that their surplus of currants, tobacco, and wine scarcely provided a balanced diet, and food shortages and starvation were very serious. This is Greece's problem, to maintain the foreign markets for her farm produce, and, at the same time, to broaden the basis of her agriculture and become less dependent upon imported foodstuffs.

The heavy dependence of Greece upon the sea reflects the poverty of the land. As with Norway, the fisheries are an important source of food, and a large number of Greeks find employment in the merchant fleet, one of the largest in the world. But unlike Norway, industrial development, which might relieve Greece's heavy dependence upon agriculture, has made little progress. Its chief branches are at present concerned with the processing of her farm goods. Greece produces small quantities of a varied range of minerals—iron ore, pyrites, emery, copper, lead, and zinc —as well as ornamental stones, such as marble. But Greece lacks fuel resources to support manufacturing industry, and is poorly off even in hydroelectric power because the rivers are too small, and their discharge too irregular, to lend themselves to power development.

Athens is by far the largest city in modern Greece, as it was also in classical Greece. Today the city itself has a population of over half a million, and its metropolitan area, which includes the port of Piraeus, embraces over a million and a half people. The city grew up around a precipitous rock, the Acropolis, which originally provided its people with a refuge in time of stress. But even by classical times this hill had been given over to temples, and the city itself, spread out below the rock, was enclosed with walls. Later it spread over the intervening plain to reach and include the port of Piraeus.

Like Rome, Athens is rich with the remains of its classical past, of the fifth and fourth centuries B.C.; here, too, as in southern Italy, we see side by side with present-day poverty the ruins of classical greatness. The Acropolis remains crowned with the most glorious group of buildings that have survived from classical antiquity, though the Parthenon itself was wrecked when the Turks used it to store gunpowder, and then, through their own carelessness, allowed the powder to explode; the marble freize that decorated it found its way to the British Museum. Parts of many other classical buildings have been burned for lime, or used as quarries by the local masons, or looted to fill the museums of Western Europe. But unlike Rome, subsequent generations in Athens never produced any works of art comparable to those of antiquity.

The second city of Greece is Thessaloníki, or Salonika, which lies on the coast of Macedonia, a few miles from the swampy delta of the Vardar River. As a port it serves northern Greece, where much of the tobacco is grown, but it is also a port for Yugoslavia and is linked by rail through the Vardar and Morava valleys with Belgrade.

The Isles of Greece, despite their beauty and their prominence in history, literature, and art, are in reality only poverty-stricken heaps of rocks. Most are dry and thin-soiled; some are uninhabited and others are visited only during the wet season when a little vegetation grows. But among them are a few of larger size and greater significance.

Across the southern entrance to the Aegean Sea lies the long, narrow, mountainous island of Crete, "the Forerunner" which received in ancient times the civilizing impetus from Egypt and passed it on to the mainland of Greece. And off the western coast of the Greek peninsula lie the rugged Ionian Islands, one of which, the "poor-soiled" Ithaca, was the home of Homer's Odysseus.

Out from the coast of Attica lie the Cyclades—the "circle of islands" —among which are Naxos, with its emery mines, and Milos, where the famous statue of Venus was found. In the northern Aegean are the rugged and inhospitable Thásos, Samothrace (Samothráki), and Límnos, and off the Turkish coast lie the Greek islands of Lésvos, Khíos, and Sámos, as well as the group known as the Dodecanese, which was held by Italy from 1912 to 1920 and then from 1923 until 1947. Largest among these is Rhodes (Ródhos), ancient center of Greek commerce and later of Christian resistance to the Turks.

And so with Rhodes we come to the point where the Christian shores of this great sea face Moslem bastions. In the remainder of this chapter we shall look at the portion of the Mediterranean coast line which is made up of the Moslem states, from Morocco to Turkey. These stand apart from the rest, both culturally and politically.

THE MOSLEM MEDITERRANEAN LANDS

Among the Moslem lands of the Mediterranean only Turkey has deliberately sought to imitate the culture of the West. The rest have been prepared to modernize only on their own Islamic terms. And so before we return to the western basin of the Mediterranean, let us look first at the state where East has met West.

The Turkish Straits have played a vital part in history since the days of Helen of Troy.

Turkey

The Aegean Sea is almost rectangular in shape. Its ragged eastern shore is formed by the coast line of Asia Minor. At the northeastern corner a narrow, twisting waterway, the Dardanelles—once known as the Hellespont—leads into the Sea of Marmara, and the even narrower Bosporus connects the Sea of Marmara with the Black Sea. These waterways constitute the Turkish Straits, the water link between South Russia and the Mediterranean, and for centuries they formed the hub of the Turkish Empire.

The Turkish Straits have been a commercial route since early classical times. The Trojan War was fought, in the twelfth century B.C., not so much to rescue Helen as to prevent the Dardanelles from passing completely under the domination of Troy. The struggle either to close or to keep open this vital waterway has gone on until the present. The Crimean War of the 1850's was Western Europe's answer to Russia's threat to control the waterway. During the First World War the costly and disastrous Dardanelles campaign of 1915 was fought in the vain attempt to force a passage through the Straits in the face of Turkish opposition. In 1923 the Turkish Straits were demilitarized; in 1936, Turkey was again allowed to fortify them, which meant, in effect, that she was free to close them if she wished.

Today, the Soviet Union, with the prospect—a remote one, it is true—

of being kept a prisoner in the Black Sea, is clamoring for a voice in the control of the Straits and a share in their military garrison. Turkey's membership in NATO is some guarantee of support for her continued resistance to these demands.

At the southern entrance to the Bosporus, on a high bluff on the western or European shore, is Istanbul, previously known as Constantinople, and before that as Byzantium. Founded by the Greeks, it later became the capital of the eastern half of the Roman Empire and seat of the Eastern or Byzantine Emperors. Its massive fortifications protected it from the Turks until 1453, when it was taken and soon afterward made the capital of the Ottoman Empire, and its churches, among them the incomparable Hagia Sophia, were turned into mosques.

From the fifteenth until the twentieth century this was the capital of the Turkish or Ottoman Empire and the seat of the sultan; it was continuously a national capital longer than any other city in Western history, from 330 to 1923.

The sultan's empire stretched into Europe, Asia, and Africa. Less than a century ago it still reached from the Danube to the Indian Ocean and through North Africa to the Atlantic. This empire was gradually whittled away during the nineteenth century, and finally it disintegrated during the First World War. From its ruins have emerged the new states of the Balkans, the Middle East, and North Africa, and the modern republic of Turkey is the direct heir to the vast, polyglot, ill-governed empire of the Ottoman sultans.

The legacy of Ottoman misrule is shared by all the successors to the vanished empire, and shows today in political instability and economic backwardness. Turkey itself has undergone a profound revolution, social as well as political, since its defeat in the First World War. From a former extent of over 1,000,000 square miles, it was reduced to about 300,000. From an empire of some 60,000,000 of mixed race, language, and culture, it was reduced to the homogeneous Turkey of today, with a population now of 28,675,000, almost all of them Turkish-speaking.

Within Turkey itself in the 1920's the accent was placed by the dictator, Mustafa Kemal Ataturk, on social reform, education, industrial growth, and, above all, on the narrow nationalism of the Turks themselves. The Greek minority, which for centuries had lived along the western fringe of Asia Minor, were driven out, exchanged for the Turkish minority in Greece. The capital was removed from the cosmopolitan city beside the Bosporus, with its mosques and palaces and memories of the vanquished Ottoman Empire, to the brash, new and aggressively nationalistic city of Ankara, built amid the dry grassland and semidesert of Asia Minor.

Modern Turkey is divided by the Straits into two very unequal parts. Northwest of the Straits is European Turkey, small, dry and steppelike, but containing the city of Istanbul, which is still, even without its governmental functions, the largest city in Turkey. Nine-tenths of the area of Turkey lies in Asia, on the other side of the Straits. It is a plateau—the Plateau of Anatolia—lying some two to three thousand feet above the level of the sea, and bordered, like the Meseta of Spain, by higher mountain ranges.

The Anatolian Plateau in many ways resembles the Meseta. It is mostly a dry steppe, cut off by the enclosing mountains from rain-bearing winds. Its temperatures are more continental and extreme than are to be found nearer the sea where the Mediterranean climate prevails. The hot, dry, dusty summers contrast with the cold winters. Ankara, set in the midst of this rolling plateau, has a July average of about 75°, and a January average of about 20°. It has the climatic range of South Dakota, in the United States, without even South Dakota's modest rainfall.

Much of Turkey is too dry for agriculture; it has no large rivers to supply water for irrigation, and rough grazing for sheep and goats is the best that much of it can offer. Good, alluvial farmland, as in Spain, is restricted to small patches around the coast, and here much of Turkey's food supply is grown. Turkey is a poor country in which to practice experiments in social and economic development. Although a small iron industry has been established, the resources in coal and iron ore are insufficient to support any large industrial growth.

Turkey is today a leading producer of chrome ore—about a quarter of the world's supply—but its industries are still predominantly those of the ancient crafts, the manufacture of carpets and silks and metal goods by traditional methods and according to traditional designs. Agriculture remains, in the main, primitive and self-sufficing, and the chief exports are still tobacco and the wool and mohair from the flocks that graze the Anatolian Plateau.

The Ottoman Empire had stretched from the Persian Gulf to the far west, to El Maghrib, or Morocco. From it have emerged at least a dozen states, together with a handful of turbulent, tribal sheikdoms, which scarcely amount to states.

Constantinople survived as a political capital for almost sixteen hundred years because its location made it a meeting place of West and East, suitable for ruling an empire that spanned three continents. Until its decline in the nineteenth century, the Turkish Empire was European, Asiatic, and African. The states which emerged in the Middle East and North Africa as it broke up have much in common with one another, and also with Turkey itself. And to these "succession states" to the Empire of the Sultans, we now turn.

Morocco, Algeria, and Tunisia

The three territorial units which make up the southern coast of the western basin of the Mediterranean have a bond, physically as well as culturally. Through all three of them, parallel with the coast of the Mediterranean Sea, run the Atlas Mountains. As we have seen, these mountains are a link between the Apennines and the mountains of Sicily and the Sierra Nevada of southern Spain.

The Atlas Mountains form a wide and complex belt of mountains, but they can be separated into the northern or Coast Range and a more southerly tier known as the Saharan Atlas and Grand Atlas. Between is a plateau, the Hauts Plateaux or the Tell, which too bears a certain resemblance to the Meseta of Spain. For most of their length the Atlas Mountains are lower than the Apennines or the Spanish Sierra, but in the Grand Atlas of Morocco, they contain some of the highest mountains in the whole Alpine system, towering in Toubkal to nearly 14,000 feet above the nearby desert.

Northwest Africa lies between the sea and the desert. Its climate is the driest form of the Mediterranean. Rains come only in the winter, and amounts are small except high in the Atlas Mountains. The landscape is similar to that of southern Spain or Italy, but is drier and browner. Agriculture is less extensive; the green patches of irrigation are fewer, and most of the hills are covered only with a thin brush. There are few rivers. Some, rising in the Coast Range, make their way to the sea. But in the interior the rivers are too feeble to do this; they dry out on the Tell, between the Atlas ranges, or on the margin of the Sahara Desert as the water gradually evaporates; the rivers thicken, turn to mud, and then cease to flow. This dry country is scarred by the deep, canyon-like wadis, excavated by violent storms of the past, but most of these are now dry and have no certain prospect of ever having flowing water in them again.

Clearly, then, the physical conditions impose more severe limitations on life in North Africa than they do on the opposite shore of the Mediterranean Sea. At the same time they require, in order to make the good life possible, a higher application of capital and of technical skills. These have been lacking in most of the area. In ancient times some parts of North Africa, notably the region of Carthage, close to the modern Tunis, achieved a relatively high level of civilization, which lasted through the period of the Roman Empire. Then it was destroyed by invaders and only the ruins of Timgad and Leptis Magna survive.

In the seventh century the Arabs, inspired by their new and militant creed of Islam, conquered the whole of North Africa, and Moslem it has since remained. It was part of the great Moslem Empire that was ruled in turn from Baghdad and Constantinople, but distance gave it a considerable freedom of action. The natives of the coastal region indulged in piracy, and, under the name of Barbary, this became one of the most dangerous coasts for the unarmed merchantman to frequent. Attempts were made, even by the United States, to clean out the Barbary corsairs, but it was not until the region came to be dominated by Europeans during the middle years of the nineteenth century that the menace ended.

In 1830 the French began their conquest of Algeria. They occupied the coastal plains, small, isolated areas of flat and fertile land which, in Mediterranean fashion, separate the mountains from the sea. Here the French *colons* settled, laid out farms, and in time built up a prosperous wine industry, supplying *vin ordinaire* to France, while France shipped quality wines to the rest of the world. The native peoples, the Berbers, for whom Barbary is named, were mostly driven back into the hills. Some were assimilated by the French, and came in time to speak and act like Frenchmen. But the rest continued to live sullen, resentful, and primitive in the wild hills of the interior, awaiting the time when they would have the strength, the weapons, and the allies to revolt and to drive the French back into the sea.

The Berbers were left with the poorer soil; little was done to help their primitive agriculture, and unless they could pass as French they were denied the rights of citizenship in a democratic country. Before independence, in a population of 11,000,000, only about 1,000,000 were French, or had been assimilated to French culture.

In the meanwhile the French had developed the coastal cities, notably Algiers and Oran, into important ports to handle their developing trade in wine, fresh vegetables and fruits, and in the products of the mines—iron ore and phosphates—which they had opened up. Algiers had been

a Turkish city, with narrow, twisting streets, a fortress—or Kasbah—
mosques, and a conspicuous disregard for sanitation. The old city remains, but beside it is the modern French city, with wide streets and
impressive buildings, gleaming white against the gray-brown background
of the encircling hills. Oran is a smaller city than Algiers, but it presents
the same contrasts between the modern French and the old Turkish or
Moorish ways of life.

To west and east of Algeria, respectively, lie Morocco and Tunisia,
each under Moslem rule until 1956, but whose local autonomy had
grown with the decline in the power and prestige of the Turkish Empire. France assumed the role of protector over Tunis in 1881 and over
Morocco in 1912. They were never incorporated into France, and the
French never replaced the native rulers. In 1956 France withdrew her
protecting hand, and Morocco and Tunisia emerged as independent and
sovereign states. Morocco resumed control over the so-called Spanish
Zone and also the internationally administered city of Tangier. This
inevitably had the effect of inspiring the Berbers of Algeria to renewed
efforts to drive out the French, and the civil war began.

Morocco has a slight climatic advantage over the rest of northwest
Africa. Facing the Atlantic Ocean and backed by high mountains, it
attracts a higher rainfall than similar latitudes farther east. A few rivers
flow to the Atlantic from the ranges of the Grand Atlas, which are snow-
capped in winter, thus providing irrigation. Agriculture and animal-
raising form the main occupation, though mining is of some importance,
and Morocco is gaining in importance as a tourist resort.

The port city of Rabat has become the capital of the new Morocco,
replacing the inland cities of Fez and Marrakech, the traditional seats of
the native rulers. But like the Algerian cities, it too is a hybrid; part congested and Moorish; part open, planned, and French. Casablanca, lying
fifty miles away to the southwest is a much larger city, and the chief
industrial center and port of Morocco. It too is a mixture of ancient and
modern, though here the modern predominates. The port exports the
minerals—phosphates, iron, manganese—and factories produce textiles
and metal goods and process the agricultural products—tobacco, olives,
and lumber.

Inland there are several quite large cities—Fez and Marrakech, the
former capitals, and Meknès—all of them crowded and congested, with
narrow streets dominated by flat-roofed houses, the whole surrounded by
massive walls of sun-dried brick.

Tunisia spans the eastern end of the high and low Atlas ranges. It is drier than Morocco, and the area of cropland is less. But much of the land which is too dry to produce grain is well suited to tree crops, and olives, grapes, and citrus fruits are widely cultivated.

Tunisia was, apart from the valley of the Nile, the most developed section of North Africa in classical times. Ancient Carthage lay only a few miles from the present-day city of Tunis, the capital and chief industrial city and port of modern Tunisia.

When the French withdrew from Tunisia in 1956, they retained the naval base of Bizerte, located nearly forty miles north of the city, where the Mediterranean Sea is narrowest and its commerce most easily controlled. Tunisian opinion demands the withdrawal of the French, just as Spanish calls for that of the British from the somewhat similar base of Gibraltar.

In Algeria the population is gathered into the plains and plateaus of the north, but three-quarters of its territory is empty, and makes up the Saharan Departments. All three of these North African countries—Morocco, Algeria, and Tunisia—pass southward into the Sahara Desert. The popular conception of a desert—an uninhabitable waste of shifting sand—fits the Sahara only locally. Much of it is bare rock, carved by erosion into fantastic shapes. There are mountains which rise in the Ahaggar

Two types of desert: Sand desert where the slopes are gradual on the windward side; rock deserts where the wind has blown away the sand, exposing buttes.

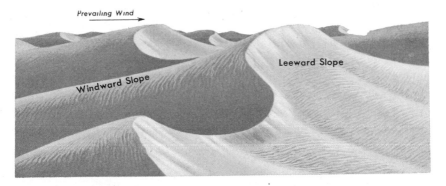

Prevailing Wind

Leeward Slope

Windward Slope

Butte

Butte

Desert Pavement

almost to 10,000 feet, and attract enough moisture for trees to grow. There are depressions in the desert floor that go deep enough to reach the water table. There palm trees grow; wells have been sunk; and if the resources are sufficient, irrigation is practiced. These are the oases, inhabited by settled communities; then there are the nomadic desert dwellers who wander with their animals—generally camels—from water hole to water hole.

There has been little change in economic life or social organization for centuries until lately. Little that was new in either technology or ideology intruded. Now, in the last few years, geologists and prospectors have come. They have found sizable deposits of iron ore and phosphate salts in the north, which are exploited for export. And in the Sahara they found oil. The strikes were rich, and reserves seem to be large. A pipeline has been built from deep in the desert to the Mediterranean coast at Bougie, Algeria, and the negotiations between the French and the Berber leaders have been bedeviled by the question of who should get the hitherto unwanted Sahara.

Libya

Tunisia's neighbor to the east, Libya, is made up almost entirely of the desert. Only near the coastal cities of Tripoli, the administrative and commercial center of the state, and Bengasi, chief city of the more easterly province of Cyrenaica, (both of which rank as capitals) is there enough moisture for agriculture. Here Mediterranean fruits are grown for export. Inland is a belt of semidesert where olive trees can be grown and sheep grazed, but behind this the desert stretches to the southern limits of the state. Libya is one of the poorest and weakest members of the community of nations; so poor and weak, in fact, that one wonders how it came to be. It is that part of the former Turkish Empire which the Italians succeeded in conquering in their war of 1911, and managed to hold until it was reconquered by the forces of General Montgomery in 1943. What to do with it? Clearly it could not be returned to Italy, and it was not politically wise for the victors to keep it. So it was given an ill-advised independence in 1952 because that was the only course on which all could agree.

Egypt (The United Arab Republic)

Were it not for the Nile, Egypt would be like Libya. This great river, the most important probably in human history, rises far to the south, beyond the belt of desert, and brings northward the water from more rainy climates. For over eight hundred miles the Nile flows across Egypt to the sea. In the south its course is sunk deeply into the desert floor; its valley is narrow and rock-walled and there is space for only a little agriculture along its banks. But below Aswan the valley widens; the strip of agricultural land, built of the silt brought down by the river and watered regularly by its floods, broadens to several miles. It continues to widen, and below Cairo it merges into the delta, as the river itself breaks up into distributaries to reach the sea.

This was the Egypt of ancient times, the narrow strip of land that could be reached by the river floods. Rainfall in Egypt is almost unknown, and without irrigation there could be no agriculture. From time immemorial the annual floods of the Nile have performed this service, inundating the soil, soaking it with water, leaving a fine layer of silt, and then either evaporating or flowing on to the sea. Not only did the regular floods make agriculture possible, they also necessitated some rudimentary political organization to supervise their use, and some means of measuring time in order to forecast their arrival, and of surveying the land and replacing boundary markers after they had retreated. Many of the early steps in human progress owed their stimulus to the Nile floods. And the surplus wealth created by the successful Egyptian agriculture provided the means to build the Pyramids, to carve the Sphinx, to lay out the temples of Luxor, and construct and furnish the tombs of the Pharaohs.

With the growth of Egypt's population it has become necessary to make the fullest possible use of the Nile's waters. Barrages, or very low dams, were built at several points to raise the level of the water and make it flow more widely across the fields in flood time. Pumps, primitive devices built of wood and leather and worked by man or beast, were erected to drive water to the fields during the off-season when the river level was low. But still the need for water grew.

During the flood season more water came down the river than could be used, and the surplus made its way to the sea, while the reduced flow of winter was almost wholly used up on the land. It was proposed to save the summer's surplus to meet the winter's needs. But where to save so vast a volume of water without inundating valuable cropland? The answer was in the narrow, gorgelike tract of the river above Aswan, where there was little cropland to ruin. So a "high" dam was planned, originally with American promises of support, and it is now being built with Russian aid. It will hold back in a vast lake the water which formerly ran to waste; it will accumulate the surplus from wet years and use it in the dry, for Egypt today, no less than in the time of the Pharaohs, is troubled by the alternation of fat years and lean, and the fatness and leanness are entirely governed by the level the flood waters reach. By means of the dam Egypt will add 2,000,000 acres to its cultivated area. The lake which will be formed will back up the Nile waters right up into the Sudan, and Egypt is to pay compensation to its neighbor for the loss of riverine lands.

If an ancient Egyptian could come back after three thousand years, he would probably recognize most of the primitive devices used for lifting water to the fields and most of the farming methods of the *fellahin* today, though not all the crops would be familiar. Corn and cotton would be new to him. He might ask, however, why foreign aid is needed to build the High Dam, while his era had built the pyramids unaided.

Ancient Egypt had its seats of power in the Nile Valley, at Thebes and Memphis. The Arab and Turkish capital was established at Cairo, close to where the Nile divides into the branches of its delta. Here were built the mosques and the Turkish citadel and here was established the foremost university in the Moslem world. Cairo has added a spacious modern city to its ancient crowded quarters, and now, with a population of four million, is the largest city in Africa.

The silt brought down to the sea by the Nile is carried eastward by the run of the Mediterranean current. All harbors on this coast tend to

silt up, but Alexandria on the western edge of the delta is the most free from silting. After its foundation in the fourth century B.C. by Alexander the Great, it grew into one of the great cultural centers of the Middle East, with the greatest library known to the ancient world. Now it is the chief port of Egypt, through which passes the export of cotton and the import of machines and consumers' goods.

All Egypt covers about 386,000 square miles, but the settled and cultivated area takes up no more than 15,000 square miles, about 3 per cent of the total area. But these acres are intensively cultivated. About 27,000,-000 people live on them, with an average of less than four persons per acre. The majority of the farm holdings are of less than an acre each, and these are made to yield two and even three crops in the year if only the water can be obtained to irrigate them. Corn, millet, and rice and wheat, barley, and beans alternate according to the seasons. Cotton is by far the most important cash crop, and accounts for almost three-quarters of the total exports of Egypt. The population is growing at an alarming rate, and if it continues to do so, only more water can save it from starvation.

By the accident of its location, Egypt has yet another asset of immense value. It contains the Suez Canal. Since early historical times the Middle East has lain at the crossroads of the Old World, crossed by the routes that run between Europe and Asia. In the past much of the traffic went overland from the Persian Gulf to the Mediterranean; now most of it goes by water through the Suez Canal. This canal, the last of several attempts to link the Mediterranean with the Red Sea, was opened in 1869. It created a revolution in world shipping, and today about 18,000 passages of the canal may be expected in a year, with a total shipping tonnage of well over 100,000,000 tons. The company which constructed and operated the canal was in origin French, though the British government, intent on keeping the canal open for British shipping, subsequently acquired a substantial holding in it. The canal henceforward became a major factor influencing British policy in the Mediterranean.

Egypt was occupied by British forces in 1882, primarily to insure the security of the canal. The British relinquished their grip on Egypt in 1922, but continued to maintain a garrison along the canal until 1954. The final withdrawal of British forces left Great Britain with a nervous sense of insecurity, which became exaggerated when, in 1956, President Nasser of Egypt nationalized the Suez Canal. A few months later, in the fall of 1956, the British, in league with the French and the Israelis,

attacked the canal in an ill-conceived and unsuccessful attempt, presumably, to re-establish their power and insure the security of their shipping.

The Suez Canal is a waterway 101 miles in length. At its northern entrance is Port Said; at the southern, Suez. It is a sea-level canal, and has no locks; it is wide enough for most ships to pass, but is now in process of being widened and deepened. By international treaty it is open to shipping of all nations, but the Egyptian authorities have consistently excluded Israeli ships and ships sailing to or from Israeli ports, on the excuse that Egypt is still at war with Israel. Since the Suez fiasco of 1956, Egypt has been undisputed master of the canal. Egypt has also been in control of the small Gaza Strip, a piece of former Palestinian territory in which live about 225,000 Arab refugees from Israel.

The State of Israel is the dominant influence in the policy of Egypt, as indeed it is on most of the Arab states. In 1958 Egypt and Syria, inspired chiefly by their common hatred of Israel, joined to form the United Arab Republic. But states need something more cohesive than a common hatred. The Union broke up in 1961; Syria again became an independent state, and Egypt clung to its empty and pretentious title of the United Arab Republic.

THE MIDDLE EAST

Most of Egypt is made up of desert, and most of it lies on the continent of Africa. But beyond the Suez Canal, the traditional boundary, the continent of Asia begins. No part of Egypt's desert, however, has the importance of the desert of Sinai, lying beyond the canal and the Gulf of Suez. This desert leads from Egypt to the Middle East, and across it since ancient times have marched Turkish and Egyptian armies. Here the Israelites wandered for their forty years of exile, and here today, in hutted encampments set in the empty desert, are hundreds of thousands of Arab refugees from Israel, the only non-Moslem state among the lands on the Mediterranean's eastern shore.

Israel and Jordan

Egypt's neighbor, Israel, is the newest of the Middle Eastern states and is the focus of the political attention of all its neighbors. To say that its presence is resented is to understate the virulence of the hatred which the Arab states, especially Egypt, bear toward it. Israel alone gives to the Arab states such unity as they possess in their foreign policies. They all pretend to fear the new, energetic, and forward-looking state of Israel, and all of them have in some degree given shelter to the Arab refugees who fled from Israel when the Israeli state was created.

The state of Israel is a creation of the present century. Part of its territory was settled by the Jews after their migration from Egypt across the Desert of Sinai in the twelfth century B.C. This was their Promised Land, and though they were scattered far from it in the Diaspora, or dispersion, they never ceased to regard it as home, and to look to the time when they might return to it. The return, however, might never have been realized if the persecutions and miseries of East European and Russian Jews in the nineteenth century had not made it imperative. The Zionist Movement, which worked for the re-creation of a Jewish State, in 1917 received the support of the British government, and in 1920 led to the establishment of the Palestine Mandate. Great Britain then assumed the obligation to develop Palestine as a "national home for the Jews."

The territory was small, poor, and neglected. Broadly it consisted of a narrow coastal plain, fronting the Mediterranean, the land of the Philistines of Biblical times, and backed by the low Galilean and Judaean hills, in the midst of which lay the city of Jerusalem. To the north lay the small plains of Sharon, and Esdraelon, and to the east, the deep, trenchlike valley of the Jordan River, the Sea of Galilee, and the Dead Sea. This was Palestine. Its abundance of milk and honey was entirely relative; it was a great deal more livable than the desert to the south and east. Its population contained a handful of Jews, but was made up mainly of Arabs, who either practiced a very primitive agriculture or were actually nomads with their flocks and herds, like the Ishmaelites of old.

The climate is very dry, closely resembling that of Baja California of Mexico. The hills on the northern border have a small winter rainfall, but this diminishes southward, and the Negev, the most southerly extension of Israel, is almost rainless desert. How to settle the refugees from Europe in this wilderness was a problem which the British authorities recognized, but never solved.

Faced with the apparently limited potential of the land itself and with the rights of the Arab inhabitants, the British kept Jewish immigration to a level far below that which the Jews themselves thought possible and desirable. The Second World War changed this. The demands of those who had miraculously escaped the gas chambers and concentration camps of the Nazis could no longer be ignored. They rushed, almost panic-stricken, to Palestine; the British authorities, no longer able in their slow, methodical ways to cope with the situation, threw the question back to the United Nations. Palestine was partitioned, and the State of Israel was proclaimed in 1948.

By the partitioning, the central hill country which had contained most of the ancient settlements of the Israelites was mostly incorporated into the neighboring state of Transjordan, which thereupon changed its name to Jordan; and the city of Jerusalem became divided. There was a flight of Arabs from the territory that became Israel, almost a million of them, into that of the neighboring Arab states. A short-lived war failed to stifle the new state at birth, and Israel came onto the political map.

The new state was beset by problems that would have intimidated a people less resolute. Every inch of its boundary was a political problem; it was short of water for agriculture; Egypt denied it the right to use the Suez Canal, and threatened its use of the Red Sea port of Elath in the desertlike, southern Negev. Above all, thousands of European Jews clamored for admission to this land which, though poor and barren, was a veritable heaven after Nazi Europe. Again the Jews look up to those brown Judaean Hills, whence came their help.

The Israelis would have chosen ancient Jerusalem as their capital if they could. It was the city of David; it had been their last defense against Assyrians and Romans. But it lay up in the dry, bare Judaean Hills, whereas recent Jewish settlement had been in the plains, which were more suited to their modern agriculture. So, when partition came in 1948, the old city of Jerusalem, with its monuments to its Jewish, Christian, and Moslem past, went to Jordan, and only the more modern sections, where most of the population lives, were left at the tip of a projecting salient of Israeli soil. This Israel made its capital.

The Jews have achieved much since the establishment of Israel. The population has doubled. The Mediterranean port of Haifa has been expanded, and Tel Aviv, almost a creation of the Israelis, is the largest city and still the seat of much of its government. Large numbers of Jews have been settled on various types of collective and co-operative farms, growing grain, cotton, sugar beets, and citrus fruit, and a beginning has been made with industries—textile, machine, chemical, and the whole gamut of consumers' goods—and with the extraction of chemicals from the highly saline waters of the Dead Sea.

For part of its course the river Jordan forms Israel's eastern boundary. It is a major source of water for both Israel and Jordan, as the Nile is for Egypt and the Sudan. After years of acrimonious bickering the Egyptian and Sudanese authorities have now reached an agreement on the division of the waters of the Nile. No such agreement has yet been forthcoming between Israel and her neighbor. The feud over how much of this small river each may take continues to embitter them and to prevent the proper use of the water. Israel, in default of an agreement, has now begun to divert water by pipeline from the upper Jordan, where rainfall is more abundant, to the dry south of Israel. But there is just not enough water for all, and we may be confident that the Jordan question will be a prominent one again.

Jordan, that is, the Kingdom of Jordan, began as the territory of Transjordan, brought into being in 1923 to satisfy the dynastic ambitions of Britain's ally, the Hashemite family, which was in process of being dispossessed of its hereditary lands in Arabia. The territory was small and poor, and was inhabited by primitive cultivators and nomadic Bedouins. It lay, as its name suggests, beyond the rocky trench of the Jordan River in what had once been the hill country of Moab.

Transjordan remained a mandate for which the United Kingdom was responsible to the League of Nations or to its successor, the United Nations, until 1946, when it gained its independence. In 1948, when the state of Israel was created from the Palestinian Mandate, Transjordan annexed most of the Judaean hill country, including the old city of Jerusalem, and at the same time received a flood of Arab refugees from Israeli territory.

Jordan is today a thinly peopled and mainly desert state. Its population of about 1,800,000 includes almost half a million refugees, who are kept alive only by a daily ration supplied by the United Nations. Its capital city, Amman, was little more than a village a few decades ago; now it is swollen, partly by refugees, to a quarter of a million. The resources of Jordan are mainly agricultural, and the aridity of the country insures that they are small—too small, in fact—to support the population. Attempts are being made to extend irrigation along the Jordan Valley and to exploit minerals like phosphorus and potash. But these resources are few, and Jordan maintains a precarious existence, its policy motivated by hatred of Israel, distrust of the other Arab states, and the preservation of the Hashemite dynasty.

Syria and Lebanon

The hills which form a kind of backbone to the state of Israel become higher and more complex as they continue northward toward Turkey. The Lebanon Mountains rise almost as high as the Alps and bear on their summits the scanty remains of the once extensive forests of cedar. Though they are themselves damp and wooded, they cut off the desert to the east from the rain-bearing winds of the Mediterranean. This mountainous region, together with its very narrow coastal plain, the Phoenicia of the ancients, and its extensive desert hinterland, makes up Lebanon and Syria. After the collapse of the Turkish Empire in 1918, this area became a prey to the rivalries of the Arab leaders and to the feuds and ambitions of the great powers. Syria, with Lebanon, emerged as a French mandate, for whose administration France was responsible to the League of Nations; Iraq and Transjordan came under British control just in order to preserve the political balance.

Syria and Lebanon proved to be as confused ethnically as they were physically. In the area as a whole Moslems formed a large majority, though Christians formed a local majority in the region of the Lebanon Mountains. This was the basis of the subsequent separation of the latter area from the rest of Syria to form the Republic of Lebanon.

Lebanon is one of the world's smallest states. Its official language is Arabic. About two-thirds of its population is Christian, though this is divided between Maronites—who are Orthodox in ritual but are members of the Roman Catholic community—Greek Orthodox, Armenians, and others. The Moslem minority is itself divided between the two dominant sects of Islam, the Shiites and the Sunnites. This internal division of Lebanon is reflected in its attitude toward the remaining Arab States. While acting with them on many issues, it maintains a more tolerant attitude toward Israel, and does not share the violent Arab nationalism of Egypt, Iraq, and Jordan.

Lebanon, like all its neighbors, is predominantly an agricultural state, though much of its surface is too mountainous to be cultivated. Industry —chiefly the making of textiles and the processing of agricultural products—is but feebly developed, though commerce is important. The capital, largest city, and chief port of Lebanon, Beirut, handles most of Lebanon's small trade, mostly the import of factory-made products and fuel, and the export of farm products, and also much of that of its Syrian hinterland.

North along the coast is Tripoli, the Tarabulus of the Phoenicians, and once again wearing its ancient name, now the most important Mediterranean terminal of the oil pipeline from Iraq.

Syria is that part of the former French mandate which was predominantly Moslem. As we have noted, in addition to the narrow coastal plain and bordering mountain ranges, Syria includes a large, semidesert hinterland. Here rainfall is small, vegetation sparse, and agriculture possible only with irrigation. Fortunately for Syria, streams descend from the Lebanon Mountains and flow out into the Syrian desert, eventually to lose themselves amid its sandy wastes. But before evaporating they are used to irrigate the oasis cities that lie along the desert edge.

Foremost among these cities is Damascus, itself no more than a very large oasis fed by the "rivers of Damascus" which flow down from the mountains of Lebanon, and produce a pool of green around the white walls of the city, amid the yellow and brown of the Syrian desert. Damascus the capital of Syria, has been a center of commerce since the earliest historical times, and it claims to be the oldest continuously occupied city in the world. North of Damascus is Aleppo, also lying to the east of the mountains, on a river that rises in the hills and loses itself in the semidesert. Aleppo has always been a commercial city on the routeway from the coast of the Mediterranean to the valley of the Euphrates.

Across the northeast of Syria flows the Euphrates, in its course from the mountains of Turkey. After it has left the mountains, its path crosses a region of steppe and semidesert, but a strip of cultivated land follows its banks, deriving irrigation water from the river itself. Syria is a predominantly agricultural country; most of its 4,825,000 inhabitants are farmers. Many depend upon irrigation, and any increase of the area under crops is dependent upon better use of the available water.

The Western World has always shown a deep interest in these three countries, Syria, Lebanon, and Israel, which border the eastern shore of the Mediterranean. For centuries European trade with Asia passed across them, and the opening of the sea route around Africa diminished, but never destroyed their importance.

Iraq

East of Syria lies Iraq, like Syria a predominantly Moslem state in which Arabic is also the official language. The separation of these two states derives from the division of the Middle East at the end of the First World War into French and British spheres. Iraq fell to the British, but in 1932 became an independent and sovereign state. Arab leadership has long been split by feuds, and this has been a factor in the coldness which has generally existed between Syria and Iraq.

Iraq consists essentially of the valleys of the Euphrates and Tigris, once called Mesopotamia, which join to form the Shatt al' Arab, and enter the Persian Gulf by a marshy delta which is building forward into the gulf at a rapid rate. It was in the deltaic region of the Tigris and Euphrates, then much farther to the northwest than it is at present, that the ancient civilizations of Babylonia grew up. Here, in Chaldea, was Ur, home of Abraham, and amid these marshes the Tower of Babel was built, in reality a great earthen mound erected to enable its builders to rise above the level of the periodic floods. Upstream from Babylonia lay Assyria.

The heir to ancient Babylon is modern Baghdad, the capital, lying forty miles to the north, and on the Tigris instead of the Euphrates. It is, with its 750,000 people, by far the largest city in Iraq. Second in size and importance is the port city of Basra, lying on the Shatt al' Arab, sixty miles from the Gulf.

All these ancient civilizations, like their successors here today, were dependent upon the annual floods of the Tigris and Euphrates. Without the rivers, this land would be only dry steppe or semidesert, furnishing at most rough grazing for sheep and goats.

The population of Iraq is 7,350,000, only a little more than a quarter that of Egypt, and it does not press, like the Egyptian, against the physical resources. Even so, Iraq is a poor country, farms are small and most of the farmers are very nearly self-sufficing. At present the irrigation system is being extended by the building of dams along the two rivers.

But Iraq, fortunately, has another resource. Along the foot of the mountains which enclose Iraq to the northeast is one of the largest oil fields in the Middle East. The most important Iraqi oil fields are around

Kirkuk, and from here the oil is piped to the Mediterranean coast for shipment to Europe. Iraq produces less than 5 per cent of the world petroleum output, but this amounts to over 40,000,000 tons and is enough to make petroleum its most important export.

This group of Arab countries, reaching from the Sinai Peninsula in the west to the Persian Gulf in the east, forms a kind of arc. To the north are mountains. To the south, within the curve of the arc, is desert. This narrow curving belt of land was termed the "Fertile Crescent" by the archaeologist James H. Breasted. Its fertility is a very relative matter, but it was from the earliest historical times a region of permanent settlements. Here the "urban revolution," in which mankind first built cities, took place, and commerce developed between the cities.

The Old Testament story moves from end to end of the Fertile Crescent. Along it Babylonian influences ran to Egypt, and Egyptian to Babylonia. But the desert which it partially enclosed, the great Arabian Desert, was a totally different environment. This was the land of the oasis dweller, who, of necessity, lived separate and apart, and of the Bedouin, the tented nomad who in small groups grazed flocks on the rough vegetation of the desert fringe.

The Arabian Desert

Amid the Arabian Desert which stretches for almost fifteen hundred miles south from the borders of Iraq and Syria to the south of Arabia, are oases where underground sources of water serve to moisten the roots of the palm trees and irrigate the barley and vegetables. Between them is bare desert, which covers most of Saudi Arabia, thus described by Charles Doughty: "This soil was waste gravel, baked hard in the everlasting drought, and glowing under the soles of our bare feet; the air was like a flame, in the sun."

The desert of Arabia is like a vast tilted land block, which slopes gently eastward from its high, fractured, western edge. Along this western rim there is rainfall; not much, but enough for intermittent streams, and for plants to grow. It is here that Arabian, or Mocha, coffee is grown. Amid the hills of the Hejaz on the west lies Mecca, home of the prophet Mohammed, the holiest city of Islam, and the place of pilgrimage of all devout Moslems. They go in their thousands to the Red Sea port of Juddah, from which they make the fifty-mile journey inland to the shrine.

East of the Hejaz Hills the land slopes gently toward the Persian

By pipeline to its ports or by tanker from the source through the Suez Canal, the Mediterranean Sea is the focus of oil transit to Europe.

MAIN OIL REGIONS OF NORTH AFRICA AND THE MIDDLE EAST

Caspian Sea

Black Sea

Mediterranean Sea

Red Sea

Persian Gulf

▲ Oil fields
--- Pipelines

0   300 MILES

TROPIC OF CANCER

IRAN
Tehran
Resht
Qum
Kermanshah
Isfahan
Abadan
Kuwait
Basra
Baghdad
Kirkuk
Mosul
Batman
IRAQ
Ras Tanura
Damman
BAHRAIN
QATAR
Umm Said
SAUDI ARABIA

TURKEY
Iskenderun
Baniyas
Tripoli
Saida (Sidon)
Haifa
LEBANON
SYRIA
ISRAEL
JORDAN
Elath
Port Said
Cairo
UNITED ARAB REP.
(EGYPT)

LIBYA
Bengasi
Marsa Brega

TUNISIA
Tunis
Bizerte
La Skhira
In Amenas
Ft. Polignac

ALGERIA
Algiers
Bougie
Sidi Aissa
Touggourt
Haoud el Hamra
Ft. Lallemand

Gulf, becoming gradually drier and more barren and culminating in the so-called "Empty Quarter" of southeastern Arabia. But in its midst are mountains where altitude moderates the temperature and occasional rains provide water for man and beast and crops.

The tribe, rather than the state, has been the unit of government in Arabia. One section of Eastern Arabia is still nothing more than a very loose federation of sheiks, the so-called Trucial Coast. But over much of the area this tribal organization, based essentially on the oasis settlement, has given place to more sophisticated types of political organization.

The "Revolt in the Desert" during the First World War brought to an end the feeble Turkish rule over Arabia. The Sultan was replaced, after a period of tribal feuds, by the family of Saud. The Western powers had fastened their hold on Palestine, Syria, and Iraq, and they operated the Suez Canal, but their interest in the interior of Arabia was minimal. At the very most, the lawlessness of the Arabian tribes might lead to friction along their mutual boundaries. But this situation changed rapidly. Ibn Saud became a more effective ruler than Arabia had ever known, and most of the peninsula was subordinated to his capital of Riyadh, in the heart of the peninsula. The personal strength of the ruler was reflected in the name of the state; it became Saudi Arabia.

The wealth of the Saudis soon came to be proportionate to their almost absolute power. Oil was discovered. Concessions were granted to the Arabian-American Oil Company, and commercial production began in 1939. Oil royalties made the king one of the richest men in the world.

The mountains of the southwest of the Arabian Peninsula escaped the clutch of the Saudis. Here the kingdom of Yemen survived, small, poor, and underdeveloped, always threatened by the expansionist ambitions of the Saudis.

Along the shore of the Persian Gulf is a succession of petty sheikdoms. Most live in a kind of primitive simplicity. The Trucial Sheikdoms of Oman in Eastern Arabia, (named on maps as the Trucial Coast) owe their strange name to the "truce" which they negotiated with the British, undertaking not to conduct their tribal forays into areas where they would be likely to obstruct Britain's commerce. The existence of two small neutral areas is itself evidence of their failure to agree on their partition among themselves.

Kuwait, near the head of the Persian Gulf, is in essence just such a sheikdom. Only a few years ago it acquired a virtual independence under its patriarchal sheik, subject only to British protection, because no one particularly wanted the difficult and unprofitable task of controlling it. British protection has now been withdrawn, and Kuwait is a sovereign state. Its minute territory—it is slightly larger than the state of Connecticut—has been found to contain one of the richest reserves of oil in the Middle East. Its small population has been swollen to 232,000 by the influx of technicians and geologists. Kuwait, the city, has mushroomed suddenly from an Arab village, and is adorned with the wealth obtained from oil; the Cadillac has suddenly become the status-symbol among its Arab inhabitants.

Southeastward along the shore of the Persian Gulf from Kuwait is the sheikdom of Qatar, a peninsula reaching into the Persian Gulf, which with the recent discovery of oil, threatens to become another Kuwait. Offshore, lies the small flat island of Bahrain, in the shallow, silting waters of the Persian Gulf. It is also a sheikdom, where oil has been found and an oil refinery built to serve not only the island itself but also the needs of the mainland oil fields.

Beyond Trucial Oman, in the extreme east of the Arabian Peninsula is the sultanate of Muscat and Oman. It is a rugged, formidable country; its scanty population mostly lives in oases, and its capital, Muscat, has only about 6,000 inhabitants. It carries on very little trade, and oil has not yet been discovered to confuse its society and arouse the cupidity of its neighbors.

Along the southeastern coast of Arabia, the mountains of the Hadhramaut rise steeply from the rugged coastline and merge inland into the so-called "Empty Quarter," one of the most waterless and uninhabitable deserts on the face of the earth. This is the British Protectorate of Aden; the population can only be guessed at, it is too restless and suspicious ever to have been counted. Aden itself, situated in the district Aden, is a city established on this bleak and waterless coast for the convenience of shipping. Its chief product is salt, made by evaporating sea water, but it handles much of the trade in coffee, hides and skins, firearms, and textiles, which is carried on by the hinterland.

Iran

On the opposite shore of the Persian Gulf across from the petty sheikdoms, is the rugged coast of Iran. In many respects Iran resembles Turkey, though in area it is more than twice as large, but has about seven and a half million fewer people. Like Turkey, it is a plateau, lying generally above 2,000 feet, and rimmed by mountains, which drop abruptly on the southwest and south to the plains of Iraq and the Persian Gulf, and on the north to the Caspian Sea and Soviet Central Asia. Toward the northwest these mountains merge into the rugged mass of the Armenian Mountains and culminate in Mount Ararat, 16,946 feet, on the Iranian-Turkish boundary. In the opposite direction the mountains and plateaus of Iran are continued into Afghanistan and Pakistan.

In the mountains of western Iran there is a rainfall of 30 inches or more a year, but in the center of the country this drops to below 10 inches. Much of the country is semidesert, and in the dry east are large areas devoid of all vegetation. In its temperature range also, Iran resembles Turkey. The fierce heat of summer contrasts with the intense cold of much of the mountain and plateau.

Iran, like every other country of the Middle East, was the scene of a civilization which blossomed here from two to three thousand years ago. It was Persians who invaded Greece and very nearly destroyed the incipient civilization of Athens early in the fifth century B.C. But Iran itself suffered more than most from invasions and conquest. The armies of Alexander the Great, the Arabs and the Turks in turn, subjugated it, modifying its ethnic composition and its culture. Today Iran is mainly a Moslem country, and its chief language is Arabic, but around its periphery are many other groups: Turkmen, Afghans, and Baluchis in the east; Kurds, Turks, and Azerbaijanis in the west.

Like its neighbor to the west, Iran has proved to be richly endowed with petroleum, and the royalties obtained from the petroleum companies are a major source of income to the Iranian state. The oil fields lie mainly below the mountain rim, on the southwest, where they are linked geologically with those of Iraq. Much of the oil is piped to the refineries built at Ābādān, near the head of the Persian Gulf.

The chief cities, however, are on the plateau. Here, beneath the Elburz Mountains and the towering peak of Mount Demavend (18,934 feet) is the capital, Tehrān. Tabrīz, the second city lies close to the Armenian Mountains, and Esfahān lies below the Zagros. Location of these population centers at the foot of the ranges indicates how the people make use of the rivers as they issue from the mountains and before they are lost by evaporation out on the plateau.

Iran is an agricultural country; yet not more than 10 per cent of its area is cropland. Much of it is cultivated by primitive methods and does little more than satisfy the barest needs of its cultivators. Wheat and other grain crops, vegetables, tobacco, and fruit are grown. Animals—especially sheep and goats—are grazed over land that is too dry or too poor to cultivate, providing the raw material of the textile, carpet, and leather industries.

Iran is a poor and underdeveloped country that finds itself today in a position of great strategic importance. To the north lies the Soviet Union; to the south the Indian Ocean. Early in the present century the British and Russians contended for influence in Iran. During the Second World War material aid was sent to the Soviet Union across Iran, and Soviet troops, brought in to guard the supply line, were with difficulty ejected when the war was over and their job was done. That pressure—diplomatic, economic, and even military—will be renewed against Iran is as certain as anything can be in the field of international relations.

MIDDLE EASTERN OIL

The Middle East today produces about 30 per cent of the world's petroleum, but, important as this is, it is less important than the Middle East's share of the total world reserves. Current estimates give the Middle East almost 70 per cent of the reserves known to geologists in the Free World, and a quarter of these reserves are in Kuwait. The rest of Asia has no more than 6 per cent; Africa, under 3 per cent, despite the recent discoveries in the desert of Algeria and Libya; and the whole Western Hemisphere has fewer reserves than tiny Kuwait.

This is only the current situation. Undoubtedly, geologists will discover other resources in other parts of the world. But it is unlikely that the primary importance of the Middle East in this respect will ever be seriously threatened. Apart from Venezuela, only the Middle Eastern countries have a large, exportable surplus of oil, and Europe, Asia, and Africa are obliged to rely on the Middle East for the satisfaction of most of their petroleum needs. Pipelines, refineries, and tanker fleets are organized for and adjusted to the Middle Eastern supply, and any interruption of the routes from the Middle East causes confusion in Europe, which is the continent most dependent on imported oil.

As we have seen, the Middle Eastern oil fields occur in two separate belts of territory. One lies close to the mountain ranges of southwestern Iran; its northwestern extremity is in Iraq, its southeastern in Iran. The other lies along the southern shore of the Persian Gulf, from Kuwait southeastward, and extends fifty to a hundred miles into the desert. The exploited deposits are in Kuwait and Saudi Arabia, but prospectors have already extended the known field southeastward, into the territory of the independent sheikdoms. The now familiar spectacle of tribal Arabs flaunting their newly acquired wealth will doubtless spread through the lesser sheikdoms to Trucial Oman, unless some means is devised in this Texas of the Old World of using the immense income from petroleum royalties more wisely than has generally been the case.

Oil makes its way to the market by two routes. Part is piped onto tankers at the Persian Gulf oil ports. The rest is conveyed by pipeline across the Middle East to the Lebanese port of Tripoli or the Syrian port of Bāniyās, and is then taken by tanker over the shorter sea route to European ports. Both routes have proved to be vulnerable. The all-sea route through the Suez Canal was closed in 1956, and each of the pipelines has at some time been interrupted. Yet their importance will increase as Europe becomes increasingly dependent upon imported oil. Politics in the Middle East would inevitably be confused, given the feuds among the Arabs themselves. And here oil does not calm the troubled waters, but rather confuses the issues by introducing also the feuds and rivalries of the Great Powers, anxious to get their hands on this precious commodity.

10 THE MONSOON
LANDS OF ASIA:

South, Southeast, and East Asia

It has produced more civilizations [than Europe],
involving a much greater proportion of mankind,
over a longer period of time, on a higher level
of continuity.

HERBERT J. MULLER—The Uses of the Past

Every second person on this planet is an Asian, and
every fourth person is Chinese. Asia, since the dawn of human history,
has had more people than any other continent, so that this phenomenon,
which seems so frightening to many of us who live in the West, is not
new. And yet only a small part of this vast continent carries this dense
population. At least two-thirds of Asia is either too cold or too dry to
be inhabited by many people. The greatest concentration of this immense
population is in the crowded valleys and plains of South, Southeast, and
East Asia. We must now examine both the physical conditions which
make such crowding possible, and the consequences of it, in terms both
of the welfare of the people who live there and of the security of the rest
of the world.

Let us look first at the physical configuration of Asia. If we accept its
traditional boundary as running along the Ural Mountains and Ural
River of Russia, and including Turkey and the Middle East, then it
appears as the largest and most compact of the continents. Indeed it
covers no less than 30 per cent of the land surface of the globe. Its limits
on the seaward side are the Indian Ocean, the Pacific, and the Arctic. It
is the only continent which stretches from the equator to the polar

regions, and it contains a greater physical variety than any other continent. And in this immense area live 1,722,000,000 people.

Lying across Asia from the Middle East to the extreme northeast is a series of mountain ranges. On the map they appear to hang like the drapes above a window, gathered into knots, between which their folds appear to hang limply. One of these knots is formed by the Armenian Mountains of eastern Turkey. To the west the Pontic and Taurus Mountains enclose the Anatolian Plateau of Turkey. Across the top of the knot lie the Caucasus Mountains. To the east the mountain ranges curve toward the south, through Iran, and then again to the north, through Pakistan and Afghanistan to reunite in the most complex of knots. This is the Pamir, the "Roof of the World," amid whose wilderness of rock and ice the Tadzhik Republic of the Soviet Union, Afghanistan, Pakistan, India, and China all meet.

Between the Armenian and the Pamir knots the curving mountain ranges enclose the high plateaus of Iran and Afghanistan. The more northerly of these loops passes through the Elburz range which looks steeply down on to the Caspian Sea, and the Kopet Dag, which rising steadily, merges into the high Hindu Kush, which merges into the Pamir. The southern loop forms the rampart of Iran against the south and then, in a thick bundle of curving mountain ranges, runs through the Baluchistan province and the northwest frontier of Pakistan until in Gilgit, the remotest corner of India, it too joins the Pamir.

The highest and most formidable mountain range in the world, the Himalayas, hangs suspended, as it were, between the Pamir knot and a point on the northeastern boundary of India. North lie other curving ranges of high mountains, the Karakorum and the Kunlun, embracing between them the high, icy, barren plateau of Tibet. In the interior of China these ranges are gathered once again, and are then allowed to fan out, like frayed and tasseled folds in the draperies, into the ranges of Southeast Asia.

Meanwhile, other ranges stretch northeast from the Pamirs; short, lower, overlapping ranges, the Tien Shan, the Altai, the Yablonovy, and countless other little-known mountains, which gradually die away into the hills that lie opposite Alaska, beyond the Bering Strait.

This is the skeleton around which the continent of Asia is built. Most of the great rivers of Asia—the Indus, Ganges, Brahmaputra, Irrawaddy, Salween, Mekong, Yangtze, and Hwang Ho—rise in these mountain ranges or in the plateaus that lie between them; and as they flow down

OUTER
MONGOLIA

CHINA

AFGHANISTAN

SIKKIM
NEPAL / BHUTAN

N.
S.
KOREA

JAPAN

FORMOSA

LAOS

PAKISTAN — INDIA

N.
VIETNAM
S.

PHILIPPINES

BURMA
THAILAND
CAMBODIA
MALAYA

BRUNEI
SARAWAK

N. BORNEO

CEYLON

INDONESIA

Most of the lands of South, Southeast, and East Asia are touched in varying degrees by the summer monsoon.

to the distant sea, they carry with them material yielded by the denudation of the mountains themselves. This they lay down on the great river plains of India, Southeast Asia, and China, and there the fertility supports that dense population which makes up half of humanity.

Asia is a continent of variety and contrast. Enclosed by the mountain ranges are the high plateaus of Tibet, of the far interior of China, of Afghanistan and Iran, and of Turkey. Cut off by mountains, these plateaus are difficult of access. Deprived of moist winds from the ocean, their surface is generally arid and little suited to agriculture. At the opposite extreme are the alluvial plains: the great plains of northern India and Pakistan; of Burma, Thailand and Cambodia; and the incomparably larger plains of China—created and irrigated by the rivers which rise in the mountains, and watered by winds from the oceans. Fingers of

The Summer Monsoon, borne by winds from the Indian and Pacific Oceans, pours phenomenal amounts of moisture over parts of India and Southeast Asia.

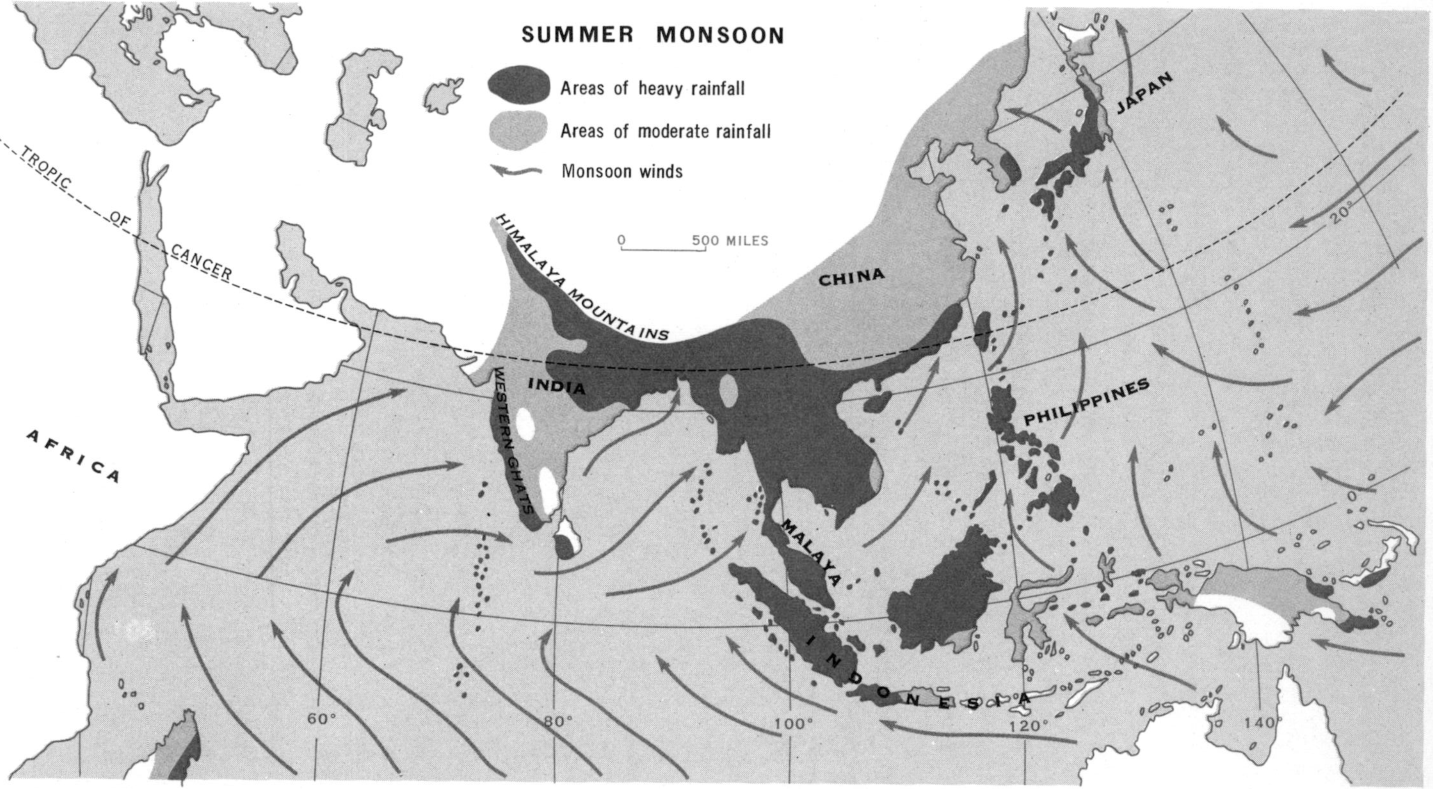

SUMMER MONSOON

Areas of heavy rainfall
Areas of moderate rainfall
Monsoon winds

0   500 MILES

mountain stretch out to separate one river basin from the next, giving to each a kind of natural protection.

Off the eastern, southeastern, and southern coasts of Asia are islands. They mostly lie in long chains which loop through the oceans, continuing the direction of the mountain ranges of the mainland. The Japanese islands lie off the eastern coast of Asia, and are continued southward in the line of the Ryukyu Islands, which in turn continue through Formosa to the Philippines. The long, narrow islands of Sumatra and Java in Indonesia continue the direction of the Arakan Mountains of Burma, and are themselves continued in the lesser islands of the East Indies. Lying between these two Indonesian islands and the Philippines are Borneo, the Celebes, and the hundreds of other islands that form a pathway in the sea that leads to Australia.

The mountains and plateaus of Central Asia, of Mongolia, of Sinkiang and Tibet; the hills, valleys, and plains that lie to the south and east in Pakistan, India, Burma, and China; and the peninsulas and islands which lie beyond in Thailand, Cambodia, Laos, Vietnam, Malaya, and Indonesia—all these together make up Monsoon Asia. The term Monsoon is derived from an Arabic word which means "season." It refers to one season in particular, the summer, when the rains come. In late spring and early summer the more southerly parts of the great land mass of Asia become intensely heated under the sun. The air becomes hot, expands and rises, not merely on a local scale as we see it happening on a hot summer's day, but on a vaster, continental scale. The most gigantic convectional system on the surface of the earth is set up. Air rises over Central and Southeast Asia, and winds are drawn in from the south, southeast, and east to take its place. They blow in from the Indian and Pacific oceans, laden with moisture.

In some places the monsoon breaks suddenly. In the midst of the hot, dry, and dusty weather of early summer the air grows humid; clouds roll in from the ocean and up over the mountains. An eerie stillness precedes the violent storms which the hot moist winds, surging in from the ocean, loose over the land. Elsewhere the monsoon breaks more gently; there is a gradual transition from the dry spring to the wet summer. But however the monsoon begins, it brings heavy rains. Over most of Monsoon Asia late June and all July are wet. In some places on the windward side of the mountains, the clouds boil up from the sea without ceasing, and interminably they empty down their rainfall. At the almost legendary site of Cherrapunji on an outlier of the Himalayan range in northeastern India, no less than 96.2 inches of rain fall to the earth in an average June, and in July the average rises to 98.2. In most of the monsoon lands, August is drier, in September the rains begin to cease, and over much of the monsoon lands October is a dry, cool month.

The winter is the dry season. The interior of the continent, which had become so hot under the summer sun, now becomes bitterly cold. Dense, heavy air forms over it and inches slowly outward toward the oceans. It streams out over the valleys and plains of China as a cold, dry air; northern India is chilled, and rainfall comes in winter only where these winds blow out over the ocean and gather moisture before again reaching land.

It is the monsoon that holds the key to the density of Asia's population. The levels of the great rivers rise in summer. They flow yellow with silt as they have done for millions of years, depositing it at their mouths, building forward new land at the expense of the ocean, and slowly fashioning a habitat for Asia's half of the human race. The rivers, fed by the monsoon, not only create fresh land; they furnish the water with which that land can be irrigated through the months when the rains do not come.

The great river valleys and plains of Monsoon Asia have unique advantages: a deep, rich alluvial soil, hot summers, and an abundance of rainfall. And in winter, when the temperature is commonly warm enough for plants to grow, the rivers themselves provide water for irrigation. It has been so in India and China since the earliest periods of human history. This is one reason why human development in these regions has been so precocious; why so dense a population has been able to grow and to maintain itself, and, despite thousands of years of continuous cultivation, to keep its land in good condition.

The people of Asia are often regarded as having some quality of mysticism denied to the more materialistic West. It is true that Western Christianity has made almost no impact on Asia, except in the Philippines, and that South and East Asia have their own religions, most of which are older than Christianity itself and have stood the test of use for a greater period of time.

The most important of the Asian religions are Islam, which is the dominant religion of the Middle East, and, within the area covered by this chapter, is represented chiefly in Afghanistan, Pakistan, Malaya, and Indonesia; and Buddhism, which has largely been abandoned in India, its country of origin, but is still dominant in Ceylon and much of Southeast Asia. These are both monotheistic religions, yet with little organized theology and doctrine.

By contrast, the prevailing creed of India, Hinduism, has a hierarchy of deities, is compounded of legend and superstition, and is overlaid with tradition and ceremonial. It is baroque by contrast with the fierce simplicity of Islam and Buddhism. In most of China the teachings of Buddha are overlain by a rather primitive ancestor worship and by the ethical code known as Confucianism, while in Tibet a purer Buddhism, sometimes known as Lamaism from its institution of lamas or monks, prevails. In Japan the predominant religion of Shintoism is also basically Buddhist, but incorporates elements of ancestor worship and reverence for the state and its personal embodiment, the emperor.

In the remote and mountainous areas, in India, the far interior of China, Southeast Asia, and Indonesia, tribal religions, mainly local and animist prevail, but their followers are numerically few.

The vast majority of Asia's population maintains itself by cultivating the soil. The picture that comes to mind is of the peasant in India, Burma, China, or where you will in the monsoon lands, planting his rice. The field is flooded, and the peasant, up to his knees in the water, bends over as he presses the young rice plant into the soft mud of the paddy fields. His farm holding is small, only an acre or two, and on this he lavishes his labor throughout the year, maintaining the irrigation works, feeding water into his fields, planting and harvesting his rice, and growing a second or even a third crop during the drier, cooler season of the year.

Through all the valleys and plains from India to Japan and the Philippines there are paddy fields. The hillsides are often terraced to grow rice. Without the heavy yielding rice, which produces more food to the acre than any other grain crop except corn, this dense population could not be fed, and without the monsoon the rice crop could not be grown. But rice is not the only crop. Even in Monsoon Asia some places are too dry for the rice crop; here wheat and barley are grown, unless water can be obtained from a river to flood the paddy fields. Other areas are too steep even for the patient Chinese to cut terraces and grow rice. There the land is left under forest, which itself yields products of value to man, like the hard teakwood.

Today there is a change in Monsoon Asia. The traditional pattern of agriculture, which has changed little in several thousand years, continues to dominate the agricultural scene and to provide most of the food required by man and beast. But beside it is a new, twentieth-century pattern of agriculture. Dams across the great rivers harness the water so that none shall flow to the sea unused. In areas where the peasant has not come, the forest is being cleared for plantations of rubber and palm trees. Even on the small peasant holdings, new methods, new tools, new fertilizers, and better seeds are being used. The Japanese have shown immense skill in mechanizing and updating this ancient agricultural structure without changing its basic pattern. The Chinese, with their communes, have tried to collectivize it by absorbing the multitude of little farms into large units, cultivated by regimented gangs of peasant workers.

In the past manufacturing industries have been little developed, except in Japan, which has made itself an industrial nation. Today, however, most of the countries of Monsoon Asia are trying to catch up with the more developed countries in the field of industrial production. Factories are rising in India and Pakistan, and in China the Communist bosses are pushing ahead with factory development in a mad rush to match and to overtake their neighbors and rivals.

Above all, the population in most of these lands is increasing faster than in any other parts of the world. Here, rather than in Europe, it threatens to outrun the resources that are available to support it. Increasing numbers are being absorbed into industry, but the numbers left upon the land are also growing. It is true that the limits of cultivation are being expanded, and that the volume of agricultural production is being increased by the use of better seed and better farming methods. But in most of Monsoon Asia the expansion of food production lags behind the growth in population, and only in Japan has the pressure of public opinion brought about some limitation in the size of families.

The population explosion is violent in most of Monsoon Asia, and its political consequences are likely to be serious. Nearly 700,000,000 Chinese exert an immense pressure on the resources of China. How much longer will it be possible to withstand their urge to expand into other and less populous lands?

Our journey through the monsoon lands of Asia will take us from Afghanistan into Pakistan and India and Ceylon; then into Burma, Thailand, and the small states of the southeast corner of Asia that have emerged from the ruins of the French empire—North and South Vietnam, Laos, and Cambodia—once known as Indochina. A detour will take us through Malaya, Indonesia, and the Philippines; then Formosa,

Japan and Korea; and China will complete our tour of the monsoon countries.

Monsoon Asia lies between the Russian Heartland and the encircling oceans. Through much of human history peoples have pressed outward from the heartland, through the mountain ranges of Central Asia, across the plateaus and down into the plains of the monsoon lands. Several of the dynasties that have ruled China came by this route; most of the invaders of India slipped down through the Khyber Pass from Central Asia. But the monsoon lands have also been exposed to the sea. Long before Europeans came, the Arabs traded with the coasts of India. Then, at about the time that Columbus was exploring the islands of the Caribbean Sea, the Portuguese sailed around Africa and reached India. They established trading bases on the coasts of India, Southeast Asia, and China, and though the Dutch and the British subsequently deprived them of much of what they had acquired, they still today retain a couple of inconspicuous footholds in Asia, Timor and Macao.

The British and the Dutch followed the Portuguese. The former made India their chief area of empire building, though they occupied also parts of Malaya and the East Indian islands and established the colony of Hong Kong off the Chinese coast. The Dutch occupied most of the East Indian islands and the Spaniards took the Philippines. The French followed, disputed with the British for the possession of India, and then went on to conquer the portions of Southeast Asia that for long were known as Indochina.

Only China, Japan, and Thailand remained immune from invasion and conquest by European peoples, but they were not uninfluenced by them. Europeans, especially the British, secured rights in parts of China, controlled the navigation of Chinese rivers, and even controlled the Chinese Customs for a period. In 1853 the American Commodore Perry sailed into Yokohama Harbor and thus broke through that hard shell of isolationism by which the Japanese had tried to insulate themselves from the rest of the world. For three centuries most of Monsoon Asia has been dominated and controlled by the sea powers, and after the Suez Canal had been opened in 1869 and the voyage from Europe shortened, this control tightened over the lands of Asia.

But the control did not go wholly unchallenged. While the maritime powers of Western Europe were occupying the monsoon lands, the Russians were penetrating Central Asia, and from here they began to threaten Iran, India, and China. During the nineteenth century this threat was

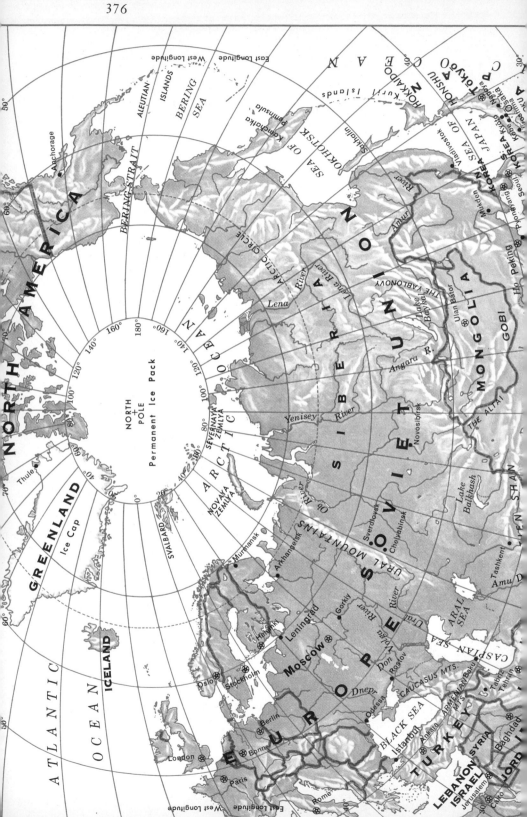

ASIA

⊛ National Capitals   ● Other Cities

Scale of Miles

0 100 200   400   600   800

COPYRIGHT 1962 BY RAND MC NALLY & CO. MADE IN U.S.A.

not severe, and though it was continuous, the British were able to contain it without great difficulty. In the twentieth century it became more intense, and today it is a steady and relentless pressure. Outer Mongolia has been brought within the sphere of direct Soviet control; Afghanistan is threatened by the Soviet Union. In China, Communist armies, trained and equipped by the Soviet Union, have taken over the whole of mainland China. Their outward advance has been halted in Korea and in Vietnam, but the Chinese and the Russians, always sounding for soft spots in the encircling ring of states, play their own kind of variations on Laos, India, Pakistan, Kashmir, Iran, and Turkey. All are in some degree threatened.

In the meanwhile the European imperialist nations have lost almost completely their control over any parts of Monsoon Asia. The Dutch were driven from the East Indies by the Japanese during the Second World War, and after the war was over, they never really succeeded in reasserting their control. In 1949 they formally transferred power to an Indonesian government which had already been in existence for four years; but they retained control over the western half of New Guinea—Netherlands New Guinea, as it is called—which culturally has nothing in common with Indonesia. Today this control is being challenged. In 1947 the British rule ended in India, with the creation from the former empire of India and the territory of Burma the three republics of India, Pakistan, and Burma. The French empire of Indochina succumbed to the hordes of Communist Chinese in 1954, and a group of small and far from stable independent republics took its place. In 1948 Ceylon and in 1957 the Federation of Malaya gained independence within the British Commonwealth. The last of the servitudes which the West had placed on China had already been removed as the Communist armies surged forward from its mountain refuges toward the sea.

All that is left of European colonialism in Asia are the British bases of Aden and the airport at Cyprus, in the Middle East, Hong Kong, Singapore, the British possessions in Borneo, and a few square miles of Portuguese territory on the China coast and in the islands of Indonesia. The Ryukyu Islands, strung out between Japan and Formosa, together with the Bonin Islands, lying a thousand miles out in the Pacific Ocean, have passed from Japanese possession to a status under United States military occupation.

Western colonialism in Asia has gone, and in its place are the new Asian nations. They are fiercely independent, but short of capital and short of skills, and are ready to receive aid from almost any quarter prepared to provide it. A new pattern of relationship has arisen between the states of Monsoon Asia and the West. They are the recipients of material, technical and military aid; their friendship is solicited by West and East and they are received into alliances for defense or development, like SEATO, CENTO and the Colombo Plan. Aid from the developed nations competes with aid proffered by the Communists.

In India three steel works have been built, one by Great Britain, one by West Germany, and one by the Soviet Union. India is preserving a nice balance between what it accepts from the Communist and from the Western World. In Afghanistan aid from the West has been completely overshadowed by that from the Soviet Union, and in China, North Korea, and North Vietnam such aid is entirely from Communist sources. Through the monsoon lands, from Afghanistan to Korea and Japan, the global struggle is being waged. In part it is a struggle for the privilege of aiding these underdeveloped and overpopulated lands. In part it is a struggle to control the governments and to influence the minds of men.

The semicircle of countries which make up Monsoon Asia begins in the west with Afghanistan, which has for centuries been the northern gateway to the Indian Peninsula. In reality it is an eastward extension of the plateau of Iran, but it is more mountainous and its peaks rise higher. At the same time the belt of mountain and plateau narrows toward the northeast, and can be crossed more easily. In fact, it is reduced to two high and complex ranges, with only a narrow and rugged plateau between them. The more southeasterly, the Sulaiman Range, rises steeply and abruptly from the plains of Pakistan, and is crossed by the deeply entrenched valley of the Kabul River, which flows down from the plateau beyond it to join the Indus River. The valley of the Kabul River contains the Khyber Pass, and provides the only significant route across the Sulaiman Mountains. Indeed, it is almost the only historically important pass across the whole mountain system that encloses India and Pakistan on the north, and through it most of the invaders of the Indian Peninsula have entered.

Behind the Sulaiman Mountains and north beyond the plateau which contains the capital city of Kabul, lies the Hindu Kush, and from the Hindu Kush the land slopes down to the plains of the Turkmen and Uzbek Republics of the Soviet Union.

Afghanistan is a poor and mountainous country, with very few minerals of economic importance and little cultivable land. Yet it has a population of 14,000,000, most of them farmers, many of them still organized in warlike tribes. The Afghans prove unruly neighbors for Pakistan and India, but their chief importance lies in the fact that across their country lies the invasion route from Central Asia.

THE INDIAN PENINSULA

The republics of India and Pakistan were created when, in 1947, the British relinquished their control of the vast and varied land that lay between the high mountains and the Indian Ocean. At the same time Burma, to the east, a territory in the Commonwealth and separate from India since 1937, formed an independent republic. Over a period of three centuries the British had gradually conquered this huge area, half the size of the United States, and to some degree they had given it a sense of unity. A network of roads and railroads spanned it. It was administered from the city of New Delhi, and trade and defense were organized for this subcontinent as a whole.

Yet the process of unifying India was never quite complete. The 400,000,000 inhabitants were mainly divided into two distrustful, even hostile, groups: the Hindus and the Moslems. As the British prepared to leave, it became apparent that it would be necessary to create two states from the unit which they had established. All that could be done was to ease the transfer of power, to make it peaceful and orderly, to establish in advance a boundary line between the two future states, and to do the least violence possible to the feelings of both Hindu and Moslem. So India and Pakistan emerged, the lands respectively of the Hindus and Moslems, with boundaries predetermined by a boundary commission.

The land which they thus divided had about it a broad simplicity, which, one might have said, would have made political unity probable if not inevitable. Along its northwestern border lay the Kirthar and Sulaiman Mountains; along the northern, the wall-like barrier of the Himalayas on which are strung the romantic land of Nepal, with its capital Katmandu, and the monarchies of Sikkim and Bhutan, which are Indian protected. There were few gaps through this enclosing ring, and only one of these, the Khyber Pass, was ever of great importance. If ever a segment of the earth's crust seemed to have a unity imposed on it in advance by nature, this was India. Both Hindus and Moslems protested that India was one and indivisible, and then quarreled about the way in which it was partitioned.

The boundary, which separated as nearly as was possible Hindus from Moslems, came to divide the Republic of India from the two fragments of Pakistan. India took nearly three-quarters of the area and five-sixths of the population. It is today second only to China in the size of its population, and in area it is exceeded only by six other countries—U.S.S.R., Canada, China, United States, Brazil, and Australia.

West and East Pakistan

The two fragments of Pakistan are widely separated by nearly a thousand miles of India. West Pakistan, the larger but less populous of the two, lies up against the mountains which separate it from Afghanistan. It lies in the basin of the river Indus, but it does not occupy the whole of this basin. It is a dry region becoming ever drier to the west, as the monsoon winds have already lost much of their moisture by the time they reach here. A large part of West Pakistan is semidesert or desert; little agriculture is possible without irrigation, and water is the scarcest and most valuable commodity in most of the area.

Unfortunately the division of the land between differing human societies does not agree with its distribution between the basins of different rivers. The most useful tributaries of the Indus River rise within India and flow across the boundary into Pakistan. India, as it were, has the first look at the waters, and we have here exactly the same problem as that which is encountered in Egypt. The upstream state has the first opportunity to use the water, and there is nothing in nature to prevent India, like the Sudan, from using it all. West Pakistan is a poor state; its 40,815,000 people are overwhelmingly dependent upon agriculture, and this in turn is dependent upon the continuing supply of water. The control of water supplies the key to much of the politics, and also to a great deal of the history of the monsoon lands. In this instance, India and Pakistan have come to a complicated agreement after years of wrangling. India will take much of the water that flows down the more easterly rivers, the Ravi, Beas, and Sutlej. Pakistan will be compensated by the construction of dams in the Indus and Chenab valleys, within the Himalayas, where these rivers originate, to conserve water which will then be fed by costly canals to its cultivated fields.

No river system demonstrates more clearly than that of the Indus the need to treat it as a single unit from the economic and technical point

THE INDIAN PENINSULA

of view, and no area illustrates more clearly the way in which political divisions resulting from the acute national feelings of modern times, renders this impossible.

East Pakistan contrasts strongly with West. It lies a thousand miles away. It embraces much of the Ganges delta, which is also fed by the Brahmaputra. Much of its area is swamp and jungle, whereas West Pakistan is arid. It receives the full force of the monsoon, whereas West Pakistan gets the monsoon winds only after they have lost most of their moisture. West Pakistan can use every drop of water that enters its boundaries and still looks for more; East Pakistan's problem is to get its overabundant water away to the sea as fast as possible. What a difference it would make if East Pakistan could pipe water across to West.

A state divided as Pakistan is, into two widely separated parts, has problems enough. But the problems of Pakistan are intensified by the veiled hostility of India which lies between them, and by differences in language, and in climate and products. Only the Islamic faith serves as a bond of union between the two parts.

The swamps of East Pakistan, where the Ganges and the Brahmaputra mingle their waters in the maze of channels that thread their common delta, are the world's greatest producers of jute, the long-stemmed fiber that provides the raw material of burlap; the chief commercial crop in West Pakistan is cotton, grown by means of irrigation in the semidesert of the Indus Valley, like that of Arizona and Southern California. The chief human food in East Pakistan is rice, produced from the level paddy fields of its deltaic lands; in West Pakistan it is generally wheat, more suited to the drier conditions. Jute and cotton, raw or spun into yarn, make up over 70 per cent of the exports of Pakistan. Manufacturing industries are little developed in either of the Pakistans, and machinery, metal goods, and chemicals make up most of the imports. Much of the raw jute from East Pakistan is, in fact, sent across the boundary into India to be manufactured into coarse fabric, though factory industries are in fact being rapidly developed in East Pakistan.

Poverty, backwardness, and territorial division into two widely separated parts, along with India's hostility, do not exhaust the problems of Pakistan. Along its northwestern boundary are restless tribes, closely related to the inhabitants of Afghanistan. This, the old Northwest Frontier of India, is a disturbed and uneasy area to which at intervals the Afghans lay claim on the basis of the common Pushtu language. If ever these claims to create a state—already as if in anticipation given the name of Pushtunistan—are backed by the might of the Soviet Union, this might be very awkward for Pakistan.

Pakistan is very far from achieving that unity and cohesion that are necessary if it is to survive as a state. Its greatest problem is not remediable. Its physical division almost of necessity made it a federal state, in which East and West Pakistan form separate units. Its federal capital has been Karachi, a cosmopolitan port city, close to the mouth of the Indus. Karachi had nothing specifically Pakistani about it; it is just a big port, and became the capital of the new state for lack of any other contender. Lahore might have become the capital but for its location close to the Indian boundary in the Punjab, and it did in fact become the provincial capital of West Pakistan. Now the Pakistanis are in process of creating a new capital, Islamabad, away in the West near Rawalpindi, which will serve both as a better image of Pakistan to the outsider, and as a focus of the loyalties of the Pakistanis themselves. Dacca, lying amid the maze of waterways which make up the delta of the Ganges and Brahmaputra, is the capital and largest city of East Pakistan. Chittagong, awkwardly placed at the end of a railroad, not far from the Burmese border, has inherited the port functions once performed by Calcutta.

To the northeast of West Pakistan is Kashmir, a province that is at present unequally partitioned between India and Pakistan. Its people are mainly Moslem; its former ruler, the Maharajah, was a Hindu. In 1947 he acceded to—that is, he allowed his lands to be incorporated in—India. The war which followed was short and none too violent, because the Himalayas proved not to be the easiest of battlegrounds. A truce followed, and each side kept what it had got, with India holding the larger area. Truce lines, if they are maintained long enough, have a habit of ripening into permanent boundaries. This could easily happen in partitioned Kashmir.

India and Ceylon

With about 1,269,000 square miles, India is nearly four times the area of Pakistan, and with a population of some 443,000,000, it has nearly five times as many people. It is a land of greater physical variety, and it is, on the whole, a richer state than Pakistan. The huge, triangular peninsula which extends southward between the Arabian Sea and the Bay of Bengal, is made up chiefly of a plateau or tableland, known as the Deccan. The Deccan contains deposits of coal and iron ore and numerous other minerals. Over large areas it has a fertile soil, formed by the disintegration of basaltic rocks, on which cotton grows well. To the west, this plateau rises to a rimlike margin, the Western Ghats, and beyond drops steeply to the narrow coastal plain. Monsoon rains, brought by southwest winds are heavy along the western margin of the Deccan. They feed rivers which flow to both seas; a more intensive, year-round agriculture is made possible. The narrow plain that encloses the plateau of the Deccan is moist at most seasons, and is intensively cultivated. Rice is the chief crop, but millet and other crops are grown in the dry season.

In the northeastern part of the Deccan are deposits of coal and iron ore. These are now being exploited for the growing iron and steel in-

0   500   1000 MILES

Ulan Bator
Amur R.
Harbin
Changchun
Hami (Kumul)
Mukden
Sea of Japan
Rawalpindi
Peking (Peiping)
Yalu R.
Pyongyang
Seoul
Tokyo
Lahore
GREAT
WALL
Ho
Tientsin
Talien (Dairen)
Pusan
Kyoto
Yokohama
Indus R.
Sutlej R.
Tsingtao
Osaka
Nagoya
derabad
Delhi
Katmandu
Lanchou
Yellow Sea
achi
New Delhi
Ganges
Lhasa
Brahmaputra R.
Hwang
Chengtu
Nanking
Shanghai
Agra
Kanpur
Lucknow
Wuhan
Ahmedabad
Banaras
Patna
Narbada R.
Jamshedpur
Dacca
Yangtze
Chungking
Bombay
Nagpur
Calcutta
Chittagong
Si
Kiang
Canton
TROPIC OF CANCER
Poona
Mandalay
Kowloon
Kistna R.
Hanoi
Victoria
Taipei
Bangalore
Madras
Bay of Bengal
Rangoon
Salween R.
Vientiane
Mekong R.
South China Sea
Quezon City
Manila
Colombo
Bangkok
INDIAN
Phnom Penh
Saigon
Penang
Kuala Lumpur
EQUATOR
Malacca
Singapore
OCEAN
Palembang
Makasar
Djakarta
Surabaja
Bandung

80°   90°   100°   110°   120°   130°   140°

PACIFIC OCEAN

ities:
- ● Over 1,000,000
- ● 200,000 to 1,000,000
- ○ Less than 200,000
- — Main railroads
- ···· Grand Canal
- ˄˄˄ Great Wall of China

Cities of Asia have the highest density of population per square mile, but the surrounding lands are also thickly settled.

dustry which the Indian government has established in this area. India now produces about 2,500,000 tons of steel a year, a small amount for a country that contains more than a tenth of the human race. It is just about 14 pounds for each man, woman, and child, but this is an important beginning.

The biggest cities of India are ports which owed their growth and even their origin to British merchants who used them for their trade with India. Many of the factory industries which the British promoted were located in the ports. Largest of these is Calcutta, which has grown from a trading fort established on the muddy banks of the Hooghly, one of the branches into which the Ganges divides to traverse its delta to the sea. Calcutta is the chief port of northeastern India. Along the river are the jute mills, built to fabricate the jute grown in the delta region, much of it now in East Pakistan. Second in extent of metropolitan area is Bombay, founded upon a small island close to the west coast of India, and now a city of almost 4,500,000 people, spreading out onto the mainland. A large part of India's cotton textile industry was established in and around Bombay.

Madras is the third largest port and city. It lies on the east coast, and is the chief port of southeast India, as well as a center of textile, machinery, and chemical industries. Other industries—many of them the traditional Indian crafts in metal, wood, and fibers, but some modern factory industries—are found in the cities over all of the Deccan; in Hyderabad, Bangalore, and Mysore; in Nagpur and Jabalpur in the northern Deccan; and in a hundred others. India is firmly set toward industrialization and her factory industries daily grow in importance.

To the north the hills of the Deccan fade out into the great plain of Hindustan. This vast and almost level area is drained eastward by the Ganges and its tributaries; and westward by the Indus system. Its deep, rich, alluvial soil has been accumulating for millions of years. The plain is the creation of its rivers, and this process of creation is still going forward, as the deltas of the two great rivers slowly extend into the sea.

As the monsoon winds blow in toward the north of India, they take a curving counter-clockwise direction. They blow toward the west coast of the Deccan, then cross back over the peninsula; then they curve northward over the Bay of Bengal toward the lower Ganges Valley. The wall-like barrier of the Himalayas forces them to blow northwestward, up the Ganges Valley. The whole of this region receives very heavy rain. Bombay has 79 inches in a year; Calcutta, 59. Farther up the Ganges Valley the rainfall tapers off. Delhi and India's capital, New Delhi, get only 26 inches and the Punjab gets even less. Crops and the seasonal rhythm of the farmer's life are adjusted to the monsoon and the coming of the rain.

In the lower Ganges Valley water supply presents no problem, and as soon as the rains break, it is easy to fill the paddy fields and set out the rice plants. There is usually enough moisture in the soil or in the rivers for a winter crop to be sown as soon as the rice has been harvested. But farther up the Ganges Valley it becomes more difficult to grow the heavy-cropping rice; the paddy fields have to be filled from the rivers, and where irrigation is not possible, drier, less remunerative crops have to be grown, capable of supporting fewer people to the square mile. This is an important matter in so crowded a country. The maps of rainfall and population look almost the same, so interdependent are they.

India need have no worries about her increasing population if only she could increase also the amount of her summer rain and spread it over a wider area. Modern engineering allows a better and fuller use of the water that does come and dams have been built on many of the Himalayan rivers as they leave their mountain valleys for the plain. But so far it has held out no hope of increasing the volume of rainfall. Meanwhile, the birth rate remains high; public health is being improved, and the survival rate is increasing.

The Indian is a farmer. No less than 70 per cent of the total population lives and works on the land. Even where the rains come at the right time and in the right amount, the Indian peasant is never far from starvation. If they are late, or too sudden and violent, or too little, or if locusts or some other pest devours his crops, the peasant, with no reserves behind him, faces starvation. He borrows from the *banya,* or money-lender, at an exorbitant rate of interest, and probably lives the rest of his life in mounting debt.

The peasant's world is his village, from which he rarely has the time or the resources to travel far. The village is closely built, as if to econo-mize with the land. There is no building stone in the deep silt of the alluvial plains, and the homes are built of brick, sometimes kiln-baked, but with the scarcity of fuel, more often sun-dried. The roofs are of thatch that can be renewed periodically from the reeds along the river bank or from the straw of the grain crops.

The narrow streets abound with animals. Pigs and poultry serve as scavengers, scouring for vegetable waste and putting on a little weight at the same time. There are cattle, rawboned and diseased, but at the same time petted and fed, because the cow is a very sacred animal to the Hindu. And there are the oxen and buffalo which pull the simple wooden plow that stirs up the soil of the paddy field. Occasionally an elephant comes through—in the drier regions it would be a camel—but the whole village collectively could not afford to maintain so big a beast. It is the Cadillac of the animals, the status symbol of the rich; it is also the work animal in the forests where its strength and reliability come in useful in the handling of heavy teak logs.

The lot of the city dweller may be even harder. Indian cities are large, tightly built up, overcrowded and unsanitary, yet colorful and picturesque. Craftsmen in metal, ivory, leather, and silk make a poor living; others are reduced to begging. Snake charmers and holy men provide unwanted services, in the need of anything more constructive to do. Most Indian cities have a downtown area of wide streets and modern shops, and nearby a bazaar where the products of Indian crafts are offered for sale. There will be temples; there may be a palace of one of the former Indian princes or a fort erected in the course of the wars between the Indian states. But much of the rest will be made up of a maze of narrow streets and alleys; of congested tenements and homes, all of them built close together and overcrowded, lacking in the modern conveniences of piped water and sanitation; bright and colorful from a distance but, on any closer inspection, mean and unhealthy. In the villages, two men guide the plow; in the city, every other man begs and conjures for alms. Such is the overpopulation of India.

The names of these overcrowded cities, are like the "magic casements" of Keats, which invite the reader to "faery lands": Srinagar by its lake in the Vale of Kashmir; Amritsar and Lahore, twin capitals of the Punjab, the one in India and the other in West Pakistan; Banaras (now Varanasi) beside the holy Ganges where devout Hindus hope that their ashes will in the end be spread upon the water; Agra, with its Taj Mahal, built of marble in 1631-45 as the tomb of the wife of the Emperor Shah Jehan; Hyderabad and Mysore, former seats of the richest and most powerful of the Indian princes.

The peoples of India entered from the north in successive waves, each advancing southward across the subcontinent and pushing earlier arrivals before it. The descendants of the earliest Indians are to be found in the south of the Deccan, and from here they have spread across the fifty miles of sea that separates Ceylon from India. Thither we must now follow them.

Off the southern tip of India is the small pear-shaped island of Ceylon. It is only about the size of West Virginia, but its population is over 10,000,000. It lies within 450 miles of the equator. Its climate, hot and humid for much of the year, is tempered by the winds from the ocean which blow across it. The mountainous core of the island rises at the center to over eight thousand feet, but around it is a low-lying plain, narrow in the south where the mountains come close to the coast, and widest in the north where most of the population lives. The most widely cultivated crop is rice, which provides the staple food of the Ceylonese. But Ceylon is also an important producer of rubber and coconut products, and tea groves have been established over much of the hilly country in the center of the island. Tea and rubber make up most of Ceylon's exports.

Colombo is the chief port and the largest city, but up in the hills, above the heat and humidity and the rice fields of the coastal plain, is the ancient capital, the small, historic city of Kandy, with its gardens, its Buddhist temples, and the burial places of the ancient kings of Ceylon. Kandy would have been the capital also of modern Ceylon if only it were larger and more accessible. In terms of the amenities required by a modern capital city, it could not compare with Colombo.

Buddhism originated in India. It was by the Ganges that Buddha himself received enlightenment and found inner peace. The religion which he founded was carried outward over much of eastern and southeastern Asia. India's neighbors on this side are Buddhist like Ceylon, but India itself no longer is. The spread of Buddhism from India to Burma and beyond is evidence of a kind of cultural community that embraces almost all of Southeast Asia.

SOUTHEAST ASIA

Southeast Asia covers the complex peninsula which extends toward the equator between India and China. It is made up of alternating mountain ranges, which radiate from the eastern end of the Himalayan system, and of flat alluvial plains. Beyond the limits of the continent the mountains are continued as chains of islands toward the continent of Australia. In this region the monsoon lasts longer than in India; water is more abundant; agriculture is easier, and the carrying capacity of the land is greater. If there is a land of plenty in crowded Asia, it is here.

Burma

Burma lies to the east of India and East Pakistan; along the boundary are the Naga and Arakan hills, high, forested, and inhabited by tribes still not wholly cured of their ancient practice of head-hunting. Burma is made up of the valley of the Irrawaddy and its enclosing mountains. The river rises in the eastern Himalayas and flows southward to the Indian Ocean. The mountains themselves form part of the ranges that fan out from the Himalayas of eastern Tibet and northeastern India.

This relief map of Southeast Asia shows the spread of mountains from Central Asia through Burma, Malaya, and the islands of Indonesia.

They are not as high as the Himalayas, more like the mountains of the Middle East. But they lie exposed to the summer monsoon. For the hot part of the year they are drenched with rain, and their slopes are covered with dense forest, huge trees of teak or sandalwood with, often enough, an impenetrable undergrowth of bamboo. Such forested mountains cut Burma off from India on the one side and from Thailand on the other. And in their recesses live the tribes—primitive and savage if you will— which are little influenced by either the government or the culture of India and Burma, and quite untouched by that of the West.

But the heart of Burma is the long, narrow, flat-floored plain of the Irrawaddy. After the rains have come it is an almost continuous rice field all the way from the deltaic swamp around Rangoon, north past Mandalay to the northern mountains. More than two-thirds of Burma's cropland is under rice; rice is the chief food of the Burmese, and rice forms their chief export. Yet the limit of cultivation has not been reached on the alluvial plains of Burma, as it has on those of India and China. Cropland can be extended, and by more careful water management additional dry-season crops could be grown. Burma is one of the few food surplus countries of Asia; in good years its rice export to countries of Southeast Asia may be nearly 2,000,000 tons, the largest rice export of any country in the world. That fact alone makes Burma important.

Nor is Burma's wealth wholly in her fields. The enclosing ring of mountains has long been known both for its minerals and for its forests. Burma is an important source of lead, zinc, and tin; and the precious metals, as well as gemstones—rubies and sapphires—are mined from its rocks. Almost 15 per cent of the area is reserved as forest for the cutting of teak and other hardwoods which figure among Burma's exports. Burma was formerly yoked unevenly with India under British rule. The Burmese always complained that their welfare was neglected; that the British favored India at their expense. Burma had been acquired later and was often last to be served by the Indian government. In 1937 it achieved separation from India, and when self-government came to these lands, Burma cut its connection completely with Britain and the Commonwealth, and chose a policy of nonalignment and of pursuing its own primitive but prosperous agriculture along the wet bottom lands of the Irrawaddy.

Thailand

Thanks to a novel, a stage play, and a musical, Thailand, or Siam, is now one of the best known countries of Southeast Asia. The land bears a superficial similarity to Burma, consisting of a broad, flat, alluvial plain, enclosed by a ring of hills. The plain is drained southward by the Chao Phraya River, or Menam, which flows to the sea near its capital city of Bangkok. Like Rangoon, Bangkok lies, about twenty-five miles from the sea, up the navigable river. Rice and lumber are brought down to it by boat, and are transshipped for export. Bangkok itself lies low beside the Chao Phraya, penetrated by the ramifying canals, or *klongs,* which were once the highways of the city, boats serving as its trucks and street-cars; the *klongs* are now being replaced by roads. Its landscape is dominated by the exuberant architecture of its Buddhist temples.

High, wild hills separate Thailand from Burma, but to the east, toward Laos and Cambodia, the hills are lower and more broken, and on this side Thailand is more easily penetrated. Therein lies its danger and its importance.

Yet Thailand was never conquered and made a colony of a European power, the only territory in Southeast Asia to escape this fate. The British were in Burma and the French in Indochina, suspicious and distrustful of one another, neither allowing the other to move a step nearer, and between them lay Siam, free and independent because neither of its would-be conquerors would let the other take it. Thailand never had the misfortune of becoming a colony; nor did it gain the advantages which came from colonial status: good schools and universities, roads and railroads, and an efficient civil service.

Thailand is like Burma, and its people are distantly related to the Burmese. The central plain of Thailand is a great rice field, and here too rice provides the chief food and the most important export. As in Burma, the limits of cultivation are very far from having been reached. Dams, now being built along the rivers to conserve water during the rains, will make irrigation possible during the dry season, and so further increase the output of rice and sugar. The hungry peoples of Asia look with envy on the rich, uncrowded plains of Thailand, and Thailand looks for protection and help to the United States and to its allies in the South East Asia Treaty Organization.

Laos, Cambodia, and Vietnam

The southeast corner of Asia, that part now broken up but still sometimes referred to as Indochina, was conquered by the French and held by them until after the Second World War. It has the same geographical characteristics as Burma and Thailand: high mountains and flat, alluvial plains; a hot and humid climate and the torrential rains of summer. Through the centuries Chinese peoples have filtered southward into Indochina, establishing little states of their own. It was these which the French subjugated late in the nineteenth century. French authority collapsed after the end of the Second World War, and from its ruins appeared three independent states: Cambodia, Laos, and Vietnam. Each was based on the cultural associations of its peoples, and reproduced, after a fashion, the ancient political pattern that had existed before the French came.

This southeastern corner of Asia is traversed by the mountains of

Annam, another of the long, narrow ranges that radiate from eastern Tibet. They lie close to the coast line of the China Sea, leaving only a narrow coastal plain between it and the sea. Like all these mountain ranges of Southeast Asia, the Annam range is high, jungle-clad, and difficult to cross. Between it and the sea is the long, narrow country of Vietnam, more than twelve hundred miles from end to end and not much more than a hundred miles wide.

West of the curving line of the Annam Mountains are Laos and Cambodia. Taken together, these two states are smaller than either Burma or Thailand. Laos is hilly, jungle-covered, and only thinly peopled. Rice fields lie along the plain of the Mekong; teak is floated down the rivers for export through Cambodia to the sea. Laos is backward and poor; no one knows for sure even how big its population is; its former capital, Luang Prabang, seat of the king, is no more than a large village; Vientiane, its administrative capital, has about 100,000 inhabitants. There has never been a careful census, and its population is estimated to be less than 2,000,000. Yet Laos lies on China's border, between China and the plains of Thailand, an obvious soft spot in the ring of states that enclose the Communist Bloc.

Cambodia lies to the south of Laos; whereas Laos is mainly hill, most of Cambodia is made up of the level alluvial plain of the lower Mekong River and its tributaries. Its population is larger, but Cambodia is far from overpopulated. Indeed, it has been estimated that only a fifth of the possible cropland is actually cultivated. Even so, Cambodia can afford to export nearly a quarter of its rice crop. How many mouths could Cambodia feed if only her agricultural resources were fully developed? The capital of Cambodia is Phnom Penh, located on the navigable Mekong, where water routes converge from the Cambodian Plain. One hundred and fifty miles to the northwest is the ruined city of Angkor Thom, once the capital of the Cambodian kings who came in from India about a thousand years ago, bringing with them the evidences of Hindu culture which are lavished upon the nearby temple of Angkor Wat.

Beyond the mountains lies Vietnam. It became independent in 1946, though it continued to be associated with France. In 1954, Vietnam was invaded by the Chinese, and in the truce agreement that followed, it was split into a Communist held North Vietnam and an independent South. Of course, this division was regarded as only temporary; free elections would heal the breach. But so far there have been no free elections; the rift between the two parts is deepening, and South Vietnam is crowded with refugees from the North. The two Vietnams are much more densely peopled than the rest of Southeast Asia, but even so they do not have the population pressure that we encounter in China. The Mekong delta in the south and the valley of the Red River in the north are intensively cultivated and even have a rice surplus for export.

The historic capital of Annam, or Central Vietnam, had been Hue, a coastal town about midway between the extremities of this long and awkwardly shaped country. Hue is now a frontier city of South Vietnam, and the function of capital has moved to the extremities, to Saigon, in the South, and to Hanoi, in the Communist North. Both lie, like most other capital cities of Southeast Asia, a few miles inland on a navigable river, the one a branch of the Mekong; the other, of the Red River. Each has grown up as a meeting place between the native peoples and the European merchant who came by sea to trade with them.

Malaya

The mountains which divide Burma from Thailand reach southward as the long narrow Malay Peninsula to within a few miles of the equator. In shape, the peninsula resembles a baseball bat. In the north it is divided between Burma and Thailand; in the middle it belongs wholly to Thailand, and in the south, where the peninsula is widest, is the Federation of Malaya. Lastly, just off the southern tip is Singapore, now independent within the Commonwealth.

The southern part of this peninsula came under British rule during the nineteenth century. Tin was discovered, and the climate proved to be suitable for growing rubber. British capital was invested to develop these resources, and as the easy-going Malays showed little inclination or aptitude for this work, the immigration of Chinese was encouraged.

Today the Federation of Malaya, with its capital in Kuala Lumpur, is a self-governing member of the Commonwealth, but its population is 37 per cent Chinese. More than a tenth of its total area is planted with rubber trees, and rubber makes up almost three-quarters of Malaya's exports. The volume of production of natural rubber in Malaya is only exceeded by its neighbor, Indonesia. Second in importance to rubber, though a long way behind, is tin. The backbone of the Malay Peninsula is made up of granite. Granite sometimes contains the ore of tin, but is heavy and also resistant to corrosion. For millions of years, the granite rocks of Malaya have undergone erosion and the tin has been laid down with the alluvium along the rivers and around the coast. From here tin is today being taken up by means of giant dredges, and separated from the sands and gravels, smelted, and exported.

Malaya, a country no larger than Florida, today produces about a quarter of the world's supply of tin and a third of the natural rubber. This alone would give it a great importance in international affairs, and this importance is reinforced by Malaya's geographical location. Thrust southward from the land mass of Asia, it forces shipping to sail around its southern extremity.

Proposals to cut a canal across the Malay Peninsula in Thailand where it is narrowest, and thus to shorten the voyage have not matured, and today the port of Singapore, on an island off the southern end of the Malayan Peninsula, is the crossroads of Southeast Asia. There is brought the produce of Malaya, of the East Indian islands, and of Southeast Asia for export, and from here are distributed imports from Europe and the New World. The self-governing island of Singapore, in all respects an independent state, linked by bridges with Malaya and by shipping with every other point in the Orient, is the most important commercial center in the whole of this broad region of Southeast Asia. The Chinese dominate the commerce of Southeast Asia. They buy the rubber and the rice, and process and export it, and the city of Singapore is almost wholly Chinese. If it were incorporated into Malaya, as perhaps it should be, the Chinese would thus be able to swamp the native Malays. The British, in their wisdom, kept the two separate, so that the Malays could remain masters at least in their own Malaya. In 1962 proposals for the Malaysia federation which would include North Borneo, Brunei, and Sarawak, as well as Malaya and Singapore, were making headway since the inclusion of Borneo populations would maintain the culture balance between Malays and Chinese.

THE EAST INDIES

Beyond Malaya lie the islands of the East Indies. These are the peaks and ridges of the submerged mountain ranges which continue those of the mainland. Most of these islands are high and rugged, and some are made up of active volcanoes. The climate is no longer strictly monsoon; it is the hot, humid, seasonless regime of the equator. The islands are naturally clad with forest, which merges into tangled jungle over the damp lowlands. Equatorial soils are rarely good, but in parts of the East Indies they have been enriched by the action of the volcanoes. Erupting at intervals through a long span of time, the volcanoes have spread their dust over large areas, and disintegrating in the hot, humid conditions of the tropics, this dust has, locally at least, produced a soil of exceptional quality. Despite the damage done by volcanoes in the island of Java, it has been said that they have, on balance, done more good than harm.

But not all the islands have had the asset of a few volcanoes. Java is one of the most densely peopled areas of the world, but other islands—Sumatra, Borneo, and Celebes—have only poor tropical soils and a thin, scattered population, much of it wild and primitive. The contrasts in development between the islands of the East Indies constitute one of their most prominent features, and these contrasts can, in part at least, be laid to the contrasts in the fertility of the soil.

It was a group of East Indian islands, the Spice Islands, that provided the magnet which drew the Portuguese and Spanish to Asia and attracted Magellan to make his voyage around the world. They are today among the smallest and least important of the islands, but a few centuries ago they were the source of the spices—the pepper, cinnamon, nutmeg, and mace—whose high price in Europe justified the sending of expeditions to the Indies to obtain them at their source. The Portuguese, the British, and the Dutch vied for possession of these islands, now known as the Molucca Islands. The Dutch won, and from the early seventeenth to the mid-twentieth century, they spread their net over them, extracting maximum production from the native peoples and monopolizing the trade.

The Dutch were ruthless and efficient. The profits of their trade with the Indies were reflected in the proud merchant houses in Amsterdam. Commercial emphasis shifted in time from spices to tin and rubber, and the focus of the Indies ceased to be the Spice Islands and became the fertile island of Java, and the tin-bearing islands of Bangka and Belitung. The Dutch set up their capital near the western end of Java in the city which they called Batavia, from the Latin name of their home country; today we know it as Djakarta. At the opposite end of the same island they developed the port of Surabaja, one of the most important in Southeast Asia. Java became, under Dutch rule, one of the most densely populated areas in the world, but the Dutch concerned themselves but little with the outer territories, and their hand lay only lightly over the forested interior of Sumatra and Borneo. In the later years of Dutch occupation plantations spread into Sumatra, and Palembang, its largest city, has grown gradually in size and importance.

The Dutch rule of the Indies appeared to face no serious challenge when the Japanese demonstrated in December, 1941, how easy it is to overthrow the white rulers of such regions. Dutch authority collapsed, and the Dutch never succeeded in restoring it. Out of the turmoil of Japanese invasion, occupation, and expulsion, there emerged the Republic of Indonesia. This is by no means one of the more solid and successful states of the modern world. The Dutch, who had never thought it possible that they would ever be obliged to quit, had done nothing to train their successors, and for several years good government in Indonesia has been obstructed by incompetence, graft, and civil war.

Neither Indonesia nor the rest of the world can tolerate the under-development of Indonesia's outer territories—first southern Sumatra, and then the coast of Borneo, and the strangely shaped Celebes, like a worm on a fisherman's hook. They contain oil, tin, and other minerals, perhaps in very large quantities; they are capable of supporting tropical plantation crops. Slowly development is penetrating them. If Indonesia does not herself open up and further develop these lands, a big neighbor of hers to the north may well come and do it for her.

Borneo is almost a byword for primitive savagery. Doubtless its popular reputation maligns the island, but it is nevertheless backward and difficult of access. Most of it belongs to Indonesia, but its northern margin fell, in one way or another, under British control. A part was occupied in 1841 by a strange, romantic freebooter named James Brooke, who managed to inherit the throne of the Rajah of Sarawak. For three generations the "white Rajahs" ruled this area as if they were enlightened eastern potentates—to the puzzled amusement of the rest of the world. Then in 1946 the last of them threw Sarawak into the lap of the British who had already, under a variety of titles and pretexts, occupied the north of the island and established the colonies or protectorates of Brunei, Labuan, and North Borneo. British Borneo has been longer exposed to European rule than the rest of the island, and once had its own traditional native kingdoms; Brunei is the last of such kingdoms. Its peoples, mixed though they are in racial and cultural origins, have affinities with the Malays, and it is quite possible that they may soon become part of a greater Malayan federation.

THE PHILIPPINES

Northeast of Borneo lies the ragged, untidy group of the Philippines. In origin their people were of the same stock as that which peopled

Malaya and Indonesia. They absorbed Chinese elements, and from the sixteenth century began to absorb Spanish. The Philippines must rank as one of the more successful attempts by Europeans to found colonies and settlements within the tropics. This success does not, however, spring from any high ideals or vigorous effort on the part of the Spaniards. It probably derives first from the physical geography of the Philippines; the fact that they are an open group of relatively small islands, among which movement has always been easy. The islands as a whole stood far enough from the equator to have the stimulus of seasonal change and to offer conditions that were fairly propitious to the Europeans who came.

Secondly, the success owes much to the lack of racial consciousness of the Spanish settlers themselves. They interbred with the native Fili-

pinos. They brought their Catholic religion to the majority of the population, and made out of the Philippine Islands the only Asian state that was largely Christian in religion. The Philippines had the further advantage of American rule from the time when they fell from the faltering hands of Spain in 1898, until 1946 when the Americans bowed out and the Philippines achieved complete independence.

The Philippines are said to consist of about seven thousand islands—nearly as many as there are lakes in Minnesota. Many of them have neither names nor importance and only one in fourteen covers more than a single square mile, and of these the largest are Luzon in the north of the group and Mindanao in the south. Manila, the largest city, and its suburb Quezon City, the new Philippine capital, lie in Luzon as does the unforgettable Bataan Peninsula, scene of the tragic American stand in the Second World War, which shelters Manila Bay from the South China Sea. Manila, one of the finest harbors in the Orient lies on the almost land-locked Manila Bay and is the commercial focus of the Philippine Islands and of much of Southeast Asia.

The Philippines are richer than all their neighbors in Southeast Asia, but that does not mean that they are well off. The average income of a Filipino—little over $200 a year—is only a tenth of that of an American. The people are mostly engaged in agriculture. Many live in small, self-sufficing communities, as they have to in a country as broken up by mountain and sea as the Philippines. Their farms are small; some are minute. Rice is grown for food, hemp (from the abaca plant) and sugar cane for export. Corn, tobacco, and the products of the coconut palm make up much of the remainder of their agricultural production.

FORMOSA (TAIWAN)

North of the Philippines a ridge rises from the floor of the Pacific Ocean. It continues the direction of the mountains of Luzon, and it supports the small islands of Batan. At the northern end of this submarine elevation is the island of Taiwan, or Formosa. It is a small, rugged island of 13,885 square miles, only twice the size of the State of New Jersey, but it rises in Sinkao Shan (13,113 feet) to mountains almost as high as Pikes Peak. Taiwan was the refuge to which the Chinese Nationalist forces of Chiang-Kai-shek retreated in the face of the Communist armies. On this embattled island, separated by a hundred miles of sea from the mainland of China, they still remain.

Taiwan has long had difficulty in supporting its dense population, and now an army and a horde of refugees have added to the population pressure. There are today over 11,000,000 people crowded onto its small area of farm land or into its cities. They are mostly farmers. Rice and sugar are their chief crops, and they grow tea over the steep hillsides. The traditional Chinese crafts have always been carried on. Now modern industries, like smelting and machinery manufacture, have been established, not only to supply the local population, but also to employ part of its surplus labor.

Taipei, lying at the northern end of the island, is the capital of Formosa; it has grown suddenly to be a city of over a million. At the opposite end is Tainan, the seat of Chiang Kai-shek's government, which claims to be the legitimate government of all China, and treats the Taipei authorities as merely the government of a Chinese province.

JAPAN

Another submarine ridge extends eight hundred miles northeast from Taiwan to the islands of Japan. From it arise the small, rocky Ryukyu Islands, among them Okinawa, the scene of the strongly resisted American landings in 1945. The Japanese islands are larger and more mountainous than any of the others that lie off the southern and eastern shores of Asia. There are four major islands, each with a fringe of islets and rocks, and together they stretch for almost fifteen hundred miles in a gentle curve, like a stretched bow pointing to the Pacific Ocean, from the southern Kyushu to the northern Hokkaido.

They span the same range of latitude as the eastern seaboard of the United States from northern Florida to northern Maine. But, whereas the eastern seaboard is backed by the huge extent of a large continent, Japan is ringed by the sea and subjected to maritime influences. It belongs to Monsoon Asia but is not intimately bound up with it, a relationship that underlies the geography and history of Japan.

Japan has an area of 142,733 square miles, about equal to that of Montana, the fourth largest of the United States, and a population slightly more than half that of the United States, or nearly 94,500,000. And it has a terrain more mountainous and rugged than Montana; agricultural land is reckoned to cover only about 16 per cent of the area, and you can be sure the Japanese have left no part of their land unused unless there was good reason for not cultivating it. All four of the main islands are mountainous. Relatively, there is less cropland in Japan than in Korea, and the population density of Japan as a whole makes that of China seem like a land of wide, open spaces. The sea has invaded and drowned much of the lowland of southern Japan, forming the delicate, island-studded Inland Sea, which separates the islands of Shikoku and Kyushu from Honshu. A good share of the cities of Japan are gathered round its shores, and small boats thread their way between the islands, linking them together.

Climate is no less important than relief in determining the settlement and agriculture of Japan. No place is more than about seventy miles from the sea, and maritime influences are always present, increasing the rainfall and moderating the temperatures. Kyushu has a subtropical climate, like that of Florida, and the southern part of Honshu and the island of Shikoku have mild winters; but northward the severity of winter increases and northern Honshu and Hokkaido are cold and snowy despite the moderating influence of the sea.

The Japanese monsoon is much less abrupt and violent than the Indian. It brings most of the rain to most of Japan, filling the paddy fields in summer. But it is compensated as it were, by a winter monsoon. This is a modest affair, produced by winds blowing outward from the Asian land mass gathering moisture over the Sea of Japan, and dropping it over the mountains on the inner side of the curve of the islands' mountains.

Wherever the terrain allows it, Japan is intensively cultivated. Farms are small, and in the Oriental tradition are tilled as if they were gardens. On average there are one and a half persons employed in the cultivation of each acre of land. Farming is not mechanized in any accepted sense of the term, but thousands of little, hand-operated rotary tillers are dragged and pushed around the tiny fields, preparing the paddy fields for the rice plants and tearing up the soil after the harvest is in. In this way Japan has reconciled her traditional ways of land holding with modern methods of cultivation.

Not all Japan can grow rice. Paddy fields cover over half the cropland, but much of the north is too cold for it to grow and ripen. There it is replaced by wheat, barley, soybeans, and temperate fruit. In Japan there is a continual struggle to increase food production. Rice production always falls short of requirements and up to a fifth of this essential food has to be imported. Over ground too rough for crops mulberry trees may be grown, and silk worms fed their leaves. The breeding of the worms

and the preparation of the silk cocoons is a cottage industry in much of Japan, providing a valuable supplement to the income from agriculture. Hokkaido is to Japan what Manchuria and Inner Mongolia have been to China. It is the pioneer fringe where, in a climate which is too severe for the Japanese to settle readily, farming and stock raising on a larger and more Western scale are spreading.

Japan can support so many people on so little land only by the intensive development of factory industry. This expansion has been extraordinarily rapid. When, just over a century ago, Japan was opened up to Western influences, its leaders decided to make it a developed, industrial power. They displayed an exceptional skill in picking up the essentials of a machine civilization and in adapting their society and institutions to make room for it. At first they copied Western methods and products, then they experimented, and lastly they developed their own characteristic products.

Japan has often been called the "Britain of the East." The similarity is only superficial. Both are crowded island groups; both have developed a factory industry based on machine power, and both have come to depend heavily on trade. Japan has been much less well endowed than Great Britain. The climate permits, over part of the country, a more intensive agriculture, but mineral resources are scanty. Coal and petroleum are found in only small amounts; there is very little iron ore, and the nonferrous metals are, in effect, represented only by copper. Raw silk is produced, but not in sufficient quantities for the industries of Japan, and most of the raw cotton has to be imported. The only significant assets which the Japanese have are the industry and skill of her people and the large resources in hydroelectric power.

No factory site in Japan can possibly be far from the sea, but most are actually on the coast. The great industrial cities are port cities, through which the coal and ores and raw cotton can be imported. Largest of them all is the urban complex that encloses the deep, sheltered Yokohama Bay, on the southeast coast of Honshu. On it lie the port city of Yokohama, through which passes a large part of Japan's foreign trade; iron and steel plants, each with their own dock facilities; and the great sprawling city of Tokyo, the capital of Japan.

West of Yokohama Bay are other industrial complexes, many spreading over small coastal plains that lie around the margin of the islands: Nagoya, Osaka, Kobe, Kyoto, Hiroshima, and Nagasaki, each with its manufacture of textiles or steel or the thousand and one little articles made with consummate skill to fit the desires and tastes of the dime-store clientele of the New World; and the city of Fukuoka and its steel-producing neighbor of Yawata. Only by trade can Japan import both the raw materials for her industries and the foodstuffs to supplement what her fields and her fisheries can supply. Trade necessitates a merchant marine, and Japan has long had a large fleet of merchant and passenger ships. Many were lost during the Second World War but Japan is now regaining its earlier level of importance in merchant shipping.

Beneath the outward calm of Japan is a deep-seated violence. A symbol of it is the near perfect cone of Fujiyama, the snow-capped volcano that wears a faint plume of smoke and rises 12,388 feet above the nearby sea, only fifty miles to the west of Yokohama. Volcanoes are often associated with earthquakes; both are indications of fracturing and instability in the earth's crust. Off the coast of Honshu, the sea floor descends steeply, almost precipitously, to depths of over 20,000 feet. The floor of the ocean and Mount Fuji, about 35,000 feet, or seven miles, apart vertically, lie within two hundred miles of one another. It is not surprising that this is one of the least stable parts of the earth's crust, or that earthquakes, most of them minor it is true, are daily occurrence. This factor influences many aspects of life in Japan. Buildings must be built either strong enough to resist the shock waves or light enough to do little damage if they collapse.

There are few old buildings in Japan. The centers of the larger cities are marked by large, modern, steel-and-concrete buildings, but all around are low, one-or-two-storied buildings and homes. Most cities have no sky-lines. The villages are clusters of small cottages, built of wood and thatched with straw, occupying a patch of land a few feet above the level of the paddy fields in the south and elsewhere built where they detract least from the extent of cropland. Fields are small, neat, and regular, covering every inch of land that can be tilled. Over slopes too steep to plow or too cut up with terraces for paddy, there are tea gardens or plantations of mulberry trees, grown to feed the gluttonous silkworms. It is a trim, well-regulated landscape, where an unusually skillful and industrious people have used their agricultural resources to the full.

EAST ASIA

As we turn from the islands of Japan to Korea and China, we come to a land cast in a bigger and more heroic mold, beside which Japan is but a garden. It's not that the Koreans and Chinese are less industrious; only their land is more rugged and its climate more severe. The Japanese, as they look at the mainland of Asia, might say, as was said by the early European settlers in the New World: "This was indeed a lustier land . . . a land of hotter summers and colder winters, of brighter and hotter sun and more tempestuous rain," than the gentler land of Japan.

The Koreas

The Korean Strait, between the Japanese island of Kyushu and the southeastern tip of Korea, is little more than a hundred miles across, yet this is no measure of the contrast between Japan and Korea. No such revolution as that which has transformed Japan ever took place in Korea. Korea is a country where the traditional modes of agriculture, practiced by the majority of the population, have continued undisturbed for centuries, except by the occasional invasion from China or Japan.

This contrast between Japan and Korea tends to hide the fact of the long, cultural community that links them. Korea is the bridge between the Chinese mainland and the Japanese islands, across which elements of Chinese culture crossed to be incorporated into that of Japan. And the Japanese people themselves in part derive from the Mongoloid peoples of eastern Asia, and probably reached their present homeland by way of Korea.

The "Land of Morning Calm" found its quiet rudely shattered that day in 1945 when it was invaded from opposite ends by Russians and Americans, and the land was partitioned between the two. It was only a short, uneasy pause before, in 1950, the calm was again broken by North Koreans invading the southern part of the peninsula. Within the next year, every corner of this country, about the size of Kansas, had been fought over, its cities reduced to ruins, its fields neglected, and a large part of the population in flight. The truce line, along the 38th parallel of latitude, reflected the stalemate in the Korean fighting. It has ripened into a political boundary and for ten uneasy years, Korea has been divided into a Communist North and a non-Communist South.

The whole country is mountainous but North Korea is more rugged than South, and South Korea has larger expanses of agricultural land than North. Korea is like a rugged inhospitable version of northern Japan. Winters are cold; the nearness of the ocean increases precipitation and adds to the snowfall. Summers are hot. Take the temperature extremes of New York City, add the snows of New England, the heavy summer rains of the Midwest, and the rugged mountainous terrain of Idaho—and you have Korea. Toward the north, the bare, brown mountains become higher, their pattern more complex, until, along the Chinese border, where the Yalu River cuts through them to the sea, they merge into the even more forbidding mountains of Manchuria.

Amid these mountains, and on the scraps of plain that lie between the mountains and the encircling sea, live about 34,000,000 Koreans. Three-quarters of them live in South Korea, and many of these are refugees from the North. However its wealth is calculated, Korea comes out as one of the poorest countries in the world, and its poverty has been intensified by warfare, destruction, and refugees.

The Koreans, like the Chinese themselves, are mainly farmers. Despite the greater harshness of their land, they are crowded along the valley bottoms and over the coastal plains in villages of small primitive wooden huts, growing rice, cotton, and tobacco in irrigated fields, and wherever water cannot be had, sowing dry crops like wheat and barley. In times of peace Korea used to have a small food surplus, over and above the modest needs of its people. Japan used to import rice from Korea.

The Japanese, who controlled Korea from the late nineteenth century until 1945, had developed a factory industry here. They had found that the poor, overcrowded Koreans were able and willing to work well for low wages. Cotton and silk mills, chemical and fertilizer factories, cement and hydroelectric works were built, and after the Japanese defeat Korea seemed set for a future in manufacturing industry. Then the Korean War shattered the hopes and expectations of the Korean people and reduced the factories to ruins. The cities of Korea were few, but they were large and growing. Not only were they the seats of industry; they were also the receptacles for those whom population pressure had crowded off the land. Both Seoul and Pusan in South Korea are vast, crowded, squalid agglomerations, each with a big city core set in a monstrously overgrown village with over a million people.

Korea, in its historical role of a bridge between Japan and China, has been controlled by these two great powers in turn. From about 1876 until 1945 the dominant influence had been Japanese. Late in 1950 Chinese forces broke across the boundary and made firm their grip on the northern half of Korea, repeating a geographical pattern of political control that has existed many times in the past. Though distinct in language and in many aspects of its culture, Korea is in some respects more than half Chinese. Its religion and social organization it shares with China, and but for the barrier of mountains that lies across the north, Korea might never have been separated from it.

China

Beyond the mountains of North Korea, beyond the Yalu River, lies China. The Western World has long been fascinated and just a little frightened by China. Its great extent, its huge population, the apparent stability and orderliness of its society, and above all the spiritual isolation of the Chinese and their contempt for all other cultures and peoples have presented Western man with a challenge. Here was a society which was civilized while his ancestors still lived in savagery. It had a coherent culture; its art and literature challenged comparison with any in the West. Apparently impervious to influences from without, it always seemed ready to expand and to engulf peoples and cultures around its borders. Chinese civilization has fascinated with its aloofness and threatened with its size and its disciplined singleness of purpose.

Long before the Chinese Communists drove down to the sea and made China a Communist state, the shadow of the Chinese had lain ominously over all the small countries of Southeast Asia. Through the centuries these countries had been invaded by Chinese peoples, and their languages and cultures had come to be derived in part from China. During the nineteenth century Chinese immigrants had filtered southward to Malaya and the East Indies, taking over small-scale businesses, dominating trade in some areas, monopolizing it in others. In all the larger cities of Southeast Asia there are colonies of Chinese; they control the rubber and tin industries of Malaya, and they have built a little China in the city of Singapore.

It is nothing new, then, for these countries to be overshadowed and threatened by the immense population of China. What is new is that a strong, vigorous, and utterly ruthless government has replaced the flabby and ineffective rule of the last Chinese emperors, and that this outward pressure of the Chinese peasant and trader is now reinforced by the power of the Communist Party.

China—Mainland or Red China as it is so often called—is not only the most populous state in the world, it has almost twice the population of the next largest, India. Seven hundred million Chinese inhabit the third largest territory in the world; only the Soviet Union and Canada are larger in area. It is the sheer size of China that is at present so frightening. Its industrial development, its power to equip its armies, is still very much less than that of the Soviet Union, but it is growing at a forced pace. If ever the technological strength of China comes to match the size of its population, then the rest of the world, including China's neighbor, the Soviet Union, will surely have cause for alarm.

China lies between the Pacific Ocean and the great ranges and plateaus of the little-known center of Asia. On the west the high, snow-capped ranges of the Tien Shan cut China off from Soviet Central Asia, and the even higher and less penetrable Himalayas separate it from India. But north of the Tien Shan and east of the Himalayas there are gaps in the mountains. The medieval traveler, Marco Polo, threaded his way from Persia, around the northern margin of the Pamir, through the Sinkiang Basin, across the southern fringe of the Gobi Desert, until at last he dropped into the Hwang Ho Valley, crossed the Great Wall, and was in China. Many a modern traveler has followed in his footsteps, and today trucks from the Soviet Union bump along the desert road. It is still a long and difficult journey, but it is being made often enough. A railroad is now being laid along the route once traversed by Marco Polo and the silk caravans that brought the products of ancient China to such merchant cities as Bukhara and "silken Samarkand" (now included in the Uzbek region of the Soviet), en route to the Mediterranean Sea and the warehouses of Venice and Genoa.

The mountains of Central Asia separate two worlds, but the barrier which they present has never been absolute. Toward the northeast these ranges—the Tien Shan, the Altai, the Yablonovy—become lower and more broken and frayed out. The grasslands of Central Asia reach between them, forming as it were a broad, irregular corridor, along which the horsemen from the Russian steppe could travel into the dried-up grasslands of Outer Mongolia, the independent republic, and the slightly less arid Inner Mongolia, which is a province of China.

Over much of Inner and Outer Mongolia stretches the Gobi Desert, the eastern extension of the belt of desert and semidesert that stretches from the Great Sahara and the Middle East. Although the latter are tracts of completely arid desert, most of the Gobi is far from extreme. It is dry steppe or semidesert, across which man could travel without great difficulty. Along this route from Central Asia to the valleys and plains of northern China came the hordes of invaders at intervals through the five thousand years of China's history; and they have been one of the great formative influences in China.

The Chinese state emerged in these northern grasslands where the invaders first met with sedentary people, and together with them created the Chinese civilization of the early dynasties. Across these grasslands later dynasties built the Great Wall, to serve as a conspicuous and unmistakable limit to their jurisdiction. The Great Wall was a formidable, though not an insuperable obstacle. It was symbolic of the division between the settled, cultivated lands of China and the steppe, with its nomadic population of wild Tartar tribesmen.

China proper lies within the Great Wall on the north, and behind the shelter of the great mountain ranges on the west. It consists essentially of the valleys of the three great rivers, the Hwang Ho, the Yangtze, and the Si. All three rise in the western mountains. The high plateau of Tibet, which covers an area of 470,000 square miles, as large as the whole Midwest of the United States, and lies mostly at an altitude of 15,000 feet above sea level, is the source of most of the great rivers of eastern and southern Asia. Toward its eastern margin, the rivers which rise from its melting snows begin to cut enormous gorges into the rim of the plateau. The more northerly of the rivers unite to form the Hwang Ho. Then comes a fan of rivers which make up the Yangtze, and in the south are the stupendous gorges of the great rivers of Southeast Asia— the Mekong of China and Laos, the Salween and Irrawady of Burma, and the Brahmaputra of India and Pakistan.

Less than five hundred miles separates the gorges of the Brahmaputra from those of the Hwang Ho, but no five hundred miles on the face of the earth presents greater obstacles. A series of gorges, each of them longer, deeper, and more rugged than the Grand Canyon, carry the drainage of the Tibetan Plateau southward and eastward. Between them, the mountains in places soar to over twenty thousand feet. This is China's western wall, beyond which lie the high plateaus of China's outer territories.

From this western barrier, ranges reach eastward across China, separating its river basins and becoming lower as they approach the Pacific Coast. Between the Hwang Ho and the Yangtze, they reach out as the Tsinling Shan, and terminate in low hills while still almost five hundred miles from the ocean; around their eastern extremity spreads the Great Plain, the vast, moist, alluvial lowland which the rivers have created throughout the long, unchronicled centuries of China's prehistory. Out in this plain, like islands rising from the alluvial sea, are steep, sharp-edged hills, relics of the mountains which once stretched farther eastward toward the Pacific. Among these is Shantung, made up of two groups of hills, which, not so very long ago, were islands in the ocean; now they are anchored to the mainland and form a hilly peninsula jutting into the Yellow Sea. The Great Plain of China, the largest expanse of alluvial soil on the face of the earth, is the creation of the two great rivers, the Hwang Ho and the Yangtze, which flow across it to the sea.

The Hwang Ho, the more northerly of these rivers, after leaving the gorges which protect the approaches to Tibet, cuts across the grasslands of Inner Mongolia. This is a vast dry land of great inherent fertility. Over it was spread during the dry, windy phases of the Ice Age a veneer of loess. This fine-grained deposit is pervious to the little rain that falls. Its surface is dry and grassy. It is soft and easily washed by the Hwang Ho in its angular course across it; the fine particles of loess are gathered up and carried downstream by the river's swift, yellow-brown current. Over the plain, the current of the stream slows; the loess sinks to the bottom; the river is choked, floods, and changes its course.

This river, known also as the "Yellow," has been aptly called "China's Sorrow." No river has changed its course with such violence and with such destruction of farms and families as the Hwang Ho, and as if to make restitution for its orgies of destruction, no river has created more and better land from the burden of silt it has brought down from the hills. A little over a century ago it flowed to the sea to the south of the Shantung Peninsula then, after a disastrous flood, it changed its course and entered the sea nearly 250 miles to the north of its old mouth.

The political center of China has alternated between the north and the south, according to which was dominant in China's political life. The more northerly capital has been in recent centuries Peking, or Peiping. It lies on the border between the Great Plain and the loess-covered plateaus of the northwest. It was the seat of the last emperors, who lived here in the "Forbidden City," and now of the Communist leaders, and is the foremost center of Chinese learning and culture.

The Yangtze is, in many ways, a better ordered river. It drops from its plateau source, through the gorges of its upper course, into the basin of Szechwan. This is a hilly region, ringed by higher hills and drained by the tributaries of the Yangtze. After gathering its ring of tributaries, as if to gain strength for the task, the Yangtze then cuts eastward, across the encircling mountains to enter the Great Plain, which it shares with the Hwang Ho. These gorges, which lie between the city of Ichang and the Szechwan Basin, are better known and less spectacular than the upper gorges. Here the river boils downward between steep cliffs, but, despite its hazards, it is regularly navigated by Chinese boatmen. Today the Yangtze is the chief link between the Szechwan Basin and the Great Plain. At Ichang the gorge of the Yangtze ends, and the Great Plain begins abruptly.

For a thousand miles the Yangtze flows across its broadening plain to the sea, passing industrial cities like Wuhan and Nanking, the "Southern Capital," which in recent years has shared with Peking the role of capital. The Yangtze enters the sea by an island-studded estuary which is in the process of turning itself into a delta. On the small Hwang Pu River, which enters the estuary from the south, lies the port and city of Shanghai, the largest city on the continent of Asia, and the chief port of China.

South of the Yangtze River is a great region of tangled hills, which covers most of south China. To the west this region merges into the western mountain wall which borders Tibet, a vast land of rugged mountains and deep valleys and narrow plains; to the east it ends along the coast of the Pacific Ocean in cliffs and a fringe of offshore islands, two of which, Matsu and Quemoy, have in recent years gained a prominence that is geographically quite undeserved. This rugged coast line is broken by small patches of plain and the branching estuaries of the short rivers that drop down from the highlands of the interior. Along this beautiful coast were the ports through which Europeans first made contact with China. There lay Foochow, Amoy, Swatow, and Hong Kong. There

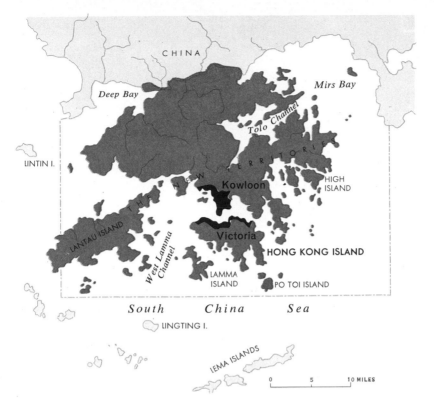

From the original offshore colony, Hong Kong has grown to these proportions.

junks gathered together the silk, the porcelain, and other products of China, and there the European merchants brought their opium and metal goods, their weapons and tools, for trading with the Chinese.

The Si, the third of the three great rivers of China flows across hilly country from the mountainous west to the hilly east. Its valley is more shallow and its plain narrower than those of the Yangtze and Hwang Ho, and it has never played so great a role in the history of China as more northerly river basins. On one of the branches of its delta lies Canton, the chief port of south China. Only eighty miles away, part almost on the delta at the entrance to the river, is the British colony of Hong Kong, with its capital Victoria, now the chief avenue of trade with China.

The original colony was a rocky, picturesque island, covering only twenty-nine square miles. It had the advantages, but also the inconveniences, of being separated from the Chinese mainland by the water which now constitutes its harbor. By successive stages the British got possession first of Kowloon across the water and then in 1898 lease of the "New Territories," which cover over 365 square miles of the Chinese mainland. Over the steep slopes of the island are the shacks of the Chinese, and in its midst lies the world of Suzie Wong. Its streets are crowded with refugees from the mainland; and its harbor, sheltered between the island and the mainland, is filled with liners and freighters, and the clumsy Chinese junks with their square bamboo sails which carry much of the trade of coastal China and house a large part of the population for whom there is no room on land.

China is a monsoon country. As the temperatures build up over Central Asia during the summer a vast low pressure system forms and winds are sucked in; winds from the south rise over the Himalayas from India, and from the southeast winds from the Pacific Ocean blow in over the coast of China. The Chinese monsoon begins less suddenly than the Indian, but it continues with just as much violence. Rain is greatest in the south. Over 100 inches of rain may fall on the hillsides facing the sea. On Hong Kong, the fierce downpours of summer may bring 60 inches in a four-month period. The rains diminish toward the interior and toward the north. Much of the Great Plain has less than 40 inches of rain, and in Inner Mongolia, where the grassy steppeland begins, the annual rainfall drops to under 20, and then to less than 10 inches.

Southern China belongs to the tropics; it is in the latitude of Cuba and Florida. Its winters are warm and its summers are hot. Trees are in leaf and crops grow throughout the year; two and even three crops are grown a year. The monsoon rains of summer fill the paddy fields, and the young rice plants are planted in the soft mud. They ripen as the monsoon rains diminish and then cease. The rice is harvested and the land is prepared for a winter crop, like wheat or sorghum, that requires less moisture. Sometimes enough moisture remains in the soil, sometimes irrigation has to be used. Sometimes the soil, climate, and water supply combine to allow a third crop of rice or wheat to be taken in spring before the rains come again.

This intensity of farming diminishes toward the north. Only rarely can two crops be harvested in the Yangtze Valley, and still farther north the increasing severity of winter freezes the soil, locks the irrigation canals in ice, and brings plant growth to a stop. There crops can be grown only in summer, and as the violence of the monsoon diminishes, so must greater reliance be placed on irrigation. Dry crops, like wheat and sorghum replace wet crops, like rice, until even rainfall and irrigation water become scarce and crop farming gives way to animal farming in the Mongolian steppe.

China is a land of farmers. For five thousand years the practice of agriculture has changed very little—until yesterday. The Chinese have irrigated and cultivated their small farms, cutting terraces into the steep hillsides in the south to hold the water in the paddy fields, cutting irrigation canals across the Great Plain in the north, returning to the soil everything that came from it and, without fertilizer or fallow, maintaining its productivity. Chinese agriculture is a miracle of economy in the use of the land, and an object lesson to conservationists everywhere.

But the traditional Chinese farming is possible only where irrigation is possible. To the west, cultivation ends against the high mountain barrier of Tibet; to the northwest and north, it fades gradually away in the dry steppe. This is China's frontier where for several generations now the farmer has been pushing out ever deeper into the dry, dusty hills. It reminds one of the American farmer advancing his frontier across Kansas and into Colorado; of the Russians, plowing up their "virgin lands." But the Chinese farmer is not at home in virgin lands. By instinct, he is a gardener. He would be more at home on the truck farms of New Jersey or the irrigated vegetable farms of southern California, than in the unending wheat fields of Kansas or the Dakotas. But population pressure has driven the Chinese out from their homeland even to these extremes.

To the northeast of China proper is Manchuria. Cut off from the sea and from marine influences by mountains, only a half-century ago it was a vast, empty region, lying between Korea and Russian Siberia. Its summers were warm, its winters bitterly cold, and over its surface a short grass covered a rich, dark soil. This region was beyond the Great Wall; it was nomads' country, where the Mongol tribes had formerly pitched their rounded tents and grazed their herds. Early in the present century the Chinese peasants began to move into Manchuria. Population pressure must have been severe indeed in China proper to drive them to settle and cultivate land so little suited to their own way of farming. The lowlands of Manchuria are now under cultivation and the peasant is inching slowly into the Mongolian steppe, lying to the west, north of the great bend of the Hwang Ho. Great cities, Mukden (Shenyang) and Harbin, both of them cities of a million or more, have grown up, and on a peninsula reaching south from Manchuria into the Yellow Sea, are the ports called Port Arthur (Lüshun) and Darien (Talien).

To the northwest are the grasslands of Inner Mongolia, potentially fertile, but too dry ever to attract the Chinese peasants as Manchuria has done; to the north the grasslands merge into the desert of Gobi. To the west is the basin of Sinkiang, ringed by mountains, and drained only by intermittent streams which evaporate and are lost in its sandy wastes. Around the margin of the plain, between it and the encircling mountains which supply them with water, are the ancient caravan cities of Khotan, Yarkand, and Kashgar, strangely disguised under their modern names of Hotien, Soch'e, and Sufu.

The snowy wastes of the Kunlun overlook the basin of Sinkiang from the south, and beyond them, reaching to the border of India, is the high, cold, barren plateau of Tibet, which rises to over 20,000 feet above the sea, and never sinks to less than 10,000. Most of it is uninhabitable waste, and the Tibetan people live mainly in the south, along the Brahmaputra Valley, where lies the Tibetan capital of Lhasa.

China has probably been the most populous country in the world since the beginning of human history, and since this time the population of China has mostly been increasing. For thousands of years it has pressed against the agricultural resources of the country, and it has usually lived on the border of starvation. In good years, when the rains came, the peasants ate, and at other times they starved, or they joined the armies of self-proclaimed "marshals," preferring to die fighting or to live at other's expense, rather than to succumb to slow starvation. So only civil wars, pestilence, famine, and the human toll taken by the periodic floods have sufficed to keep the human race within the bounds set by food supply.

Today the rivers are better controlled and floods less disastrous; disease is not as rampant as it once was, and temporarily at least, there is no war within China. The population is mounting and growing demand for food has necessitated extraordinary steps to satisfy it. Most recent has been the formation of farming communes, antlike settlements in which the human being is just a work unit, ordered and regimented by the commune boss. This may be justified as "primitive communism"; in reality it is a means of extracting more food from an acre of soil. It is demography, not dogma, which explains and excuses it. The fact is that it is very difficult, and locally it is almost impossible, to intensify the agriculture of China. The communes appear to have been a failure in their declared objective—to increase agricultural production. China is bursting at the seams and, Communist or not, presents a threat to all

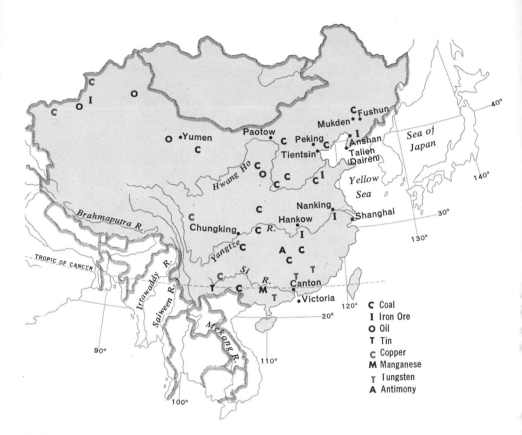

THE MINERAL RESOURCES OF CHINA

the lands to the south and southeast, where the density of population is less than her own.

Can the development of factory industry provide any kind of solution to China's problem? It can absorb labor which is superfluous in the fields; it can supply the farmer with better tools and with fertilizer. It can create the modern means of transportation by which farm surpluses in one region can be supplied to others, and lastly, factory industries can manufacture goods for export, to pay for her import of foodstuffs.

China has large resources. Coal is abundant in many parts of the interior; there are extensive reserves of iron ore, and many important nonferrous metals also occur in large quantities. The potentiality for generating hydroelectric power from the rivers as they emerge from the mountains is almost unlimited. Industrial crops, cotton and hemp, oil seeds and silk, are grown or produced to supply Chinese mills. The use of these resources in a small way began many decades ago. Cotton mills in Shanghai and other cities of central China were established by outside capitalists, Japanese or British. A small iron-smelting industry was formed. These industries are being expanded at a rate which appears to the rest of the world to be frighteningly rapid.

China is not yet one of the great manufacturing countries of the world, but she is well on the road to becoming one. She has only to maintain her present rate of progress, and her industrial power may become proportionate to her population. In 1960 her coal production was 420,000,000 tons, the largest in the world, exceeding that of the United States, and her steel output of 18,450,000 tons was as much as the United Kingdom produced less than ten years ago.

But in the last accounting, it is the huge population which is China's greatest resource. Patient and long-suffering, hardworking and intelligent, untrained but capable in a very short time of picking up the techniques and processes of factory production, and above all able to live on little more than a handful of rice a day and conditioned over generations not to expect more, the half billion Chinese peasants present a labor force such as no previous empire has ever known. When all allowances have been made for technology and training, sheer weight of numbers still has importance. One cannot escape the fact that every fourth child born into the world is Chinese.

The West first came to know China through the writings of Marco Polo, who traveled overland in the later years of the thirteenth century. He described, in terms that have lost none of their vividness and clarity, the ordeals on his journey from Persia, across Asia, and so down into the valley of the Hwang Ho, "over mountains and through valleys, in perpetual succession, passing many rivers and desert tracts, without seeing any habitations or places of verdure. Every article of provision must therefore be carried along with you."

It was then, as it has since remained, a long, arduous, and dangerous journey. Human foes added to its risks: "Even amidst the highest of these mountains, there live a tribe of savage, ill-disposed and idolatrous people, who subsist upon the animals they can destroy, and clothe themselves with skins."

This barrier of mountain and desert held the worlds of Central Asia and of China, of Islam and of Confucius, of the pastoral nomad and of the farmer away from one another, minimizing the contacts between them. The barrier itself has not changed; only movement across it has become easier. A railroad was built more than a half-century ago from Manchuria into Soviet Siberia. Another crosses Outer Mongolia, and a third is slowly inching across the desert of the Sinkiang, along the camel trails that Marco Polo used.

This region, so long a cultural and political barrier between Central Asia and the Chinese world, has become almost suddenly a zone of contact. Chinese rice appears on the menus in the Communist countries of Eastern Europe; a liqueur, advertised as Chinese brandy, replaces cognac; Russian and East European technicians are training Chinese factory workers, and their machines are set up in Chinese factories. Much of this trade is carried on by the roads and railroads that cross the mountain and desert, and it is time now to ride one of the twentieth-century caravans out of China and into the Soviet Union.

11

THE NEW EMPIRE
OF THE SOVIETS':

The U.S.S.R. and Eastern Europe

*Is not the pivot of the world's politics that
vast area of Euro-Asia which is inaccessible
to ships, but in antiquity lay open to the horse-
riding nomads, and is today about to be covered
with a network of railways.*

Sir Halford Mackinder, 1904

The Soviet Union covers no less than a sixth of the land surface of the globe, and contains about a fourteenth of all its population. Its size alone would make it important. It is the neighbor of too many countries ever to have been unimportant, however weak its rulers might at times have been. One interpretation of world history, in fact, attributes the changes that have taken place in Europe, in the Middle East, and in South and East Asia during thousands of years to the play of influences emanating from the Russian Heartland. This may be oversimplifying the course of history, but the immense importance of the land which today makes up the Soviet Union to the whole of humanity cannot be denied. And this is nothing new. The Soviet Union occupies the whole middle of the land mass of Europe and Asia, the so-called Heartland of the Old World. Its power and importance are due not so much to the policies of autocratic Russian Tsar or of Communist Commissar as to the simple facts of geography; for, however we look at it, the Russian or Soviet land is the core of the Eastern Hemisphere around which the other and smaller countries are grouped.

419

In the last three chapters we have skirted the territory of the Soviet Union and of its satellites, following a curving path that has taken us from Northern and Western Europe to the Mediterranean; then on to the Middle East and lastly to South and East Asia. Away to our left there always lay the Soviet Union. Each country along our path has its own problems, and it also has those between itself and the Soviet Union. The Soviet Union is always watching them from beyond the Iron Curtain. The Western World, too, is concerned with Soviet pressure on Finland or Berlin, with Soviet desire to control the Turkish Straits or to dominate Afghanistan. This anxiety is not new. In the eighteenth century the Russian Tsars were pressing westward into Europe. In the nineteenth, Great Britain and France fought a war to keep the Russians away from Constantinople; the British occupied the island of Cyprus in order to have a Mediterranean base conveniently placed for operations against Russian expansionism. Russian pressure on Iran and Afghanistan was a continuous threat to the Middle East and India, and the Japanese fought the Russo-Japanese War in the early twentieth century to keep the Russians away from the Pacific Ocean.

Yet, today, there is one change: the Russian Tsars were cunning and ruthless; the Communists are efficient as well. The Tsars were supported by the whole force of national feeling in Russia; the Communists have that too, but they have added to it the strength of international Communism which sees in the Soviet Union, not the image of the age-old Russian nationalism, but a leader in an ideological struggle for the minds of men and women.

THE UNION OF SOVIET SOCIALIST REPUBLICS

It is time now to look inside the curtain that encloses the Communist World, and to see at close quarters what sort of land it is that the Communists have made their own, and how its resources as well as its location contribute to Soviet power. A teacher in the flat plain of eastern England used to take his students to the summit of a low and inconspicuous hill and, directing their attention to the east, he would assure them that there was nothing between them and the Ural Mountains. There is in fact nothing that rises more than a hundred or so feet above the curving surface of the earth. The sea and the low, flat plain stretch for over two thousand miles, all the way from England to the Ural Mountains, and these mountains, which were presumed to shut in the distant view, are

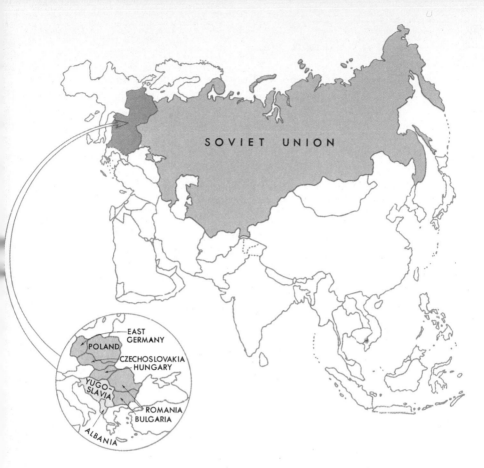

The Soviet Union stretches almost halfway around the world and extends its sphere of influence to Eastern Europe, but not to Yugoslavia or Albania.

themselves only low and rounded hills. Beyond them the vast Russian plain stretches on and on until, at last, it merges into the low mountains that border the Pacific Ocean or ends against the high ranges that separate it from China.

In fact, most of the Soviet Union is made up of a great plain, as flat as the plains of the United States' Middle West, and incomparably larger. To the north this plain stretches to the Arctic Ocean; to the west, it extends into Poland and Finland. To the south it is enclosed by mountains—the high, snow-capped ridge of the Caucasus; the tangled, pathless Pamirs, the so-called "Roof of the World," and the Hindu Kush; the Tien Shan, the Altai, and all the ranges which rise in a never ending succession along the borderland of Russia and China. On the map only the Ural Mountains are seen to break the regularity and uniformity of this plain, and they are only worn-down stumps of a former mountain range, rising at their highest point to little more than six thousand feet. They may be the conventional boundary between Europe and Asia, but in reality they are no boundary at all.

The Russians themselves have never recognized the division of Eurasia into two continents by a line which follows the Ural Mountains and then runs roughly along the Ural River to the Caspian Sea. Their land stretches from the borders of Finland, Poland, Czechoslovakia, and Romania in the west, to China and the Pacific Ocean; it spans Europe and Asia and takes in more than half of the one and nearly half of the other. It belongs to both worlds, sharing the land which is traditionally Europe and that which is traditionally Asia. This is part of the enigma of Russia: it belongs to two worlds. Scratch a Russian, it is said, and you will find a Tartar. Penetrate beneath the veneer of Western sophistication and you will find a poker-faced Oriental. The Soviet Union belongs to the West in its modern technology, its factory industries, and its armaments; but behind these is a non-Western scale of human values.

The Soviet Union has come a very long way in a very few decades. The science of the West has spread over much of this huge country. But it is slower and harder to change the ways in which people think and act than it is to alter their methods of production. The Soviet Union has become a modern Western state in terms of technology and production; it remains basically Oriental in many other respects. The Romans had a god named Janus, who gave his name to our month of January. He was always represented as having two faces, one looking back into the old year and the other forward into the new. Russia is the Janus among the nations.

The Russian Land and Its Climates

The vast plain which makes up most of the Soviet Union is drained by rivers which are among the broadest and longest in the world. Across the European section flow the Don, Dnepr, and Dnestr to the Black Sea. The Volga flows to the land-locked Caspian Sea; the Nemunas (Niemen) and the Western Dvina to the Baltic, and the Northern Dvina and Pechora to the Arctic Ocean. All these rivers of European Russia flow outward, like the spokes of a wheel, from a region with Moscow near its center. Only very low hills, many of them composed merely of the material brought here and dropped by the ice sheets, separate their drainage basins from one another. In earlier centuries a short portage was all that was needed to cross from the valley of a river flowing west to the Baltic into that of another discharging to the Black or Caspian Sea. The early Russian people could travel through European Russia by boat in much the same way that hunters and trappers traversed the Canadian North—a fact that has been of incalculable importance in the rise and expansion of the Russian state.

East of the Ural Mountains a few great rivers, with their tributaries, drain the Siberian plain northward to the Arctic Ocean: the Ob, with its tributary the Irtysh, the Yenisey, and the Lena. Part of the Soviet Far East is drained to the Pacific Ocean, chiefly by the river Amur. Southern parts of Asian Russia are not drained to the ocean at all. Here rainfall is too small for a large and integrated river system to have developed. Instead, a number of relatively short rivers have formed, flowing from the mountains into the nearby depressions, where they form heavily saline seas, like the Caspian and Aral; lakes like Balkhash, or just brackish swamps, which dry out when the rivers cease to flow in summer.

The Soviet Union stretches nearly halfway around the globe; it is 167° of longitude from the Polish boundary in the west to the shores of the Bering Strait, and only 193° from the Bering Strait back again around the world to the Polish boundary. In more familiar terms, the Soviet Union is over 5,000 miles from one end to the other.

In the poleward direction, the Soviet Union extends from about the latitude of North Carolina to that of northern Greenland. It embraces all climates except those of the equatorial and tropical regions. It can grow all crops except those which require great heat and great moisture. And furthermore, an area covering one sixth of the land surface of the earth may reasonably be expected to contain, if not also a sixth of the earth's minerals, then at least a very good share of them; and it does.

In any geographical study of North America the primary divisions of the continent are most likely to be based upon the contrast of mountain, plateau, and plain. Enough has been said to show that a division of the Soviet Union on the basis of similar criteria would not be particularly meaningful. A very large extent of the country would appear as a featureless plain, unbroken by hills or mountain ranges. The contrasts between one part of the Soviet Union and another lie far more in the differences in climate and in the resulting vegetation, than in the relief of the land's surface.

Plants in general, and trees in particular, may not be the most sensitive measures of climate and of the variation in climate from place

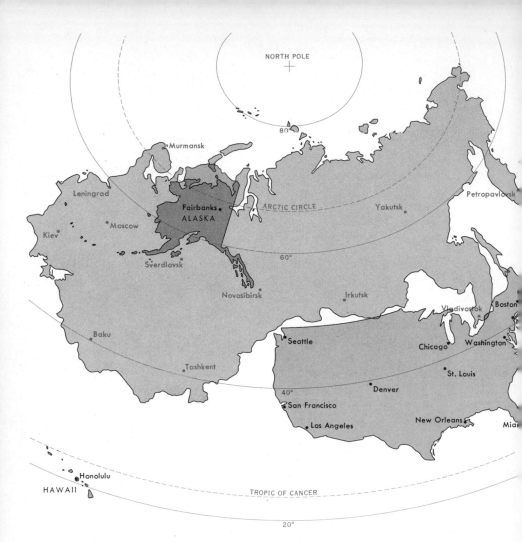

At their correct latitudes, both countries in the same scale, the United States is shown superimposed on the Soviet Union.

to place. Yet vegetation is primarily a natural response to climate; and man, who is much less sensitive in these respects than are the plants, responds to climate indirectly, through the impact which vegetation—including the cultivated species—makes upon him. The only other major division of the earth's surface where we shall find that the kinds and qualities of vegetation make the most meaningful division of the land is Australia.

A land about 14 per cent larger than the whole of Anglo-America might be expected to have a wide range of climates, and one that lies up to 1,700 miles from the sea, to have an immense range in temperatures. The north coast of the Soviet Union lies in the latitude of Baffin Land or central Greenland. Its southern extremity, where the Turkmen Soviet Socialist Republic borders Iran, is in the latitude of northern Texas. The whole of the Soviet Union lies within the middle and high, or polar, latitudes and at no point does it even approach the tropics; yet it experiences great summer heat, as Texas does.

In the popular imagination Russia is a land of cold winters with deep snow, where people wear heavy topcoats and fur-lined hats. Snow seems to pervade the gloomy canvasses of the Russian novelists and the jangle of sleigh bells runs through Russian popular music. But even in the coldest parts of the Soviet Union, winter lasts for only a part of the year, and even there the snow is not always abundant.

In fact, almost the whole of the Soviet Union has a climate of seasonal extremes. The distance of most of it from the Atlantic reduces the moderating influence of the sea. During winter a great mass of cold, heavy air settles over the area and edges outward into Central Europe and China. Until a lower temperature was registered by an expedition in the heart of the Antarctic continent, the lowest natural temperature recorded by man had been the $-90°$ registered at Oimekon, Eastern Siberia, on February 6, 1933. But summers are hot in Russia, except in the far north. Moscow, despite its high latitude, can be like New York or Chicago in summer, and the deserts of Central Asia may be as hot as the Sahara.

The snowy winters of Russian folklore and story are met with in Western or European Russia. There the humid winds from the Atlantic bring moisture that is precipitated as heavy snowfalls in winter and as storms—often violent—in summer. Only European Russia can possibly be described as wet, and even here it is the wetness of the Mississippi Valley rather than that of the Pacific Northwest or of New England. Most of Russia has less than 20 inches of rainfall a year, and Soviet Central Asia has less than 10. In terms of the United States, most of the U.S.S.R. is as dry as the plains of Colorado or of Wyoming, and in climate much of it resembles Nevada or Arizona.

The vegetation zones of the Soviet Union are a series of west to east belts, which mark by their transition from one to the next the passage from arctic cold to an almost subtropical heat. The most northerly of these is the tundra, which borders the Arctic Ocean and extends over the Soviet Union's arctic islands, such as Novaya Zemlya and Severnaya

Zemlya, all the way from the Finnish border in the west to the Bering Strait in the east. Fingers and islands of tundra occur farther to the south amid the coniferous forest, wherever a mountain ridge lifts itself high enough above the surrounding plains. Along this arctic coast of the Soviet Union, the average temperatures in January are generally below zero, and in the most northerly and coldest parts, below $-20°$. In summer, the average temperature in July is rarely much over $40°$.

Inland the summers gradually become warmer, but winters are even colder. The period when the surface of the ground is free of frost is short —it may be only a couple of months—far too short for almost every cultivated plant. In fact the frost never completely disappears from these northern lands which make up about 45 per cent of the Soviet Union, not even in summer. During winter, with month after month of sub-zero temperatures, the frost penetrates the soil and reaches down into the subsoil. In summer only the surface thaws out. A few inches or a foot of slush and mud covers the still frozen subsoil; this is the permafrost, which the roots of trees cannot penetrate, which animals cannot burrow through, and the miner has difficulty in cutting. It is as if nature had set a vertical as well as a horizontal limit to man's use of the soil.

Yet the tundra is not wholly without vegetation. Much of its surface is strewn with boulders and stones, which have lain here, without accumulating soil around them, since the movement of the great ice sheets left them. But mosses and lichens have grown over them. In depressions and hollows, where water accumulates in the short summer, peat forms—frozen solid in winter and an impassable quagmire in summer. Tree growth is restricted by the low temperatures, by the permanently frozen subsoil, and above all by the wind which cuts off every living thing that grows in its path. Yet there are sheltered hollows where the severity of the Arctic is moderated, and a few stunted and twisted conifers take root and grow.

Toward the southern margin of the tundra the trees become more numerous, larger, and better formed. They begin to form a forest of low trees that can grow only waist or shoulder high. But gradually, as the growing season lengthens toward the south and the permafrost goes deeper and disappears, these dwarfed trees merge into the tall forest of the taiga. The taiga reaches from Sweden, through Finland, and across the Soviet Union to the Pacific Ocean. It covers almost a tenth of the land surface of the earth. It is not completely uniform. Human settlements. have penetrated it from the south; the forest has been cleared in thousands of small areas, and the land brought under cultivation or sown with permanent grass. But the damp, cool climate does not contribute to the formation of a good soil. Not much humus is added by decaying plant material, and the soluble constituents of the soil, upon which plants depend for their sustenance, are dissolved and removed by the rain or washed out by the spring floods which spread out over the plains after the melting of the winter snows.

Winter temperatures very gradually moderate as one passes southward and southwestward across the taiga. But everywhere January temperatures are far below freezing and over the whole central area of the taiga, below zero. Southward summers become warmer; there are generally seven months, from April through October, with an average temperature above freezing, and July, the warmest month, has average temperatures in the sixties and occasionally in the seventies. There may be even short spells of really hot weather when the thermometer climbs to well over 80° and the mosquitoes come out in their myriads to enjoy the unaccustomed warmth.

Fur trappers were the earliest Russian travelers in these forests. They came in search of muskrat and beaver, and before the end of the sixteenth century, they had penetrated deep into Siberia. More recently has come the lumberman, cutting the softwood timber and shipping it out. The taiga is incomparably the largest stand of softwood lumber in the world today; yet it is one of the most inaccessible. Everywhere in the world the rivers provide the most convenient means of transporting lumber, but these Russian rivers flow northward to an ocean that is difficult of access and is icebound for much of the year. The Northern Dvina, the Pechora, the Ob with its great tributary the Irtysh, the Yenisey, the Lena, and a hundred lesser rivers take their winding courses through the northern forests, and far within the Arctic Circle, they enter the cold Arctic Ocean. They are broad rivers, slow-flowing, and deep.

On the map these rivers look as if they had been shaped by nature to provide routes into the northern forests. In reality, however, they are little used. Summer is short and cool here. The ice clears from the rivers and the coast only for a month or two. Furthermore, since these rivers flow from south to north, spring comes first to their headwaters and then travels slowly downstream, unlocking the ice and melting away the snow from the plains. Spring floods come first on the upper stream and the flood crest moves slowly downstream toward the north, while the lower river remains still locked in ice. The melt water, unable to

keep to its proper channel, floods out over the land on each side, converting it into a vast impassable swamp.

The mouth of the Yenisey remains frozen for 260 days or more in each year, and for an even longer period sea ice obstructs the approaches from the Arctic Ocean. The open season is so short that freighters cannot sail from either the Atlantic or Pacific to the small ports that have been established along the lower reaches of the arctic rivers and return again with a cargo of lumber or pelts or minerals without the help of ice-breakers to guide them through the pack ice. If only the climate allowed an easier access to the mouths of the great northern rivers of Russia, then the Soviet Union could inundate the world market with cheap softwood lumber.

The taiga is far from uniform in the kinds and qualities of trees that it supports. Over much of its area the commercially valuable pine and fir predominate, but in Siberia this merges into forests of the less valuable larch or tamarack, which sheds its needle leaves in fall. The best commercial lumber thus occurs in the western forests of the Soviet Union, where as it happens, roads, railways, and human settlement have penetrated the forest more deeply, and it is easier to ship out the lumber.

The prevailing weather systems come in from the west; moving off the Atlantic and across Western Europe to the Soviet Union. They bring moisture in from the ocean and carry the fall-out eastward toward the Pacific and North America. The western part of the Soviet Union has milder temperatures in winter, owing to the moderating influence of winds from the ocean. At Leningrad, close to the coast of the Baltic Sea, the annual temperature range, that is the difference between the normal temperatures in January and July, is about $40°$; at Moscow, over three hundred miles to the east, it has risen to $50°$. In the Ob Valley it is $70°$ and in eastern Siberia it rises to over $100°$, before diminishing to a range along the Pacific coast similar to that found in Leningrad.

The results of these climatic changes are seen in the vegetation. South of the belt of taiga in European Russia lies a region of mixed forest. The conifers are intermixed with oak and ash, and toward the south the broad-leaved trees take over almost completely, and relegate the conifers to the areas of high ground and of poor and sandy soil. The climate is more suited to cultivated plants, and the autumn leaf fall of the broad-leaved trees adds humus to the soil, and over the centuries has built up a fertility which is still being used.

This region is wedge-shaped. Its base lies along the Baltic coast and against the boundaries with Poland and Romania. Eastward it tapers away toward the Ural Mountains. To the north is the taiga; to the south, where both warmth and drought increase, is the steppe. Beyond the Ural Mountains the taiga and the steppe meet, with just an occasional narrow belt of mixed or broad-leaved trees to mark their junction. This wedge is driven into the great land mass of Russia by Europe; it is European in its climate and vegetation, and it separates the characteristically Asian environments of taiga and steppe.

This wedge-shaped region of broad-leaved and mixed forest served as a funnel through which European peoples and European technology and skills entered Russia. Within this wedge-shaped region they found a climate more severe than that of Central Europe, but nevertheless broadly familiar; they found trees that they knew and soils that they could cultivate with the tools and equipment which they possessed. And within this region they had some degree of protection. To the north there were few enemies; there lived only the Finns and scattered tribes related to the Lapps.

But the steppe to the south was like an unknown sea to the early Russian settlers. Out of its depths came horse-riding nomadic peoples— the Tartars—who in the early centuries of the growth of the Russian state were a constant threat. The forest gave some protection; it slowed down the Tartar inroads, allowing cities in the Moscow region to develop with a great deal less interruption than those of the steppe. And in later centuries, the Russian peoples moved outward from the region of mixed and broad-leaved forest where they had, as it were, rested and recouped their strength, into the steppe and through the taiga. Without this wedge-shaped area, driven deep into the heart of the Russian land, there could be no Russia and no Soviet Union as we know them, for these are the product of Asian elements, fertilized, and vivified by Europeans.

To the south of the wedge the forest thins gradually away, just as the woodland of the Midwest disappears at the margin of the prairie. Beyond the forest lies the steppe, the grassy plain covered with tall grass that stretched on to the Black Sea, westward to Poland, and eastward into Asia. Thus, in the nineteenth century, the Russian writer Turgenev, described the transition. "Round low hills tilled and sown to their very tops, are seen in broad undulations; ravines, overgrown with bushes, wind coiling among them; small copses are scattered like oblong islands; from village to village run narrow paths . . . between willow-bushes glimmers a little river. . . . The hills are smaller and there is at last—the boundless, untrodden steppe."

It is a region of tall grass where the trees thin out and disappear. Winters are cold, but without the severity of Siberia, and summers are hot. Rainfall, from 15 to 20 inches along the forest margin, begins to decline toward the southeast. The tall grass merges imperceptibly into short, and the short grass grows shorter and drier until it merges into the semidesert which lies around the north and the east of the Caspian Sea. And the semidesert merges into the true desert, with the rock fields and shifting sand dunes of Turkestan, and these reach on until the land rears itself above the level of this torrid waste in the cold, snow-capped mountains of Central Asia. Between the Black and Caspian seas, the steppe and semidesert are bordered by the high straight crest of the Caucasus Mountains. Beyond are the hills and high valleys of Transcaucasia.

Desert and semidesert cover the southern extremities of the Soviet Union, as the cold desert of the tundra does its northern. Between these extremes stretches the taiga and the steppe. The latter is reduced to a narrow and in places discontinuous strip, where the rainfall falls off rapidly from the forest to the north to the semidesert lying to the south.

The steppe reaches its broadest extent in European Russia, where it forms the Ukraine. Agriculturally, the Ukraine is to the Soviet Union what Kansas, Nebraska, and the Dakotas are to the United States. It was formerly the chief source of wheat, and is now the source of much of the corn, barley, and fodder. A century and more ago much of the wheat entering the world's commerce was from the Ukraine. It was shipped down the rivers which rise within the forest belt to the north and flow into the Black Sea: the Dnestr, Bug, Dnepr, and Don. Ports—foremost among them Odessa—grew up near the mouths of these rivers and transshipped the wheat. Toward the west, where the winters are shorter and milder, the wheat is sown in the fall as it is in Kansas. But as the

steppe belt is traced to the east and northeast into Kazakhstan, where wheat growing has been greatly expanded in recent years, the winters become longer and more severe, and spring-sown wheat, like that of the Dakotas, is grown. The frontier of Russian agriculture lies to the east, in Siberia and Kazakhstan, where at the price of a slowly mounting severity in the climate and a shorter growing season the cultivated area can be expanded almost indefinitely into the so-called "virgin lands."

To the south of the grassland belt in Central Asia is Russia's subtropical south. Rainfall is far too small for agriculture under any normal conditions. The land is scrub desert, but across it flow the perennial rivers, fed by rain and melting snow from the Pamirs, the Tien Shan, and Altai. Along these watercourses, until they dry away into the desert, there are long narrow oases, where cotton, rice, sugar, and tropical fruits are grown. The biggest of these rivers are the Syr Darya and Amu Darya, which flow into the shallow, saline Aral Sea. But there are many others that wilt and dry away in the desert as their water either evaporates into the dry air or is taken to irrigate the cotton and rice fields and the fruit orchards.

The Settlement of the Russian Land

Such is the tableau before which has been enacted the drama of Russian history, and that drama itself cannot be understood apart from its physical setting, so closely are they interwoven. The state of Muscovy, from which modern Russia has developed, originated in the ninth century in the wedge-shaped area of mixed forest, near the point from which the rivers of European Russia radiate to the three seas. It was well placed to benefit from the natural routes opened up by the rivers, and in its earlier and more vulnerable days it had the natural protection of the forest. From here Russian adventurers and conquerors moved outward during the following centuries, north to the Arctic, northwest to the Baltic where in 1703 they founded the city of St. Petersburg, as their "Window on the West," and south to the Black Sea. Their slow spread to the east into the frontier of the Siberian forest and the Ukrainian steppe is like the westward movement of the American pioneers from the Atlantic seaboard. Only the Russian movement began earlier, lasted longer, and went farther.

These people who traveled as pioneers outward from the Moscow region into the forest and the steppe were Europeans. They spoke a Slav language; through the centuries they had filtered eastward from the plains of Poland; they had received and absorbed immigrants from Scandinavia, the so-called Rus, who gave their name to the land of Russia. They had received Christianity at the hands of missionaries from Constantinople, and from the earliest times they had possessed a veneer of West European civilization and sophistication. But as they spread outward they absorbed Tartars and Turks, Lapps and Mongols. The European or Western heritage was gradually diluted by the traditions and cultures of the peoples of the vast Asian plains. The great Russian dichotomy began to take shape.

By the end of the Middle Ages the Russian pioneers had spread over much of European Russia. From the sixteenth century onward they pushed their frontier of settlement out into Siberia. Once they had got beyond the Volga, the rivers gave them little help, and, indeed, offered them every hindrance. The broad marshy valleys had to be crossed, one after the other, while the rivers themselves, flowing majestically toward the Arctic, where the ice glint could be seen in the northern sky even in summer, offered them a route in a direction which none of them wanted to follow.

In the United States the pioneer was led westward mainly by his desire for land and yet more land. But the early Russian never had this insatiable hunger; he had land in plenty, but what he most wanted was the skins of the fur-bearing animals that lived in the northern forest; and the gold that could be panned along the beds of the northern rivers; and above all freedom from the restrictions and controls exercised by the feudal society of European Russia. The Russian pioneers had no danger quite like that which the American pioneers faced from the Indians, but they had to endure a climate of incomparably greater severity. And when at last they reached the Pacific Ocean, it was not the mild, blue Pacific of California or Oregon, but the cold, gray, foggy Bering Sea. The search for pelts took them across it and into Alaska beyond, and even into California. Still today at Sitka in Alaska you can see a Russian church, with its onion-shaped dome reminiscent of St. Basil's, built by the Russian pioneers early in the nineteenth century. Southward they spread, through what is today the Alaska Panhandle, trading for furs and claiming the land for the Tsar wherever they went.

Within the Old World the Russian pioneers kept to the forest, because it was the forest that yielded the things they most wanted. The tapering belt of steppe that is gradually pinched out toward the east between the forest to the north and the desert and mountains to the south, did not attract them. They had not come in search of land to cultivate, and this land in any case was too dry for them to till. The Russian expansion into the steppe and into the desert of Central Asia came almost a century after the penetration of the northern forests.

The steppe was exposed and dangerous and it had its own savage, nomadic horsemen, the Tartars, who, in the course of history built up short-lived empires over the grasslands, threatening and even destroying the settled communities and societies which they bordered, only to disintegrate as the temporary alliances of their chieftains broke up. The Russians, following the maxim which urged them to set a thief to catch a thief, established some of these Tartars as a kind of frontier guard, the Cossacks. For a long time they were as dangerous and unruly as the Tartars themselves, and only gradually did they allow themselves to be turned into settled agriculturalists in the Ukraine. In the eighteenth century the Russian government set out to subjugate and control the steppe; in the nineteenth, they began to develop it.

The great divide in Russian history and in the story of the development of the Russian land came in the twentieth century when the Bolsheviks overthrew the government of the last of the Tsars in 1917, seized power, and a few years later carried through an economic revolution to match the political revolution they had already accomplished.

A few years before the Bolshevik revolution, an English geographer, Halford Mackinder, had argued very persuasively that this great land mass, so difficult to penetrate from the outside, nevertheless had exercised a profound influence on the course of history in the encircling ring of lands, from Scandinavia through Central Europe, the Middle East, and India to China and Korea. This is no place to discuss how profound was this influence of Mongols and Tartars, who at intervals through history came raiding outward from the heartland. The point is that Mackinder had said that if the unorganized power and the undeveloped resources of the heartland could have been so important in world history, how much more so would they have been if they had been organized and developed by a technically trained people. The Russian revolution was the beginning of just this.

Russia was a rich land, but its croplands were poorly cultivated, its forest resources scarcely touched, and much of its fuel and mineral reserves scarcely known. In these lay the future wealth of Russia. Up to now the Russians had just picked and chosen; their exploitation and development had been haphazard. Industry was concentrated in a few sections of European Russia, and farming had made little impression upon the vast empty spaces of Siberia. The revolution in the environment began ten years after the political revolution, and was incomparably the more important of the two. Communism was a revolutionary political and social doctrine, but without power—economic power that is based on the firm control of land and people and the exploitation of resources —the doctrine would not have been able to menace the world.

The Land of the Commissars

Agricultural practice had been traditional and simple in the villages of prerevolutionary Russia. Equipment was primitive; plow and harrow were of wood, and the crops were harvested and the hay cut with nothing more than sickle or scythe; rough buildings were put together with simple tools, often little more than the hammer. An immense labor was expended to achieve little. Most of the population lived in the large villages of wood-built huts and worked on the land. Holdings were small, and poverty intense, and all around was the immensity of Russia. The revolutionary plan called first for changes in agriculture. The expenditure of labor was to be reduced, and the output increased. Farm units were to be made larger; there was to be more mechanization, improved farm stock and better seed. And the food surplus would be sent to feed the cities in which industrial production was to be increased.

Such was the rationale of collectivization. This change in the organization of agriculture was carried through in the face of strenuous opposition by the peasants, who preferred the relative independence of their own poor holdings to the illusory delights of the collective farm. Yet collectivization succeeded in its primary objective, to produce more food with the expenditure of less labor, and in this it laid the foundation for the industrial revolution that followed.

The pattern of agriculture in the Soviet Union is fixed by the great climatic and soil belts of this huge country. The farming region par excellence is the steppe, with its immense potential for growing wheat and other grain crops. To the south are the irrigated lands set amid the deserts of Turkestan. But here a limit is set to cultivation by the volume of water that is available. The rivers Amu Darya and Syr Darya, and the smaller ones, rise in the mountains of Central Asia; like the Nile in Egypt or the Gila in Arizona, they have created long, striplike oases through the desert. On their banks cities grew up in ancient times, and under the Soviets these have been expanded and increased. Today the greatest possible use is being made of the water that flows down from snows of the Tien Shan and Hindu Kush to grow cotton and rice and other subtropical crops, for this is the only part of the Soviet Union which combines a long hot summer with the availability of water in sufficient quantities for such crops to grow. But a strict limit to agriculture in Soviet Central Asia is set by the amount of water that comes down from the mountains. There, as in Egypt, Pakistan, and parts of India, in Nevada, Arizona, and southern California of the United States, it is not land that is scarce, it is water.

North of the steppe the forest is characterized by poorer soil and harsher climate. Winter gets longer and harder toward the north and east, and agriculture correspondingly more difficult and less important. Toward the west the forest is largely cleared, and cultivated fields have taken its place. Northward through the forest belt wheat is gradually replaced by more hardy cereals, rye and oats. The dark rye bread replaces white bread as a food, and potatoes become more important. North of about the latitude of Moscow, even potatoes and hardy cereals become more scarce, and north of Leningrad they are rarely seen in the fields. Hay and fodder crops for the animals, and a few quick growing summer vegetables, are all that can be grown here.

During the past half century, there has been a rapid expansion in the area under crops. Without making allowances for boundary changes, the cultivated area has expanded from about 46,000 square miles in 1913, to 50,000 in 1933; to 65,700 in 1958, and 78,400 in 1960. The expansion of the last couple of years reflects the recent Soviet policy of plowing up the "virgin lands" of the eastern steppe. In 1960, rather less than 10 per cent of the total area of the Soviet Union was actually under cultivation (as against 25 per cent in the United States), and already, in order to expand food production, the Soviet authorities had been obliged to plow up and cultivate the dry eastern margin of the steppe. Unquestionably more food can yet be grown from land already under cultivation by the use of better seed, more fertilizer, and more scientific land management. It will have been implicit in the previous pages why the extension of cropland is proving so difficult, and it is a chastening thought that the biggest political unit in the world can suffer from a shortage—not so much of land—as of good land to grow crops.

The population of the Soviet Union is growing fast. At the beginning of 1962, it was estimated to have been about 220,000,000. Despite the immense losses during the Second World War, it had increased on the basis of present Soviet territory by about 25,000,000 since 1939. At the beginning of the century the population of the Russian Empire is estimated to have been about 130,000,000. In this rapidly growing population lies the primary reason for the need to increase the area under cultivation. A second reason is the growth of industry, the expansion of the urban population, and the need to produce ever increasing quantities of foodstuffs for the nonagricultural population. In 1960, for the first time in Russian history, the urban population exceeded the rural. Twenty years before a little less than a third had lived in cities.

The agricultural revolution, the transformation of a primitive and largely self-sufficing peasantry into farmers, cultivating giant farms with machinery and with the use of all the aids that modern chemistry and biology can furnish was a necessary prelude to the industrial revolution. Without the agricultural revolution labor would not have been set free from the fields for work in the factories; nor would food have been available in adequate quantities for the provisioning of the cities' ever growing number and size. The agricultural revolution insured a sufficient food base for the growth of the Russian industrial economy. The country already had a large and in many ways generous base in fuels and mineral raw materials.

How great the mineral resources of the Soviet Union really are we can still only guess; and we do not know precisely how great is the production of many of them. Today the Soviet Union produces about a fifth of the world's production of bituminous coal—about 374,933,000 tons in 1960—as well as large quantities of lignite, and in output follows China and the United States. The coal fields are widely distributed. The first to be opened up, and still the largest in production, is the so-called Donbas, lying in the Donets Basin in the eastern Ukraine. Much of the earlier industrial growth of Russia was carried on on the basis of Donets coal. There are also other smaller reserves in European Russia, but all these pale before the resources of Siberia, beyond the Ural Mountains.

Coal occurs along the flanks of the Urals themselves, and also in immense quantities in the Kuznetsk Basin, near the city of Novosibirsk; in the Karaganda Basin in the semidesert of Kazakhstan, and the Irkutsk Basin, in the mountains that enclose Lake Baikal. Other and smaller coal fields are strung out eastward across Siberia right to the most easterly peninsulas of the Soviet Union. Coal is abundant, but the large deposits of lignite, found near Moscow and in Siberia are also important, especially for power generation. Lignite is only a low-grade fuel, but it burns in furnaces designed to take it as well as any other, and constitutes for the future an almost inexhaustible source of thermal-electric power.

Petroleum is less widespread. Longest known and most intensively worked of the oil fields of the Soviet Union borders the Caucasus Mountains, wrapping around their eastern extremity and the shores of the

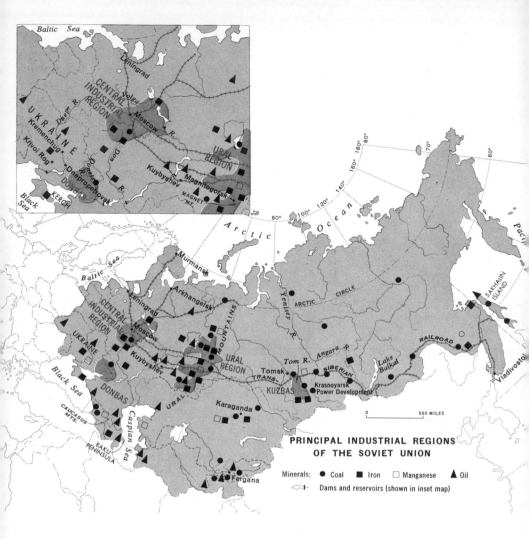

Minerals: ● Coal ■ Iron □ Manganese ▲ Oil

**PRINCIPAL INDUSTRIAL REGIONS
OF THE SOVIET UNION**

◁─┤ Dams and reservoirs (shown in inset map)

Caspian Sea, in the neighborhood of Baku. From here the petroleum has been piped across to the Black Sea port of Batumi. But this oil field has long been worked, and its reserves are diminishing sharply. In the meanwhile, a "second Baku" has been discovered to the north, between the Caspian Sea and the Ural Mountains, and smaller oil fields are now known and worked between the Caspian and Aral Seas and along the foothills of the mountains of Central Asia.

Petroleum production in the Soviet Union has been increasing far more rapidly in recent years than in the world as a whole. In 1951 output was 42,253,000 tons, about 7 per cent of the world production, and a little more than an eighth of that of the United States. By 1960. this production had risen to 147,859,000 tons or 14 per cent of the greatly increased world production. Yet the petroleum industry of the Soviet Union is not without its problems. Modern society—and Soviet society in particular—is increasingly dependent on petroleum. In the Soviet Union there is concern over whether resources are in fact adequate, and this concern is reflected in a deep Soviet interest in the Middle East, and a desire to replace in that area the influence of West European powers by its own.

Iron ore occurs very widely over the earth's surface. Most of the supply for Soviet industries has come from a large reserve at Krivoy Rog in the Ukraine, and much of the remainder from massive deposits at Magnitogorsk—"Iron Mountain"—in the Urals. But the biggest reserve of ore runs out in time, and the reserves in each of these are diminishing. Just as the approaching exhaustion of the Mesabi ores in the United States has been followed by the discovery of large resources in Labrador, and by the development of means of processing and using low-grade ores like taconite, so in the Soviet Union careful prospecting has revealed many other sources of ore; however, these are not all as large or as conveniently located as the older deposits that are becoming exhausted.

The most important of the new reserves are in the southern part of the Ural Mountains, where Magnitogorsk constituted a mountain built almost entirely of high-grade ore, and in Central Siberia, where ores were found quite close to the Kuznetsk coal field. Yet other iron ore fields have been located in the arctic region of European Russia, in European Russia itself, in the steppe of Kazakhstan only a few hundred miles from the coal of Karaganda, and in the Soviet Far East. Some of these ore deposits pose difficult transportation problems, and others present difficulties in the actual mining or smelting of the ore; but of iron ore itself there is no scarcity; nor is there likely to be.

The Soviet production of iron ore has been rising even more sharply than that of petroleum, and in 1960 reached 61,770,000 tons, measured as the iron content of the ore, rather than as the total weight of material shipped from the mine to the smelter. This amounted to over 27 per cent of the world output of iron ore and was almost half as large again as United States production.

But this is not as menacing as it may seem. In all the more advanced countries, like the United States, Great Britain, and West Germany, scrap metal is produced in very large quantities, and is recycled through the steel furnaces to come out again as new metal. This does not require the use of iron ore, and is in fact cheaper and easier to produce than metal that has to be reduced from the ore. Secondly, the United States imports large quantities of ore from Canada, as well as from Latin America and Africa. It is difficult to believe that the flow of Canadian ore, at least, could be seriously interfered with. On the other hand, the Soviet Union has stimulated the growth of iron-smelting industries in several of her satellites. Some of these have little or no ore of their own, and the Soviet Union is obligated to keep them supplied.

Nature is as capricious as any woman in bestowing her favors, and her caprice is nowhere more conspicuous than in the way she has scattered minerals through the earth's crust. The Soviet Union appears—the lack of reliable statistics compels us to be cautious—to produce about a half of the world's manganese, and considerable though rather indefinite quantities of many others, including gold, which the Soviet Union periodically dumps on the world market to the confusion of currencies and prices. The Soviet Union is also a significant producer of tin, but copper production is well below domestic needs.

Much of the northeast of the Soviet Union is built like the northeastern sector of North America, of a vast mass of ancient rock of great hardness. It was there, and of continental proportions, long before the rest of Russia was formed. During the geological ages it has accumulated a great range and variety of minerals within itself. Like the great Canadian Shield, it is of vast extent; it lies far to the north where the climate makes travel, prospecting, and mining difficult. And like the Canadian Shield, this great Siberian massif is still far from completely explored, mapped, and prospected. There the Soviet Union may hope to find more minerals.

On the basis of a more abundant food supply and the ample reserves of minerals and of industrial raw materials the Soviets moved to build an industrial society. Manufacturing industry was not wholly new to the Soviet Union. Long before the Communist Revolution there was an iron industry. Iron smelted in the Ural Mountains in the eighteenth century supplied much of Europe, and during the nineteenth century a great iron industry was developed in the Ukraine; the ore of Krivoy Rog and the coal of the Donbas were brought together, under the direction of Western technicians, and a modern industry created. Similarly in many of the cities of western Russia there were textile, woodworking, and other industries. But the pace of this industrialization was slow; and its scope was limited.

The Soviet Five Year Plans, which began in 1928 and continued in an unbroken sequence, except for the interruption of the war years, envisaged a radical change, a fuller utilization of the natural resources, a wider distribution of production, and an output of rapidly mounting proportions. The Soviet Union aimed to be largest in production of agricultural and industrial goods, just as it was largest in area among the states of the world. In 1959 a Seven Year Plan, encompassing similar objectives, was initiated.

Modern U.S.S.R.

Let us not underestimate the Soviet achievement. The Soviets have changed the geography of their country. It is no longer a vast, sprawling, undeveloped land, with a rather primitive industrial growth in its western corner. There remain vast empty areas, but between and scattered through them are lands newly broken-up for farming, mines newly opened and, above all, newly planned industrial cities. Expressed in the simplest terms this prolonged period of planned growth has been one of investing in new industry, utilities, and transportation a large fraction of the total production of each year. This means simply that the Russian people have consumed less and saved more than other peoples. They did not do this voluntarily; the plans were imposed on them by the Communist Party, and occasionally and locally they resisted the stringencies that resulted.

It is difficult for a country to pull itself up by its own bootstraps, particularly when it tries to do so within the span of a very few years. The West European countries industrialized slowly, over a period of a century or more. They had time to experiment, to consolidate each step forward without at the same time taking the next. The Russians, in their mad haste to catch up, did not. They exchanged Soviet petroleum, lumber, and grain for the machine tools and the even scarcer technicians of the West, and this necessitated increased production from their own forests, fields, and mines. After the early phases of this development, technical assistance from other countries ceased to be so necessary. The Russians had equipped themselves to make their own machines, and they had learned the skills required by a complex, modern society.

The map of Soviet industry is today quite different from that of a generation ago. Then, manufacturing was confined to European Russia, and there its scale was small and its equipment backward. Now it spreads from the Baltic Sea to the Pacific Ocean. Communist planners, both in the Soviet Union and also in other Communist countries, have tended to emphasize the heavy industries. The production of iron and steel in adequate amounts they regarded as a necessary preliminary to the manufacture of almost all other factory-made goods; the mechanization of agriculture was dependent upon a supply of metal, and transportation could not be developed without it. It is not surprising then that the iron and steel industries bulked large in the Soviet plans. The old centers, in the Donbas, were modernized and extended; a vast new metallurgical center was established in the Ural Mountains, where the ancient charcoal-iron industry had once flourished, and away in Central Siberia, in the valley of the river Ob, the Kuzbas industrial region began to take shape. The resources in fuel and ore were large, but so was the Soviet Union.

Transportation was one of the greatest problems facing the planners. Existing railroads were used to capacity; an increase in the railroad net was essential for increased production, and greatly increased steel output was only possible with the aid of better transportation. Slowly these problems were solved. The great west-to-east trunk line, the Trans-Siberian railroad, which runs from Moscow in Europe to Vladivostok on the shore of the Pacific, was double tracked. Spur lines were built from it. A new line was built to swing northeast from the Caspian Sea, through Turkestan to join the Trans-Siberian. The existing net was intensified in the region of the Ural Mountains and in the developed areas of European Russia.

Developments in transportation were not limited to the railroads. The rivers were improved, deepened, and straightened. River ports were built, and connecting canals were cut between the river basins of European Russia. It was not possible to link up with canals the great rivers of Siberia, which flow north to the Arctic Ocean; instead, it was planned to make greater use of them by developing a shipping lane along the arctic coast of the Soviet Union. Now, the use of faster ships and of heavy icebreakers permitted ships to carry away the lumber and other products of the Soviet Arctic that are being floated down the great northern rivers to the small ports near their mouths.

The smelting of other metals—lead, zinc, manganese, nickel—was established in the Ukraine, in the Urals where many of these metals were mined, and elsewhere. The machine industries were expanded, especially in the cities of European Russia. The production of textiles was increased from the cotton and woolen mills of Ivanovo and Vologda; of pulp and paper, from the lumber mills in the northern forests; of fertilizers and chemicals, from the factories built near the coal fields and oil refineries.

Thus was the pattern of human activity changed in forest, farm, and factory. The population has risen to 220,000,000 and will in the near future rise very much higher. This population, which is exceeded only by the population of China and India, is far from evenly scattered, but it is now found more widely than ever before. In 1890 the Bureau of the Census declared that in the continental United States, the frontier, as a continuous line fronting a vast and almost uninhabited region, had ceased to exist. It will be a very long time before such a declaration can be made in the Soviet Union. There still remain vast, uninhabited, and little-known regions of the country. Much of this may never be permanently settled and used; its climate is too severe, its soils too poor; only the possibility of mineral wealth beneath its surface may bring in the prospector and miner.

The distribution of population conforms very closely to the pattern of vegetation regions that was described earlier in this chapter. Almost the whole of the Soviet Union's population is found in only two of these regions: that of broad-leaved and mixed forest which covers much of European Russia and that of the grassy steppe. In the west these two adjoin one another, giving a populous area from Leningrad in the north to Odessa on the Black Sea coast, and extending eastward through the Ukraine and beyond Moscow, until it tapers away in the southern Ural Mountains. Beyond this only a thin line of cities, settlements, and farms straggles eastward, following the discontinuous belt of steppe and the Trans-Siberian Railway which winds its way through it until, at last, it reaches the Pacific Ocean.

Away from this relatively densely peopled area are two important and several minor centers of population. One lies along the flanks, both north and south of the Caucasus Mountains, where there is water for irrigation, and corn, cotton, and subtropical plants can be grown. The other is similarly located along the foot of the Pamir and the Tien Shan. It also relies upon irrigation, and the long, thin fingers of population reach outward from the mountains along the rivers for as far as they have water in them. There are isolated centers of population along the dry northern and eastern shores of the Caspian Sea; at mining centers and lumber camps scattered through the northern forests; at the arctic ports of Murmansk and Archangel (Arkhangelsk) and at the dozens of little river stations scattered through the Soviet northland.

A map showing Soviet population distribution in one of the accepted ways—by dots—resembles a picture of the sky, with the long winding line of settlements across Siberia serving as a kind of Milky Way. Amid the ground mass of stars of feeble magnitude there shine a few bright stars; these are represented by the great cities of the Soviet Union. It is not often realized how many and how large these cities are. According to the census of 1959, no less than 149 had populations exceeding 100,000. Most of these would not even be familiar names to Western readers, not only because of the Russian practice of naming cities for rising political personages, and then of changing their names as these personages decline, but simply because only a few years back many of these cities were not there. The development of new industries on new sites necessitates new, planned workers' cities. These consist most often of a group of tall blocks of apartments rising from a still unfinished street; a few state-operated shops, in which little more can be purchased than the barest necessities of life; and the factories which are the justification for it all.

But some will be familiar enough. Moscow itself, with its population now of about 8,000,000 lies on the Moskva River, where it was founded during the Middle Ages. It was defended against the Tartars; it became the center from which the Russian people and Russian political power spread outward to occupy this huge land. Still today, the core of the city is medieval—the walled town of the early Tsars, with the finest surviving assemblage of early Russian architecture in the Kremlin. Around this heroic center are the few large stores and government buildings and away from it in all directions stretch the one- or two-storied wooden buildings, now being replaced by multistory apartment buildings, interspersed with factories, which make up most of Moscow.

The second city is Leningrad, now with 3,875,000 people. It is the city which Peter the Great founded beside the river Neva in 1703 and destined to become the avenue of communication between Russia and the West. He made it his capital, thus emphasizing the Western orientation which he gave to Russia, and it remained the capital until 1917 when the Bolsheviks cut themselves off from Western civilization, turned inward upon themselves, and returned to the more exclusively Russian and less cosmopolitan city of Moscow, making it their capital. Yet Leningrad also retains the symbols of its period of two centuries of rule in the Hermitage and the Winter Palace, built by the eighteenth-century successors to Peter the Great, and in the old Peter and Paul Fortress.

Kiev, or "Kiev the Golden," grew up on the high bluff that commands the west bank of the Dnepr, where it flows across the Ukraine to the Black Sea. The river and its own bluffs gave it some protection from the Tartars, though none from the Germans who came from the opposite direction. It became a commercial center, and a focus of the life of the Orthodox Church of Russia. Today its population numbers more than a million; it contains not only an eleventh-century cathedral, but also twentieth-century factories which turn out metal goods, glass, and chemicals and process the foodstuffs grown in the agricultural Ukraine.

Many cities should be added to this list and their function examined if space permitted: the industrial cities of the Moscow region—Yaroslavl, Ivanovo, Smolensk, and Tula; the western ports—Riga in Latvia and Kaliningrad, the former German Königsberg; the cities of the Volga— Gorkiy, Kazan, Kuybyshev, Saratov, and the familiar Stalingrad, now made unfamiliar by being renamed Volgograd. Then would come the industrial cities and ports of the Ukraine—Donetsk (formerly Stalino), Dnepropetrovsk, Kharkov, Rostov, Zaporozhye, and Krivoy Rog; those of the more recently industrialized Urals—Chelyabinsk, Sverdlovsk, Magnitogorsk; and of the yet more recently developed Kuznetsk Basin— Novokuznetsk (formerly Stalinsk), Barnaul, and Novosibirsk.

Then would come the old cities of Soviet Central Asia—Mary (formerly Merv), Bukhara, Tashkent, Fergana, and "silken Samarkand" itself, which grew up on the caravan routes between Europe and Asia; in each today, beside the crumbling mosques of an older culture, are the stark new factories and hydroelectric stations of the newer. Beside the colorful costume of the Tadzhik and Uzbek, the oriental craftsmen and markets, are the Soviet planners and engineers. Nowhere are the extremes of Soviet society, of Western technology and Eastern tradition brought into harsher juxtaposition than in the Soviet Socialist Republics of Central Asia.

Lastly, the string of cities which mushroom along the route that runs eastward through the steppe to the Pacific would be included: Omsk, Tomsk, Krasnoyarsk, Irkutsk, Ulan-Ude, Chita, Khabarovsk, Komsomolsk, and the Soviet Union's eastern gateway, Vladivostok itself.

The Union of Soviet Socialist Republics is a federal state, in which a somewhat variable number of units has been devised to meet the aspirations of a very varied people. At present, there are fifteen republics, each with its own constitution, government, and limited executive functions. In theory they are designed to fit the settlement pattern of the largest of the ethnic groups which make up the population of the Soviet Union. Where the groups are small—as are for example, the Mari, Tartar, Chu-

The fifteen republics are listed below. They can be located on the map by number.

Name	Population	Area (sq. miles)	Capital
1. Russian S.F.S.R.	122,200,000	6,592,800	Moscow
2. Ukrainian S.S.R.	43,725,000	232,050	Kiev
3. Kazakh S.S.R.	10,900,000	1,064,000	Alma-Ata
4. Uzbek S.S.R.	8,950,000	157,900	Tashkent
5. Byelorussian S.S.R.	8,325,000	80,150	Minsk
6. Georgian S.S.R.	4,280,000	33,450	Tbilisi
7. Azerbaidzhan S.S.R.	4,120,000	25,150	Baku
8. Moldavian S.S.R.	3,120,000	13,000	Kishinev
9. Lithuanian S.S.R.	2,850,000	26,900	Vilnius
10. Kirghiz S.S.R.	2,305,000	76,650	Frunze
11. Latvian S.S.R.	2,170,000	24,600	Riga
12. Tadzhik S.S.R.	2,170,000	55,200	Dushanbe
13. Armenian S.S.R.	1,960,000	11,500	Yerevan
14. Turkmen S.S.R.	1,690,000	118,400	Ashkhabad
15. Estonian S.S.R.	1,235,000	17,400	Tallin

UNION REPUBLICS OF THE SOVIET UNION

0   500 MILES

vash, and several similar groups in European Russia—they have been constituted as Autonomous Soviet Socialist Republics (A.S.S.R.'s) within the limits of the union Soviet Socialist Republics (S.S.R.'s). At a lower level of theoretical self-government, and reflecting smaller numbers and an alleged lesser degree of political maturity are the Autonomous Oblasts and National Okrugs. On paper the system appears to give every possible concession to democracy and the expression of national feeling, and is in reality so complex that it is almost unworkable. Yet it should not be dismissed as merely a façade. It does serve to decentralize certain functions of government, and it actually allows for the cultural expression of the subject peoples of Russia's empire.

The Russian people themselves are said to number about 114,000,000, a little over half the total of the Soviet Union; and the largest unit in the federal structure of the U.S.S.R. is the complex and unwieldy Russian Soviet Federated Socialist Republic, a federation within a federation, occupying about three-quarters of the whole area of the Soviet Union. In terms of numbers the 37,000,000 Ukrainians and 8,000,000 Byelo- or White-Russians come next, each with their own S.S.R.'s in European Russia and their seats in the United Nations. Then come the smaller groups: the Lithuanians, Latvians, Estonians, and Moldavians, though the actual numbers assigned to each of these peoples is somewhat suspect; then the nationalities of Central Asia: the Uzbeks, the Kazakhs, the Tadzhiks, the Kirghiz, and the Turkmen, and those of the area lying south of the Caucasus—the Azerbaidzhanians, Armenians, and Georgians.

Each of these peoples constitutes the nucleus of a separate S.S.R. There still remain numerous and important groups, like the Tartars, the Bashkir, and the Chuvash, who have not been accorded this theoretical degree of freedom and independence, and yet others: Jews, Germans, and Poles among them, who live scattered over wide areas and are not recognized in the constitution.

There is more continuity than is often realized between the Soviet Union and its predecessor, the empire of the Russian Tsars. They cover much the same area, and their territorial policies have much in common. The Tsarist Empire grew slowly through the centuries, its limits fluctuated with the relative power of the Tsars and their neighbors. The Soviets have consistently tried to maintain, strengthen, and even extend the territorial limits which they inherited from the last of the Tsars. The eastern and southern boundaries were fixed in the nineteenth century, and despite intermittent pressure on Mongolia, Iran, and Turkey, these boundaries have stood with no substantial change, beyond the incorporation of Tannu Tuva, southern Sakhalin, and the Kuril Islands after the Second World War.

This is not true of the western boundary of the Soviet Union. Here

the boundary changes made during the present century have been revolutionary. Before the First World War, Tsarist Russia extended westward
to embrace all of modern Finland, the Baltic States, and much of Poland,
including the capital city of Warsaw. In 1917 the Russian armies suffered
a complete defeat at the hands of the Germans. A year later the Germans were also defeated, leaving, as it were, a power vacuum in Eastern
Europe. Five new republics appeared on the political map, carved
wholly or partly out of the territory of Tsarist Russia.

Finland was created in the north. Along the eastern shore of the
Baltic Sea, the three small Baltic States—Estonia, Latvia, and Lithuania—
established themselves by successful revolt against the Russians. Farther
to the south the new Poland, created in part from former German territory, extended her boundaries far to the east, incorporating peoples who
were Byelorussian or Ukrainian, rather than Polish. And Romania, one
of the weakest of the East European states, profited from the defeat and
anarchy of Russia to incorporate the province of Bessarabia. Along the
whole western border, from the Arctic Ocean to the Black Sea, the Russian boundary withdrew before the pressure of the vigorous young
nation-states of Eastern Europe.

But this retreat was not permanent, and in their hearts the Russians
never regarded it as such. As soon as they had become strong enough
the Soviets clearly intended, at the very least, to regain the lost Tsarist
territory. They began, in 1939, with the Soviet agreement with Germany
to divide Poland between them, and in September of that year, Soviet
forces occupied approximately the eastern third of Poland. This was
followed by pressure on Finland for the cession of territory which was
regarded as strategically valuable to the Soviet Union. These demands
were resisted, and the Winter War of 1939-40, and Finland's defeat followed. The Soviet Union took what she wanted and turned her attention
to the Baltic States. First she demanded bases, then secured the formation in each of them of a government favorable to herself; the final
event, reached in June, 1940, was for these governments to seek admission to the Soviet Union and to be welcomed enthusiastically into the
fold. At the same time Romania was required to cede Bessarabia.

Between Romania and Poland the Soviet Union, as it were, extended
a grasping hand across the Carpathian Mountains, and laid it firmly on
the northeastern corner of the Hungarian Plain, annexing the eastern
extremity of Czechoslovakia. With the defeat of the German armies, the
Soviet Union also took over the northern third of the former German

East Prussia. Along the whole front, from northern Finland to the mouth of the Danube, the western boundary of the Soviet Union was pushed to the west.

The legal boundary does not always mark the limit of Soviet jurisdiction. Beyond it lies a Soviet sphere of influence. The depth of this influence varies from one country to another. A few years ago it might have been said that Soviet influence in China was powerful, almost controlling. Today that can be said no longer, though Soviet influence in Outer Mongolia is considerable. To the south lie three non-Communist states: Afghanistan, Iran, and Turkey, the first neutralist, though apparently under strong Soviet influence, the other two in alliance with the West.

Along the European boundary of the Soviet Union, from Romania through Hungary and Czechoslovakia to Poland, lie the satellites, a group of countries tied economically, politically, and even militarily to the Soviet Union, preserving independence of action only in the less important fields of government. Bulgaria has no common boundary with the Soviet Union, but is a satellite no less. Beyond Hungary and Romania, which are firmly attached to the Soviet Union, lie the Communist states of Yugoslavia and Albania, both in their different ways in revolt against Russian direction. The Yugoslav revolt has gone on since, in the summer of 1948, Tito broke with the Kremlin, without in any way affecting the Communist organization of the Yugoslav state. It is the best example so far of national Communism, and proof that a Communist state is not necessarily under Soviet Russian domination and control.

Albania presents a different problem. It is small in population, relatively undeveloped in its resources, and is cut off by Yugoslavia and Greece from other members of the Soviet Bloc. In its isolation, it has become susceptible to Chinese persuasion. Geographical separation has prevented the Soviet Union from reinforcing its prestige and political standing, and it looks today as if Albania might provide another example of national Communism in Europe.

Lastly, we have Finland, twice defeated by Soviet armies and twice deprived of territory by its Communist neighbor, capitalist in its organization and westward looking in its culture. Finland has had neutralism imposed upon it, and there is always the danger that some alleged deviation from the narrow path of nonalignment may bring down upon this small nation of only 4,517,000 the wrath of the Soviet Union.

EAST CENTRAL EUROPE

So we turn from the Soviet Union itself to the group of states which border it on the west. Finland, which is overshadowed by the Soviet Union though not a member of the Soviet Bloc, we have already examined. There remain Poland and East Germany, Czechoslovakia, Romania, Bulgaria, and the two Communist states of Yugoslavia and Albania, which in their different ways stand aloof from the Soviet Union, if not also from the rest of the bloc.

This East European area is a confused one. It might be said that, geographically, all that it has in common is its acceptance of the Communist ideology. It is peopled by no less than a dozen distinct peoples, each with their own language. Eight of these peoples are Slav, representing more than three-quarters of the total population; and they are so numerous and so widespread that their distribution might be said to be a second factor giving unity to Eastern Europe.

The Slavs originated within the territory of modern Poland. From here they spread southward into the Danube Basin and on into the Balkan Peninsula early in the Christian era, and at the same time eastward into European Russia. The Slavs settled in widely scattered agricultural communities. Their language evolved differently in different parts of the vast area which they came to inhabit, giving rise to the distinctive Slav languages: Polish, Czech and Slovak, Slovene, Serbo-Croat, Macedonian, and Bulgarian, as well as the Russian language and the closely related White Russian and Ukrainian.

The Slavs had reached approximately their present area of settlement almost a thousand years ago. But the continuity of the settlement of Slav Europe was interrupted by groups of earlier peoples who had lived on through the Slav invasions. Among these were the Albanians, descendants of the ancient Illyrians, who enjoyed the protection which the ruggedness of their country gave them. Others were descended from Roman settlers. They retained their language, a Latin which borrowed words and constructions from the Slavs and others. Some of these peoples were later concentrated as the Romanians; other and smaller groups continue to inhabit some of the more mountainous regions of the Balkans under the name of Vlachs.

Into this Slav sea, with its islands of Albanian and Romance languages, there came from the east the Magyars, or Hungarians, and the

Turks, and from the west, the Germans and Italians. Magyars settled the plains of the middle Danube Valley, where today is the state of Hungary. The Turks spread, like a tidal wave, through the Balkans and were checked for a time along the line of the Danube; they flowed on across Hungary and then ebbed back almost as quickly and suddenly as they had advanced. Like the ebb tide, they left only a few pools of Turkish influence and culture behind them.

The Italians spread along the western coast of the Balkan Peninsula, but penetrated no farther inland than the extent of the mild Mediterranean climate. The Germans came from the west with greater deliberation, and with the thoroughness that has always characterized them, settled and Germanized the western borders of Poland and Czechoslovakia, and sent an advance guard of German settlement eastward as far as Russia.

Thus was created the complex pattern of peoples and cultures which lies between Germany to the west and Russia to the east. The Second World War brought changes—the Germans, in all some ten millions of them, were driven from western Poland and Czechoslovakia—but the geographical pattern remained much the same. The antipathies between the many national groups remained as strong, though their open expression has been prevented by the imposition of Soviet control. Only where the division between the peoples of Eastern Europe coincides with the rift between East and West, as it does between Bulgaria and Greece and between Albania and Yugoslavia, are the ancient animosities encouraged. To these peoples, with their national aspirations and their lingering hatreds, first those of East Central Europe and then those of the Balkans, we now turn.

Poland

Poland is in many ways the most important and the most interesting of this group of states. Poland is the land of the plain. It is usually held that the term Poland derives from the Slav word *pole,* meaning a field, and implying a broad, level, open area. Today Poland is a segment of the great North European Plain. It stretches from the Baltic Sea in the north to the mountains, the Carpathians, that enclose the plain on the south. Rivers flow lazily across this plain, from the mountains to the sea, the Oder—or Odra, as the Poles call it—and the Vistula. Their small sluggish tributaries drain the land between them, cutting damp, shallow valleys into the almost level plain. It was amid these river valleys, and pro-

tected from attack by their wet, ill-drained valley floors, that the Polish state emerged a thousand years ago. This state grew outward, becoming at one time territorially one of the largest states in Europe. The greatness of early Poland is a memory which continues to haunt the Poles. It gives them a pride in their past, and a hope for the future that is not found among all the satellites.

The tragedy of Poland is that these marshy valleys, which gave shelter and protection to the infant state, were not barriers enough to keep out stronger and more numerous peoples from west and east. First, the Germans moved into western Poland, settling there and taking over the territory. The Poles, as if to compensate, spread east, carving for themselves great tracts of land out of the vast territorial mass of Russia. Then Russia grew to strength, began to take back what had been lost, and Poland, caught between the upper and the nether stones of a giant mill, was slowly pulverized and extinguished.

Late in the eighteenth century Poland disappeared from the map of

Europe. It came back in 1918, with the defeat of both Russia and Germany. It was liquidated again in 1939, as these two powers, grown to strength once again, turned and divided Poland between them. But undaunted by these misfortunes, Poland appeared on the map again in 1945, smaller in area, changed in shape, and pushed bodily westward. Poland had reversed its centuries-long creep toward the east. Now the east, represented by the Soviet Union, was stronger than Germany, and Poland lost territory to the former and recouped by gains from the latter.

Despite the devastation of war and the complete destruction of its capital city, Warsaw, Poland is now a richer and more homogeneous country than before. Its population of over 30,000,000 is made up almost entirely of Poles. It has acquired from Germany good farm land along the Odra River, and it has got possession of the whole of the important coal field of Upper Silesia, second in size and importance among the coal basins of Europe.

Outwardly Poland is a poor state, but potentially it is rich. Only wars, boundary changes, and exploitation by more powerful and aggressive neighbors have prevented it from developing its resources. But now this is being done. The Upper Silesian coal field, in both resources and production ranks next to the Ruhr coal field of West Germany. Its present output of about 100,000,000 tons a year supplies an important export trade and a rapidly growing domestic industry.

On the coal field itself are the industrial cities of Katowice, Bytom, Gliwice, and Chorzów, each engaged in some branch of the metallurgical industry. Industry is being re-equipped and extended, and fifty miles to the east, near the beautiful old city of Kraków, is the new steel town of Nowa Huta, with the newest and largest steel mill in all Eastern Europe. In the Carpathian Mountains, to the south, hydroelectric power is being generated from new installations built on the rivers that flow down to the Vistula. A shipbuilding industry has been established in the northern ports of Gdansk (Danzig) and Szczecin (Stettin). The old textile industry in Lódź, established when much of Poland was under Russian rule, is being extended. The mining of copper, lead, zinc, and sulfur is being developed, and everywhere there is a new drive toward the building up of industry.

The new Warsaw typifies the new Poland. The old city was wiped out. The new recaptures the atmosphere of the old. The old Town Square and much of the old city have been rebuilt just as they were before their destruction by the Germans. They are even more ornate, colorful, and picturesque than they were before. They demonstrate Poland's pride in its past, proved by its willingness to sacrifice modern housing and amenities in order to rebuild these architectural and artistic monuments.

East Germany

Beyond the Oder and the Neisse rivers is East Germany, that part of the former Reich which passed in 1945 under Russian occupation. To the countries of the Communist Bloc it is the German Democratic Republic; to the West, just the Russian Zone. It is less than half the size of the German Federal Republic, and has less than a third of its population. It has for many years been losing people by flight to West Germany, and it has shared with the Republic of Ireland the unique distinction of being the only country in the world with a diminishing population.

Yet East Germany is neither poor nor unviable. It is made up of the eastward extension of two of those physical regions which make up the Federal Republic; the Northern Plain and the Central Uplands. The former consists of heavy-soiled clay plain; of light, infertile sandy tracts, and of rich loess in alternating bands stretched across the country from west to east; the latter is only a fringe of hills, in which rise most of the East German rivers.

The Elbe, which rises in Czechoslovakia and enters the sea below Hamburg in West Germany, serves as a kind of natural axis for East Germany. Berlin communicates with it by river and canal; Magdeburg and Dresden lie on it, and Leipzig and Halle are on its tributaries. The tributaries in the Ore Mountains (Erzgebirge) which lie on the Czechoslovak border, once provided power for the textile mills of Plauen, Zwickau, and Chemnitz (Karl-Marx-Stadt); now these industries use coal from the small deposits that are found in this part of Saxony. In addition to the small reserves of coal are large deposits of lignite, of rock salt, and of potash, which form the basis of the highly developed chemical industry of East Germany.

In its seaborne commerce the territory which now makes up East Germany formerly made use of the port of Hamburg. This is now cut off by the Iron Curtain, and the East German government is today developing the Baltic port of Rostock, which had previously been of only small importance.

As in all the East European satellites, heavy industry is being expanded and integrated into an over-all plan which has been shaped in

Moscow. A new iron and steel works has arisen to the east of Berlin, at Eisenhüttenstadt (formerly Stalinstadt) on the Oder, and is supplied with fuel brought down the river by barge from Polish Upper Silesia. The resources and industry of East Germany make an important contribution to the economic strength of the Communist Bloc.

But neither resources nor factories are of much value without manpower to exploit and work them. This has been East Germany's problem; too many people have escaped during the period from 1945 to 1961. They had only to travel into East Berlin, the capital of the East Zone, and to slip quietly across into West Berlin, where asylum would be awaiting them, together with a job in one of the booming West German industries. In all, some two million had been lost in this way, and these were drawn in the main from the younger and economically more valuable age groups. The remedy should have been simple: to improve conditions in East Germany so that workers would not want to leave. But the remedy to which the East German authorities had resort was to build a wall across the city of Berlin.

Czechoslovakia

Its name is a longer and more complex name than Poland, and it describes a more elongated and a more complex country. The land of the Czechs and Slovaks cannot be described in simple terms. It is made up of hills and mountains, separated by valleys and plains. In the west is a diamond-shaped area, ringed by hills, with lowland set in the midst of this rough frame. This is Bohemia, homeland of the Czechs. Through it flows the upper Elbe (Labe) River, and on a hill overlooking one of its tributaries, the Vltava, the city of Prague grew up. Prague suffered only negligible damage in the Second World War; it remains one of the glories of European Gothic and baroque art and architecture. Coal is mined in this central basin of Bohemia, and industrial centers, notably Plžen (Pilsen), famous for its beer and its steel, have grown up.

East of Bohemia is a kind of trough, the Province of Moravia, which joins the Polish plain to the north with the Danube Valley lying to the south. This trough has been a routeway between northern and southern Europe throughout history. To the north it leads to Kraków and Warsaw; to the south, to Vienna. Its flat floor is good farm land; in the north there is coal, and Ostrava has become the most important Czechoslovak center of the iron and steel industries. To the south, on the edge of the rich farm land of the Moravian plain, is Brno, chief city of the province, and in the extreme southeast of the country, where the first of the mountain ridges which make up the Carpathians curves down to the river, is Bratislava. The city nestles beneath the steep cliff, crowned by the ruins of its castle and commanding the Danube. Upstream lies Vienna and the hills of Austria; downstream is the plain of Hungary. To the northeast are the Carpathian Mountains, their long, fingerlike ridges reaching out toward the river.

Moravia is a part of the Czech lands, but to the east, beyond the outermost of the curving ridges of the Carpathian Mountains, are the Slovaks of Slovakia. Slovakia is more mountainous and rugged, poorer and less developed than the Czech lands. Culturally, there are also differences. The Slovak language is similar, but distinct. The Slovaks had formerly been ruled by the Hungarians; the Czechs, by the Austrians. The Slovaks received less encouragement. Their land was not industrialized; few roads were built, and, compared with the Czechs, they have always been more primitive and self-sufficient. Despite the attempts of the last forty years to level up the living standards of Slovakia, there remains an element of suspicion and distrust between Czech and Slovak.

Today industrial development in Czechoslovakia is being pushed ahead no less than in Poland, and, as part of this process, new industries are being located in the previously backward Slovakia, where a primitive agriculture and lumbering operation had once formed the main branches of human activity.

Along part of Slovakia's southern border flows the Danube, and almost all of Slovakia is drained to the Danube. The river Danube, brown or green, but never blue, flows down from south Germany and across Austria. On the western outskirts of Vienna a low hilly ridge runs out to the river, which winds around its foot. This is the Wiener Wald, the familiar Vienna Woods. From the summit of the Wiener Wald, the eye ranges eastward over the city, and beyond it to the level plain which borders the river. In the blue distance this plain widens and merges into the Hungarian Plain. Across the plain flows the Danube. One or two low hilly ridges reach out from the Alps, northeastward across the plain, as if forming hurdles for the river to jump. Instead the river, like a saw, has cut narrow defiles across them. The last of these is at Vysehrad, only thirty miles above Budapest.

Near Vysehrad the river swings to the south, passes Budapest, and flows on across the plain, gathering tributaries from the Alps and the Car-

pathians. It flows beneath the cliff on which old Belgrade—the "white fortress," now the capital of Yugoslavia—was built, and then in the biggest defile in its whole course, the gorges of the Iron Gate, cuts across the mountain system, separating the Transylvanian Alps, lying to the north, from the Balkan Mountains, to the south. The lowest part of its course is through a plain dividing Romania and Bulgaria, until at last the Danube reaches its delta in Romania and empties into the Black Sea.

The Danube forms a kind of link between the countries which share it—Czechoslovakia, Hungary, Yugoslavia, Romania, and Bulgaria. It is a navigable river even as far up as south Germany, but below Vienna it is used increasingly by barges which carry the products of the Danubian countries down to the Black Sea, and bring back Soviet coal, iron ore, and petroleum for the Soviet Union's Danubian empire.

Hungary

The middle part of the Danube's course, from Vienna down to the Iron Gate, is across the most extensive area of plain in its whole course—the Hungarian Plain. The mountains draw back on each side, to rejoin again where they overlook the defile of the Iron Gate itself. This plain is the homeland of the Hungarian people, or Magyars, as they call themselves. The Magyar tribes invaded and settled the mid-Danubian plain about the year 900. They came from the grasslands of southern Russia; they were a seminomadic and at least partly a pastoral people, but in the Danubian plain they turned agriculturalists, and built up one of the more important states of medieval Europe. The Magyars, interbred with the peoples they found there, dominated the plain and extended their control, if not also their settlements, into the surrounding hills.

This has remained the Magyar sphere, the plain set in its frame of mountains. Their language, with its affinities with Finnish and with languages still spoken in Central Asia, spread over the plain, but the hills remained Slovak, or Romanian, or Serb, or Croat. Mountain and plain supplemented one another, the one with its forests and mines, the other with its croplands and animal industries. Economically they constituted a unit, but between the two there was a cultural conflict which led, at the end of the First World War, to the break-up of the old Hungarian state.

Modern Hungary is only a fraction of its earlier size; it has lost its physical frame of mountain and hill, which is now included within its neighbors, Czechoslovakia, Romania, and Yugoslavia, and it is now reduced to the heart of the plain, the essentially Magyar region. Hungary has been left with depleted resources and a yearning for revenge. Its membership in the Communist Bloc helps to supply the one and suppress the other. If the Communist rule of Eastern Europe could miraculously vanish, in its place as a threat to peace would be the national ambitions of countries like Hungary, looking for the restoration of their past greatness and the former extent of their territory.

Hungary is today predominantly an agricultural state. Crop farming, the cultivation of corn and wheat and food for the cattle and horses, as well as the crops associated especially with Hungary, like paprika, has spread over the once grassy puszta, or steppe.

Resources for modern industry are limited in both quantity and variety. There is a little coal, a scrap of iron ore; the only resource that is abundant is bauxite, the ore from which aluminum is obtained. Yet the city of Budapest has long had a number of light industries, which included an important manufacture of electrical equipment and some food processing. Up in the hills on the northern border of Hungary there was an ancient iron industry that used charcoal. Now a modern heavy industry is being created. On the bank of the Danube, below Budapest, a new iron and steel works has been built at Dunaújváros (formerly Sztalinváros). Iron ore is brought up the river in barges all the way from the Soviet Union; another instance of the way in which the Soviet Union is making its satellites increasingly dependent upon itself.

Budapest is to Hungary what its neighbor, Vienna, is to Austria, a vast overgrown capital city that dwarfs the rest of the country. And, like Vienna, it is one of the liveliest cities in Europe. Up on the hill to the west of the wide curving Danube, is old Buda, once the castle of the Hungarian kings, and now the site of government buildings, which still bear the scars of the Russian attack in 1944. Beyond the impressive bridges which cross the Danube is Pest, the flat, sprawling residential, commercial, and industrial part of this twin city on the Danube. Here are the scars left by a later Russian attack, when in the fall of 1956 Red Army tanks rumbled through the streets and suppressed the short-lived Hungarian bid for independence.

THE BALKANS

The three states of Poland, Czechoslovakia, and Hungary are uncompromisingly Western in their way of life and in the political outlook of the people. In the past they sought their friends and allies in France and Germany. Their capitals bear the stamp of elegance that puts them beside Paris and Brussels and Bern. But just beyond the eastern border of Hungary, the plain ends against the hills of Romania and to the south, against those of Yugoslavia. Physically, historically, and culturally Romania, Bulgaria, Yugoslavia, and Albania are quite different from Hungary. They are mountainous; for long periods they were under Turkish misrule; for them peace has been only the short intervals between wars.

Romania

This country is grouped around a central region of mountains; rivers flow outward in all directions from the center, and give the country no physical unity. The forested ridges of the Carpathians curve through the state, continuing as the Transylvanian Alps, enclosing the rugged, hilly massif of the Bihor Mountains. These mountains remain today one of the most backward, least penetrable parts of Europe, where truly medieval feuds and superstitions linger on into the twentieth century. Between the Carpathians and the Bihor Mountains is the rolling, mountain-girt basin

of Transylvania, a sunny region with rich soil, into which Germans and Magyars came and settled in the Middle Ages between the mountains where lurked the Romanians.

Romania is as complex geographically as Czechoslovakia, and far more complex in its cultures and communities. A core of mountains holds apart from one another the surrounding segments of plain. The nucleus of the Romanian state was the plain to the south and east of the mountains, the provinces of Walachia and Moldavia, whose union in the mid-nineteenth century laid the foundation of the modern state. The rest was added later, and it must be admitted that, although Romania in 1939 lost possession of the province of Bessarabia to Russia, her growth has been remarkable. Her allies of the First World War helped her to territory to which her neighbors, Hungary, Yugoslavia, and Bulgaria could each put up a respectable claim. Again, it can be said: Remove the Communist tyranny, and the old national rivalries will reassert themselves.

Romania does not belong to Western Europe, in spite of its claim to derive its name, its language, and even its people from those Romans who, in the second century A.D., settled within the curve of the Carpathian Mountains. Romania is Eastern; its Christianity is that of the Eastern, or Orthodox, Church. For centuries it was the battleground of Turks and Tartars. Invaders from south of the Danube, or from beyond the Prut on the northeast, in turn devastated its fields and destroyed its cities. Time and again incipient industry and commerce were destroyed by invaders, and Romania was forced back over and over again to its primitive self-sufficiency, made worse by the graft, the incompetence, and the greed of its rulers, whether Turkish or its own kings and native aristocracy.

Romania remains poor today. Although, near Ploesti, it contains the largest reserves of petroleum in Europe, these have never brought much profit to the people. There is coal, and metalliferous ores, neither of which has ever been properly exploited. There are some of the most fertile soils of Europe in the plains of Moldavia and Walachia, and until recently there were neither roads nor railroads sufficient to carry much of the surplus to market. Today there is change in Romania, as in all the satellites. Much of the land is collectivized. The minerals are being worked as never before, and a small iron and steel industry is growing. The capital city of Bucharest, once no more than an overgrown village, is transforming itself into an industrial city, and traffic is increasing along the Danube and through the branches of its delta, which lead to the Black Sea and the ports of the Soviet Ukraine.

Bulgaria

Across the Danube from Walachia is Bulgaria, a smaller and simpler country than Romania. Like Romania, from the collapse of the Roman Empire in the fifth century it has known invasion and war, punctuated by only short periods of peace and prosperity when the short-lived Bulgarian state appeared only to be extinguished in the invasions that followed. For five hundred years Bulgaria was ruled and misruled by the Turks. As their power grew weaker during the nineteenth century, government became more corrupt and oppressive, and collapsed less than a century ago in massacre and war. The British statesman, W. E. Gladstone, called for the expulsion of the "unspeakable Turk . . . from the continent he had defiled and defaced." During the next half-century, the Turks were reduced to a small foothold in the hills behind Constantinople. The Bulgarian state was re-created and endowed with extravagant hopes of dominating the Balkans.

Urged on by the memories of the medieval Bulgarian state, Bulgaria planned too big, ran into similar imperialist ambitions of her neighbors, and forfeited her gains in the Balkan Wars of 1912-14. Like Hungary, whose experience was broadly similar, Bulgaria was reduced to a small and compact size. Any territory to which her neighbors could put forward even the most shadowy claim, was taken from Bulgaria. Bulgaria, like Hungary, was shorn of territory, of outlets to the Mediterranean Sea, of subject peoples, and left, suspicious and revengeful, to await the opportunity to repair her losses.

The Communist Bloc does not readily tolerate any rift in its monolithic façade. The feud between Bulgaria and Romania is suppressed. But the same does not hold for Bulgaria's western and southern neighbors, Yugoslavia and Greece. Here the old, almost traditional hostility is reinforced by the wider conflict between East and West. Bulgaria is permitted to lay claim to parts of Macedonia, shared by both her neighbors, because to do so is to absorb into the Cold War one of the basic disputes of the Balkan Peninsula; but so far Bulgaria has done nothing to enforce her claim.

For five centuries Bulgaria was less exposed to Tartars than Romania, and more exposed to Turks. But whichever was the enemy and conqueror, economic development was inhibited. Bulgaria remains today an overwhelmingly agricultural state. Its resources for modern industry are more limited than those of Romania, and only in the last few years have even these small resources been used. But the Bulgarians have always shown great skill in managing their small farms, on which they grow corn and sunflowers, tobacco, grapes, and vegetables. In a valley on the southern flank of the Balkan Mountains, roses are grown as a field crop, and from their petals, which are collected each summer, is distilled the oil, or attar of roses, which serves as the base of many scents.

In its physical features Bulgaria is quite unlike Hungary. It is a mountainous country. The Carpathian system, which provides a sinuous backbone to Romania, comes down to the Danube as the Transylvanian Alps, and beyond the narrow cleft eroded by the river at the Iron Gate continues its curved path through northern Bulgaria as the Balkan Mountains. These are a formidable barrier to movement; they held up the Russian invasion of the Balkans in 1876, and they continue to divide Bulgaria into two contrasted regions, the plains along the Danube and the Maritsa Valley. The former are like the plains of Romania, hot in summer, cold in winter, open to the climatic as well as the human influences

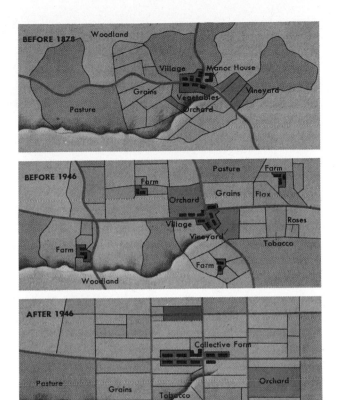

Under the Turks Bulgarian farms were large and centered on the manor house. Then the peasants became small landowners. Collectivization restored large units.

that flow outward from Russia. The Maritsa Valley is a corridor lying between the Balkan and the Rhodope Mountains. Since ancient times it has provided a routeway from Constantinople, through the passes near Sofia, to the Hungarian Plain. It broadens southeastward toward the Black Sea. It is a kinder and more genial region, more Mediterranean in its climate and its crops. The capital of Bulgaria, Sofia, lies near the head of the Maritsa Valley, in the trough that leads through the mountains to Serbia.

The Rhodope Mountains bound Bulgaria on the south. They are a steep-sided, rough massif of old rock which has throughout history repelled settlement and offered a refuge to those who flee from invaders and tyranny. Beyond the Rhodope and to the west lie the dry, hilly plains of Macedonia, with its medley of languages, peoples, and historical claims. Here is a sea of troubled waters in which the Bulgarians often fish. If they have so far caught little, they have, nevertheless, succeeded in muddying the waters and making them unpleasant for others.

Yugoslavia

To the west of the Balkan and Rhodope Mountains is a hilly depression, drained by the Morava northward to the Danube and by the Vardar south to the Aegean Sea; west of this depression are the Dinaric Alps of Yugoslavia and Albania. This mountain range branches southeastward from the Alps of Austria and borders the Adriatic Sea as far as Greece. In the north the mountains are low, narrow, and easily crossed, but to the southeast they become broader and more difficult to cross, and present a serious barrier to communications between the coast and the interior of Yugoslavia.

The Dinaric Mountains are made up of steep, dry limestone ridges, carved into fantastic shapes by the solution of the softer beds in the limestone itself. Much of this Dinaric region is without soil or water. The white or gray limestone shows at the surface; it is pervious to water; the small winter rainfall is absorbed by it, leaving the surface without pools or flowing rivers. This is the land that rises precipitously from the eastern shore of the Adriatic, where we took leave of it in Chapter 9.

The coastal strip has a Mediterranean climate, but this changes a few miles inland to one more typical of Eastern Europe, with severe winters and hot and rather rainy summers. The grape and the olive are the characteristic crops along the Dalmatian coast; inland it is corn.

Much of the interior of Yugoslavia is hilly or mountainous. Villages crowd along the valleys that drain down to the Danube, but between them rise the high, bare mountains of Bosnia, Hercegovina, Montenegro, and Serbia. Yugoslavia is a large country, as large as Wyoming or Oregon. Its northeastern quarter lies within the Hungarian Plain. It is traversed by the Danube, and is good farm land, well cultivated, in contrast with the rest of the country.

The mineral wealth of Yugoslavia is varied but rather small in quantity; coal, iron, copper, lead, zinc are mined in insufficient quantities to make Yugoslavia important for any of them. Only bauxite is found in quantity, and Yugoslavia lacks the electric power to use it. Centuries of Turkish rule hindered economic development, and more recently the feuds between the dominant Slav peoples, the Serbs and the Croats, the one Orthodox and the other Catholic, have torn the country politically. The picture is complicated by the presence in Bosnia of Serbs who became converted to Islam when under Turkish rule; and the presence of Albanian, Bulgarian, Hungarian, Macedonian, and Romanian minorities, as well as German—some of them only small groups—adds to the variety of the people and the problems of government. Yugoslavia is now organized as a federal republic, and as far as possible these groups each constitute a separate and largely autonomous unit.

The most developed parts of Yugoslavia are in the northeast; the cities of Belgrade, Subotica, and Zagreb are on the margin of the Hungarian Plain; other large cities include Ljubljana, Sarajevo, and Skopje. Yugoslavia has a long coast line and numerous natural harbors—among which Rijeka is the most important and Dubrovnik the most picturesque —all of them cut off from the interior by the Dinaric system, across which there are so far few means of transportation. Yugoslavia faces grave difficulties in her attempts to use her resources more fully and to broaden her economy. The problems of lack of capital and industrial skills she shares with her neighbors, but the problem of transportation—the rugged terrain, the mountainous barrier between the interior and the Adriatic coast, the centuries of Turkish rule when little was done to develop communications, and the paucity of good roads and railroads today—are peculiarly her own.

Albania

Near the southern boundary of Yugoslavia, the Adriatic coast line makes a turn to the south, and the mountains which lie behind it become yet higher and more rugged. These mountains are so difficult of access that they have formed a refuge for peoples driven here by invasion and war in the surrounding areas. Here are traces of ancient peoples and cultures. Languages extinct elsewhere still flourish. These mountains are, as it were, a museum of vanished cultures, but there is nothing leisurely or academic about these survivals.

The Albanians are the descendants of the ancient Illyrian peoples, who inhabited the Dinaric Mountains in ancient times and fought against the Roman invaders. Their language is a European speech that is older than the classical and the Slavic languages of these regions. Their ways of life remain simpler, almost primitive. Their literature is folklore, and until recently the blood-feud absorbed their energies and resolved or perpetuated their disputes. Albania has always been one of the least penetrable and least known parts of Europe.

As a state, Albania appeared on the European map in 1913, not because it was fit for statehood or able to rank with Greece and Italy, but because there was nothing else to be done with this unruly territory once Turkish rule, which had in fact been little more than nominal, vanished from the area. Western—mainly Italian—influences in time crept into the Albanian mountains, but left no lasting political influence. During the Second World War, the Albanians shook off their ties with Italy, and forged new ties with the Communist Bloc. But isolation, the rugged terrain, and the difficulties of transport and communication restrict the Communist control over the area. The Albanians are true to themselves, if only in their refusal to accept outside direction and control. Today they have become collectively a wayward, rebellious, problem child of the Communist Bloc. If now they hitch their destinies to the star of Red China, this is in part because China is distant, in part because the Soviet Union has shown favors to their enemy Yugoslavia.

The Albanians, whose memory is longer even than that of their Balkan neighbors, still regard their tribal enemies, the Serbs and the Greeks, whom they have fought for centuries, as their bitterest foes. With both Bulgaria and Albania gnawing at her southern portion, Yugoslavia has reason for concern. But Albania is weak; her industry only feebly developed; her agriculture, despite claims to have been collectivized, backward. She will need all the aid her Chinese ally can give her before she can pose a serious problem to her neighbors.

In this chapter we have ranged over a territory immense both in its size and in the variety of environment and culture that it offers. Some good reason must be given for including such an area within the limits of a single chapter. This area is defined, not in physical or cultural terms, but in political. It is, with the addition of Mainland China and North Korea and North Vietnam, the area which has adopted, or has had imposed upon it, a Communist system of government. It is, with the exception of Yugoslavia and Albania, the area which is obedient to the command of Moscow. In these political circumstances alone lies its unity. This unity was achieved during the years immediately following the Second World War. The Red Armies had swept westward into Germany, occupying the countries of Eastern Europe on their way. In each of these during the next three years, Communist governments replaced non-Communist. Factories and other means of production were nationalized; experiments were made in crop farming, and a structure of government and of society, roughly modeled on that of the Soviet Union, was built upon the ruins left by the war itself.

This political bloc soon began to assume the characteristics of an economic bloc. Plans for industrial development were initiated in each, and the detail of each country's plans was shaped by the Soviet Union itself. To varying degrees the economies of all these East European countries were subordinated to the needs and the policies of the Soviet Union. At this Yugoslavia revolted. Refusing to accept regimentation by the Kremlin, it has since pursued a policy of national Communism. In the others, with the possible exception of Albania—small, poor, and remote—there has been some degree of integration in their economic development. The branches of industry in which each specializes are designed so as not to overlap or compete with those of other countries within the Communist Bloc. Trade between them in fuel, raw materials, and finished goods is increasing. Each is helping in the industrial development of the others, and their combined industrial production is increasing at a rapid rate.

These East European countries, which only a generation ago were primarily agricultural, are now becoming increasingly industrialized as their development plans are one by one implemented and completed. There would have been some economic growth in these countries, whatever their political regime. The present enforced expansion with all the hardships which it brings to the people, made to work harder and rewarded with less, is the work of the Communist governments. It is a major event in the history of Europe, transforming the landscape, the geographical pattern of production, and society itself. In the words of W. Wszelaki, "The Communist system may endure or perish, but what has already been done can hardly be undone: Middle Europe will not return to its pastoral era."

12 VANISHING EMPIRES, NEWBORN NATIONS:

West, East, Central, and South Africa

"Balkanisation" is becoming an obsolete word:
it should be "Africanisation."

—The Economist, January 6, 1962

Many elements in our Western civilization originated on the fringes of the African continent. The fountains of Egyptian civilization were watered by the river Nile which reached Egypt from some then unknown source in the heart of Africa. The Pharaohs ruled and the Pyramids were built in Africa. The Phoenicians founded colonies along the African shore, and the Romans expanded their empire into it until they were repelled by the sandy waste of the Sahara Desert. The early Christian saint and teacher, Augustine, was born in North Africa, and medieval Christian tradition represented him as black.

Yet none of these peoples and empires knew Africa. Theirs was a narrow rim of the continent bordering the Mediterranean, set between the sand and the surf. Movement outward over the sea was easier than inward across the desert, and very few of them ever concerned themselves with what lay beyond the unknown, untrodden waste which made up most of North Africa.

Nevertheless, some curiosity was displayed. The Phoenicians, in particular, ventured in their ships along the African coast, both westward from the Strait of Gibraltar and southward along the coast of the Red Sea. There is even a story that about 600 B.C. the Egyptian Pharaoh Necho

469

sent an expedition, manned by Phoenicians, to sail right around Africa. Legend reports that they completed their long hazardous voyage in two years, and that in order to replenish their food supplies they landed on the African coast and remained long enough to sow and reap a crop before sailing on. But we know nothing more about this expedition. Least of all do we find that it brought back any substantial knowledge of the continent of Africa.

In the fifteenth century the Portuguese navigators began to push southward along the west coast of Africa. In 1487 one of them, Bartolomeu Díaz, reached the Cape of Good Hope, which is almost the most southerly point of the continent. A decade later, his fellow countryman Vasco da Gama rounded the south of Africa, and sailed along the east coast and so across the Indian Ocean to India. He had opened up a sea route from Europe to India, but he did not add to mankind's knowledge of Africa.

It continued to be the dark, unknown continent. Here medieval people located the kingdom of the legendary Prester John, and no one could prove them wrong. Even in the eighteenth century the English writer, Jonathan Swift, reflected the contemporary ignorance of Africa when he wrote:

> So geographers in Afric-maps,
> With savage-pictures fill their gaps;
> And o'er unhabitable downs
> Place elephants for want of towns.

By the end of the sixteenth century South America had been crossed in many directions; and Marco Polo's travels through the heart of Asia were widely known at a time when people in Europe had no idea of where the river Nile originated. Indeed the source of the Nile was not known to Europeans until Speke discovered it in 1860.

For this prevailing ignorance of the African continent, there was very good reason. Africa in past centuries was a difficult continent to penetrate. No important land mass on the face of the globe has a straighter or more regular coast line; not one has fewer bays, openings, and estuaries to shelter ships and welcome and entice them into the interior. It was a forbidding continent.

When, in the late Middle Ages, the Portuguese sailors began their slow progress around Africa, they encountered first the desert coast of the western Sahara. Then the coast became less forbidding; there were

In West, East, Central, and South Africa the European colonial empires have almost disappeared, and independent nations have taken their place.

signs of vegetation, and one headland they called Cape Verde, though its greenness was wholly relative to the yellow and brown of the desert which the voyagers had just left behind. Then, with only a short transition through the savanna came the forest. Dense forest reached down to the coast, and even invaded the ocean. As if wading on tall stilts, the mangrove trees spread outward into the sea itself. On beyond the equator the dense forest continued, awe-inspiring and impenetrable to those who had just come from Europe, ignorant of its secrets. And when the forest ended the desert began again.

Rivers flowed down to the coast from the far interior—the Nile into the Mediterranean; the Niger, Congo, and Orange into the Atlantic; the Zambezi into the Indian Ocean—yet they provided no avenue of penetration. The fact is that much of Africa is made up of a kind of plateau. Its surface relief is simple; it has few high mountains, and almost no deep valleys. It is as if someone had cut it out with a saw from a sheet of plywood, and bent it to fit the curvature of the globe. It is sharp, steep-edged. Rivers meander across the rolling surface of the plateau in

which they have, at the most, cut for themselves wide, open, shallow valleys. Then they plunge over the edge, dropping by falls and cataracts to
the narrow plain that fringes the coast.

Sometimes in the interior the rivers drop abruptly, as in the great
Victoria Falls of the Zambezi; sometimes in a series of rapids or cataracts, like those of the Nile. But, however they drop, the rivers cease to
be navigable. We can imagine those early navigators heading up a small,
swamp-fringed estuary, attracted by the fresh water that met them. Then,
just as the forest began to thin out, their course was blocked by white
foaming water, up through which they could not sail. That is why the
Egyptians did not know where the Nile came from; they could not sail
a boat upstream, through the series of cataracts, between Aswan and
Khartoum, through which the river descends from the plateau into the
valley which is the heart of Egypt.

Africa is mostly made up of a tablelike mass of hard, ancient rock. It
has stood aloof from those violent movements of the earth's crust which
raised the Alps and the Himalayas. Only in the Atlas Mountains in
North Africa, do we find the evidences of this furious mountain-building
activity. The rest of Africa has been stable since before Europe began to
form in the shallow seas of the more recent geological past. Apart from
the extreme northwest, Africa took no part in those violent contortions,
but it could not help being jarred and shaken by them. Its surface was
stretched and cracked; breaks, or faults, were formed.

In fact, a series of such faults developed, reaching from the Middle
East through the Red Sea, and across the plateau of East Africa to
Nyasaland in the southeast. The faults lay parallel to one another and
formed two series, generally not more than fifty miles apart. As the crust
of the earth was stretched, the rocks lying between the lines of faulting
subsided, and a wide, deep valley resulted. This is the origin of the Rift
Valley which traverses the continent as an irregular, winding trench; its
banks towering many thousands of feet above its damp, hot floor; cool,
crisp highlands spread out on each side. Lake Rudolf, on the border of
Ethiopia and Kenya, lies in the Rift Valley; Lake Nyasa occupies its
southern extremity. A kind of spur curves back westward from the main
course of the Rift Valley and is distinguished on every map of Africa
by the succession of elongated lakes—Tanganyika, Kivu, Edward, and
Albert—which occupy it.

This Rift Valley and the highlands which form the rim constitute
one of the most conspicuous features in the physical map of Africa. An

observer from a satellite, as he spun across Africa, would see the greens of the forest merging with the sage greens of the savanna and then turning into the yellow brown of the desert. The Rift Valley would stand out like a great, raw scar on the face of a dueller. It is the scar left on the face of Africa by the violent earth movements that took place so near, to the north and northeast.

Africa is so old that it was there long before the Great Plains of the United States were formed and the Rocky Mountains were raised out of the shallow seas where their substance had been accumulating. The continent is so ancient that it was there, stable and almost immovable, before the great swamps began to form in which were laid down the coal beds. It dates so far back in geologic time that its rocks were largely formed before the organisms from which petroleum is derived began to live in the seas and accumulate on the rocks. The rocks of Africa took shape during the youth of this planet. There is little coal and no petroleum except in the Sahara.

On the other hand, age brings its rewards. Those minerals which came into the earth's crust from deep in the interior, rising through cracks and fissures in a liquid or gaseous condition and impregnating the rocks, have had abundant time to form. The Republic of South Africa is favored with great beds of manganese and immense deposits of gold. South Africa at present produces about two-thirds of the world's gold, and in manganese production comes next after the Soviet Union, India, and Brazil. Vast reserves of copper are found in Katanga, the southernmost province of The Congo, and in neighboring Northern Rhodesia. Together this area produces over a quarter of the world's copper. Reserves of tin lie within the borders of Nigeria and The Congo, and yield at the present about 12 per cent of the world production of a mineral that is otherwise heavily concentrated in Southeast Asia. There are very few of the metalliferous minerals that are not obtainable in some quantity or other from the continent of Africa, and many of them are produced in important quantities.

About 92 per cent of the world's production of natural—as distinct from synthetic—diamonds is in Africa. South Africa was for long the most important and the most famous source. Here the diamonds occur as hard grains in a soft claylike rock produced by the decomposition of "pipes" of igneous rock, which rise almost vertically through the crust to the earth's surface. Most of the famous gemstones have come from the diamond pipes at Kimberley and Pretoria, but the forces of erosion

OCEAN

EQUATOR

KENYA

Mombasa
Zanzibar
Mt. Kenya
Nairobi
Mount
Kilimanjaro
Dar es Salaam

UGANDA
Entebbe
Lake
Victoria
Lake
Edward
TANGANYIKA
Lake
Tanganyika
Lake
Nyasa

RUANDA
RWANDA
BURUNDI

MADAGASCAR
Tananarive
MALAGASY REPUBLIC

MOZAMBIQUE CHANNEL

INDIAN

MOZAMBIQUE

THE CONGO
BASIN

Stanleyville

River
Kasai
River
Congo
River

KATANGA
Elisabethville

FEDERATION OF
RHODESIA AND
NYASALAND
Lusaka
Zambezi River
Victoria Falls
Salisbury

Lourenço Marques
SWAZILAND
Durban
BASUTOLAND
Pretoria
Johannesburg
Kimberly River
Orange River
Port Elizabeth

SOUTH AFRICA

BECHUANALAND

SOUTH-WEST AFRICA
Windhoek

ANGOLA
Luanda
Lobito
Benguela

CONGO
GABON
Libreville
Brazzaville
Leopoldville
Ubangi
River

Cape Town
Cape of
Good Hope

ATLANTIC
OCEAN

St Helena
Island

Ascension
Island

EQUATOR

South Latitude

TROPIC OF CAPRICORN

West Longitude   0°   East Longitude

AFRICA

Scale of Miles
0 100 200 400 600 800

⊗ National Capitals   ☆ Other Capitals   ● Other Cities

COPYRIGHT 1962 BY RAND MC NALLY & CO. MADE IN U.S.A.

which have been at work for centuries, have distributed the diamonds from these and other similar sources along the river valleys and over the alluvial plains of much of South Africa. These alluvial diamonds are now of increasing importance. At the same time new sources are being discovered, especially in Central and West Africa, and The Congo has now far exceeded South Africa in the production of the coarser type of diamonds used for industrial processes. The engagement ring and the diamond necklace, however, are likely to continue to be furnished by South Africa.

We cannot overlook iron ore, which is widespread throughout the continent, though production itself amounts at present to little more than 1 per cent of the world's output. Improved transportation may make iron mining far more significant than this would suggest is possible.

It is true that the mineral wealth of Africa lies more in its metals than in its fuels. Coal is scarce, and the African continent produces little more than 2 per cent of the world's coal, most of it from South Africa and Southern Rhodesia. Until recently the discoveries of petroleum in Africa had been negligible, and it had been supposed that the continent was devoid of liquid fuels. Within the last few years, discoveries of petroleum have been made in the younger rocks of the Sahara Desert, especially in Libya and Algeria. Reserves have been proved to be large, and North Africa may become one of the major oil producers of the future. There appears, however, to be little hope of obtaining petroleum from most of the remainder of this continent.

Africa lies spread out on each side of the equator, through a total of 72° of latitude; the most northerly point lies 37° North, the most southerly, 35° South of the equator. Africa has a climatic symmetry unknown to other continents. So perfect is its balance, it can be considered the classic example of our earlier discussion of climates and vegetation regions.

Across the middle lies the equator. On each side of it lies the region of perpetual heat and moisture, where dense forests of broad-leaved trees fringe the rivers and clothe the lower ground and, over the higher, merge into open woodland. Here there are no seasons, at least none sufficiently well marked for man to distinguish them without the aid of scientific instruments. The only climatic changes which he recognizes are those between the hot humid lowlands and the drier and cooler conditions of the higher parts of the plateau.

Away from this region of equatorial evenness seasons begin gradually to show themselves, and the short winter break in the rains grows longer until the wet season coincides with the months of summer and winters are mild and dry. This is the parklike country of big trees and big game, where the grass grows tall during the summer rains and dries out in the warm, winter drought. Toward its outer margins—to the north in the Northern Hemisphere and the south in the Southern—plant life wilts. The summer rains become short and uncertain. Sagebrush takes over until even this becomes stunted and rare, and the desert replaces the arid savanna.

Africa is broad across the north; it is 3,600 miles from Cape Verde in the west to the Red Sea, and all this is desert. The Sahara is the biggest, the most formidable, and the least penetrable desert on the face of the earth. It has always separated two worlds, the world of the Mediterranean Sea and the world of Africa. The corresponding region in the south of Africa, the Kalahari Desert, is in every way less formidable. There the continent is narrower; oceanic influences are able to penetrate to its interior. The Kalahari Desert is smaller and less arid than the Sahara; it does not reach across the continent from sea to sea. Instead it becomes a little moister and a lot greener along its eastern margin as it passes into the grasslands of the Veld. And below the steep edge of the African plateau, in the lowlands of Mozambique and Natal, there is moist, wooded country where corn, sugar cane, and cotton grow.

But it is the extremities of the continent that offer the greatest attractions. The Mediterranean coast in the north and Cape Province in the south are blessed with that most provocative of all climatic regions, the Mediterranean. The dryness which accompanies the heat of summer; the rains in winters which are still warm enough for plants to grow; the prolonged sunshine, the limpid air, and the distant mountains faintly etched in blue against the pale blue of the sky—all characterize the northern rim and the southern extremity of this otherwise rather inhospitable continent. Between these extremes, Africa has until the last century been isolated and almost unknown. No part of the world was ever completely cut off, like Samuel Butler's country, Erewhon, from influences and contacts from without. But Africa, enclosed by the great desert on the north, the straight, forbidding coasts to west and east, was more cut off than most.

Human societies grow and prosper by the cultural contacts they make with others. It is as if African cultures were inbred, drawing upon one another over and over again; always, as it were, marrying within their own African societies, without any invigorating cultural infusions from without. The broad lines of African history were implicit in the geography of the continent. In both Europe and Asia contacts were maintained with contrasted societies and the progress of civilizations, both Western and Asian, proceeded by the incorporation of foreign elements. In Africa craftsmanship in wood, bone, and leather, and in bronze and iron, reached a consummate level, but for anything that may be called a civilization we look in vain south of the Sahara.

THE EUROPEAN IN AFRICA

Europeans entered Africa in the most hospitable areas—the extremities. No other parts of the continent tempted them for several centuries, even after they had learned to sail around it. All along the northern shore, from the borders of the Promised Land of Palestine in the east to El Maghreb el Aqsa, or Morocco, the "Far West" of the Arabs, there were civilizations or fragments of civilizations from the dawn of history until now. The Egyptian civilization grew up here. There, too, were outliers of the Greek and Roman, the Islamic and modern civilizations. Each was built on the foundations left by those that went before, and each derived stimulation and inspiration, as well as more material aids, from beyond the blue waters which it bordered. North Africa is thus bound up culturally with the civilizations of the Mediterranean region. Even Egypt, which, thanks to the Nile, penetrates farther to the south than any other part of this cultural province, is bound up with the Mediterranean region and the Middle East, not with the rest of Africa.

All other bases on the African coast were regarded at first merely as staging points on the route to India. Two of them even gained the names of Algoa Bay and Delagoa Bay, evidence of their significance in the routes to and from the Portuguese trading base of Goa in India, which India recently took over.

The first permanent European settlements south of the Sahara were made by the Portuguese at the Cape of Good Hope, where the westerlies blow in winter, and the blue skies of summer reminded the settlers of home. Then came the Dutch, who also established a base at the present Cape Town in 1652, for the watering and provisioning of their ships as they sailed to the East Indies. A few French, mostly Huguenot refugees, joined them later in the century and introduced the grapevine which now supplies a flourishing wine industry in the hills which lie inland from Cape Town. Then the British, who already controlled India and dominated the sea, swept this southern province of Africa into the net of their empire in 1806.

When the British replaced the Dutch as the rulers of the small colony at the Cape, they had already begun, in a somewhat half-hearted way, to interest themselves in the interior of Africa. Their interest was prompted in part by scientific curiosity, in part by greed for whatever wealth might be found. This wealth seemed indeed limited. Gold and ivory gave their names to the stretches of West African coast where each was found, but quantities were small. It was the "black ivory," the West African Negro, that proved to be for centuries the most abundant and lucrative article of trade with Africa, both West and East.

The African slave trade began in the fifteenth century and lasted in West Africa until the end of the eighteenth. As a result, the South American, West Indian, and North American population is now in part of African origin. The slave trade was formally abolished in 1808, but in East Africa, where it was controlled by Arab traders, it went on much longer. The missionary explorer, David Livingstone, has left a harrowing description of the slave trade as it was conducted from the coast of East Africa by the Arabs. Only slowly, during the course of the nineteenth century, was this trade suppressed. This brings us to the Africans themselves, who thus for several centuries appeared to be its only, or at least its most desirable, form of wealth.

Africa was thinly peopled. Its tribes were numerous, if not large, and only a few of the African peoples had formed "kingdoms," or political organizations covering a large area and embracing many people. Altogether, it has been estimated the population of Africa was only about 90,000,000 when Europeans began to press into the continent; today it is estimated at 261,000,000. These peoples belonged to many racial stocks and cultural groups, but the majority were Negro.

It seems that the inhabitants of Africa had come from the north or northeast in successive waves. The earliest were probably the most primitive. We cannot be sure who are their modern representatives, or do we know for certain whether they have descendants among the African peoples of today. But in parts of the forest of the Congo and in the semi-desert of South-West Africa, are primitive peoples who had not risen even to the level of agriculture when they were discovered. These are the Pygmy and Bushman peoples, who live today in a modern Stone Age. They are few in number, nomadic, retiring, and difficult to find. A similar people, the Hottentots, have become extinct since Europeans began to settle in South Africa. It is as if these peoples had been driven back into the desert and the jungle by the stronger and more numerous Negro peoples who followed them.

The Negroes had advanced south across Africa from the northeast. Westward they moved through the savanna of the Sudan, into West Africa as the Sudanese; and southward, down across the highlands above the Rift Valley in East Africa, and so into South Africa as the Bantu. Left to themselves, they kept to the savanna country; they hunted the big game, cultivated the soil, and built large villages of straw-thatched homes. But a later wave of invaders—the Hamitic peoples—seems to have driven the Negro out of some parts of the savanna and into the forest, and it was here, in the West African forest, that the sixteenth-century slavers found them.

The true Negro is primarily an agriculturist. He is adept with the hoe, and his normal crops, which he cultivates in his small gardenlike fields, are corn and root crops like the manioc and sweet potato.

The groups of invaders who came after the Negro, known collectively as Hamites, were brown rather than black; they were a tall, thin people, and their facial features differed in many ways from those of the Negro. The ancient Egyptians were mainly Hamitic. These peoples spread south and southwestward into tropical Africa, driving the Negroes before them here, subduing and ruling them there, and in many areas producing a hybrid, part Negro, part Hamitic people. Many of the present-day Sudanese form such a mixed group; so, too, do the Masai, the cattle-raising peoples of the East African highlands.

Whereas the Negro had been primarily an agriculturist, the Hamitic peoples tended to be more pastoral. Though they practiced agriculture, they tended to regard it as a menial occupation, more suited to conquered and subject peoples than for their noble selves. And when they did engage in cultivating the land, they commonly left the field work to their wives.

This distinction, blurred by time and by the leveling influence of the money economy that the conquering Europeans have introduced, tends yet to be present. The Masai still measure their wealth in head of cattle, and the growing of crops is still left to their women. And in West Africa today the pastoral Fula and Hausa, who are only partly Negro, continue to lord it over the sedentary, agricultural Negro. In several of the new states that have emerged in recent years from the ruins of the colonial empires, the clash of these African cultures is still present.

The latest comers to Africa, before the arrival of the Europeans, were the Arabs. They didn't come as settlers, or even as conquerors. Their role was that of traders. From their bases in the Middle East they traded with the East African coast, penetrating as far inland as was necessary for their commercial purposes. Arabic came to be spoken along this coast, and the Islamic religion practiced. It was Arab merchants who guided the earliest Portuguese from the East African coast across to India, and today the last relic of this Moslem empire is the Sultanate of Zanzibar, with its Moslem ruler and partly Moslem population.

This was the Africa which Europeans found when they penetrated below the Sahara. Their penetration of its interior was slow, as we have seen. At first it was inspired more by missionary zeal and scientific curiosity than by the greed commonly associated with imperialism. David Livingstone, who explored much of Central Africa, was an idealist. Henry Stanley, who was sent to look for him when no word had come from him for many months, was a man of different fiber.

Stanley was a journalist turned explorer who put himself at the disposal of those who were eager to open up Africa for commerce. His journey across the Congo Basin was the prelude to the founding of the Congo Association, one of the most grasping and least scrupulous of the many organizations that engaged in the contest for Africa. It was through his participation in this rather unsavory venture that King Leopold of Belgium got his hands on the Congo and bequeathed it as a none too welcome inheritance to the Belgian nation.

At this time, in the 1870's, Europeans awakened quite suddenly to the potentialities of Africa. These had hitherto not been apparent. The difficulties in penetrating the continent slowed down its exploration and occupation. Its resources were of a kind that were at this time only just beginning to be valued: forest products like hardwood lumber and vegetable oils, which, a generation earlier, Europeans would not have known what to do with. But now a need was experienced for rubber and palm oil, cacao and hardwoods, and the scramble for Africa began.

The dozens of bases around the coast served each as a springboard for the invasion and conquest of some part of the interior. The British pushed inland up the Gambia River, and from the coastal bases of Freetown, Accra, and Lagos, to carve out their West African colonies of Gambia, Sierra Leone, the Gold Coast (now Ghana), and Nigeria. The French advanced east from Dakar on the west coast of Africa; they reached the Niger, and went on again through the Sudan until they met the British who had pushed inland, following the Nile Valley from Egypt. They ran fingers of French territory down to the coast, between the spheres marked out by the Portuguese, and the Spanish, and the British. And the Germans, latest comers in this race for African real estate, acted like Autolycus, the "snapper up of unconsidered trifles," which had somehow escaped the attentions or the grasp of those who were in the race earlier.

The land was not properly surveyed. The features of its interior were only roughly known. There was no question of thorough exploration and settlement, only of pioneer reconnaissance and claims to territory. These claims were ironed out and reconciled not in Africa but in Europe. The African boundaries were drawn on maps, which were frequently inaccurate and always inadequate, at council tables in Europe and by people who knew little of Africa and cared less. The nineteenth-century European cartographers could add a few towns and ports around the African periphery, and within the continent they could show with some degree of accuracy at least the larger and more important rivers. But over much of the continent they could add little to the downs and the elephants pictured by Swift in the previous century.

The boundaries that came to separate the colonial empires from one another represented not the cultural divisions between the Africans themselves but the compromises and balances which Europeans had arrived at in their mutual struggle for mastery. And these boundaries, arbitrary as they are, have in turn become the limits of the new African states.

By the end of the nineteenth century claims to all of Africa had been staked out by these colonial prospectors except for two small areas, Liberia in the west and Ethiopia in the east. Liberia had been established in 1822 as a home for slaves who had been liberated in the United States, and, though its internal affairs not infrequently afforded an excuse for intervention, the colonial powers were obliged to restrain their acquisitiveness. Ethiopia, thanks to a combination of rugged terrain and fierce inhabitants, was able to repel Italian invaders, and, in fact did not succumb to European conquerors until 1936. By 1941 it was freed of invaders and has since enjoyed political independence again. Only Liberia never became someone's colony. Every other part of the continent was occupied and ruled for a period, long or short, by British or French, Portuguese or Spanish, Germans or Italians.

The freeing of Africa from colonial rule began gradually and spread at first only slowly. In 1910 the Union, now the Republic, of South Africa

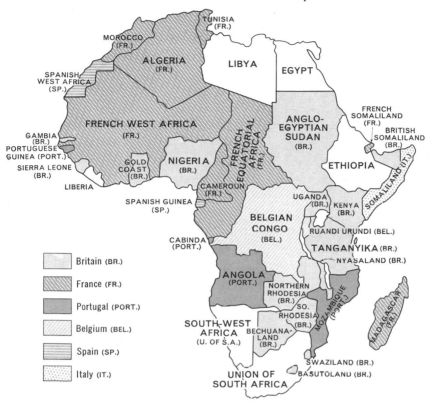

AFRICA AFTER WORLD WAR II

Britain (BR.)

France (FR.)

Portugal (PORT.)

Belgium (BEL.)

Spain (SP.)

Italy (IT.)

European colonial empires were still in existence in Africa in 1945. By the 1960's the break-up into small, independent nations was almost completed.

was the first to gain virtual independence from Great Britain; then the British control in Egypt was gradually relinquished and finally abandoned in 1922. The policies of the colonial powers differed widely. The British and French, in their own peculiar fashions, prepared the African peoples for independence, but showed a surprising reluctance to bow gracefully out of the ring. The Germans had their colonies taken from them in 1919; the Italians lost theirs during the Second World War; and the Belgians hesitantly gave independence to The Congo in 1960. Only the empires of Portugal and Spain remained.

Britain and France yielded to the growing demand for independence. They protested all the while that the Africans were not ready, but always yielded in time to avoid serious bloodshed. It was as if the heavy cloud of colonialism that had lain over the continent had gradually thinned away, until, as happens so often to the clouds in summer, the heavy pall broke up suddenly into fragments and was dissipated.

In the last few years colonialism has vanished from most of Africa, and the emergence of twenty-five new republics in this continent which had long been dominated by colonialism is the major development of recent years. Those areas in which Great Britain continues to exercise some degree of control—Gambia, in West Africa, Uganda and Kenya, in East Africa, the two Rhodesias and Nyasaland, and Zanzibar—already have a large degree of self-government, and are destined for complete independence in the very near future; in fact, late in 1961 Tanganyika, formerly in this list, was granted its independence. But the High Commission Territories are jealously guarded protectorates, enclaved within the Republic of South Africa, and the smaller offshore islands of the Seychelles and Mauritius still retain colonial status. The French Empire in Africa—except for the territory of French Somaliland in East Africa, the Comores Islands off the East African coast as well as Reunion—has gone, and in its place is a swarm of small, independent nations.

For centuries the colonies of Spain and Portugal had been little troubled either by enlightened rule or by the yearning for freedom that comes from it. But now the liberation of West Africa and the revolt in The Congo have created such a political storm that waves from it have spread outward to beat against the bastions of Portuguese rule in Angola and Mozambique. The Spanish Empire, long in retreat, has been diminished to the large and almost uninhabited Spanish Sahara; some minute footholds on the coast of Northwest Africa; Rio Muni on the west coast of Central Africa, Fernando Póo, and a few other small islands in the Gulf of Guinea; in all an area of about 114,000 square miles and only 455,000 people.

Let us turn now to the major divisions of this continent, recognizing that any division of it for the convenience of description and analysis must necessarily be an arbitrary one. It will also be misleading because it will imply differences and contrasts on each side of the dividing line that in reality are not present. North Africa, that strip between the Sahara Desert and the Mediterranean Sea, has been described along with the Mediterranean lands to which it belongs in Chapter 9. There remain five broad divisions of the continent: the Sahara, West Africa, East Africa, Central Africa, and South Africa.

The boundaries between these divisions have been made to follow the political boundaries which divide their component states. This is desirable, because the state is the primary division of the earth's surface; it is at the same time inconvenient because many—if not most—of the African states and colonial dependencies extend across two or more of the climatic and vegetational divisions of which the continent is made up.

THE SAHARA

The problem is encountered right at the start. Across the middle of the Sahara Desert, from the Atlantic Ocean to the Red Sea, a zigzag boundary takes its course. To the north of it lie Morocco, the southern territories of Algeria, Libya, and Egypt; to the south are the Spanish Sahara, Mauritania, Mali, Niger, Chad, and Sudan. The more northerly of these territories reach to the Mediterranean Sea; the more southerly, with the exception of the Spanish Sahara, extend southward into, and even in certain instances across, the savanna to the border of the equatorial forest zone. And so we must discuss the Sahara Desert in general terms, letting the description apply to any one of the ten political divisions which share it, and of which the desert forms a significant part.

The Sahara Desert covers about 3,500,000 square miles, about a third of the area of the whole African continent. On the north it ends somewhat abruptly against the southernmost ranges of the Atlas Mountains or, in Libya and Egypt, against the surge of the Mediterranean Sea. Its southern limit is more gradual; it passes into a sort of mesquite or sagebrush, and then into savanna, with short, dry grass. Very approximately, its southern limit is along the parallel of 15° N. latitude, across southern Mauritania, through Mali, Niger, Chad, and Sudan.

For all its immense size the Sahara need not detain us long. It is a part of that great tabular mass which makes up the largest part of the continent. Mostly its surface is undulating, but rises in the Tibesti and Ahaggar regions of the central Sahara to mountains that are impressive by virtue both of their ruggedness, and also of their height. This is a dry, hot region. It is predominantly one of high atmospheric pressure, where a mass of cool air sinks slowly downward toward the earth's surface and blows outward. As the air sinks it is heated; its relative humidity diminishes and it becomes a dry, scorching wind, which draws the moisture from the rocks and parches and suffocates plants and human beings.

The Sahara is a region of intense sunshine. Cloud is rare because the humidity is so low. The unprotected ground heats up during the day to temperatures far higher than those attained by the sidewalks of New York in July. During summer, afternoon temperatures regularly reach 120°. After sunset the western glow quickly fades from the sky and the heat of the bare rocks is radiated back into the atmosphere; the temperature drops suddenly, abruptly. The nomad who has endured the intense heat of the day has now to protect himself against the chill of the night air. The shorter nights of summer remain warm, rarely dropping below 60°, or at the lowest 50°, but in winter there may be frost.

The rocks, expanded under the heat of the sun, suddenly contract as they cool; stresses are set up, fragments of rock are broken off, and by alternately heating and cooling, expanding and contracting, they are reduced to sand. As we have already noted, the popular picture of the desert is one of sand, driven by the wind into giant dunes, which advance like the waves of the sea to beat against whatever protection man or nature may have raised against them. Over the ground swell of the giant waves are the small sand ripples which make a swiftly changing pattern of interlacing lines. Yet this picture fits only a part—a small part—of the desert. In general the sand characterizes its margins, whither it is swept by the outblowing winds from the interior. It is this desert margin that the traveler most often sees. If he made the difficult journey across the shifting sand, he would find much of the center a region of bare rock swept clean by the wind.

Rainstorms are rare in the desert, but they do occur, and the wadis, or dried-up watercourses, are evidence of their immense powers of erosion. But however violent, the storms are short-lived, and the rivers they produce surge down the wadis, sweeping up silt, sand, and boulders. Then the water evaporates into the dry air. The river turns to mud and dies of suffocation.

From every storm, however, some water penetrates the rocks and supplies the springs. The springs are few, but wherever they occur, they support patches of green amid the brown of the desert. These are the oases. Generally they occupy depressions in the desert floor. Sometimes they contain self-supporting communities which have lived since time immemorial on the fruit of their date palms and the barley, wheat, and squash of their irrigated fields. These communities are Moslem. They were among the last of African peoples to become known to Europeans, and they remain the least influenced by contacts with Europeans. Yet this aloofness of the Tuareg and other "veiled" peoples of the Sahara may not last very many years longer. The Sahara is being opened up.

Every inch of the desert has been surveyed by aircraft, and it is regularly crossed by trucks and jeeps. This in turn has allowed geological prospecting to move ahead, and prospectors have been rewarded by the discovery of petroleum deep within the Algerian and Libyan Sahara. There is every indication that these resources are large, and every possibility that other minerals will be discovered as the desert becomes more fully explored.

For most of the ten political divisions into which it has been carved up, the Sahara constitutes a vast empty quarter which, unless minerals are found there, will contribute little to their wealth and welfare. For the Spanish Sahara and for the Republic of Mauritania, the desert is almost all they have. These two territories lie in the western Sahara, bordering the Atlantic Ocean. Mauritania, with an area of about 420,000 square miles, a population of under 750,000, and a density of under two to the square mile, is one of the poorest and most thinly peopled of all sovereign states. It was with difficulty that it found a village—Nouakchott, near its Atlantic coast—adequate to serve as its capital.

WEST AFRICA

The northeast trade winds blow from the desert toward West Africa. During the dry season the air may be heavy with Saharan dust. On the ground, the desert passes to the south gradually into the semidesert and then into the savanna and forest. The vegetation forms belts lying west to east across West Africa. The savanna covers most of the West African plateau; the equatorial forest spreads over the narrow strip of lowland that fringes the ocean, and sends fingers up the valleys of the rivers that come down from the plateau. Most of these rivers, like the Senegal and the Gambia and the Volta in Ghana, are fairly short. As they approach the margin of the plateau they cut deep narrow valleys, from which they escape onto the flat, marshy coastal plain by way of falls or rapids. These are ideal conditions for the hydroelectric engineer, and they are likely to furnish the power for the future industries of West Africa. Dam construction has already begun on the Volta River in Ghana.

The greatest river of West Africa, however, is the Niger, a river almost as legendary as the Nile itself. It rises in the steep rim of the African plateau, within two hundred miles of the coast, but, instead of

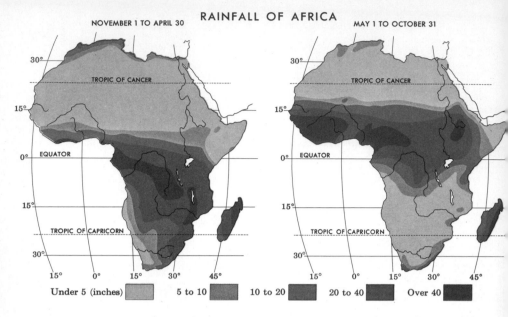

RAINFALL OF AFRICA

NOVEMBER 1 TO APRIL 30   MAY 1 TO OCTOBER 31

Under 5 (inches)   5 to 10   10 to 20   20 to 40   Over 40

In the rainfall pattern of Africa there is a key to the change of climate north and south of the equator and one hope of progress in agriculture.

cutting directly through the hills to the nearby plain, it takes the longest way round. It meanders northeastward, out into the desert margin. Near Tombouctou, it reaches its most northerly point, and from here it curves back again toward the coast, traverses Nigeria, where it descends from the plateau to the plain, and enters the Gulf of Guinea through the many branches of its delta. Along its most northerly reaches the Niger receives little water; instead it gives it, providing the means of irrigating the semidesert through which it flows with water that fell as rain hundreds of miles to the southwest. In this it fulfills a similar though less conspicuous role to that of the Nile.

The Niger, like the Nile, was a magnet which attracted explorers into the interior of West Africa. Great rivers have always exercised an unusual fascination, and the number of explorers who have devoted themselves to following their courses and finding out where they rise may well be greater—and their contribution far more significant—than those who have striven only to get to the summits of mountains. Rivers hastened the exploration, and now they are speeding the industrialization of Africa.

The political map of West Africa is the strangest pattern of lines on a map to be found anywhere on the world's surface. Around the coast the political units are like fingers, interspersed with a few broad thumbs. Each reaches inland from a narrow frontage on the ocean, like those long narrow farms in Quebec which stretch for miles into the back country from their short waterfront along the St. Lawrence. Each originated in a trading station, set up by some European colonial power along the coast. The station itself, a damp unhealthy place, usually occupied some slightly raised ground—a bank of sand piled up by the ocean perhaps—to give it better drainage; and it had some protection, like an offshore bar of sand or gravel, from the wild surge of the Atlantic.

From such coastal stations the West African colonies, most of them now independent states, emerged: Cameroun and Nigeria, near the head of the Gulf of Guinea; next to them to the west Dahomey, Togo, Ghana, and Ivory Coast in origin French, German, British respectively and again French; then Liberia, independent since its creation, and Sierra Leone, which gained its independence from Great Britain as recently as 1961; Guinea, formerly French, and another Guinea, which is still ruled by Portugal. Then comes the Republic of Senegal, wrapping round the tiny British colony of Gambia, and lastly Mauritania. These are just the hinterlands which the traders and imperialists of the nineteenth century claimed for themselves.

The development of each of these fragments of territory depended upon the policy of the respective colonial powers. Each introduced its own language; in some of the West African republics today the official language is French, in others English. It encouraged the production of those tropical crops which best suited its needs—cacao in the Gold Coast, palm oil in Nigeria. It confiscated or acquired the Africans' land and preserved it, as in Nigeria; or as in parts of French Africa, broke up the African tribal order and associated the Africans in widely differing degrees in the business of administering an African territory along European lines. The only exception was Liberia, where the Africans ran the show themselves. But they were Africans from America; they constituted an Americanized aristocracy, no less cut off from the native Africans of the territory, in spite of having the same color. Indeed Liberia, like the rest of West Africa, came to have a dual society, made up of the Africans themselves and the newcomers. The only difference was that here the newcomers were also in origin African.

The century of colonialism in West Africa is almost over, but the legacy of colonialism is a hard one. It appears most conspicuously in the political map, the jigsaw pattern of political units that arose from European rivalries; it shows in the broken tribes and the varied levels of cultural and economic development that were achieved among peoples who are basically similar. Tribal loyalties were eroded during colonialism and loyalty to the state was never fully developed to take their place. One of the many problems—perhaps the overriding problem—is to fill out those compartments which spread their crazy pattern over the political map with the new spirit of nationalism.

The lesson of Europe is that national feeling took centuries to develop; the example of the European experience, combined with the means of social communication which the Europeans have introduced, may hasten the process in Africa. On the other hand, the hatred which it has generated between people and people, tribe and tribe, may in fact hold back the realization of stability, cohesion, and unity.

Some of the new states, Ghana for example, have been able to build upon the stable foundation of a competent European-run administration, and have made great progress in a short time in creating and projecting an image of themselves. In others, such as Cameroun, the European administration never succeeded in bridging the gap between hostile tribes, and with the removal of the strong-handed European imperialists, Cameroun seemed for a time to be slipping back toward tribal anarchy.

Another problem is that these states are small. In a sense, this is an advantage, because a feeling of unity and coherence will develop more quickly in a small than in a large group. But some are too small to be viable. In West Africa there are no less than fifteen separate sovereign states, if we include those which lie partly within the Sahara, and this number may be expected to increase as the three remaining colonial dependencies achieve statehood; of these, twelve have fewer people than the Chicago metropolitan area, and only one of them, Nigeria, has more than that of New York City. Some of these states, like Togo and Dahomey and the still dependent territories of Gambia and Portuguese Guinea, are almost too small for statehood. Mali, Niger, and Chad, in part Saharan, are large in area but small in population.

The formation of this mosaic, begun when European states established trading bases on the African coast, was completed when the French empire in Africa broke up in 1958. This had been in extent the largest of the African empires. Whereas the British had, in general, tried to preserve, and even to fossilize, native African institutions and practices, the French aimed rather to replace the native African culture with that of France and to develop a native elite that would be in all significant respects French. If they had succeeded, they would doubtless have given some feeling of unity to the whole of their sprawling empire. They failed, and the empire fell apart. Eleven new West African states appeared, from former French West Africa and from part of former French Equatorial Africa, none of them unified or coherent, all preserving, for lack of anything better, the lines which had separated the administrative divisions of the former French Empire as their international boundaries.

In physical terms the eighteen territories of West Africa differ greatly. The coastal group, from Cameroun to Gambia, is built of forested coastal plain, backed by savanna-covered plateau. The inner tier, from Senegal to Chad, consists of plateau, over which the savanna of the south passes northward into the desert. These political units differ no less in their peoples, ranging from the Negroid peoples of the forest and of the moister and more southerly parts of the savanna to the pastoral tribes of the north, Moslem in religion and racially akin to the Berber of North Africa. Everywhere the political boundaries conflict with the racial and cultural groupings. Not a single state is without some element of conflict between its tribes or its cultural groups.

The solution to the problems raised would appear to lie in boundary adjustment, coupled with the federal union of groups of the West African states. But those territories that have already gained their freedom are jealous of their independence; those still colonial are thirsty for political freedom. Once they have acquired independence and a seat in the United Nations, none of these states show any willingness to give it up. These peoples did not struggle for independence only to surrender it to an African federation. Mali and Senegal formed a short-lived federation which broke up after only a few months. Political independence is a heady sort of wine, and these new nations have drunk deeply. Yet the fact of so many small states threatens to bring political anarchy into West Africa.

In this modern world size is important. There are economies to be had from administering large areas; a greater population and a wider range of resources are a basis of political power and some assurance of security. Europe is finding that its states are too small for modern needs, and groups of states are associating themselves in free-trade areas. West Africa, as a whole, is not yet mature enough for this. But if this medley of small political units is to remain, then some association or federation becomes increasingly necessary.

And now to turn to what the people produce and what they need in this vast area from Senegal to Cameroun. The West African is a village dweller and cultivator. He is not particularly crowded, except in a few areas, and in general West Africa still has many wide-open spaces. His products are those of the tropical savanna and forest. West Africa produces vegetable oils, cacao, soybeans, peanuts, and rubber for export. Sometimes these are grown as cash crops on the small African farms; sometimes they are produced, with more attention to quality and economy, on plantations established by Europeans. Ghana produces no less than 33 per cent of the world's cacao; Nigeria, 37 per cent of the palm oil.

The rest of the world needs these products of West African agriculture, and West Africa needs in return the manufactured goods from the factories of Europe and North America. But a simple exchange of cacao beans for automobiles is not enough. The West African countries are underdeveloped. They are desperately short of good roads and of the public services which Western peoples take for granted. The revolution of rising expectations has reached them; they want the better homes, tools, and equipment that they hear of; they demand a more scientific agriculture and a superior medical service to that which the witch doctor can offer. This rising demand is not found everywhere; it appears first among the more advanced and more sophisticated and among those who were better governed in the colonial period. But rumors that better things are possible have spread through even the stagnant jungle of Portuguese colonialism.

And so a revolution is slowly changing West Africa. The young nations, increasingly conscious of themselves as groups of people with an individuality and a destiny, want power stations and factories not only to satisfy their own very real needs, but to show the world that they too belong to the twentieth century. There is a danger that the things which the new African states will demand will not really be those which they need and can make the best use of, like the manufacture of fertilizers and instruction in better farming methods.

The eighteen states and territories that can in some way be described as West African form a double tier, stretching from west to east. The more southerly fronts on the Atlantic Ocean; the more northerly, except at its western extremity, lies inland. A survey of these states might begin at the head of the Gulf of Guinea, with the Republic of Cameroun. This state of about 4,000,000 inhabitants is the most equatorial and forested, and economically the least developed. Its society is more tribal than that

of the rest of West Africa; and a national image is almost nonexistent. Most of its population practices only a self-sufficing agriculture, and its small export trade is limited to cacao, palm oil, rubber, products of the few plantations established by the French, and the hardwood lumber taken from the forests which cover much of the state. In the whole state of 183,000 square miles there are only about 325 miles of railroad, made up chiefly of a line from the port of Douala to the capital city of Yaoundé.

Nigeria, lying to the west of Cameroun, is about twice as large and nine times as populous. It is, in fact, the most densely populated African state. To accommodate its variety of peoples and cultures, it has built upon foundations laid by the British and has created a federal state, with its capital in the port city of Lagos. A higher degree of political maturity has been achieved in Nigeria than in most other West African states. Its economy is based upon a vigorous peasant agriculture, and very little land was ever allowed to be transferred from the Africans to the operators of commercial plantations. The result is a prosperity and a stability not often met with in the new Africa. Peanuts and palm oil, well suited to the native agricultural practice, make up most of the exports, and the rest consists of cacao, rubber, and a few other items.

Dahomey and Togo are merely two small strips of territory lying side by side between Nigeria and Ghana. Both until very recently had been ruled by France, and they owe their somewhat illogical separation one from the other to the fact that Togo had, from its occupation in 1884 until 1919, been a possession of Germany, and as far as France was concerned was a mandate and then a trusteeship territory. Each presents a cross-section through plateau and coastal plain, and both produce palm oil and palm kernels for export, supplemented by cacao, coffee, and the inevitable peanuts. The chief ports—Porto Novo in Dahomey and Lomé in Togo—serve also as capitals, and each is linked by a single axial railroad with its hinterland. Cotonou in Dahomey has lately rivaled Porto Novo and plans are under way to make it the capital.

Ghana is a bigger and more aggressive operation. It is larger than Togo and Dahomey together and has a population of over 7,000,000. In all West Africa it is second only to Nigeria in size of population and in resources, and is one of the most viable of the new states in Africa. The foundation of its prosperity is the cacao plantations established here in the nineteenth century by the British. Ghana is by far the biggest producer of cacao, and almost a third of the world's total is shipped out through the ports of Accra and Sekondi-Takoradi. Minerals, especially the gold for which the colony was originally named, manganese, bauxite, and diamonds, are growing in importance.

Between Ghana and Liberia is the Ivory Coast. It is larger, less populous, and less developed than Ghana. Its export trade, chiefly in coffee, cacao, bananas, and tropical hardwoods, is poorly developed, and the traffic in ivory for which it was once noted has entirely ceased. Its capital and chief port, Abidjan, is however the terminus of a railroad that runs northward through the state and into neighboring Upper Volta, for which it provides the only practicable outlet to the highways of the world's commerce.

The name of Liberia, with that of its capital city of Monrovia, witnesses to its American origin. The first settlement of freed American slaves was made here in 1822, and was named for James Monroe, the American president at the time. In the strict sense Liberia was never a colony, and until quite recently its commerce was small and its economic development neglected by most Western powers, reluctant to invest in a territory whose destinies they could not control. This has been changed. The United States got permission to establish air bases—which have since been vacated—during the Second World War. Lavish aid and investment by the American government and by the governments of certain West European countries is bringing about a rapid development and an expanding trade. The chief vegetable products are from the oil palm, but minerals—especially iron ore, bauxite, and industrial diamonds—are growing in value and importance.

The capital of Sierra Leone is the city and port of Freetown, which owed its origin to a British venture closely similar to the American undertaking that created Monrovia. It was founded in 1788 as a home for liberated slaves, and the colony of Sierra Leone gradually took shape around it. In area it is one of the smaller West African republics, and its population of about 2,500,000 is engaged mainly in subsistence farming in which the West African trio of palm oil, peanuts, and cacao predominate. But here, as in most of the other republics, mining is increasing and the export of iron ore and bauxite is gaining in importance.

From a narrow frontage on the ocean, where lies the capital and port of Conakry, Guinea expands inland on to the higher West African plateau. The coast of Africa here swings toward the north; the area of equatorial forest is small, and most of Guinea is made up of savanna. This is peanut country rather than palm oil, but the native peoples are engaged primarily in self-sufficing agriculture, and also produce a significant crop of bananas; the small volume of foreign trade is dominated by the products of the mines, chiefly iron ore or bauxite.

Portuguese Guinea and Gambia amount to little more than the humid tracts which extend up the valleys of two or three of the West African rivers. Their populations are small—about 580,000 and 315,000 respectively—and their trade is limited to the export of their simple agricultural products and the import of manufactured goods. Before long they may be freed from their dependence on European imperial powers, but even by the standards of West Africa, they seem too small and weak for independence. Beside them lies Senegal, ready and even eager to take them over.

On the coast of Senegal is Cape Verde, the Green Cape, so-named by the Portuguese voyagers because here the prevailing colors of the African coast line began to turn from the browns and duns of the desert to the faint green of the savanna. Senegal is a savanna country, it is drier; movement is easier, and a railroad has been run far into the interior from Dakar, its capital and chief port. The forest crops, which have been seen to characterize most of West Africa so far, are here replaced by dry-zone farming; millet, peanuts, and corn, which grows well during the hot moist summer, predominate. Animals, which had been lacking in the humid forested regions, have become more numerous and much of the dry savanna supports sheep and goats.

North of Senegal lies the almost wholly desert state of Mauritania and the wholly desert dependency of the Spanish Sahara, sometimes known as Río de Oro. To the east, linked to the Senegalese port of Dakar by a railroad, is Mali, one of the largest in area of the new republics. It lies astride the upper Niger, part savanna and part desert. In the southwest, where its capital city of Bamako lies, irrigated agriculture—the cultivation of cotton and rice—is carried on along the Niger Valley. Elsewhere peanuts and millet are grown; and rough grazing lands, where the scanty summer rains fall; merge northward into desert.

Upper Volta, enclosed within the great bend of the Niger River, lies entirely in the more humid savanna. Its rivers mainly discharge to the south, into Ivory Coast and Ghana. Its greater productivity is reflected in its denser population—about 3,700,000 in just over 100,000 square miles. They grow corn, sorghum, yams, peanuts, and cassava, use irrigation to produce cotton and rice, and the capital city of Ouagadougou is the terminus of a railroad which runs down through the Ivory Coast to the sea. Over these tracks is carried most of the small foreign trade of Upper Volta.

The republics of Niger and Chad, both of them of about the same area as Mali, but with only about 2,800,000 people each, belong more to the desert than to the savanna. The focus of the political life of both of them is in the more humid south, at Niamey in Niger, and Fort-Lamy in Chad. Neither has a railroad link with the outside world. The population in the south of both is mainly sedentary and agricultural, growing millet, corn, peanuts, and yams, and where there is water for irrigation, cotton and rice. Over the northern two-thirds of each a small population clusters around the oases or wanders from water hole to water hole, with its flocks of sheep and goats and its camels, which here constitute the universal beast of burden.

East of Chad lies the republic of the Sudan, and this, in our arbitrary classification, belongs to East Africa.

EAST AFRICA

East Africa is different in many respects from West. The African plateau of which it is built, lies higher above the level of the sea than West Africa, and this reduces the temperature and the humidity. It is a more rugged region in its relief. It is scarred by the great Rift Valley, whose precipitous sides form in many areas an obstacle to movement. From the surface of the East African plateau rises the shapely volcanic cone of Kilimanjaro to a height of 19,590 feet, little over two hundred miles from the equator and yet wearing at all seasons its white cap of snow. Almost on the equator are the Ruwenzori, the legendary Mountains of the Moon, which rise to 16,821 feet, and Mount Kenya which reaches even higher, to 17,040 feet.

East Africa lies over against Asia. The distance across the Arabian Sea to India was not too great for early navigators. East Africa, therefore, felt the impact of the Asian and Middle Eastern worlds during the first millenium B.C., whereas West Africa knew no overseas contacts until the Europeans arrived in the sixteenth century. Lastly, the Africans of East Africa were later arrivals than the Negro population of West Africa, and they are predominantly Hamitic, rather than Negro.

The high plateau is too dry, even on the equator, for the lush vegetation of the lowlands. The rubber tree, the cacao tree, and the oil palm do not grow here; only along the narrow coastal fringe that borders the Indian Ocean and in the depths of the Rift Valley are they likely to be found. Instead the cultivated crops are corn and soybean, peanut and yam, the coffee tree, the tea shrub, tobacco, and the spiky agave that yields sisal fiber from its tough leaves. Much of this area, too, is cattle country. Over parts there is no tsetse fly to spread disease to man and animal, and the malarial mosquito is mainly left behind in the lowlands.

Toward the northeast, the East African plateau rises into the tangled mountains of Ethiopia, which so long resisted the Italian invasions, and for centuries gave protection to the kingdom.

There is only one great river in East Africa, just as there is only one in West. The Nile rises in Lake Victoria, a large, shallow lake that occupies a depression in the surface of the plateau, its shores shared by the three countries of Uganda, Kenya, and Tanganyika. The source of the

The main Rift Valley lies west of Mt. Kenya and Mt. Kilimanjaro. In its westward spur lie the elongated lakes Albert, Edward, Kivu, and Tanganyika.

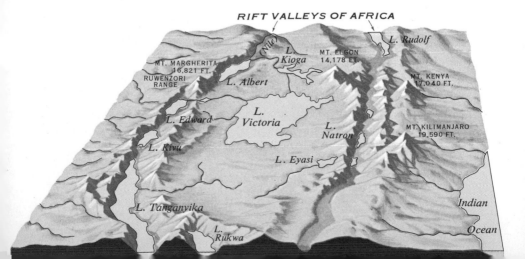

RIFT VALLEYS OF AFRICA

Nile was long one of the mysteries of the African continent, until in 1860 the African explorer, J. H. Speke was able to write in his journal; "I saw that old father Nile without any doubt rises in the Victoria Nyanza (lake). . . ." The Nile drops in steps from the plateau, gathering the drainage of parts of the Rift Valley, and then meanders sluggishly through the Sudan toward Egypt.

From the western edge of the high East African plateau, the western highlands of the Rift Valley, short streams descend to the level of the lower plateau of Central Africa, where they join the Congo. From the south of the East African region the rivers flow to the Zambezi River, and along the east they cataract down to the Indian Ocean.

This is the physical framework of East Africa, outwardly so different from West Africa, yet so similar in its customs, its development, and its problems.

Lands Along the Upper Nile

The Sudan spreads across the savanna and the desert. In the south its rainfall is enough to support a thin cover of vegetation, which burns away toward the north. Irrigation is less important here than in Egypt, where there is no rainfall, but, all the same, commercial agriculture cannot be carried on without it. While the Sudanese tribesmen graze their sheep and goats over the dry grasslands, the cultivators draw water from the Nile to irrigate the cotton fields of the Gezira, the tract of fertile country that lies in the angle between the Blue and the White Nile. Modern dams impound the water and allow it to be led to the fields. Subsistence crops are also irrigated. Sudan's population of about 12,300,000 is not large for so vast a country and its demands on the water of the Nile have hitherto been fairly small. Most of the water continues on downstream to Egypt; but there is a lot of potentially good cotton land in the Sudan, and the Sudanese could quite easily dip more deeply into the Nile waters and irrigate more extensive cotton fields—and this would be hard for Egypt.

In the 1820's the Sudan was conquered by Egyptian forces, and remained under a rather loose Egyptian control until 1883, when the Sudanese, under a fanatical religious leader known as the Mahdi, revolted and drove out the Egyptians. It was not until 1896-98 that the Sudan was reconquered by a joint British and Egyptian force. Until independence was gained in 1956, the Sudan was jointly administered by the two powers as the Anglo-Egyptian Sudan.

Egypt fondly hoped to retain some control over the Sudan, if only to regulate the use which the Sudanese make of the Nile's waters. Since independence the Sudan has successfully asserted its right to use more water from the river that flows through its territory. Today the irrigated cotton fields of Gezira are being extended, and Egypt is having to plan her water use more carefully. In the center of the irrigated land where the White and Blue Nile meet is the city of Khartoum, capital of the Sudan. Its metropolitan area includes a population of about 250,000, making it one of the greater cities of Africa by African standards.

Ethiopia, which contributes the abundance of water to the Sudan and Egypt via the Blue Nile, has hitherto used little of it. This has been partly because it is difficult to take water from the deeply incised valleys of the Ethiopian highlands; partly because the population, with its strong leaning toward pastoral activities, has not created a very great demand for water. But the situation is slowly changing. The population of about 20,000,000 is growing, and demand for water is rising, and Ethiopia is increasing her own use of the rivers that rise within her borders, both to generate power and also to irrigate the lands along her mountain valleys.

Ethiopia, with its capital city of Addis Ababa, located in a high mountain basin, is one of the oldest political units in Africa. It was the Sheba of Biblical times, when it reached down to the shores of the Red Sea and maintained contact with Arabia and the Middle East. Through this route it received the Christian religion in the fourth century. Ethiopia lost control of this coastal region of Eritrea and Somaliland, which was occupied by the British, French, and Italians. The French still retain the small colony of French Somaliland, with its capital Djibouti, but Ethiopia has now, since 1945 returned to the Red Sea coast with the incorporation of Eritrea. As its contacts with the outside world are being intensified, this ancient kingdom is gradually grafting modern institutions and practices onto its ancient folkways.

The Eastern Horn

To the east and southeast of the Ethiopian highlands is a rough, semi-desert country, where nomadic herdsmen have grazed their flocks since time immemorial. A little agriculture is practiced along the watercourses, which are dry for much of the year. This region, formerly part of the British and Italian empires, now constitutes the Somali Republic, one of the poorest and least populated of the new states of Africa, with its capital on the coast at Mogadiscio.

The Heart of East Africa

The three adjoining countries of Kenya, Uganda, and Tanganyika make up the heart of East Africa. They lie between the Rift Valley and the Indian Ocean. Except along the western and eastern margins, the altitude is enough to take the edge off the temperature and humidity, while the rainfall is better distributed and more adequate than in the lands to the north. In Kenya the plateau lifts up into highlands which are cool and pleasant, rather like a perpetual European summer. The British, by a variety of legal titles, gained possession of Kenya and Uganda. The Germans occupied Tanganyika, but lost it during the First World War, and it has since been administered by Great Britain, first as a mandate under the League of Nations and since 1945 as a trusteeship territory under the United Nations; late in 1961 it was given its independence.

Uganda is the smallest of the three, and with about 6,900,000 inhabitants by far the most densely populated. The Africans of Uganda are highly organized in groups of tribes, through whose mechanism of kings, chiefs, and tribal councils the British government has been wisely content to administer the territory; its independence is scheduled for fall, 1962. The people practice a highly developed agriculture in which the banana palm plays a very important role. The southeast boundary of the state is formed by the shore of Lake Victoria, on which lies its capital, the little town of Entebbe. Kampala, a short distance inland, is the major town. A great deal of shipping and commerce passes to and fro on the lake, linking Uganda with its East African neighbors. The White Nile discharges northwestward, dropping by way of the Ripon (Owen) and Murchison Falls—now being harnessed for hydroelectric power—to the lower plains of the Sudan.

On the plateau of Kenya were numerous pastoral peoples who grazed their herds over the savanna. The region was not densely populated, and a change from pastoralism to crop farming would have allowed it to support far more people than in fact it did. Into this region came Europeans, not to supervise the exploitation of cacao and rubber and palm oil, but to settle, build homes, hunt imported foxes, and live the lives of English country gentlemen along the railroad that runs up from the port of Mombasa. Their numbers have not been great; no more than about 70,000 ever settled in the Kenya Highlands. But their impact has been immense.

They helped themselves generously to the land, which had all the appearances of being but thinly settled and little used. The African tribes were forced into reservations, made up generally of the poorer soil, where crowding became acute; meanwhile up in the healthful highlands around Nairobi, the capital, the white settlers laid out their coffee plantations, their tea groves, and their cotton and tobacco fields. The inequality between African and European, the latter living in ease, if not always in affluence, on lands which the former insisted had been stolen, provoked one of the most bitter communal struggles in Africa. Its leaders were the Kikuyu tribe, one of the agricultural peoples which had suffered most by losing its best lands. The terrorism provoked by the Mau Mau secret society was suppressed, but the Kikuyu made their point. Reforms are under way, and independence, with some safeguard for the white minority, is promised for the near future.

Tanganyika's is a different story. The few Germans who settled here left at the end of the First World War, and as a trusteeship territory Tanganyika ripened rapidly toward independence, which came in 1961. The conditions of the mandate prevented Great Britain from treating Tanganyika as she had Kenya, allowing Europeans to settle all the more desirable land. Tanganyika has over 50 per cent more area and almost 50 per cent more population than Kenya. But the population is almost wholly African. There is only a handful of Europeans, and the largest non-African group consists of Indians and Pakistanis.

Tanganyika is a savanna country, with a fringe of mangrove forest along the coast. Over the plateau the Africans practice mainly a subsistence agriculture, but produce also large quantities of sisal hemp, which is the most important export of Tanganyika.

The port of Tanganyika is Dar es Salaam, which is also the capital. A railroad climbs up from the narrow coastal lowland onto the plateau and then runs across the country west to the shore of Lake Tanganyika, the western boundary of the country. Offshore is the small island of Zanzibar, and its even smaller neighbor, Pemba, which together form an independent sultanate under British protection. Zanzibar has an area of only about 1,000 square miles, a population of 300,000, and an agriculture that is dominated by the production of cloves, which are the island's chief export and provide most of the world's supply.

The communal problems of East Africa are not only those of African versus European. The exposure of the East African coast to Asian influence has already been mentioned. The result has been an influx of

Indians and Arabs. The Indians in East Africa are not numerous, though they are many more than the Europeans—but they are almost all petty traders. They buy up the African's surplus peanuts, beans, cotton, and tobacco; and whether their trading methods are fair or otherwise, they are distrusted and disliked by the African, who usually suspects he is being victimized by someone a little sharper than himself.

The Arab role in East Africa is similar to the Indian, and has been practiced for a very much longer period of time. The Arabs are merchants all along this coast. The local Swahili language has been strongly influenced by Arabic. The dominant group in the little island protectorate of Zanzibar is Arab, and the ruling sultan is a Moslem. There are some parts of East Africa where it is the role of the European to hold the balance between the African and the Asian.

CENTRAL AFRICA

Any physical distinction between West or East and Central Africa is one of convenience. The forests of Cameroun pass into those of Gabon and the Republic of the Congo, and the savanna of Chad stretches across the Central African Republic to Sudan and Uganda, which we have placed in East Africa.

Near the eastern boundary of Nigeria the coast turns to the south and approaches the equator. The climate becomes more equatorial, the rainfall more evenly distributed through the year, and the heat and the humidity consistently higher. Central Africa is the only other region of the world that may be said to resemble the selvas of the Amazon. Yet the similarity is not close. Both lie astride the equator, but whereas the Amazon plain is low and flat, rising only a few feet above the level of the sea, and in consequence wet and ill-drained, the basin of the Congo River is a depression in the surface of the African plateau.

Central Africa lies from a thousand to about four thousand feet above the level of the sea, and the Congo River, which draws toward it the drainage of almost all this region, tumbles down to its coastal plain and to the sea by cataracts that remain unnavigable. The result is that the forests of the Congo are neither as continuous nor as dense and impenetrable as those of the Amazon. Throughout the Congo Basin, even on the equator, there are areas where the forest thins out and exposes patches of rising ground where the drainage is easier and areas of parkland where Negro tribes have built their villages.

The Central African region, which consists in the main of the drainage basin of the Congo River, is more thickly peopled than the Amazon plain, and if its agricultural resources are no greater, they are at least capable of being developed and used more easily. The Congo Basin is today an important producer of palm oil, of rubber, coffee, cotton, bananas, and lumber. But it is as a source of minerals that this region is perhaps likely to be most important in the future. Today the area ranks high as a producer of a number of important minerals, including copper, tin, gold, manganese, and diamonds. But the most important of these is copper.

Great beds of copper occur in the southern part of the Congo Republic, or The Congo, in the province of Katanga. This region today supplies about a tenth of the world's production of this essential mineral. The copper mines, near Elisabethville, have been the chief source of income for The Congo, and with the proceeds of the sale of copper, The Congo has imported much of what it needs from overseas. Behind the attempts of Tshombe to form a Katanga state, independent of The Congo, and behind the anxiety of the rest of the republic to retain Katanga, lies the mineral wealth of this province. The internal struggle between the authorities in Elisabethville and those in Léopoldville is, in essence, a contest for control of the copper mines.

The Congo River is one of the great streams of the world. It spreads across the equator, drawing its tributaries from the savanna lands to the north and south. It is also a great navigable river. Its flow is as steady as the equatorial rains. Its broad, shining surface is a highway through the forest and savanna and gathers to the dozens of small river ports along its course the oil, the rubber, and the minerals of the basin of the Congo. No railway system has ever been built, and none was needed; there are at most a few fairly short lines running down to the river or circumventing the rapids that occasionally obstruct this otherwise perfect river. Unfortunately the rapids begin a little over a hundred miles from the mouth of the river where it descends from the plateau to the west coast. It was these rapids that prevented the early explorers from sailing up the Congo from the sea into the heart of Africa. Today they interrupt the flow of commerce along the river and make it necessary to send it by rail from Léopoldville, above the rapids, to Matadi, lying below this obstacle, where ocean-going ships can ascend.

The Congo Republic was the result of the financial juggling of King Leopold of the Belgians, who bequeathed this burdensome legacy to

Belgium. In a physical sense it is one of the most united areas in Africa. The river system holds it together, and it has a simplicity in its relief, climate, and vegetation unknown in most areas of so great a size. Yet the Belgians never succeeded in building a cultural and political unity to match the physical. Little attempt was ever made through education to attach the Congolese to the concept of a Congo state. The primary loyalties of the Congolese in most instances remained to their tribes, and tribal rivalry has been more significant to most than any ideal of a Congo state. Thus the end of Belgian rule was followed by a period of chaos in which tribal and local loyalties asserted themselves, as they had done before the arrival of European conquerors in this continent.

The Congo problem has raised in an acute form the question of how to organize politically a vast, thinly peopled region in which a common loyalty to a single central government has never emerged. This problem was faced by the British before they left Nigeria. There, too, there were

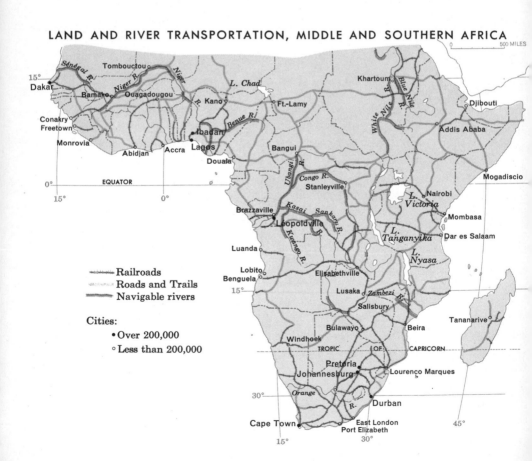

LAND AND RIVER TRANSPORTATION, MIDDLE AND SOUTHERN AFRICA

warring, feuding tribes whose political horizon had never embraced the whole of Nigeria. The solution was federalism: a central government to conduct foreign policy and to administer internal transportation and commerce; and local or provincial governments to focus the loyalties of the tribes. The same solution is being proposed in The Congo, but the problem here is made more difficult by the mineral wealth, especially that of Katanga. The Katanga government has no desire to share this with anyone, and its reluctance to be associated with the rest of The Congo springs in part, at least, from its unwillingness to subsidize less well-endowed parts of Central Africa.

In the course of the partition of Africa during the last decades of the nineteenth century, the Congo River and its tributary, the Ubangi, came to be adopted as the boundary between the Belgian and the French spheres in Central Africa. Beyond it to the west and north was French Equatorial Africa, now divided into the states of Chad and Cameroun—which we have already examined—the Central African Republic, Congo, and Gabon.

The Central African Republic spans the transition from the northern savanna to the equatorial forest. On the north it is drained toward the saline swamps which make up Lake Chad; on the south its rivers flow to the Ubangi, and thus to the Congo. Its population of only a little over 1,200,000 is engaged mainly in subsistence agriculture. It has few roads, little commerce, and no railroads, and its more important centers of population, including Bangui, the capital, lie on the navigable river Ubangi, which alone provides a reliable route along the southern borders of the state.

The Republic of Congo—to be distinguished from The Congo which it faces across the Congo River—is in all respects smaller than the Central African Republic. But it is more accessible from the ocean and for that reason is more developed. A railroad links its Atlantic port of Pointe Noire with its capital city of Brazzaville, which lies on the broad navigable highway of the Congo River across from Léopoldville, the capital of its similarly named neighbor.

Gabon is yet smaller and less populous, and many will know it as the primeval forest on the margin of which Albert Schweitzer established his hospital at Lambaréné. Its capital and chief port, Libreville, lies on the coast, but only river and forest track link it with its hinterland. In all three of these small republics the native Negro population lives in small forest clearings, and lives mainly by subsistence agriculture.

Two small enclaves on the coast of Central Africa deserve mention: Rio Muni, or Spanish Guinea, a small relic of Spain's nearly vanished empire, notched in between Cameroun and Gabon, and Cabinda, in reality an outlier of Portugal's Angola. Both are thinly peopled, underdeveloped, and politically backward, and if they have been free from the disturbances that have marked the recent history of their neighbors, this may be only the peace that goes with backwardness and oppression. It may also be the calm before the storm.

On the other side of the vast sprawling territory of The Congo are the two new nations (1962), Rwanda and Burundi formerly the Belgian-controlled Ruanda-Urundi. They lie up in the hills which border the Rift Valley. Ruanda-Urundi formerly was German, but in 1919 Belgium acquired the mandate to administer it. The area is more healthful and far more densely populated than The Congo itself, and served as a source of labor for the Belgian-operated mines. Political independence along with The Congo in 1960 was postponed by the feuds which have in the past divided its tribes.

SOUTH AFRICA

Africa south of the Congo Basin and the East African plateau presents problems even more important and even less easily solved than West, Central, and East Africa. And again it is the geography of the region that chiefly accounts for them. The forests which cover parts of Central Africa thin away toward the south and are replaced by more open, healthful country. Like East Africa this is mostly a high plateau. The rivers are etched into it and flow through deep valleys to the sea. Between the valleys is the rolling, grass- or savanna-covered plateau of Rhodesia. Rainfall diminishes toward the south and becomes more seasonal, and in the Republic of South Africa the open woodland—the Bush Veld as it is called—passes into the grasslands of the High Veld. At the same time the plateau rises to a high rim, and then plunges steeply and abruptly to the narrow coastal plain that separates the plateau from the ocean.

South Africa lies in the belt of the trade winds. They blow continuously off the Indian Ocean, cross the narrow plain, and pile up over the rim of the plateau. The coastal plain is a moist region, where the on-shore winds bring rain at most seasons of the year. The climate is tropical, hot and humid, with only a short dry season: the perfect climate for sugar cane and citrus fruit. This is the climate of Portuguese Mozambique and of Natal. But up beyond the rim of the plateau it is drier. The winds drop down from the Drakensberg Mountains, where this rim is highest and most rugged, toward the interior of the plateau as dry winds. They bring little rainfall to the central areas of the plateau, and even less to its more westerly parts. A journey across the south of Africa from the Indian Ocean to the Atlantic would pass from the lush vegetation of the coastal region to the tall grass of the High Veld and on to the even shorter, drier, grassland of the western Veld; then to the semidesert of the Kalahari and the Namib Desert, a true desert which borders the Atlantic Ocean.

The extreme south of the continent, where the coast faces the great southern ocean, is a region to itself. This is the region of Mediterranean climate, too far south for the trade winds to blow regularly, where the westerlies of the Southern Hemisphere blow across the extremity of the continent in winter.

There is more variety of relief and climate in South Africa than in other large divisions of the continent, and in this variety lies the source of part, at least, of South Africa's problems. Settlement by Europeans has been negligible in West and Central Africa, and in East Africa has been limited to the highlands of Kenya. But South Africa offered greater possibilities.

The Southern Point of Africa

In the area now embraced by the Republic of South Africa, Europeans first settled and farmed in the small region of Mediterranean climate near the Cape of Good Hope in the mid-seventeenth century. As their numbers grew, they spread into the interior of what today we call Cape Province. There they ran into certain primitive African peoples, notably the Hottentots, who offered no resistance to the newcomers. In this direction the plateau rises in a series of huge, broad steps, called the Great and Little Karroo, to the plateau of the interior. The Karroos were arid and forbidding, and Europeans did not penetrate into and beyond them until the thirties of the last century. Then occurred one of those great, formative events, which give a character and tradition to a people. The British had abolished the slave trade several years before; now they abolished the institution of slavery itself. The Boer farmers, descendants of the Dutch settlers, resented and resisted this. Though they were offered compensation by the British for the services they would lose of their

African slaves, they nevertheless packed up their farm tools, saddled their horses, and moved out, with their ox-drawn covered wagons, up through the Karroos and on to the grasslands of the Veld.

This was the Great Trek, the focal event in the history of South Africa, the revolution by which the Boers threw off British control and carved out a state for themselves beyond the Great Karroo and the Drakensberg Mountains. British authority was slow in catching up with the Boers. That it did in fact do so was due in part to the Africans themselves. There had been very few Africans in Cape Province, and most of these had been the simple Hottentots. But up on the High Veld the Boers met the advancing wave of Negro peoples. They were war-like and well organized into tribes, such as the Zulus, Swazis, Matabele, and Mashona. There were bloody battles on the Veld, in which the Boers were fully as ruthless as the Africans. The fact is that the Boers looked upon themselves as a kind of chosen people, directed to create a society along somewhat Biblical lines up here in this grassy, pleasant, promised land. They established the two small, independent republics of the Orange Free State and, beyond it to the north, the Transvaal in the 1850's. Then for a time the Boers again accepted a kind of British protection, but again threw it off in 1881.

It is time to look briefly at what was happening at the same time down below the rim of the escarpment, in Cape Province and, farther to the northeast, in Natal. Some Boers had remained behind in the Cape, when most of their community had trekked north, but the Europeans at the Cape became mainly English-speaking. They spread into Natal, where, the warm, moist climate soon led them to the growing of sugar cane. Africans were not numerous, nor were they too willing to work on European-owned plantations, so Indians were brought in. Usually the Indians contracted to work for a period of years in return for their passage, and after their obligations had been terminated, many of them settled permanently in Natal, where there remains today a sizable Indian community. At the end of the nineteenth century there were thus two colonies which were ruled from London, and up on the Veld, two more which ruled themselves.

Relations between the two pairs were never happy, but they greatly worsened with the discovery of gold and diamonds in the Transvaal. The precious minerals held little attraction for the Boers, who wanted nothing so much as to be left alone. The mines attracted personalities—as gold and diamond fields always do—that were diametrically opposite to the stolid, deeply religious, and fundamentalist Boer. They also attracted British capital, and this, in turn, led to watchful interest by the British authorities at the Cape. Incident was piled on incident; tension mounted until at last war came. This was the Boer War, a three-year struggle, 1899–1902, in which the Boers took full advantage of the terrain which they knew so well, to harass the attacking British forces. The resistance of the Boers was finally overcome. For a few years the British controlled the whole of South Africa, and then, in 1910, created the Union of South Africa as a self-governing dominion within the Commonwealth.

But the Boer War and the conferring of dominion status were merely incidents in a continuing struggle. Hostility between the English-speaking population and the Boers, whose Afrikaans language was derived from Dutch, was diminished, not ended. The Boers still retained the same views about the role of the African peoples which had led them almost a century earlier to make the Great Trek. They regarded the Africans as a race apart, born to be the hewers of wood and drawers of water, the modern Canaanites to this new chosen people; and their opinion of the half-castes, the so-called "Cape Colored," was no higher. The number of the Boers grew faster than that of the English, and today the latter are outnumbered. With this change in the balance of the two peoples, the extreme nationalists came to the fore among the Afrikaans. Their policy has become one of *Apartheid*, of the rigid segregation of white from African, Indian, and also from those of mixed blood. Nowhere has so extreme and rigid a policy of segregation ever been attempted. When it ran into adverse criticism from the members of the Commonwealth in 1961, the Union of South Africa just quit the Commonwealth, and changed its title to Republic.

South-West Africa is the desert and semidesert which lies to the northwest of the Republic of South Africa. It was first annexed by the Germans in 1883, but in 1919 was entrusted to the Union of South Africa as a mandate by the League of Nations. When, in 1945, the former mandates were transferred as trusteeship territories to the United Nations, South Africa refused to recognize the change. It treated South-West Africa as part of its sovereign territory, and when its policy was criticized in the United Nations, replied by denying the competence of the United Nations to intervene.

South-West Africa is a large territory of about 318,000 square miles, but its total population is only about 500,000, many of them members of backward and mainly pastoral tribes. Agricultural resources are negligible, and such wealth as there is lies mainly in rough grazing. The production of karakul lambs for the sake of their pelts is increasing. But the economy is based mainly on the mining industry. Diamonds, extracted from the alluvium along the Namib coast, are the most important. In addition lead, copper, zinc, and tin are mined and exported.

When the Union of South Africa was created, the British, as if with a kind of foreknowledge of what was to happen, held back three areas as reserves for the Africans. These are the so-called High Commission Territories—Bechuanaland, Basutoland, and Swaziland. As land goes in South Africa, they were not of the best, but at least they were Africans' land, where there was neither segregation nor discrimination, nor, in fact Europeans, except for a few administrators. Today the three territories remain under British control; they are embedded deeply within South Africa, an example to the Africans within the former union of a freer, more equal society. One of the foremost objectives of the nationalists is to destroy the High Commission Territories, and to absorb them into the segregated Republic of South Africa.

South Africa, today, must be one of the loneliest of states. It sacrificed many of its allies when it left the Commonwealth. It is the object of the violent hatred of all the new states of Africa, and within its borders the African majority—about 68 per cent of the total population—is poor, disfranchised, and seething with discontent. Those stolid Dutch colonists may yet reap a bitter harvest from the seeds of hatred they have sown.

In the meanwhile South Africa does fairly well materially. Much of South Africa is blessed with a good climate and endowed with great mineral wealth. Cattle and sheep are raised in immense numbers on the Veld, and their skins and hides make up the most valuable single group of agricultural exports. Subtropical fruit, especially oranges from Natal, and the products of the grape, including wine, from Cape Province, make up another important group of exports. But all are outclassed by minerals.

South Africa is one of the most important and most varied of the producers of minerals in the modern world. Copper, diamonds, manganese, chrome, and uranium are obtained from South Africa's mines, but most important of all is gold. Gold makes up almost two-thirds of the mineral output by value, and gold has the peculiar advantage that, unlike copper and others which can so easily be overproduced, it is something which someone always wants. Most of the gold comes from the Witwatersrand, or Rand for short, an area of about 1,200 square miles in the Transvaal, where the first strike was made in 1886. Here is the city

of Johannesburg, with its population of nearly 2,100,000, founded where the first gold strike had been made and named for Johannes Rissik, surveyor-general of the Transvaal. Johannesburg, a fine modern city, is the capital of the gold-mining industry. Around it the skyline is made up of the pointed spoil heaps, the waste of the mines and of the ore-dressing floors.

Second in value to the gold output is that of diamonds, obtained from mines at Pretoria in the Transvaal, from Kimberley in Cape Province, and from many sites in the Orange Free State as well as from South-West Africa. Among the metalliferous minerals the most important is manganese, and South Africa, as has been seen, ranks high in the world production of this essential material of steel manufacture.

Most of the foreign commerce of South Africa passes through the ports of Cape Town and Durban. Cape Town lies a little to the north of the Cape of Good Hope. Its sheltered bay—Table Bay as it is called—provided a secure anchorage for the earliest settlers. The first vineyards and farms were laid out over the rolling hills which stretch inland from Cape Town, and the flat-topped Table Mountain, with the city nestling at its foot, must be one of the most familiar sights in all South Africa.

North of South Africa

Between South Africa and the countries which make up Central and East Africa lie the two largest fragments remaining of the Portuguese Empire—Angola and Mozambique—and the most extensive of Britain's remaining dependencies—the Federation of Rhodesia and Nyasaland. These are intermediate between Central and South Africa in more ways than one. Climatically they lie between the perpetually hot and humid Congo region and the cooler, drier lands of the Veld and Cape Province. In terms of suitability for European settlement, they also lie between the equatorial regions, which are not reckoned suitable, and the eminently suitable lands of the Cape. This is reflected in the numbers of Europeans who have settled here: Europeans are most numerous in Southern Rhodesia, where they make up almost 10 per cent of the population; they are fewer in Northern Rhodesia, about 3 per cent, and in Nyasaland, about 1 per cent. Europeans are few also in Portuguese Mozambique, which is mostly low-lying and located to the east, in the path of the wet trade winds. Portuguese Angola, on the other hand, lies on the western side of the continent, and it is drier. Most of it is savanna land passing southward into the Kalahari Desert and northward into the forests along the lower Congo. The Portuguese have made no great efforts to settle this territory, but almost 200,000 of their people have set up home there, and the total population is about 5 per cent European.

Much of this belt of dry savanna country between Angola in the west and the borders of Mozambique in the east, where it is too dry for the mosquito to trouble human beings or the tsetse fly his cattle, is one of those crucial meeting places of African and European. To the north, nearer the equator, the European generally takes up no permanent residence, and when he has finished his career in plantation or mine, he goes home. In Angola, the Rhodesias and Nyasaland, he occupies the higher, cooler, drier lands, and remains; even in the less favorable Mozambique he stays, though in smaller numbers.

These Europeans are a small fearful minority, knowing that if a broadly based democratic society were to be established in Africa, they would be outnumbered; that if it came to a physical clash of cultures, they would be defeated. They have seen the handful of Belgians driven from The Congo, and to many of them their future seems to be in a heavy-handed policy of segregation, like the *Apartheid* of South Africa. That is why the calm of Rhodesia may be only the calm before the storm.

The storm has already broken upon Angola, and storms usually move forward, covering a wider area before their energy is spent.

The chief ports of Angola are Benguela and nearby Lobito, and Luanda 250 miles to the north. From each of them a railroad winds up onto the dry highlands of the interior, and that from Benguela passes Nova Lisboa, the chief center of European settlement, and runs on across the rest of Angola to Katanga and the copper mining center of Elisabethville. It is along this line from Angola that supplies are sent to Katanga and the copper itself is shipped out.

Angola is a kind of geographical bridge between the Congo Basin and the Kalahari. It is not a region of great promise; wherever the rainfall is adequate, the soils are poor, and over much of the territory the rainfall is too small for agriculture. The Portuguese have settled in moderate numbers to farm and ranch, forming a small ruling aristocracy amid the African majority.

Mozambique, on the opposite coast, is like Natal, but more tropical. As in Angola, the Portuguese never gave much thought to their policy here and have done little to develop the region's great resources.

When the rest of Africa was torn by the conflict of the Africans demanding independence and the Europeans trying to cling to their possessions and power, Portuguese Africa seemed a haven of peace. But the peace of Angola and Mozambique was not the peace that comes from good administration, progress, and good will. It was rather the quiet that results from the forcible suppression of discontent. The hand of Portugal lay heavy on her African colonies, but in the end not heavily enough to prevent their becoming inflamed by the revolt in The Congo and the freedom of most of tropical Africa.

Rhodesia and Nyasaland—the two Rhodesias, South and North, and the Protectorate of Nyasaland—lie geographically between the two large fragments of Portuguese Africa. British rule was established here during the closing years of the nineteenth century. There had been several proposals for a closer union of these three territories before, in 1953, the Federation of Rhodesia and Nyasaland was created. Boer farmers from the Cape never pushed their settlements this far into the bush. African tribes were more numerous and more formidable than they had been farther south in the Veld; the climate was more tropical, and the Boers stopped at the Limpopo River. But the British imperialist, financier, and one-time prime minister of the Cape Province, Cecil Rhodes, dreamed of building an empire in the interior of Africa, and of linking it geographically with British territories in East Africa, and then with the Sudan and Egypt. A railway was planned to run from the Cape to Cairo. This has remained a dream, but Rhodes was the architect of the Rhodesias, to which he gave his name, and here in the rough Matopo Hills he was buried, after bequeathing his large fortune, made in the diamond mines of South Africa, for the endowment of scholarships at Oxford University where he himself had studied.

The Rhodesias and Nyasaland are part of high Africa. The plateau lifts them above the humid heat of the lowlands. Their climate is sunny and invigorating. Their soils, which do not match the excellence of their climate, grow corn, cotton, and tobacco; the hillsides support coffee plantations. The plateau itself is trenched by the deep valley of the Zambezi River and by the southern prolongation of the Rift Valley, which contains Lake Nyasa. But between these valleys stretches the rolling, savanna-covered plateau, where the African grazes his cattle and hoes his plot of mealies.

The wealth of the region lies more in its bedrock than in its soil. It is highly mineralized. Northern Rhodesia contains the southern prolongation of the Katanga copper belt. Copper is the most valuable export of the region, and prominent among the remaining exports are asbestos, chrome, zinc, lead, gold, and cobalt. An impressive list of metals passes into world trade from Rhodesia and Nyasaland, and in some of these this region ranks among the world's leading producers. The Rhodesias are not without mineral fuels, though in this respect no part of Africa is well off. The coal of the Wankie coal field in Southern Rhodesia will soon be supplemented by water power generated at the dam now built across the Zambezi River at Kariba. Slowly industries are growing up; first those which process the local raw materials, to be followed by those which manufacture textiles and metal goods.

These territories of South Africa are generously endowed with favorable climate and physical resources. They do not, like the lands of South and East Asia, experience the pressure and the poverty of too many people living on too little land. The picture is one of golden opportunities lost on account of racial conflict, which no amount of technical aid can either reduce or resolve.

Offshore Africa

About 250 miles off the coast of Mozambique, out in the Indian Ocean, is the island which we had all learned to call Madagascar, until in 1958, it became the Malagasy Republic. It is a compact island, with a backbone of high mountains which descend steeply to its straight, rocky east coast. On the west the land sinks more gradually to a coastal plain, and here is most of the island's agricultural land.

When Europeans first reached Madagascar early in the sixteenth century, they found here a people with a developed culture and political organization. They were descended in the main from invaders who had crossed the Indian Ocean from Malaya and Indonesia, but they had received some infusion of Negro blood from the mainland of Africa, and there was a trace also of Arab racial and cultural influence. To this day the people of Madagascar protest that they are not Africans. Both the French and British established naval stations on the coast of Madagascar, but it was not until 1882 that the French attempted to impose their rule as protector on the whole island, and not before the early twentieth century that this rule became effective.

The Malagasy Republic is almost as large as Texas, but has a population of only about 5,600,000. It lies perpetually in the path of the trade winds. There is heavy rainfall in the mountains, and the lowlands to the west are moist, warm, and well cultivated. The chief native crops are rice, corn, manioc; coffee, cloves, tobacco, sugar, and the vanilla plant are grown for export; in the drier southwest cattle breeding has become important on the savanna.

The capital of Malagasy, Tananarive, lies up in the hills near the center of the island. The chief port, Tamatave, lies to the north below it, on the rockbound east coast, linked to it by one of the island's few railroads.

There are few islands in the South Atlantic Ocean, but the Indian Ocean, more like the Pacific, is strewn with islands and island chains. Between the northern tip of Madagascar and the African mainland are the Comores Islands, a volcanic group now ruled by France. North of Madagascar are many small groups of coral islands, of which the largest is Seychelles, a British colony, which exports coconut products, cinnamon, and vanilla. Between four and five hundred miles off the east coast are the small British island of Mauritius and the French island of Reunion. Both have a warm humid climate, and their prosperity is based upon the cultivation of the sugar cane and the export of sugar.

The African continent covers about 20 per cent of the land surface of the earth and has less than 8 per cent of its population. Much of Africa—the Sahara, the Kalahari and Namib deserts for example—are unlikely ever to be inhabited except by nomadic pastoralists and mining communities. But most of the continent has far greater resources in both soil and minerals than have ever been used. In contrast with Southeast Asia, the Middle East, or Central America, Africa is not poor because it is overcrowded, but poor because its resources have gone largely undeveloped. In Nigeria there are about 100 people to the square mile; in Ivory Coast, about 30, with little conspicuous difference in the quality of the two environments. The range in the national income of fundamentally similar areas is equally apparent. In Ghana, a recent computation put the national income per head at $135 per year; in the territories of former French Equatorial Africa—that is from Chad to Gabon—at only $58. The level of welfare, like the density of population, is more uneven and also far lower than the facts of physical geography alone would serve to indicate.

There is no simple explanation of this and yet an understanding of this inequality would be a halfway point toward remedying its evils. The more apparent of the many reasons can be listed: The quality of the soil, and the uncertainty in many areas of the rainfall; but modern technology provides a remedy in chemicals and plants to condition the soil and in dams to conserve and regulate the supply of water. Then there are the pests and diseases; and again, remedies for the scourges of malaria, sleeping-sickness, and other diseases of tropical Africa are known, and chemicals exist that can reduce the dangers to crops from insects and fungi. Modern machines exist that can clear the brush and pull out the trees by their long, deep roots; machines that can build all-weather roads and deepen and make navigable many rivers which have never yet been used for commerce.

Africa—or at least Africa south of the Sahara Desert—appears to be poorly endowed with mineral fuel which throughout the world has been a basis of industrial growth. But it has immense and largely untouched resources in hydroelectric power in the rivers of equatorial Africa, which vary little in their flow and are never obstructed by ice. Only a beginning has been made—on the Zambezi, the Volta, and the Upper Nile—in using this resource.

One is forced to conclude that it is not a grudging nature, but man's misuse or his inadequate use of natural resources, that is here the chief source of the poverty and backwardness of most of this continent.

The reason and the remedy both lie in society. Most of Africa has been subject to colonial rule for most of modern times. But it cannot be demonstrated that colonialism has necessarily been bad; after all the former colony of Gold Coast, Ghana, has one of the highest levels of income in Africa. But, as will have been implicit in previous pages, colonial policy and colonial practice have rarely been directed to the improvement of welfare among Africans. Then, too, the present has inherited from the pre-colonial period a legacy of tribal organization, with its concomitant tribal conflict. At its best colonial rule has tried— as in Nigeria and Uganda—to reconcile tribes, to diminish their hostilities, and to create a cohesion between all peoples of the territory or colony. At its worst colonial rule has intensified the hatreds which it found. And colonialism has added to the problems by creating plural societies, made up of strata of Europeans, of Asians sometimes as along the whole east coast, of half-castes like the "Cape Colored" in South Africa, and of the Africans themselves.

In this stratified society the African is always found at the bottom. Almost half the continent is vexed by this communal problem. The danger is not that a bloody revolution in Angola, Kenya, or Northern Rhodesia may wipe out the small white minority—though this may well happen—but that this animosity, infecting a whole continent, may prevent the African from learning by co-operation and collaboration the technological and political skills which Western man has to give. Events in Angola, in Northern Rhodesia, and in the Transvaal give cause for the gravest fears; then the smoothness and the success of Western and of African co-operation in, let us say, Uganda or Nigeria, serves to restore our hope in the future of Africa and our faith in the fundamental sanity of human nature.

13 CAPTAIN COOK'S WORLD:

Australia, New Zealand, Antarctica, and Oceania

. . . he had loved the Australian landscape, with the remote gum-trees running their white nerves into the air, the random streets of flimsy bungalows, all loose from one another, and temporary seeming, the bungalows perched precariously on the knolls, like Japanese paper houses, below the ridge of wire-and-tuft trees.

D. H. LAWRENCE—Kangaroo

Thousands of islands, like stepping stones in the ocean, stretch out from Southeast Asia to Australia; and thousands more, strung out in lines and loops, stretch out across the Pacific Ocean toward the Americas. This is the world which Captain Cook opened up to Western knowledge in the eighteenth century. It was a world with its own native peoples, Polynesians, Melanesians, Micronesians, and, most primitive of them all, the aboriginal peoples of Australia. There had been movement between and among the islands, yet, until Cook showed the way, Europeans had never sailed from island to island until they at last reached the great southern continent.

AUSTRALIA

No sailing ships crossed the Timor Sea, or the Arafura, or even the Torres Straits between New Guinea and Australia, to satisfy a curiosity about the "Down Under." Australia was, excepting only Antarctica, the last continent to be discovered, and the last to be settled. Europeans were the first to reach Australia, early in the seventeenth century. They found here a native people, a poor, almost Stone Age group, which had not learned to cultivate the soil, and had made very few of the steps in the ladder of progress that leads from savagery to civilization. Why had Australia been cut off for so long from contact with other continents and other peoples? Why was Australia so primitive?

Dutch sailors of the seventeenth century, bound for the West Indies, would round the Cape of Good Hope and then sail due east to take advantage of the westerly winds before turning north to their destination. It is nearly six thousand miles sailing from South Africa to the East Indies, and over five thousand miles from South Africa to Australia, and occasionally a ship would hold to its eastern course too long and make a landfall on the west coast of Australia. In this way the Australian coast came to be well known, but nothing that the Dutch navigators saw ever attracted them to explore it more fully. It was a barren desert coast that they struck; it did not even provide water to provision their ships, and beyond the shore line the scrub stretched inland until it merged into desert.

In 1642, a few years after the Dutch sailors had first sighted Australia, Abel Tasman set out to explore its coast more fully. But the ocean is a big place and Tasman missed Australia completely. He discovered the smaller island of Tasmania, which now bears his name, and he touched the rugged west coast of the South Island of New Zealand, but he made no contribution to man's knowledge of Australia itself.

So Australia still remained an unknown continent for another century. It was not until the age of James Cook, in the second half of the eighteenth century, that much progress was made. In the course of his three great voyages, made between 1768 and 1779, Cook circumnavigated and mapped the islands of New Zealand and explored the eastern coast of Australia as well as many of the island groups in the Pacific Ocean. He was as fortunate as Tasman had been unlucky. His exploration of New Zealand revealed that these islands were not all mountainous, and in Australia he had the good fortune to see the warm, humid east coast. There he was greatly impressed by the wealth of its vegetation, and one particularly luxurious inlet he christened Botany Bay.

Even so, his glowing reports would probably have done little if the successful revolt of Britain's North American colonies at this time had not deprived Great Britain of the places to which debtors and other

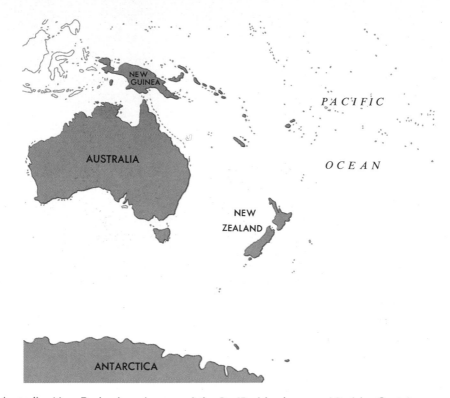

Australia, New Zealand, and many of the Pacific Islands were visited by Captain Cook. He also reached the great ice barrier which guards the Antarctic.

undesirables had been customarily sent. The problem this raised threatened to become serious until it was suggested that the land recently explored by Cook combined all the advantages of climate, fertility, and distance from Britain's hallowed shores the former penal colonies had had.

In 1788 the first consignment of convicts reached Botany Bay. Conditions here actually seemed less suitable than a few miles north, and a shift was made to Port Jackson. There, on the shores of a deep, sheltered inlet was founded the settlement that grew to be the city of Sydney.

The factor of distance, which had recommended Australia as a site for a penal colony, deterred the emigration of free settlers. Although a few arrived, the distance from Europe and the impossibility at first of exporting farm products prevented them from developing commercial colonies such as existed at that time in North America. It was not until well into the nineteenth century that free settlers began to arrive in any considerable numbers.

About the beginning of the nineteenth century the most significant innovation in the history of Australia was made. The merino sheep was introduced from South Africa, whither it had been taken from Spain. Australia had grassland in abundance, the merino sheep produced a fine fleece, and the textile mills of England could use all the wool that Australia could produce. Captain John Macarthur began to experiment with his merino sheep in the Sydney area in 1794, and early in the following century, sheep ranching spread outward in all directions and soon came to be concentrated up on the Blue Mountains, a hundred miles inland from Sydney.

So the fortunes of Australia were founded on the wool trade, and the prospects began to attract free settlers from England. The search for grazing lands drew explorers into the interior of the continent. Up over the abrupt hills of the Blue Mountains of the Great Dividing Range they went from the narrow, coastal plain along the east coast near Sydney, gradually opening up the rolling grasslands beyond. Sheep were to open up a continent, and the fortune that lay in their golden fleece was to draw men far into the interior of Australia.

Botany Bay, and its neighbor and successor Sydney, was not the only penal institution in Australia. Either crime was serious in England, or the courts were very active, and the numbers sent to Australia grew; the convicts were best kept in small and widely settled colonies. The coast of eastern and southern Australia was gradually explored, often by the military who had been sent to guard the criminals. In 1803 a fresh colony was established on the shore of a deep, natural harbor that had been discovered on the south coast, and had been called Port Phillip; later, in 1835, Tasmanians also settled the area and it grew into the city of Melbourne.

At the turn of the nineteenth century the island of Tasmania began to attract the settlers by its mild, moist climate and its wooded beauty, and beginning in 1804 colonists—both voluntary and involuntary—went there and established the city of Hobart. In 1833 an association was formed to settle South Australia, and the city of Adelaide was founded a few years later. Earlier, in 1829, a settlement had been made on the Swan River, at Perth, in the southwestern extremity of Australia, which later grew into the colony of Western Australia.

Settlers also moved northward from Sydney, though in this direction they quickly encountered a warmer and more humid climate with which they were quite unfamiliar. In 1824, the settlement which eventually became Brisbane was founded.

Up to 1830 the majority of the immigrants were convicts, though from the early days of Australian settlement there had been a minority of free settlers. Many of the convicts, whose crimes in any event had often been only trifling, were liberated and turned themselves into farmers or ranchers on the expanding Australian frontier. And during the nineteenth century the number of free settlers gradually increased. Thus the English settlements came to be spread out along the eastern and the southern coasts, with a small outlier in Tasmania. No roads linked them, and they were held together only by the ships which sailed the 3,500 miles from the most northeasterly settlement in the future Queensland to the most southwesterly, beside the Swan River. The settlements developed in virtual isolation from one another; jealous and suspicious, they formed the nuclei from which each of the Australian states evolved. When the time came, at the beginning of the twentieth century, to weld these states into the Commonwealth of Australia, they joined reluctantly and reserved extensive powers to themselves. Australia, as it were, had come into being divided, and the social system introduced by the British served only to emphasize the divisive influence of the continent's physical geography. And to this we must now turn.

Australia is the smallest and most compact of the continents. In area it is a little smaller than conterminous United States; 2,974,581 square miles as against 3,082,809. For great distances along the west, south, and east coasts the coast line is straight and fringed by cliffs, calculated to repel rather than to attract settlers. Much of the west and south coast is backed by desert; the northern coast is fringed with swamp; and lying off the east coast of Queensland, ranging 20 to 150 miles from the shore, is an almost continuous reef of coral, the Great Barrier Reef, which endangers shipping and restricts access to the coast. Captain Cook was himself shipwrecked on this reef. No continent ever welcomed its explorers and settlers less warmly than Australia.

Australia is the least diversified physically of the continents. It is a vast plateau of tableland, rising near its center to heights of less than five thousand feet. Its hills are only ridges rising above its generally level surface, and the valleys of its few rivers are only shallow depressions. A sense of somberness lies over the land. Only along the eastern margin in the Great Dividing Range, which lies behind the whole of Australia's eastern coast and in its southern portion often called the Australian Alps, is there a region of stronger relief. This range is the highest in Australia, but at its greatest elevation, Mount Kosciusko in the southeast part, it reaches only 7,328 feet. Snow falls in winter over its summit.

AUSTRALIA
AND SOUTHWEST PACIFIC

Scale of Miles

0   100   200   400   600

⊛ National Capitals   ☆ State Capitals   ● Other Cities

COPYRIGHT 1962 BY RAND MC NALLY & CO. MADE IN U.S.A.

150°   160°   10°

North Latitude

South Latitude

OLINE   ISLANDS

P   A   C   I   F   I

ATOR   0°

dia

RTHEAST
NEW
GUINEA

PUA
(STL.)

Port Moresby

Cape York

Bismarck
Archipelago

New Britain

Solomon
Islands

170°   180°

Ellice Islands

Santa Cruz
Islands

Banks
Islands

New
Hebrides

WESTERN
SAMOA

Fiji
Islands

CORAL   SEA

C

O

Great Barrier Reef

GREAT DIVIDING RANGE

Townsville

River

NSLAND

GREAT
RTESIAN

BASIN

I   A

Rockhampton

Loyalty
Islands

New
Caledonia

TROPIC OF CAPRICORN

Tonga
Islands

10°

20°

Brisbane

g River

NEW
SOUTH
WALES

Murrumbidgee R.

River

TORIA

Melbourne

BASS STRAIT

Newcastle

Sydney

Canberra

Mount
Kosciusko

Lord Howe
Islands

TASMAN   SEA

North Cape

Auckland

NEW

ZEALAND

North
Island

Wellington

Kermadec
Islands

A

N

30°

TASMANIA

Hobart

Mt. Cook

Christchurch

South
Island

South Cape   Stewart
I.

Dunedin

150°   160°   170°   East Longitude   180°   West Longitude   170°   160°

40°

and the city-dwellers from Sydney and Melbourne turn out for a little skiing. This is the only snow they are ever likely to see.

The Great Dividing Range has a steep, fractured face toward the east, which for many years halted the sheep farmers in their movement toward the interior. On the west it merges into a rolling plateau, which drops slowly, imperceptibly south toward the basin of the rivers Darling, Murray, and Murrumbidgee, the only important river system that Australia possesses. The Great Dividing Range rises to its highest points in New South Wales. To the north, in Queensland, it becomes lower and more spread out and runs on to Cape York, the most northerly point, as a line of low, softly rolling hills. At its other extremity, on the border of New South Wales and Victoria, the range swings round to the west, runs through the state of Victoria and dies away as it approaches the great shallow indentation, known as the Great Australian Bight or Bay, which is the chief feature of the south coast of this continent.

Only two of the great wind systems of the world affect Australia, the westerlies and the trade winds of the Southern Hemisphere. The west winds blow only across the southern promontories. Only the southwest and southeast of the country experience them, and then only in winter, thus giving these areas a kind of Mediterranean climate. The island of Tasmania lies about 140 miles south of the coast of Victoria, far enough south to have the moist, west winds blowing across its mountains throughout the year. If we may again look for climatic analogies, southern Australia resembles the San Francisco region, and Tasmania to the south is more like Oregon and Washington.

The rest of Australia is blown upon by the southeast trade winds. They blow on to the coast of New South Wales and Queensland, and as D. H. Lawrence observed, "there is the wide Pacific rolling in on the yellow sand: the wide fierce sea, that makes all the built-over land dwindle into non-existence." The trades build up a heavy swell, and "so the Pacific belied its name and crushed the earth with its rollers."

Winds from the Pacific bring rain to this eastern coast. The rains come at all seasons, and up in the hills they are heavy. Sydney, New South Wales, has a climate like Charleston or Savannah in the United States; farther north the climate is more like that of Florida, and northern Queensland is more tropical than any part of the United States, and resembles the West Indian Islands or Central America.

To the west, in the shadow of the Great Dividing Range, the rainfall diminishes. The woodland of the eastern coastal regions, characterized by typically Australian trees like the wattle, or gum-tree, and tree ferns, gives way gradually to the rolling grasslands that allowed much of interior Australia to become one large sheep run. But as the center of the continent is approached, the grassland too dries out. It passes into sandy waste or into bush. Australia lies in the latitude of northern Chile and of the southern part of Africa, which makes it almost certain that much of its surface will be too arid for human use.

Only small areas are true desert. Much of it is covered with bush, gray, charred, and ghostly. From it rise the tall, straight, pale trunks of the gum trees. Most leaves are a dark gray-green. There is little life; birds and animals are few, and water is scarce. This is the dead heart of Australia. This is why Australia is the most sparsely populated of the continents, why, after nearly two centuries of European settlement, it still has only 10,740,000 people.

The great Australian Desert, made up of the Great Sandy, Gibson, and Great Victoria deserts, is not utterly arid like the desert of Atacama or the Sahara, but it is dry and repellent, and it covers a half of the continent. On the margin of the desert there are many lake basins. On occasion these may contain water if the rains have been more than usually generous, but for much of the time they are dry and covered with salt, formed on their surface by the evaporation of the water. Lake Eyre, near the southeastern margin of the desert, which looks so large on the map, is an illusion. Most of the time it is a sheet of hot, white, dry salt, shimmering in the heat. When there is water in the lake, it is too salty for use by man, beast, or growing plant.

Across the north of Australia there lies a belt of moister land. The extreme north of Australia lies within 11°—less than eight hundred miles —of the equator. The coastal fringe has tropical rains in summer and is hot and humid throughout the year. Mangrove swamps fringe parts of the coast and in the short rivers there are crocodiles. But Australia's jungle covers only scattered areas along the north coast, some of which extend for short distances up the rivers into the interior. It quickly passes southward into a wooded savanna. This is only a strip, about a hundred miles wide, and it passes into drier savanna, which yields within five hundred miles of the coast to the dead, dry heart.

In the west the desert reaches right to the coast. Here the trade winds, which blow toward the continent along the coasts of New South Wales and Queensland, blow offshore; they are dry winds, blowing from the hot, dry land to a cool sea, and they bring no rain.

The world as a whole is not short of good soil to produce crops; it is only short of water. And no continent is as deficient as Australia. Perhaps two-thirds of the continent receives too little rainfall for crops to be grown. The only extensive river system, that of the Murray and its tributaries, provides some water for irrigation, and fruit orchards have been established along its banks. But the Murray basin embraces only southeastern Australia. No rivers flow through the dead heart of the continent to bring water from the wetter to the drier parts, and the local streams are short stream-beds, dry most of the time. They grow smaller and more muddy until they at last lose themselves in the desert. Australia has no Nile or Indus, and that is the great misfortune of this continent.

Yet the interior of Australia does not depend entirely on rainfall and rivers for its small supply of water. Most rocks contain water, which can be reached by wells and pumped to the surface, and Australia is unusually rich in such sources. Water-bearing basins underlie large areas, especially in the eastern half of the continent, including some areas that are now desert. Furthermore the water from some of these water bodies gushes to the surface when tapped by a drill hole, and is available to water stock or irrigate cropland. This so-called artesian water is an important factor in using some of the drier lands of the interior. Most extensive of these is the Great Artesian Basin, which covers much of the interior of Queensland and New South Wales. Smaller artesian basins occur on the northern, western, and southern margins of the Australian desert. If rainfall should fail, as it not infrequently does, it can in these areas be supplemented from within the rocks.

A shortage of water on the continent is, as it were, matched by a shortage of labor. Australia has always had a labor problem. Immigration from Europe was slow. Perhaps it was the association of Australia with criminals and debtors that deterred free settlers from coming; perhaps it was the distance from Europe, the high cost of the voyage, and the consequent problems of importing necessities and exporting Australia's staple products. Even today, after the Commonwealth government has for many years been encouraging immigration, its population is only as large as that of Illinois in the United States.

As we have seen, the far northern part of the continent has a hot, humid climate. Europeans thought the climate too extreme for them to work in the fields and mines, and determined that if this area were to be developed, it should be done with non-European labor.

The native Australian could not be used. They were never numerous, and today the total number of full-blood and half-caste does not exceed 70,000. The Europeans found their way of life to be the most primitive known to them. The aborigines knew nothing of agriculture or of the use of metals, and they lived by hunting and collecting. They had not progressed to the bow and arrow, and they knocked down their prey with the curved boomerang. Neither in quantity nor in quality could the aboriginal Australians provide the farm labor which the European settlers needed.

The Australians resorted to the people of the South Sea Islands for their labor force. The peoples here were as varied as the islands themselves, but all were incomparably more advanced than the aboriginal Australian. They were tempted by the promise of monetary rewards to enlist for work on the plantations of northern Australia, and when voluntary enlistments failed to meet the need for agricultural labor, the Australians were not above using more forceful methods of persuasion.

These laborers were known as Kanakas, a Polynesian word meaning "man," and the process of recruiting, which in its essentials differed little from slave-raiding, came to be called "black-birding." Many thousands were brought to Queensland and with their aid, the cultivation of sugar and other tropical crops spread through parts of the damp coastal region. Without them these areas would probably never have been opened up.

But how to keep them in the areas where their labor was most wanted? There was nothing to prevent them, as soon as they had fulfilled their contract obligations, from spreading south into New South Wales and Victoria, where the climatic argument for using Kanaka labor did not apply and where the population aimed to exclude rivals who were prepared to work for less.

The presence of the Kanakas was not the only problem raised by the presence of non-European peoples. Australia's nearest neighbors were the densely peopled lands of East and Southeast Asia. The Chinese in particular were spreading at this time through Malaya, the Japanese were settling in Hawaii; and the population pressure behind their outward movement was such that Australians began to fear that Asian peoples might be invading their own shores before many years had passed. So the internal danger—that of the competition of Kanaka labor with European—and the external—the threat of unrestricted immigration from Asia—led Australians to close their doors.

The policy of excluding colored peoples, the so-called "White Australian Policy," was not adopted without opposition. Queensland, the hot, humid northeastern province which was coming to the fore as a sugar producer, objected strongly and threatened even to separate itself from the rest of Australia. A situation somewhat analogous to that in the United States a century ago developed, with Queensland threatening to "secede" in order to retain the right to employ colored labor. Queensland, however, did not press her point; the need for political unity within Australia, in the face of gathering problems of population growth and aggression in Eastern Asia, proved to be too great, and Queensland along with the remaining five states, was merged into the Commonwealth of Australia in 1901.

In the end most of the Kanakas were shipped back to the islands whence they had come, and the Australian government introduced a drastic immigration law. A literacy test was introduced for would-be immigrants, and was made so stringent and applied with such discrimination that all unwanted immigrants were excluded. Australia thus has the distinction of being a white man's continent, for the remaining aboriginals are not to be reckoned with and are in fact commonly excluded from the population figures.

White Australia was achieved at a high price. The sugar fields of Queensland are now worked with white labor; sugar in Australia costs about three times as much as elsewhere; and large areas across the north, which are capable of producing crops, remain under forest and savanna because Australians are unable or unwilling to work there. The resources of Australia are thus far from fully utilized.

In parts of Southeast Asia the pressure of population has not only led to the almost complete utilization of resources, but leaves part of the population underemployed. It is true that Australia could absorb only a minute fraction of the continuing population increase in Asia, and could not provide even a short-term solution to the problem of over-population. Nevertheless the existence of empty lands so near to over-crowded must necessarily raise hopes and ambitions in the minds of Asians and fears among the Australians.

The Australian federation came in part as a response to the dangers and problems that have just been discussed. The early settlements were a fringe of colonies around the edge of a barren and empty continent. These colonies grew in almost complete isolation from one another. Overland communication between them was slow, difficult, and costly, if not actually impossible. Contacts were maintained by sea, and in fact the hinterlands of each of the larger and more important colonies were administered as separate and distinct units.

Thus it happened that six colonies emerged, and each grew into a self-governing state. New South Wales was the hinterland of the port of Sydney; Victoria grew from the colony and port of Melbourne; Queensland was in origin the tropical coast of northeastern Australia. South Australia grew from Adelaide, and Western Australia from the city of Perth in the far west of the continent. The island of Tasmania made the sixth colony.

The so-called Northern Territory, consisting of much of the arid interior and part of the north coast of Australia, formed part of South Australia at the time when the Commonwealth was formed. But it presented serious administrative problems; at this time its population was under 1,000 and even now is only about 21,000. It had no railroad and its northern parts were inaccessible, except by sea from Adelaide. In 1911 South Australia exercised its right under the Australian constitution to transfer this unwanted territory to the Federal Government, and it is now administered by the Commonwealth.

Before federation each state had its own postal and railroad system. Co-operation between them had been minimal. Transportation was never planned on a continental basis, and the Australian railroads today have no less than three different railroad gauges.

Drawing the six colonies into a single state met with strong resistance from the deeply entrenched separatism of the colonies. It took strong persuasion by Great Britain as well as active fears of colored immigration and Asian imperialism to bring the six together. Even so, the states retained extensive rights and privileges, and each continues to attract the major part of the Australian's loyalty. Indeed it has been said that, until quite recently, the only manifestation of an essentially Australian consciousness or enthusiasm has been on the occasion of a cricket match between Australia and England.

The chief market for Australia's products has always been in Europe, and Western Europe is halfway round the world from Australia. Today it is a five weeks' journey in a freighter, and during the years when Australia was being opened up, the sailing ships took several times as long, oftentimes several months. Distance, of necessity, made Australia an exporter of those farm products that could stand a long voyage without deteriorating. The accidental introduction of the merino sheep, coupled with the excellence of the grasslands of southeastern Australia, determined that wool should be the staple export. For very many years it was almost the only export. Ships loaded raw uncombed wool straight from the shearing sheds in the "outback" in the ports of Melbourne and Sydney, and carried it to the ports of Western Europe, returning with cargoes of factory goods. The pattern of trade has changed over the past century. Mutton and lamb have been added to wool. Australia has itself become an industrial country, and exports, though mainly agricultural in origin, are more varied. But still raw wool makes up almost 40 per cent of the total exports; the rest is made up of meat, dairy produce, fruit, grain, and—of negligible importance—ores and minerals. Wool is the largest single item, and Australia is still the world's largest producer and exporter of wool.

But agricultural production within Australia has been greatly diversified. The refrigerator ship, which came into regular use about 1880, the growing population, and the widening demand within Australia stimulated a wider range of production. Sheep runs once covered the hills within a few miles of Sydney and Melbourne. Then as population increased and land values rose, a more intensive use was made of the land, and these areas were plowed and sown with wheat and the sheep were pushed deeper into the interior. Mixed farming, dairying, and the growing of produce for the great cities then came in, and wheat farming was itself forced farther from the coast.

This is a familiar course of development, the dirt farmer driving out the rancher; we have seen it in the American and Canadian prairies, in the pampas of Argentina; and in the Russian steppe also the peasant replaced the Tartar and the Cossack. The agricultural pattern depends upon climate, but above all on access and transportation.

Agricultural Australia today lies like an arc, curving around the eastern and southeastern coast of the continent. Nearest the coast line and the ports is a belt of more intensive farming—sugar growing in the northern portion, with cotton and subtropical fruits, and toward the south of this area dairy, mixed, and fruit farming taking over. Farther inland are the wheat fields; Australia is the fifth largest producer of wheat, and the second largest exporter of it. Gradually the drier wheat lands merge into the sheep runs. It is not an abrupt transition, and it varies with the relative price of meat and wool. On their inner margin, the sheep runs merge into the bush.

In the extreme southwest this pattern is repeated, progressing in from the coast. Behind the port of Fremantle and around the city of Perth, capital of Western Australia, is a small region of Mediterranean climate, where fruit trees and the grapevine are grown. This passes eastward into wheat fields, and about two hundred miles inland the wheat fields pass into sheep runs, until these fade into the West Australian bush.

The diversification of agriculture during the later years of the nineteenth century was accompanied by the opening of mines and the establishment of factories. Australia consists mainly of a tableland of ancient rock, like South Africa and the highlands of Brazil, and such areas are often highly mineralized. Australia is no exception. Gold was found in the Great Dividing Range at about the same time that it was discovered in California in the middle of the nineteenth century. But the gold rush to Australia was restricted by the difficulties of getting there. Many miners came in search of gold, and some stayed to work in other fields.

Ore deposits occur at many points in the Great Dividing Range and over the vast plateaulike expanse of central and western Australia. Silver, lead, zinc—metals often found in close association with one another—gold and iron are the metals found most abundantly and worked the most intensively. The Broken Hill mines in western New South Wales make Australia one of the world's leading producers of lead and zinc, with about 17 per cent of the production of the former and nearly 10 per cent of the latter. Copper comes from Queensland, and gold from the Kalgoorlie and Coolgardie mines in the desert of Western Australia, though in the

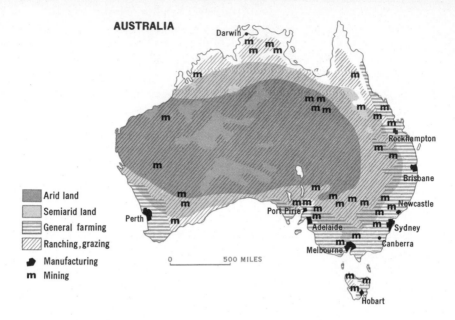

AUSTRALIA

Darwin

Rockhampton

Brisbane

Newcastle

Port Pirie

Perth

Adelaide

Sydney

Canberra

Melbourne

Hobart

Arid land
Semiarid land
General farming
Ranching, grazing
Manufacturing
m Mining

0 _____ 500 MILES

The modern Australian economy shows a significant shift. Manufacturing accounts for 63 per cent of the value of the country's total product.

production of neither of these does Australia contribute more than 3 per cent of the world's output.

In the long run, perhaps it is the iron ores that hold the greatest promise for the future of Australia. They occur the most abundantly in the tropical north, and near the desert coast of South Australia. Only the most accessible deposits have hitherto been exploited, but in all probability large reserves exist also in the still little-known interior.

Those geological conditions which make it possible for Australia to have large and varied resources in the metalliferous minerals make the widespread occurrence of coal and petroleum an improbability. Nevertheless there are a number of coal fields along the eastern coast, between the Great Dividing Range and the ocean, and these make Australia the leading coal producer in the Southern Hemisphere.

Australia is rapidly becoming an industrial country. Already the value of factory products greatly exceeds those of farms, sheep range, and mine taken together. In 1958–59, out of an estimated value for all the products of Australia of almost seven billion dollars, manufacturing accounted for 63 per cent, mining for 4 per cent, and agriculture in all its branches for only 33 per cent. The population, which now exceeds 10,000,000, is sufficient to provide a market for many branches of factory industry. Iron smelting and steel making are being expanded, an automobile industry has been established, and the manufacture of textiles and chemicals has been introduced.

The most important centers of Australian industry are close to the original settlements in New South Wales and Victoria. Both Sydney and Melbourne are great industrial cities, the former with a population of over two million, the latter only slightly smaller. Coal is mined near Sydney, and iron and steel industries have been established at coastal sites, at Newcastle, eighty miles to the north of Sydney, on a site near the coal field and accessible to ore freighted around the coast from South Australia, and at Wollongong, south of Sydney. More recently an iron works has also been established at Whyalla, on the coast of South Australia, where the situation is reversed; the ore occurs nearby, and the fuel is brought by sea from New South Wales.

The industrial growth which has characterized Australia in recent years has served to increase the size and importance of its few large cities. In three out of the six states, more than half of the population lives in its capital and largest city; two-thirds of the population of Victoria live in Melbourne, and in Tasmania and Queensland the capital cities have about a third of the states' population. This phenomenon has developed from the early focus of life, commerce, and transportation on a few widely separated centers of settlement. It has made Australia a country of a few large cities and of many small towns.

Largest is Sydney, the oldest permanent settlement, founded in 1788 when the earliest party of settlers had found neighboring Botany Bay not wholly suited to their needs. Today Sydney, with its 2,165,000 inhabitants, spreads out over the rolling hills which enclose the branching waterways of its harbor. Sydney Harbor is famous not only as one of the most beautiful, but also as one of the deepest and most commodious in the world, and through it passes about a half of Australia's seaborne commerce.

Second in age and size among the cities of Australia is Melbourne, the capital of Victoria and second port of Australia. The city spreads along the shore of a deep, protected inlet, Port Phillip Bay, which penetrates deeply into the southern shore of Victoria. Melbourne has a population of about 1,890,000; the second largest city, Geelong, about 90,000, and most of the remaining cities have less than 50,000 people.

Adelaide is a smaller capital, and of a less populous state. It has no port facilities, but is closely linked with its docks in Port Adelaide, seven miles away. Like Sydney and Melbourne, it is a focus of railways which fan out over the southeastern part of the state where most of the agriculture and mining are carried on.

Western Australia, we have seen, is mostly desert and bush, and the population is concentrated in its southwestern corner. Here is the city of Perth, built on the Swan River, about ten miles from its mouth. At the river's mouth is Fremantle, the chief port of Western Australia.

In Queensland the original settlements were less concentrated; they were spread out along the narrow coastal plain which stretches from the New South Wales border in the south to Cape York, 1,400 miles away to the north. Although Brisbane, established on the Brisbane River about 14 miles from the ocean, now has over a third of the state's population, there is a succession of small towns of about 50,000 people or less, almost regularly spaced along the coast to the north: Rockhampton, Mackay, Townsville, Cairns, from each of which a railroad runs up over the hills and into the grazing country of the interior.

Hobart is the smallest capital and lies in the smallest state, Tasmania. By the standards of Australian capital cities it is quite small—only about 112,000 people—and it lies on a sheltered opening in the rugged and beautiful southeast coast of the island.

Two other cities deserve mention, not because of their size—for they are among the smallest—but because of their political importance. Darwin, in size no more than a village, lies on the tropical north coast, where it was briefly attacked by the Japanese during the Second World War. It is the port and the chief administrative center of the Northern Territory, and the terminus of a short railroad into the grasslands of the interior. The other is Canberra, the Commonwealth or Federal capital, lying up in the rolling hills of New South Wales between Sydney and Melbourne. The site was chosen as far back as 1909, and the construction of government buildings was begun in 1913. But still it has no more than 45,000 people. It is an unfinished city of strikingly beautiful and original architecture, of distant vistas, like Washington, planned in its design and specialized in its function.

Australia's growth has been conditioned by the problems of transportation and travel, and transportation remains one of the biggest problems faced by Australia today. Much of the road and railroad system has been built through sparsely populated countryside, and its cost of maintenance is high. Some was built entirely for political and strategic reasons.

As in the case of British Columbia, Canada, one of the conditions exacted by Western Australia as the price of joining the Australian Commonwealth was the building of a railroad westward from Adelaide in South Australia to Perth. For most of its length this railroad runs across the open barren plateau of desert—here known appropriately as the Nullarbor (no-tree) Plain. Unlike its Canadian counterpart, few trains use the road, and its economic advantage is outweighed by its political significance. The role of the railroads, in every way possible, is now being taken over by airlines.

A north-south railway through the central Australian desert was begun but never finished; there remains a distance of five hundred miles in the Northern Territory, between Alice Springs and Daly Waters, with only a road. Traffic is insufficient to justify the very heavy cost of railroad construction. The chief need for the railroad is strategic—access to the militarily exposed and thinly peopled north coast—and this is at present being met by a highway over which trucks can carry supplies into the far north, while passengers most often travel by air.

Australia is today the least populous of the larger states of the world; it is in many respects underdeveloped, and it lies remote and isolated. Its nearest neighbors, Indonesia and the states of Southeast Asia, are not likely to be its friends. Australia's policy of excluding all except white immigrants offends them, while Australia's unused land arouses their envy. In this position, Australia's policy is to encourage immigration from Europe; to develop further her industries, especially her heavy industries, and thus to increase her political and military strength; and to strengthen her ties of friendship with the United States and the Commonwealth and with her neighbor, New Zealand, "four days . . . over a cold, dark, inhospitable sea."

NEW ZEALAND

Among the islands of the Pacific Ocean, those that make up New Zealand are in every way exceptional. They are larger, more mountainous, and more populous. New Zealand is made up of two islands—together having an area of 103,736 square miles, about equal to that of Colorado in the United States—and a few small islands, of which the largest is Stewart Island, off the southern end of South Island.

New Zealand was discovered in 1642 by Tasman, who named it for the Dutch province of Zeeland in which he was born, and it was explored by Cook; but the beginning of European settlement did not come until early in the nineteenth century. Unlike Australia, New Zealand had a native population that was able, intelligent and warlike, and capable of offering a formidable resistance to the newcomers. These were the Maoris, who had come to New Zealand not long before from the islands of Polynesia. They had settled in the North Island of New Zealand where they had built up a society with its own distinctive culture.

From the first New Zealand has experienced the consequences of its remoteness. It was the last really habitable land to be discovered; no state was in any hurry to take over the islands, and Great Britain, after proclaiming its sovereignty, took no steps for many years to follow this up with actual occupation. Meanwhile New Zealand had become the haunt of desperadoes of all kinds, confident that here they were beyond the arm of any nation's law. Conditions came to such a pass that in 1840 Great Britain extended her effective control to New Zealand, appointed a governor, and began to encourage regular settlement. North Island, in many ways the more attractive, contained most of the Maoris, with whom the white settlers were obliged to fight a series of wars. Settlement of South Island was less troubled in this respect, but at the same time it was more restricted by the physical environment.

New Zealand lies within the belt of the westerly winds, and as no part is more than eighty miles from the sea, the climate is mild and humid at all times. South Island, however, is mountainous. The Southern Alps, which border its west coast, rise to over 12,349 feet in Mount Cook. In the south they have been eroded into fjords of great beauty. To the east lie the plains of the South Island. These plains are cut off by the mountains from the westerly, rain-bearing winds and are in consequence very much drier than might be expected in a fairly small island at this latitude. The grasslands which have resulted proved to be admirably suited to sheep farming.

Here, too, the coming of the refrigerator ship revolutionized the economy of this region. Sheep were raised, not so much for their fleece, as in Australia, though the export of wool was important, as for lamb and mutton, which were exported chilled and frozen. Canterbury lamb, from the Canterbury Plains of South Island, is familiar in the stores of Great Britain.

North Island is more irregularly shaped than South, and it has a central mass of mountains around which the plains are distributed. Most of the mountains are volcanic, and some volcanoes are still active. Asso-

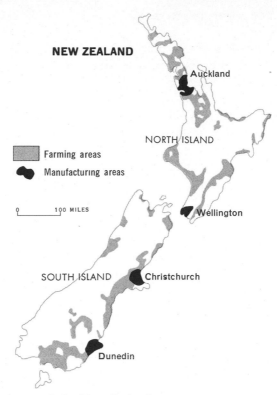

NEW ZEALAND

Auckland

NORTH ISLAND

Farming areas

Manufacturing areas

0   100 MILES

Wellington

SOUTH ISLAND   Christchurch

Dunedin

Farming is still the mainstay of the New Zealand economy.

ciated with the volcanism are geysers and hot springs, and not unrelated to it is the liability of North Island to earthquakes. North Island is warmer than South, and rainfall is more evenly distributed over it. It is more suited to dairy cattle than South Island, and the production of butter, cheese, and bacon for export form its most important branch of agriculture.

The exports of New Zealand are made up almost exclusively of agricultural produce—wool and hides, frozen meat, butter, cheese, and other animal products. Imports consist mainly of factory-made goods. The products of the metallurgical and machine industries dominate, followed by textiles and clothing, chemicals, and such foodstuffs as tea, coffee, and sugar, which New Zealand is incapable of producing.

The many branches of agriculture make up together by far the most important occupation in New Zealand, which is predominantly a farming country. The largest cities are the ports of Auckland and Wellington in North Island, and of Christchurch and Dunedin in South. New Zealand is a great deal less urbanized than Australia; its total population of about 2,466,000 is only a little greater than that of the metropolitan area of Sydney.

The largest city is Auckland with nearly 500,000 people, located on the narrow subtropical panhandle of North Island. It lies where the land is narrow, and though the city fronts on to Hauraki Gulf and the Pacific Ocean, it has also docks a few miles away on an inlet of the Tasman Sea, Manukau Harbour. Wellington lies at the southern extremity of North Island, looking across the Cook Strait to the mountains of South Island. It was made the capital of New Zealand, replacing Auckland, because it is the most centrally located of New Zealand cities; its population totals about 250,000.

The largest city of South Island is Christchurch, with almost 225,000 people. It lies on the margin of the sheep-raising Canterbury Plains, and eight miles inland from its small port of Lyttelton. Dunedin, the port and chief urban center of the far south, lies at the head of a small coastal inlet. Its hinterland is mountainous, and its trade small, but it is the most southerly harbor in New Zealand, and has many times served as the port of departure for expeditions to the Antarctic. Its population has risen to over 100,000. Most other urban settlements are very small; their function mainly being to serve the needs of their surrounding agricultural countryside; and the balance between farm and factory is much the same as we find in one of the agricultural states of the United States.

Farms in New Zealand are large; their average size is over five hundred acres, and comparatively few have an area of less than fifty acres. Farms, mostly owned by the farmers of English origin, are efficiently managed and highly mechanized. Only in this way can New Zealand compete from a distance of thirteen thousand miles in the European market for meat and dairy products.

This, of course, raises serious problems for New Zealand. The country is dependent upon an overseas market for its farm product, and this market is necessarily a very distant one; and, as most of it is in Great Britain, it could not possibly be more distant. New Zealand lamb and bacon, butter and cheese, sell in the British market in competition with the products of much more favorably placed Denmark and Ireland. The New Zealand products, however, in common with those of the whole Commonwealth of nations have the advantage of a tariff preference in the British market.

New Zealand's dependence upon imports for the supply of manufactured goods could, of course, be reduced by building up factory industries there. New Zealand is not without fuel; there are coal deposits and the hydroelectric power potential is large, but the population, and thus the size of the domestic market, is small. A factory large enough to be competitive would, in many fields of production, be too large for New Zealand. New Zealand cannot hope to manufacture automobiles or railroad equipment, for example, because its market is too small to absorb the output of a factory large enough to be efficient.

New Zealand is thus economically weak and vulnerable. It is also weak militarily. It is too small in population to be able to operate munitions factories or to maintain an effective navy. It is dependent upon its friends and allies. Membership in the British Commonwealth insures, at least for the time, a privileged position in the British market, and partnership in the South East Asia Treaty Organization gives her some political guarantee against attack.

Australia and New Zealand, though made up of islands, have a twofold frontier. One lies to the north and northeast, in Indonesia and the islands of the Pacific Ocean. The other is to the south more than fifteen hundred miles beyond the stormy southern ocean, where the Antarctic continent reaches on to the South Pole.

THE ANTARCTIC

The immense land mass of Antarctica, almost twice the size of Australia, is the least-known part of the earth's surface. This is due in part to its location, over and around the South Pole, with a protective barrier of pack ice guarding the approaches to it. But in part it is also due to the fact that it is covered by a cap of ice, many thousands of feet in thickness, which masks the continent almost completely.

The rocks of which Antarctica is composed show through only around the margins of the ice sheet. Over the continent as a whole they are not only covered, but also depressed by the weight of the ice. It is probable that these rocks resemble those of most of Australia and South Africa, which means that there is, at the very least, a strong possibility that they contain minerals of economic value. Mining is at present impracticable, and it is likely to remain so for very many years.

The Antarctic continent was approached only very gradually during the eighteenth and nineteenth centuries. In 1773 Captain Cook, in the course of his second great voyage of discovery, crossed the Antarctic

Circle and reached the ice barrier which guarded the approach to the unknown continent. "It was, indeed, my opinion," he wrote, "as well as the opinion of most on board, that this ice extended quite to the Pole, or, perhaps, joined on some land, to which it had been fixed from the earliest time."

One by one the bleak barren islands of the southern ocean—South Georgia, the South Orkney and South Shetland Islands in the South Atlantic, and Kerguelen to the southwest of Australia itself—were discovered. The whaling fleets which frequented these southern waters, added greatly to our knowledge of them, but the southern continent itself long remained unseen. Between 1819 and 1821 the Russian explorer Bellingshausen circumnavigated the polar continent and added very greatly to man's knowledge of it; this was the only Russian venture into Antarctica before the recent Soviet participation in the work of the Geophysical Year. But the Antarctic continent itself was not seen until 1843 when James Clark Ross penetrated the pack ice and at last saw the snow-capped ranges and smoking summit of the active volcano of Mount Erebus, in what he named Victoria Land.

Later in the century explorers and whalers combined to piece together a fairly complete picture of the southern seas. Then, early in the present century, expeditions led by the Swede, Nordenskjöld, and the Englishman, Shackleton, began to press their explorations into the interior of the continent. The next task was to reach the South Pole itself. In 1911 two expeditions set out to achieve this, one under the leadership of the Norwegian Roald Amundsen, the other commanded by the Englishman, Captain Robert F. Scott. They set out from different bases on the Antarctic continent, to the south of New Zealand. It was a race to the Pole. The Norwegian party got there first and returned safely to its base. Scott's party was slower. It reached the Pole a week or two later and on its return journey ran into severe weather, failed to reach its next food store, and the five members who had gone on this last part of the journey perished.

For the next generation expeditions were less ambitious; they limited themselves to lesser objectives of greater scientific value than merely getting to the Pole. Details of the coast of Antarctica were filled in, and flights across the Pole, notably those of the American Admiral Byrd, not only added greatly to knowledge of the region but showed also that there were easier ways of exploring this continent than trudging across it on foot, pulling a sled.

Modern science has made exploration much easier than in the days of Scott and Amundsen. Subsequent voyages in specially constructed ships have filled in our knowledge of the coast line. In 1958-59 a combined onslaught on the Antarctic was made by a group of nations, each undertaking a limited task of scientific value and importance. As part of its contribution the United States maintained a station at the Pole for a whole year, observing the weather, terrestrial magnetism, and other phenomena. The contours and thickness of the icecap were examined; temperatures were recorded, and isothermal maps made for its surface, and the distinction of having the lowest recorded temperature was stolen from Oimekon, in Siberia, and transferred to an unnamed spot on the Antarctic continent.

Sovereignty over parts of the Antarctic continent has been claimed by no less than seven countries—Argentina, Australia, Chile, France, Norway, New Zealand, and the United Kingdom, but the United States which has hitherto made no territorial claims, has also not recognized any of

The United States makes no claim to Antarctica and recognizes none of the claims.

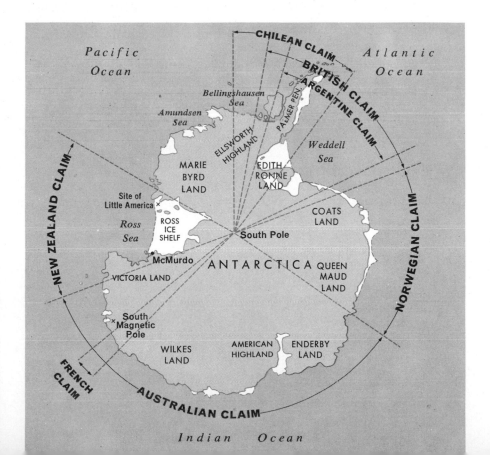

these claims by other nations. But sovereignty here has little meaning. There is no permanently resident population, or is it likely that in the foreseeable future there ever will be. It is impossible to mark boundaries on the very slowly moving surface of the ice, and no profit to be had from doing so. Some of the claims to the sovereignty in Antarctica are over-lapping, but the states with rights here have agreed not to press their demands, but to demilitarize the area and to use it only for scientific and peaceful purposes.

The Antarctic continent, it has already been demonstrated, has re-sources of minerals that are of economic importance. These include coal, tin, lead, and copper, and it is reasonable to suppose that many others also occur. Their exploitation, however, lies in the distant future, for the technical difficulties of mining in the Antarctic are so great as to deprive these resources of all practical value at present.

THE PACIFIC

The other frontier of Australia and New Zealand lies to the north and presents problems more urgent and more serious than those which the empty waste of Antarctica can offer. For these territories are far from empty, and they are so distributed through the ocean that they constitute a path to the southern continent.

Nearest of these is the island of New Guinea, which lies only a hundred miles across the Torres Strait from Queensland. This strangely shaped island is at present divided. The western half, Irian, is held by the Dutch, who managed to retain it when the rest of their East Indian Empire was transformed into the Republic of Indonesia, despite the claims to it by the Republic of Indonesia, which again in 1962 pressed its claim. The eastern half, once made up of a German and a British colony, is controlled by the government of Australia. It is a large, moun-tainous, forested island. Its population is sparse and primitive; much of the interior of the island remains unexplored and unmapped. During the Second World War, New Guinea was occupied by the Japanese, and since their expulsion the Australian government has maintained as firm a grip on its share of the island as the geographical conditions permit. The population of New Guinea is not known with any degree of cer-tainty, but for the island as a whole is estimated to be about 2,200,000. The chief settlements and the administrative centers of West—that is Dutch or Netherlands New Guinea—and East New Guinea are respectively Hollandia and Port Moresby, both of them no more than large villages with some port facilities and a handful of white residents.

Away to the northeast of the Queensland coast, at least eight hundred miles from the coast of Australia, there stretch chains of islands, sometimes known collectively as Melanesia, the region of "large islands." Hundreds of them dot the surface of the ocean; most are small, even minute; only a few are large enough to have a sizable population. No one who remembers the battle of the Coral Sea, and the bloody fighting from island to island during the Second World War, is likely to underrate their importance to Australia.

These and many island groups that spread eastward and northeastward across the Pacific Ocean toward Hawaii and the coast of Chile are of two kinds. Some are high and rugged, rising to sharp peaks which stand many thousands of feet above the sea. Others are low, flat, and built of the sand which is formed by the ceaseless beat of the waves on the banks of the coral.

These two types of island are, in fact, closely related. Both rise from the great depths of the deep sea plain or floor. In the case of the "high" islands, the rock, often the product of volcanic eruption, breaks the surface of the sea and rises high above it. The "lows" are created by the building activities of the small coral polyps on rocky foundations which rise from the ocean floor, but fail to reach its surface.

Coral islands may be of almost any shape, but most often they form a lagoon, a ring of patches of coral enclosing a rounded area of shallow water. Such a form is known as an atoll. Bikini, in the Marshall Islands, is an atoll, and recent nuclear explosions have taken place within the lagoon. The islands are made up of dead coral, with a growing fringe of living coral around the margin. Finely broken-up fragments of coral in turn form a kind of soil in which palms and a few other plants can root, and they in turn contribute humus to the soil.

There appears to be neither order nor pattern in the distribution of the islands of the Pacific, except that they are more numerous in the south and west than they are in the north and east. Yet a closer examination shows that their distribution bears some relationship to that of the neighboring land masses. They are—both the high and the low islands—merely the exposed summits of submarine ridges. Like the Aleutian, the Kuril, and the Ryukyu Islands, they continue, however vaguely and imperceptibly, the directions of mountain and hill ranges on the continents themselves. They form curving lines or festoons, drawn

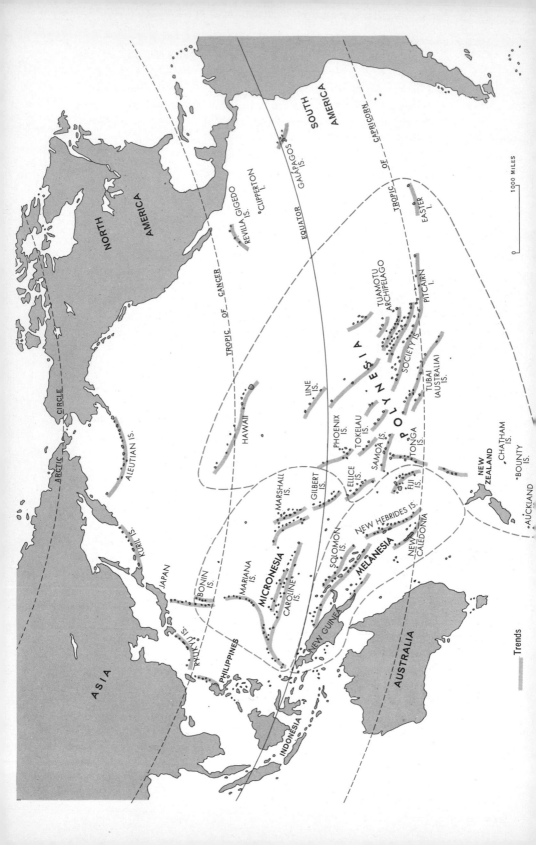

through the oceans, rather like the pattern of curving mountain chains on the land.

The island chains of the Pacific are best thought of as lying in a series of roughly concentric curves, to the north, northeast, and east of Australia. In the first and nearest of these curves lie New Guinea and New Zealand, and about halfway between them, the small French-owned island of New Caledonia, which along with Canada contributes most of the world's production of nickel. Only two or three hundred miles to the northeast is the next line of islands, that which includes the Bismarck Archipelago, administered by Australia, the British-held Solomon Islands, and the New Hebrides, jointly ruled in a quaint con-dominium by Great Britain and France.

The succeeding arcs of islands which collectively make up Micronesia, or the region of "small islands," are longer, and more interrupted. The widely spread atolls of the Carolines, once German, then ruled as a mandate by the Japanese, and now held in trust by the United States, stretch out from east of the Philippines toward Nauru, famous for its phosphate deposits, and then, curving to the south, to the Fiji group and back toward New Zealand. North of the Caroline Islands is Guam, the first of an arc of islands which runs through the Mariana and the Bonin Islands to the Japanese mainland.

Fiji, a group of islands which passed under British rule in 1874, is one of the larger and more prosperous of the island groups. It is made up of high islands, large enough to be significant though small exporters of sugar and coconut products.

Next come the Marshall, Gilbert, Ellice, and the Tonga or Friendly Islands, each group made up of a great many small coral atolls. Several contain deposits of phosphate which is quarried and exported for use as a fertilizer. Their chief agricultural export is copra, the dried meat of the coconut.

Out beyond the Marshall-Tonga arc, the islands are more scattered. They still occur most often in chains varying from a hundred to a thou-sand miles in length, but there is less pattern and order among the arcs and chains of islands themselves. This is Polynesia, literally the region of the "many islands" which lie scattered in disorderly array over the Central Pacific. Ellice Island, geographically in the Marshall-Tonga arc, is the most western of the islands peopled by Polynesians.

In the south Polynesia includes Samoa, a group of rugged, volcanic islands, clothed with a lush tropical vegetation; a new state, Western

Samoa, has been formed from those islands formerly held by New Zealand, but the other islands of Samoa remain under United States control. Polynesia also includes the Cook Islands, the French-held Society Islands, discovered by Cook and named for the Royal Society of London which had supported his expedition, and the thousand atolls of the spreading Tuamotu Archipelago. Largest of the Society Islands is Tahiti, like Samoa, a volcanic island of great beauty, where Robert Louis Stevenson lived and Gauguin painted the Polynesian women and the rugged mountain landscape.

Out beyond the reefs of Tuamotu lies Pitcairn, a small, rocky and volcanic island of only two square miles, where the mutineers of the *Bounty* settled in 1790 and remained, unknown to the rest of the world, until they were discovered in 1808. Descendants of this group, to the number of about two hundred, still live on Pitcairn.

Even farther out, and only 2,300 miles from the South American coast, is Easter Island, one of the most remote and romantic islands in the world. It was discovered by a Dutch sailor on Easter Day, 1722, and soon became known for the gigantic stone statues, carved here by some unknown people at some undetermined date. Whether the inspiration that led to this enormous work came from the west, from Polynesia, or from South America to the east across the empty Pacific Ocean has not been settled.

Farther to the north among the islands of Polynesia are New Zealand's Tokelau Islands, the Line Islands, and the Phoenix Islands. In the last group are the Canton and Enderbury Islands, held jointly by Great Britain and the United States for the sake of the airfields that are used as staging points in long Pacific flights.

The islands of the South Pacific have become almost legendary for their soft and sunny climate, their freedom from the harsh rigors of winter in the middle latitudes, their fertility and the general ease of living which they make possible. Writers, artists, and musicians, from Robert Louis Stevenson and Gauguin to James Michener and Rodgers and Hammerstein, have used the setting for their creative efforts. Yet the popular image is not wholly accurate. The islands are not all fertile, and many of the coral atolls are dry and barren. Typhoons or tropical storms of exceptional violence sometimes occur, and the native peoples include head-hunters and cannibals as well as the gentle creatures of fiction.

The larger islands are visited more or less regularly by ships. The Fiji Islands, for example, carry on a quite large trade in sugar and coconut products. But the smaller and more remote—and that is most of the islands of the Pacific—very rarely see a ship put into their shores. They remain primitive and self-sufficing in conditions far removed from those of the tropical world of the imagination.

Away to the north, the outermost of the Polynesian islands, is the Hawaiian group. It stretches for 1,700 miles from Kure in the northwest to Hawaii itself in the southeast. It is, like most other Pacific Islands, made up of the summits of a chain of volcanic mountains which rise through complex foothills, deeply submerged in the ocean, to summits of over 13,000 feet above the sea level. The volcanic peaks of Hawaii, still smoking and active, and the mountains of neighboring Maui are the highest within the Pacific basin. The Hawaiian group differs also in another respect. They are part of the United States, and as such have already been described and discussed. They are more developed than any other island group in the Pacific. Despite their population, drawn predominantly from Polynesia, Japan, and the Asian mainland, these islands belong to the Western World. Though the last of the island groups of Polynesia, and belonging to Asia or Australasia according to how one regards them, they may also be considered the first of the United States, separated from the continental states by more than two thousand miles of empty ocean.

With the return to the territory of the United States, we have in the words of Shakespeare's Puck, "put a girdle round the earth," though we may have taken a good deal more than Puck's "forty minutes." We have examined as fully as was possible between the covers of a single book each continent and each country. We have seen, though briefly and superficially, their resources and their beauty, their problems and their poverty. It is time now, on that journey across the empty ocean to the mainland from whence we began, to gather together the threads and the arguments that have been started; to make comparisons, and to draw what conclusions this examination has made possible about man and his future on "this goodly frame, the earth."

14 THE TWO WORLDS

There remaineth yet very much land to be possessed.

—Book of Joshua

In the last chapter our journey about the earth took us to Australia, that vast and still largely empty continent, upon whose spaces many crowded people have looked with envy. The world's empty spaces have provided one of the themes of this book; another, written in a kind of counterpoint with it, has been the theme of the crowded lands, where people have insufficient space to grow their crops and satisfy their everyday needs. Two more such themes, also closely related, the one the reverse of the other, have been well-being and poverty. It is time to draw them all together, to see if from the facts that have been related, any general conclusions can be drawn about man's relations with this planet on which he lives.

The map has given us a crude measure of the density of population. The maps of gross national product, pages 144–45, and of food consumption, pages 148–49, are a rough measure of the variations in human welfare, incomplete and inadequate because they omit so many factors in human welfare and because they generalize for too large an area. But they are the best we have, and upon them, supplemented by what has been given in this book, the argument of this chapter must rest.

It is easier to explain the well-being of the rich and prosperous nations than the backwardness of the poor. The former possess resources, and show skill and ingenuity in using them. By implication the others do not. It is easy enough to ascribe the relative prosperity of the peoples of Western Europe and North America to their generous endowment in agricultural and mineral resources, and to their wise use of them. It is not so easy to explain why other and basically similar areas have made little material progress, and it is very difficult, if not impossible, to ex-

551

plain why today we find degradation and backwardness in areas which once stood in the forefront of material progress.

The difficulty has not deterred many people from proposing their simple explanations for such complex phenomena. The fact is, however, that there are no simple explanations. The more these major phenomena of human geography and history are studied, the more complex, the more inscrutable do they seem to become.

There, first of all, are the racists who explain progress and backwardness in terms of race, of biologically inherited characteristics within allegedly homogeneous groups of people. This is a simple and dangerous view which appeals to simple and uninformed people. Such homogeneous racial groups have not been identified, and the qualities that matter in the human race are socially not biologically inherited.

Then there are those who explain it all in terms of climate and the vagaries and variations of climate. They can point to a respectable ancestry for their opinions. Aristotle, Plato, and Hippocrates all considered climate to be the dominant factor in the energy, the initiative, and the achievement of peoples. Hippocrates, for example, was quite specific: "The deficiency of spirit and courage observable in the human inhabitants of Asia has for its principal cause the low margin of seasonal variability in the temperature of that continent." This lack of spirit and courage in Asians is not as apparent to us as it was to Hippocrates in the fourth century b.c. Hippocrates has had his successors in very recent years who have refined and refurbished his theory, introducing the fact that climates have changed and fluctuated during the span of human history, and finding in this the cause of the rise and decline of civilizations. "The suddenness and severity of storms in the United States are highly stimulating. . . . The passive Egyptian peasants know nothing of any such stimulus."

Such a line of thinking is fatalistic; it implies that there is no possibility of progress, development, and change in Egypt, and other places which share its climatic disabilities, because its backwardness is allegedly rooted in those physical circumstances which man lacks the skill to alter and adapt.

Climatic fluctuations there have been, but none of such magnitude within historical times as to provide conditions that could bring about the decline of a civilization. It is as difficult to lay man's inequality against the door of climate as it is against that of race.

Toynbee, in his monumental *A Study of History,* looks at this problem from the opposite side. He does not see an immutable nature controlling the destinies of man; instead he visualizes man as challenged and stimulated, frightened and deterred by nature. He sees the Arctic, the equatorial forests, and the tropical deserts—all of them savage environments—presenting a challenge to man, daring him to settle in their midst and live on their meager resources. He visualizes rich and fertile regions encouraging man to settle and to multiply, assuring him of abundant and steady returns on his labor, and ease and well-being. Then he visualizes the environments intermediate between the extremes of ease and harshness, where effort and endurance are rewarded, where the good life is possible but at the price of effort, thought, and initiative. It was in such settings as these, he argued, neither extremely propitious nor forbidding, that material progress was made. Human skills were developed and ambitions sharpened with each obstacle faced and successfully overcome. The process became cumulative. Each step in material progress left man better equipped, both mentally and materially, to grapple with the next problem and take the next step forward.

It is irrelevant to our present argument whether some small degree of adversity provides the most stimulating conditions for human progress. What is important is that Toynbee leaves the initiative with man. Progress and stagnation in his view—and also in ours—are not conditions preordained by nature; they spring from man's readiness or his reluctance to take risks, to experiment, to tear himself out of the narrow groove of his routine in the expectation or the hope of greater material rewards.

Every phenomenon in the geography of man is the end product of a multiplicity of factors. The cultivation of a dominant crop in any area—sugar in Cuba, coffee in Brazil, corn in the Midwest—is the resultant of the conditions of soil and climate, of facilities for transportation, of the demand in the world market for the commodity. Production is determined also by the level of technology which man can bring to bear. The rise of a large city depends upon the convergence on it of routes, on the existence of a suitable site for the city to spread, of water supply, of raw materials for its industries. In neither instance are the factors which we might list exhaustive or are they equal to one another in importance.

In the first place there must have been an individual—or a group of individuals—who made the decision to grow this particular crop; to choose this site for their settlement, to locate their industrial plant in that particular area. Did they make their decision after a careful evaluation of all the factors—or after an evaluation of those factors which were known to them? How subjective was their judgment? To what extent were they influenced by factors that were merely personal prejudices and predilections? To what extent, in other words, were they capricious or irrational? These are questions we cannot answer. Not even today when such decisions are made by planning authorities or by the boards of big corporations, whose discussions are minuted and recorded, can we know all that went into—or was left out of—the process of making the decision. The purpose of this discussion is to show that we cannot know the reasons for human action. We can only rationalize after the event, weaving ingenious tissues of explanation in which we assume our forebears to have been more rational than perhaps they were, and we guess at the motives that might have inspired their actions.

The geography of man, like man's history, is made up of contingencies, happenings that perhaps were never foreseen or intended. It could all so easily have happened differently. Our geographical pattern of well-being and poverty could have been so different if people unknown to us had not at some indeterminate period in the past made different choices and different decisions.

So when we talk about the resources of any country or any region, we must regard it, in the words of Paul Vidal de la Blache, as "a storehouse of dormant energies, laid up in the germ by Nature but depending for employment on man." It is man, he continued, "who reveals a country's individuality by molding it to his own use"; it is he who "establishes a connection between unrelated features, substituting for the random effects of local circumstances a systematic co-operation of forces." This reversal puts man in the forefront. As Vidal de la Blache's contemporary and compatriot, Lucien Febvre, expressed it, "There are no necessities, but everywhere possibilities; and man, as master of the possibilities, is judge of their use."

Let us now return to our problem, the unevenness of population, of welfare, and of the utilization of the resources of the earth. When we come upon an underdeveloped country, or a former center of civilization now neglected and abandoned, let us not say here nature failed to provide, or to continue to provide. Rather, let us be prepared to admit that here resources may lie unrecognized and unused, either because no one has recognized their value, or because none has had the skill, the capital, or even the desire to use them.

There are two conditions for all advances in human welfare: the first is that society must be able to make the adaptations necessary, to adjust itself to a smaller consumption of manpower, perhaps, or to different conditions of work. Such a change might be the concentration of the scattered fragments of land which in many parts of the world make up the farmer's holding. In England this process of creating compact, manageable farms, on each of which a farmer would have freedom to experiment without being held back by the dead weight of tradition and apathy, began in the Middle Ages. Its virtual completion was a prelude—perhaps it was an essential prelude—to those changes in the technology of production which we call the Industrial Revolution. This process was never necessary in the United States; it has made some progress in Western Europe, but in much of the world, little or none.

Why did the pioneer English cotton manufacturing industry establish itself in Lancashire? Probably because this was one place where the vested and organized interests of the woolen manufacturers proved to be inadequate to keep it out. Why is agricultural production backward in its methods and limited in its capacity in many areas of the world? In part because it is organized on the basis of great estates, poorly administered, and worked by underprivileged and scientifically uneducated labor. These are just a few examples of the many that could be cited—some from the earlier chapters of this book—of social restraints on progress.

When a society no longer welcomes and encourages the entrepreneur, when it puts stability before experiment and refuses to innovate, its stagnation and decline are surely imminent. Chinese society, which remained static for a period of two or three thousand years, is an example of hidebound conservatism which refused even to recognize the fact that other societies might have something to offer it. In 1793 the representative of Great Britain approached the Chinese Emperor with a request for trading facilities in the Chinese ports. He received the crushing reply: "As your ambassador can see for himself, we possess all things. I set no value on objects strange and ingenious, and have no use for your country's manufactures."

Such cultural arrogance, which fortunately has not characterized Chinese society throughout all its history, and such a refusal to welcome and learn from other societies has over the centuries reaped a reward in the poverty and backwardness of the unindustrialized Chinese peasantry. The virtue of stability in Chinese society has been purchased at a high price, and the attempts of this present age to make a giant technological leap forward, to lift agriculture and industry suddenly onto a higher plane, appear to be meeting with resistance and achieving only a very limited success.

The second condition of material progress in human societies is in the field of communication. If a society lived remote from others, cut off by insuperable barriers to the flow of ideas, it might still make considerable progress. But the probability is that its advances would be slow and halting. In fiction and legend lost societies are usually depicted as static and thus backward. The stimulus to progress comes usually from without. It is the stranger who comes into its midst who suggests changes and makes innovations, and from the union of two cultural traditions invention and progress are born.

The slowness of technical and material progress in past ages was, partly at least, a function of the slowness of social communication, of the obstacles to the flow of ideas and of techniques. The Stone Age Australian aborigines and the primitive African peoples are backward in part because they have been cut off from outside contacts, and in their seclusion have allowed their folkways to harden into an immutable law of life.

There is not a single backward or underdeveloped people today whose welfare could not be benefited by the skills and techniques of the more advanced. In the past there was no means whereby these skills and techniques could be conveyed to them. Societies just did not communicate; there was no cross-fertilization of techniques.

Perhaps the most important revolution of modern times is not to be found in the spheres of power engineering or of chemistry or medicine, but in social communication, without which these other advances might not have been achieved and certainly could not have been communicated to other societies. The Point Four agricultural scientist who urges the primitive farmer in Iran or Pakistan or West Africa to use improved strains of seed or to breed from blooded stock is part of this revolution in communication. He exemplifies, in fact, both the conditions on which we suggested that advances are predicated: the communication of ideas, skills, and techniques, and the existence of a society sufficiently plastic to be able to accept and assimilate them.

Now let us return to the main argument. Granted that the surface of the earth is pretty uneven in its capacities and resources, has man made the most of what is there? The general conclusion reached in these

pages has been that different skills and techniques, coupled where necessary with different social attitudes to land tenure and the organization
of production, could lead to an increase—sometimes a very great increase
—in total production in both food and manufactured goods. A careful
examination of the geographical potentialities suggests that there are
few areas that could not be made more productive and that could not
contribute more to the totality of human welfare.

The need for greater production is urgent. The world's population
is increasing at a rate of about fifty-five millions a year, requiring about
a 2 per cent increase in total production each year merely to maintain
the present average level of consumption. At the same time the revolution
in communications, to which we just referred, is bringing home to the
vast mass of underprivileged and underfed the extent of their backwardness and their poverty. Their expectations are rising. It is true that this
same revolution in communications may be expected to bring them the
skills and the techniques needed to realize higher agricultural and industrial production. But in this there is always a time lag. Expectations
begin to rise as soon the underdeveloped peoples hear of the higher
levels elsewhere, but it will take them time to learn to achieve higher
levels through increased production, partly because the human mind
learns only slowly the strange techniques and acquires the new skills
necessary for their realization, partly because an even slower adjustment
of society itself has usually to be made. To revert to examples used on
an earlier page, land reform and the ending of such practices as the
fragmentation of minute holdings, should precede the introduction of
farm mechanization and better crop rotations, seeds, and blood-stock.

Since the increase in total food production is probably the most
urgent of the problems, it would be well to pause, to look at the map
and to see where this increase could most easily be made. The map
showing density of population, pages 26–27, shows vast empty or only
thinly peopled areas in every continent except Europe; and even in Europe
there are small areas of relative sparsity. The whole of the west and
the north of the North American continent, the interior of South America, much of Africa, most of Australia and the Asian heartland are
all relatively empty lands. As a rough estimate, the empty lands cover
three-quarters of the land surface of the earth.

We used earlier a quotation from Vidal de la Blache: "A country
is a store-house of dormant energies, laid up in the germ by Nature, but
depending for employment on man." What dormant energies, the reader

may ask, are locked in the ice sheets of Greenland or the Antarctic, or hidden beneath the jungle of the Amazon or New Guinea, or fixed in the steep slopes of the Andes or Tibetan Plateau? It must be admitted that they are few indeed: that in some of these extremes agriculture, at least as we conceive it, is not possible, and in others it is confronted with immense difficulties. But nature has laid up in germ some elements of usefulness in the most unlikely areas. The mere fact that we mentioned the probability of mineral resources in the Antarctic continent, beneath the ice, shows a possible line of development for what is today the only continent wholly without permanent inhabitants.

The extremes of cold in the Arctic and Antarctic make the cultivation of plants impossible; and with the exception only of the harvest of the sea, the food supply of mankind comes directly or indirectly from plants. The extremes of drought in other areas of the world make cultivation of crops difficult or unlikely. The deserts have usually certain of the prerequisites of agriculture—a long growing season and, locally at least, the rudiments of a soil, sometimes relatively rich in the soluble minerals which serve as plant food. What they lack is moisture, the medium by which this plant food is absorbed into the plant itself. Where the deserts have been watered either by the springs of an oasis or by a river which, like the Nile or Indus, flows through its midst, there it has truly been made to blossom as the rose. It was observed that the earth is short rather of water than of land. But already, locally and on a relatively small scale, this deficiency is being made good. Water from the moist north of California is being sent to the arid south; water from the headwaters of the Jordan is being diverted to the waterless Negev, and dams to be built in the Himalayas, supplemented by a net of concrete-lined canals, will deliver more water to the parched fields of Pakistan and India.

Together these irrigation projects will make only a very small dent in the total area of desert, but they are an example of the technical skills of one society, namely the Western, being used to remedy the backwardness and poverty of others in Pakistan, India, and elsewhere. The water that is evaporated is never lost. It is recycled and will fall again as rain at some future date perhaps at some distant place. The reservoir from which it came and to which it will eventually return is the ocean. If man could dip into the ocean for the water which he needs, he would not lower its surface, and in millions of years he would not exhaust the supply because in time it would all make its way back to the ocean again.

But using salt sea water for irrigation raises serious problems. The process of extracting the salt is costly, and is at present used only on a small and almost experimental scale. But if it could be operated cheaply and on a gigantic scale, it could effect a revolution in the extent of man's cultivable land.

Next among the empty lands are the vast areas of equatorial forest and tropical savanna. Their exuberant vegetation, we have seen earlier, is deceptive and does not indicate a rich soil. In the equatorial region soils are poor and basically unsuited to field crops. In the savanna region the winter drought is long and locally at least the rains are uncertain. Severe erosion is a danger once the natural vegetation is disturbed, and locusts and other insect pests do not so much limit the usefulness of these regions as make them harder to use.

The equatorial forest region remains a vast area that could be developed for tree crops like the oil palm, cacao, and rubber; the savanna is potentially a far greater source than at present of corn, sugar, peanuts, soybeans, and a great variety of other tropical crops. The dismal failure of the "Ground-nuts Scheme" in East Africa will unquestionably discourage efforts to develop the savanna region; but it should only demonstrate that far deeper study and far more careful planning are needed before the machines and methods of agriculture, developed in other climates, are applied in the tropics. The belief that the interior of South America and much of tropical Africa and Australia must always lie outside the limits of cultivation and of profitable land use must not continue to prevail. Hope must not be abandoned. None of these lie beyond the capacity of present-day and future technology to develop and use.

Of all these currently empty lands the savanna probably offers the greatest potentialities, and Africa, where the extent of the savanna is the greatest, has the most. Africa has the further advantage that its population is adapted to these physical conditions and able to work in them. The usefulness of the Australian savanna is limited by the unwillingness of the Australians either to settle in their own tropical north or to admit people willing to do so. The opening up of the South American savanna has been restricted by the lack of means of transportation and by the discouraging instability of the Latin American political scene. But, in the words of L. Dudley Stamp, "of all the underdeveloped or undeveloped lands in the world the tropical savannas call most urgently for careful study." And since, in the same author's words, "the tropical climate is par excellence the climate of Africa," one is forced to conclude that this is the continent in which one may look for the greatest advances in food production.

The more intensive development of all these underdeveloped regions is closely linked with, or even dependent upon, four other problems of the modern world, all of which have been touched upon at various points in this book. They are vanishing colonialism, technical and economic aid to underdeveloped peoples, the rapidly growing number of political entities with their brash young nationalism, and human migration.

We are witnessing the sunset of the old imperialism. At some time or other within the past four centuries, no less than two-thirds of the land surface of the earth was held as a colonial dependency by one or other of the great powers. This included all Latin America; all Africa except only Liberia and Ethiopia; most of South and Southeast Asia, together with Australia. Today, a little less than 10 per cent of the land surface has any kind of dependent status, and this is certain to diminish yet more within a very few years. The old empires have vanished. Does their legacy consist of anything more positive than the frustration of the former colonial peoples and their deep hatred toward their former masters? It would seem that in some parts of the world colonialism has left little more than this behind it. Then we come upon colonies, like some in West Africa, where a half-century or so of colonial rule has left a lasting legacy of respect for law, order, and good government, together with material things like roads, railroads, and harbors without which progress is impossible.

The great danger is that the ghost of vanished colonialism will continue to dominate the new states, its visage made more fearful in the imagination than it may ever have been in reality, poisoning the relations between the new states and the old, the non-Western and the Western worlds. Political freedom among the rapidly increasing number of new states does not mean, as many of them seemed to think, the dawning of economic prosperity. The underdeveloped world in independence is more, not less, dependent upon the developed. It needs loans and equipment, technical aid, and guidance in the intricate paths of the modern world. How to ask for and how to accept such help, without at the same time exposing the new state to a renewal of the old controls from without, is their most formidable problem.

This is the problem of neocolonialism, of the control which the great powers of the world are allegedly establishing over the underdeveloped through the supply of technicians and materials. Unquestionably the leaders of many of the new states have been attuned through their years of struggle for independence to regard the peoples of the Western World as exploiters. Old attitudes of suspicion linger on even when there is in reality no justification for them. Suspicion breeds suspicion. The advanced peoples give their aid more grudgingly; the less advanced accept it with jealousy and resentment. "The rich and the mighty," in the words of a report to the United States Senate, "have always in history had difficulty understanding the poor and the weak. When the world is so good, they feel, why are people always trying to change it? The fact is that the world does not look as good to the poor and weak as it does to the rich and mighty, and many a class and nation have fallen precisely because of their inability to understand this."

Yet aid there must be, technical, educational, and economic aid, from the developed nations to the underdeveloped. Gone is the time, as we saw in the opening chapter, when societies can live in isolation from one another. Today "no man is an island." In its preamble to the Mutual Security Act of 1959, the Congress of the United States recognized "the basic identity of interest which exists between the people of the United States and the peoples of other lands who are striving to establish and develop politically independent and economically viable units, and to produce more goods and services, and to improve ways of living by methods which reflect the popular will, and to realize aspirations for justice, for education, and for dignity and respect as individual human beings, and to establish responsible governments."

The advanced nations of the world still carry their "White Man's Burden," though today we would not express it so completely in terms of color. And still they cannot demand the price for the job, the proper reward for their services and materials in the shape of commodities and political control. It is as true now as when Kipling wrote it more than half a century ago, that the bearer of the burden will:

> . . . reap his old reward
> The blame of those ye better,
> The hate of those ye guard.

Aid to the underdeveloped nations cannot possibly be requited in any measurable fashion. It must be given largely in the hope and expectation that at some future date it will result in a betterment of the human lot. We cannot think of aid to underdeveloped peoples mainly—or even partly—as a weapon to be used against Communism, nor as a means of stimulating exports and keeping the home industries busy. "The question is still asked," wrote Frederic Benham, "what do *we* get out of it? The answer is that we should expect nothing, not even gratitude. The purpose of economic aid is simply to relieve the poverty of our much less fortunate fellow human-beings and to help them speed up the economic growth of their economies."

How closely intertwined are the problems of upgrading the technical level and modifying the social attitudes of underdeveloped peoples we have already seen. How difficult and at times discouraging it is to perform both tasks we already know from the experiences of those in the field. But the revolution in social communications which makes them possible also makes them necessary. This point cannot be made more forcibly and eloquently than in the words of the Senate committee report that has already been quoted:

"One of the greatest social consequences of this technological revolution is the idea that starvation and poverty are no longer inevitable. For most of men's history the welfare of the masses depended on the harvest. If the weather was good, people ate well for that year; if it was bad, they starved that year. Not their efforts but the will of the gods determined men's lot on earth. The technological revolution has forever banished this passive response to material welfare. Thinking people in all lands start from the assumption that if poverty exists, it is not because of the gods but because of men's ignorance or lack of will since it is believed to be within the competence of men to change man's fate. The task of changing it has become one of the deepest obligations of the political and intellectual leaders of every underdeveloped country."

The maps of gross national product and of food consumption, to which we have already turned several times, form a rough measure of where aid is needed. Without external help these areas cannot hope to break the vicious circle of poverty, backwardness, and dependency against which all of them are rebelling.

The United States in its many, varied, and confusing programs which it has initiated since the end of the Second World War, has given aid more generously and more widely than the rest of the world's givers together. Yet what it has done has in many parts of the world scarcely touched the problem. Its aid has, by and large, been politically oriented. To some extent this has been inevitable. It would be unnatural if the taxpayer did not expect to see some return on the money which his government gives. And, as he is preoccupied with the international situation, he prefers to see the money invested in the territory of firm friends and trusted allies rather than in that of needy peoples whose friendship he does not need or whose alliance he does not trust. Pakistan, Thailand, and the Philippines are trusted friends; India, Indonesia, and Ghana, so far, have not won many friends or influenced many people in Washington. Yet their needs, hopes, and aspirations are as great, and their poverty and distress as disruptive of the world's economy as that of America's closest friends. The pattern of American technical and economic aid shows its political orientation. It shows how little help has been given to Latin America and tropical Africa, regions of the world whose need for it is perhaps the greatest and where, as our previous discussion may have indicated, such aid may reap the largest rewards.

The aid provided by other countries—the Soviet Union and the states of Western Europe—has been relatively small. Soviet aid has been opportunist, designed rather to buy friends and embarrass enemies than to raise the general level of welfare among the underdeveloped peoples. It has been on a large scale only to India, Egypt, and Indonesia, though Afghanistan, Iraq, and Cuba have received substantial sums. The United Kingdom's help has chiefly been to members of the Commonwealth, among which it has sometimes been on a large and generous scale.

In addition to the individual aid which the developed countries have given, sometimes with little expectation of a direct return, mention should be made of the collaborative efforts of several groups of countries. The World Bank, for example, uses money subscribed by its member nations to invest at interest in approved projects anywhere in the world. The World Bank can only participate in projects whose success is so well-assured that they can service the loan and repay the capital, and these projects are in general in the fields of irrigation, land reclamation, power development, transportation, and industrial development. The Colombo Plan, in which most of the countries of Southeast Asia, together with Australia, New Zealand, the United Kingdom, and the United States participate is similar, and the administrators of the plan insure a minimum of overlapping and a maximum of collaboration between the member states which form a compact group in Southeast Asia. The Alliance for Progress is the latest of such regional groupings of states for capital investment and economic development, though in this instance the donor is the United States and the recipients, the sadly neglected countries of Latin America.

Closely related both to the vanishing world of colonialism and to the need which the more advanced countries feel to aid the more backward is the multiplicity of new and emerging states. The people of the United States have learned the advantages of scale. It is cheaper in the long run to administer the large areas or to operate the large factory than several of smaller size. The new states, however, have not struggled for independence only to surrender it at once to a federation, whether in Africa, Central America, the Middle East, or Southeast Asia. Too many careers are at stake; too many cultural groups would feel themselves threatened by being thrown in with a larger grouping. Yet a broad union of states is what each of these areas urgently needs. The United States learned the advantages of federation the bigger part of two centuries ago; even Europe is learning the advantages of a closer functional unity and is moving toward it at a speed that a generation ago would have been regarded as unbelievable.

It is not impossible that groups of young, poor nations might merge to some degree—a consummation to be worked for and devoutly to be wished. It is a mark of maturity among nations to be able to give up a little of their sovereignty and power, to compromise with others without feeling that they are losing face.

At several points in this book reference has been made to the advantages of regional co-operation, not only for trade, as in the European Common Market and in the incipient free-trade area of Central America, but also in resource development like the Colombo Plan and the utilization of river basins like the agreements between India and Pakistan, Egypt and the Sudan. Every move in this direction helps to soften the sharp angularities of nationalism and to minimize the harsh consequences of the division of the earth into about a hundred and twenty-five independent countries.

A last problem is that of international migration. We have all through this book been meeting with crowded and with empty lands, and the question has inevitably arisen of migration from the one to the other. This was the way in which overpopulation in Ireland and Italy and Central Europe was remedied during the nineteenth century to the immense advantage of the United States. Can migration again solve the population problem in the overcrowded lands?

Let it be admitted that overpopulation is a relative matter. A density of 561 per square mile in the United Kingdom, or of 784 in Belgium is not only tolerable, it is an advantage; whereas 353 per square mile in India, 190 in China, and 70 in Egypt are too many. One has to consider

THE TWO WORLDS 565

the capacity of the soil to support a farming population; the proportion of the population engaged in manufacturing and mining; and the importance of such tertiary occupations as banking, commerce, and transportation.

The overpopulated countries are, in general, those in which a large majority of the population is engaged in agriculture, and generally subsistence agriculture. Their overcrowding consists in the existence of more people in the villages than are necessary to guide the plow, to scatter the seed, and to reap the harvest. We have already seen examples of underemployment and of duplication in the labor on the peasant farm in many parts of the world. This surplus population might migrate; it might also be absorbed in factory industry or mining, or even in land reclamation or the construction of capital assets like roads and docks. In the countries of Western Europe the surplus population from the farms has been absorbed into industry, and in general it was essential to modernize the agriculture in order to squeeze more people into industry. The countries with the labor surplus were mostly those like Ireland or like the southern parts of Italy or parts of Poland, Hungary, and the Balkans, where modern industry did not make its appearance until very recently.

And so we may say of the underdeveloped, overcrowded lands today that migration, even if it were possible, would provide only a short-term remedy. The solution is to absorb the surplus population into other profitable employment. This is the essence of the economic revolution that was effected in the Soviet Union between the two world wars, which is being employed in the East European satellites, and which has been imposed violently and perhaps unsuccessfully on the people of China. The challenge to the open societies today is to achieve the same ends—a shift of the labor force from agriculture to industry and thus a great increase in total productivity, without the violence, the cruelty, and the repression that has in these instances accompanied it.

Migration is not then the only solution, and it may not in all instances be a solution at all, to overcrowding on the land. Yet migration is desirable and even necessary, as much for the benefit of the empty as for the relief of the crowded lands. Some empty countries—Australia and New Zealand, for example—have the wisdom to appeal for immigrants, though they may fairly be accused of being unnecessarily discriminating in whom they will admit. Africa and South America need substantial numbers of immigrants if their resources are to be developed and used. Though here, as almost everywhere, the hostile social attitudes on the part of both immigrant and host threaten to make any large scale movement of people difficult.

We are not likely to witness any large movement of people from the crowded to the empty lands. Apart from those social attitudes which stand in the way, the logistics—the simple business of moving the people in large numbers from one to the other—and the capital equipment needed to set them up in their new homes present insuperable difficulties. The population of China is said to be growing at the rate of perhaps fifteen million persons per year. Even if there were lands ready to receive this huge annual increment, there does not exist the shipping to take them there, and if they were willing to go to the African or South American savanna, it is doubtful whether the world's factories could produce, or the world's generosity pay for the equipment necessary to clear the brush and settle the immigrants into their new homes on a scale as vast as this.

Migration will continue to provide relief for the persecuted minorities, and will always offer some slight relief to the overpopulated lands. But the crowded people are poor, and the costs and obligations of migration are beyond—very far beyond—their resources. And, too, the empty lands of today are in general not those which are capable of being settled by subsistence farmers, cultivating the soil by their traditional methods. They call for all the resources of the soil chemist, plant breeder, mechanical engineer, and many other specialists. Primitive societies cannot provide these.

In these concluding pages, which in their turn summarize the main themes of this book, we see that there are just two worlds, the rich and the poor. Sometimes they are called the Western and the Eastern; sometimes, less invidiously, the Western and the non-Western. But they cannot be defined by compass direction, by political ideologies, or by attitudes of mind. They are the developed and the underdeveloped, and together they form a spectrum from the United States at the one end to the poorest community in Africa or Asia at the other. If the order in which countries lie in this spectrum could be established incontrovertibly now— which it cannot—the order would be likely to change within the space of a few years. Change and development are rapid in many of these countries. In Pakistan or Thailand or Ghana, or the formerly agrarian societies of Eastern Europe, factory industries are being established and the surplus rural population is being employed in manufacturing.

It may be that not all the factory industries which the new states choose to establish are wisely chosen. Many of them are prestige items. The steel mill newly built in Egypt has been described as "a modern equivalent of the Pyramids except that the maintenance expenses are higher." Too many of the new industries are designed rather to enhance the military power of the state than to improve the level of welfare. But the new governments in the underdeveloped countries are inexperienced and naïve, their pride is easily hurt, and they tend to a little showmanship which the older and more developed states do not need. Yet, judge them by whatever standard you will, they are making progress, slow and halting though it is, along the paths of a more diversified economy, of fuller use of resources, and of a higher level of material welfare. In the words of a former British Ambassador to Moscow, "our political end should be the actual raising of the living standards of Asia and Africa, in the interests of the people of those countries, but also in the interests of a stable and peaceful world."

The world is crowded, but the crowding is relative only to a former technology and organization. There remains today much land, but its possession demands different methods from those used in the past. "This goodly frame, the earth," is not, in Hamlet's words, "a sterile promontory," unless we wish it to be. Man has it in his power to create a bounteous and a peaceful world. If he does not succeed in doing so, he cannot blame nature for his failing. "For the fault, dear Brutus, lies not in our stars, but in ourselves."

TABLE OF CHIEF POLITICAL DIVISIONS

Region or Political Division	Area in sq. miles	Estimated Population 1/1/1962	Pop. per sq. mi.	Capital; Largest City (unless same)
Aden [Colony]	80	157,000	1,963	Aden
Aden [Protectorate]	112,000	775,000	6.9	Aden, Aden Colony; Al Mukallā
Afghanistan†	250,000	14,000,000	56	Kabul
Albania†	11,099	1,680,000	151	Tiranë
Algeria	917,537	11,150,000	12	Algiers (Alger)
American Samoa	76	21,000	276	Pago Pago
Andorra	175	9,000	51	Andorra
Angola	481,351	4,900,000	10	Luanda
Argentina†	1,072,747	20,500,000	19	Buenos Aires
Australia†	2,971,081	10,740,000	3.6	Canberra; Sydney
Austria†	32,374	7,090,000	219	Vienna (Wien)
Bahama Is.	4,375	108,000	25	Nassau
Bahrain	231	153,000	662	Manama
Basutoland	11,716	700,000	60	Maseru
Bechuanaland	275,000	345,000	1.3	Mafeking, S. Afr.; Kanye
Belgium†	11,778	9,230,000	784	Brussels (Bruxelles)
Bermuda	21	53,000	2,524	Hamilton
Bhutan	19,300	675,000	35	Thimbu
Bolivia†	424,163	3,530,000	8.3	Sucre; La Paz
Bonin Islands	40	200	5.0	....
Borneo, British	78,614	1,365,000	17	........; Kuching
Brazil†	3,286,478	73,400,000	22	Brasília; Rio de Janeiro
British Guiana	83,000	592,000	7.1	Georgetown
British Honduras	8,866	93,000	10	Belize
Brunei	2,226	90,000	40	Brunei
Bulgaria†	42,729	7,975,000	187	Sofia (Sofiya)
Burma†	261,789	21,650,000	83	Rangoon
Burundi (Urundi)	10,747	2,300,000	214	Usumbura
Cambodia†	66,606	5,100,000	77	Phnom Penh
Cameroun†	183,333	4,150,000	23	Yaoundé; Douala
Canada†	3,851,809	18,460,000	4.8	Ottawa; Montreal
Canal Zone	553	42,000	76	Balboa Heights; Rainbow City
Cape Verde Is.	1,552	208,000	134	Praia
Central African Republic†	238,224	1,275,000	5.4	Bangui
Ceylon†	25,332	10,300,000	407	Colombo
Chad†	495,800	2,750,000	5.5	Fort Lamy
Chile†	286,397	7,880,000	28	Santiago
China (excl. Taiwan)	3,691,500	700,000,000	190	Peking (Peiching); Shanghai
Colombia†	439,513	14,625,000	33	Bogotá
Comores Is.	834	187,000	224	Dzaoudzi
Congo (Rep. of Congo; Capital: Brazzaville)†	132,000	850,000	6.4	Brazzaville
Congo, The (Rep. of The Congo; Capital: Léopoldville)†	905,381	14,500,000	16	Léopoldville
Cook Is.	90	18,000	200	Avarua
Costa Rica†	19,600	1,254,000	64	San José
Cuba†	44,217	7,000,000	158	Havana (Habana)
Cyprus†	3,572	586,000	164	Nicosia
Czechoslovakia†	49,366	13,840,000	280	Prague (Praha)
Dahomey†	44,696	2,060,000	46	Porto Novo
Denmark†	16,619	4,635,000	279	Copenhagen (København)
Dominican Republic†	18,816	3,150,000	167	Santo Domingo
Ecuador†	104,506	4,500,000	43	Quito; Guayaquil
El Salvador†	8,260	2,550,000	309	San Salvador
Ethiopia (incl. Eritrea)†	457,147	20,000,000	44	Addis Ababa
Falkland Is. (excl. Deps.)	4,618	2,200	0.5	Port Stanley
Fernando Póo	785	65,000	83	Santa Isabel
Fiji	7,055	415,000	59	Suva
Finland†	130,119	4,517,000	35	Helsinki
France†	212,822	46,200,000	217	Paris
French Guiana	35,100	32,000	0.9	Cayenne
French Polynesia	1,550	79,000	51	Papeete
French Somaliland	8,500	69,000	8.1	Djibouti
Gabon†	103,100	450,000	4.4	Libreville
Germany, East	41,804	17,170,000	412	Berlin (East)

† *Member of the United Nations (1962).*

569

Region or Political Division	Area in sq. miles	Estimated Population 1/1/1962	Pop. per sq. mi.	Capital; Largest City (unless same)
Germany, West (incl. West Berlin)	95,924	56,680,000	591	Bonn; Berlin (West)
Ghana†	91,843	7,050,000	77	Accra
Gibraltar	2	26,000	13,000	Gibraltar
Gilbert & Ellice Is.	349	47,000	135	Tarawa
Greece†	51,169	8,435,000	165	Athens (Athinai)
Greenland	840,000	32,000	0.04	Godthaab
Guam	212	70,000	330	Agana
Guatemala†	42,042	3,930,000	93	Guatemala
Guinea†	94,925	3,000,000	32	Conakry
Haiti†	10,714	3,570,000	333	Port-au-Prince
Honduras†	43,277	1,925,000	44	Tegucigalpa
Hong Kong	391	3,225,000	8,248	Victoria
Hungary†	35,919	10,065,000	280	Budapest
Iceland†	39,800	182,000	4.6	Reykjavík
India† (incl. part of Kashmir)	1,224,967	443,400,000	362	New Delhi; Calcutta
Indonesia†	572,582	95,800,000	167	Djakarta
Iran (Persia)†	636,300	20,925,000	33	Tehrān
Iraq†	171,599	7,350,000	43	Baghdad
Ireland†	27,136	2,805,000	103	Dublin
Israel†	8,000	2,232,000	279	Jerusalem; Tel Aviv
Italy†	116,303	49,800,000	428	Rome (Roma)
Ivory Coast†	124,503	3,340,000	27	Abidjan
Jamaica	4,411	1,650,000	374	Kingston
Japan†	142,726	94,500,000	662	Tōkyō
Jordan†	37,301	1,800,000	48	Amman
Kenya	224,960	7,400,000	33	Nairobi
Korea, North	47,861	8,200,000	171	Pyongyang
Korea, South	37,424	25,700,000	687	Seoul (Soul)
Kuwait	5,800	232,000	40	Kuwait
Laos†	91,400	1,875,000	21	Vientiane
Lebanon†	4,000	1,850,000	463	Beirut
Liberia†	43,000	1,300,000	30	Monrovia
Libya†	679,358	1,225,000	1.8	Tripoli and Bengasi; Tripoli
Liechtenstein	61	17,000	279	Vaduz
Luxembourg†	998	317,000	318	Luxembourg
Macao	6	225,000	37,500	Macao
Malagasy Republic (Madagascar)†	227,800	5,625,000	25	Tananarive
Malaya†	50,680	7,225,000	143	Kuala Lumpur
Mali†	464,874	4,150,000	8.9	Bamako
Malta	122	330,000	2,705	Valletta
Martinique	425	285,000	671	Fort-de-France
Mauritania†	419,230	740,000	1.8	Nouakchott; Kaédi
Mauritius (incl. Dependencies)	808	685,000	848	Port Louis
Mexico†	760,375	36,650,000	48	Mexico City
Midway Is.	2	3,000	1,500	
Monaco	0.6	23,000	38,333	Monaco
Mongolia†	591,100	950,000	1.6	Ulan Bator
Morocco†	171,599	11,950,000	70	Rabat; Casablanca
Mozambique	297,846	6,500,000	22	Lourenço Marques
Muscat & Oman	82,000	575,000	7.0	Muscat; Maṭraḥ
Nauru	8	4,600	575	
Nepal†	54,362	9,480,000	174	Katmandu
Netherlands†	12,529	11,710,000	935	The Hague (s' Gravenhage) and Amsterdam; Amsterdam
Netherlands Antilles	371	197,000	531	Willemstad
Netherlands New Guinea	160,600	750,000	4.7	Hollandia
New Caledonia (incl. Deps.)	6,531	80,000	12.2	Nouméa
New Guinea, Ter. of	94,430	1,450,000	15	Port Moresby, Papua; Rabaul
New Hebrides	5,700	61,000	11	Vila
New Zealand†	103,736	2,466,000	24	Wellington; Auckland
Nicaragua†	48,600	1,550,000	32	Managua
Niger†	458,995	2,900,000	6.3	Niamey
Nigeria	356,669	36,100,000	98	Lagos; Ibadan
North Borneo	29,388	475,000	16	Jesselton; Sandakan
Norway†	125,064	3,629,000	29	Oslo
Pakistan† (incl. part of Kashmir)	399,373	96,600,000	242	Rawalpindi; Karachi
Palestine (Gaza Area)	78	390,000	5,000	Gaza
Panama†	28,753	1,100,000	38	Panamá
Papua (excl. New Guinea Ter.)	90,600	530,000	5.8	Port Moresby
Paraguay†	157,047	1,835,000	12	Asunción
Peru†	496,222	11,400,000	23	Lima
Philippines†	115,707	29,200,000	252	Quezon City; Manila
Pitcairn (excl. Dependencies)	2	150	75	Adamstown
Poland†	120,359	30,265,000	251	Warsaw (Warszawa)

† Member of the United Nations (1962).

Region or Political Division	Area in sq. miles	Estimated Population 1/1/1962	Pop. per sq. mi.	Capital; Largest City (unless same)
Portugal†	36,376	9,000,000	247	Lisbon (Lisboa)
Portuguese Guinea	13,948	580,000	42	Bissau
Portuguese Timor	7,332	510,000	70	Dili
Puerto Rico	3,435	2,410,000	702	San Juan
Qatar	8,000	59,000	7.4	Doha
Reunion	969	352,000	363	St. Denis
Rhodesia & Nyasaland, Federation of	484,529	8,625,000	18	Salisbury
Rio Muni	10,045	185,000	18	Bata; Evinayong
Romania†	91,698	18,665,000	204	Bucharest (Bucureşti)
Rwanda	10,169	2,725,000	268	Kigali
Ryukyu Is. (Southern)	848	900,000	1,061	Naha
St. Helena (incl. Dependencies)	119	5,900	50	Jamestown
St. Pierre & Miquelon	93	5,000	54	St. Pierre
San Marino	23	17,000	739	San Marino
Sarawak	47,000	800,000	17	Kuching
Saudi Arabia†	617,800	6,200,000	10	Riyadh; Mecca
Senegal†	76,124	3,050,000	40	Dakar
Seychelles	156	43,000	276	Victoria
Sierra Leone†	27,925	2,500,000	90	Freetown
Sikkim	2,744	162,000	59	Gangtok
Singapore	224	1,720,000	7,679	Singapore
Solomon Is., British	11,500	130,000	11	Honiara
Somali Republic†	246,202	2,035,000	8.3	Mogadiscio
South Africa†	472,926	16,350,000	35	Pretoria and Cape Town; Johannesburg
South-West Africa	318,099	535,000	1.7	Windhoek
Soviet Union (Union of Soviet Socialist Republics)†	8,599,300	220,000,000	26	Moscow (Moskva)
Spain†	194,345	30,700,000	158	Madrid
Spanish Sahara	102,703	25,000	0.2	Aiún
Sudan†	967,500	12,300,000	13	Khartoum
Surinam (Neth. Guiana)	55,145	324,000	5.9	Paramaribo
Svalbard (Spitsbergen)	24,101	4,000	0.2	Longyearbyen
Swaziland	6,704	270,000	40	Mbabane
Sweden†	173,649	7,540,000	43	Stockholm
Switzerland	15,941	5,520,000	346	Bern (Berne); Zürich
Syria†	71,227	4,825,000	68	Damascus (Esh Sham)
Taiwan (Formosa) (Nationalist China)	13,884	11,150,000	803	Taipei
Tanganyika†	361,800	9,500,000	26	Dar es Salaam
Thailand (Siam)†	198,500	27,000,000	136	Bangkok (Krung Thep)
Togo†	22,000	1,475,000	67	Lomé
Tokelau (Union) Is.	4	2,000	500	........; Fakaofo
Tonga	269	67,000	249	Nukualofa
Trinidad & Tobago	1,980	864,000	436	Port-of-Spain
Trucial Coast	32,300	88,000	2.7	........; Dubayy
Tunisia†	48,332	4,260,000	88	Tunis
Turkey†	301,381	28,675,000	95	Ankara; Istanbul
Uganda	93,981	6,925,000	74	Entebbe; Kampala
United Arab Republic (Egypt)†	386,000	27,000,000	70	Cairo (Al Qāhirah)
United Kingdom of Great Britain & Northern Ireland†	94,205	52,860,000	561	London
United States†	3,675,633	185,200,000	50	Washington; New York
Upper Volta†	105,839	3,735,000	35	Ouagadougou
Uruguay†	72,172	2,380,000	33	Montevideo
Vatican City (Holy See)	0.2	1,000	5,000	Vatican City
Venezuela†	352,143	7,600,000	22	Caracas
Vietnam, North	59,933	16,900,000	282	Hanoi
Vietnam, South	65,948	14,600,000	221	Saigon
Virgin Is., British	59	7,400	127	Road Town
Virgin Is. of the U.S.	133	33,000	248	Charlotte Amalie
Western Samoa	1,130	110,000	97	Apia
West Indies Federation	1,614	701,000	434	........; Bridgetown
Yemen†	75,300	5,000,000	66	San'ā'
Yugoslavia†	98,776	18,700,000	189	Belgrade (Beograd)
Zanzibar	1,020	313,000	307	Zanzibar
World	57,295,000	3,075,000,000	54	........; New York
Africa	11,635,000	261,300,000	22	........; Cairo
Antarctica	5,100,000	....	.....	....
Asia	17,075,000	1,792,000,000	105	........; Tōkyō
Europe	3,835,000	583,600,000	152	........; London
North America	9,420,000	273,100,000	29	........; New York
Oceania (incl. Australia)	3,295,000	16,400,000	5.0	........; Sydney
South America	6,870,000	148,600,000	22	........; Buenos Aires

† *Member of the United Nations (1962).*

TABLE OF WORLD'S LARGEST CITIES

This table includes all cities with 1,000,000 or more population. The populations are estimates for January 1, 1962. Metropolitan populations are given for as many cities as possible, and identified by a star symbol (*). Some metropolitan areas include more than one large city. In such cases, the entry for the first-named city carries the entire metropolitan population, and other cities in the metropolitan area carry a reference to the first-named city with a star symbol.

Ahmadabad, India (*1,425,000).......1,175,000
Alexandria, U.A.R. (*1,525,000).......1,490,000
Amsterdam, Netherlands (*1,650,000)...865,000
Antwerp, Belgium (*1,000,000).........255,000
Athens, Greece (*1,890,000)............635,000
Atlanta, Georgia (*1,060,000)...........500,000
Baku, Soviet Union (*1,185,000)........685,000
Baltimore, Maryland (*1,695,000).......936,000
Bandung, Indonesia (*1,025,000).......975,000
Bangalore, India (*1,250,000)..........915,000
Bangkok, Thailand (*2,250,000).......1,500,000
Barcelona, Spain (*2,070,000).........1,585,000
Berlin, East, Germany (*Berlin)......1,070,000
Berlin, West, Germany (*4,000,000)...2,175,000
Birmingham, England (*2,590,000)....1,112,000
Bogotá, Colombia (*1,200,000).......1,050,000
Bombay, India (*4,475,000)...........4,250,000
Boston, Massachusetts (*3,000,000).....680,000
Brussels, Belgium (*1,930,000)..........170,000
Bucharest, Romania (*1,375,000)......1,245,000
Budapest, Hungary (*2,150,000).....1,835,000
Buenos Aires, Argentina (*7,175,000)..2,965,000
Buffalo, New York (*1,370,000)........525,000
Cairo, U.A.R. (*4,000,000).............3,400,000
Calcutta, India (*6,450,000).........2,950,000
Canton, China (*2,025,000)..........2,025,000
Caracas, Venezuela (*1,550,000).......800,000
Casablanca, Morocco (*1,080,000).....1,015,000
Changchun, China (*1,125,000).......1,125,000
Chengtu, China (*1,275,000)..........1,275,000
Chicago, Illinois (*6,735,000).......3,540,000
Chungking, China (2,400,000▲)......*2,050,000
Cincinnati, Ohio (*1,250,000).........503,000
Cleveland, Ohio (*2,150,000)..........870,000
Cologne, W. Germany (*1,500,000).....820,000
Copenhagen, Denmark (*1,365,000).....722,000
Dairen, China (*1,200,000)..........1,150,000
Dallas, Texas (*1,090,000)............710,000
Delhi, India (*2,750,000)..............2,150,000
Detroit, Michigan (*4,110,000)........1,645,000
Djakarta, Indonesia (*2,950,000).....2,400,000
Donetsk (Stalino), Soviet Union
   (*1,675,000)........................775,000
Düsseldorf, W. Germany (*1,035,000)...705,000
Essen, W. Germany (*4,825,000)........733,000
Frankfurt am Main, W. Germany
   (*1,405,000).........................690,000
Fushun, China (*1,150,000)...........1,150,000
Glasgow, Scotland (*1,885,000).......1,055,000
Gorkiy, Soviet Union (*1,380,000).....1,035,000
Hamburg, W. Germany
   (*2,280,000)........................1,850,000
Harbin, China (*1,800,000)...........1,800,000
Havana, Cuba (*1,550,000).............885,000
Houston, Texas (*1,335,000)...........970,000
Hyderabad, India (*1,400,000).........960,000
Istanbul, Turkey (*1,900,000)........1,510,000
Johannesburg, South Africa (*2,100,000).580,000
Kanpur (Cawnpore), India (*975,000)....870,000
Kansas City, Missouri (*1,070,000).....510,000
Karachi, Pakistan (*2,000,000)........1,675,000
Katowice, Poland (*1,925,000).........273,000
Kharkov, Soviet Union (*1,200,000)....998,000
Kiev, Soviet Union (*1,300,000).......1,210,000
Kōbe, Japan (*Osaka)...............1,145,000
Kowloon (*Victoria), Hong Kong....1,350,000
Kunming, China (*1,025,000).........1,025,000
Kuybyshev, Soviet Union (*1,010,000)...890,000
Kyoto, Japan (*1,510,000)............1,300,000
Lahore, Pakistan (*1,375,000)........1,250,000
Leeds, England (*1,335,000)...........512,000
Leipzig, E. Germany (*800,000)........590,000

Leningrad, Soviet Union (*3,875,000)..3,050,000
Lima, Peru (*2,025,000)...............1,750,000
Lisbon, Portugal (*1,350,000).........820,000
Liverpool, England (*1,660,000).......744,000
London, England (*10,900,000)........3,190,000
Los Angeles, California (*6,955,000)..2,565,000
Madras, India (*2,050,000)...........1,750,000
Madrid, Spain (*2,430,000)...........2,325,000
Manchester, England (*2,815,000).....658,000
Manila, Philippines (*2,650,000).....1,170,000
Mannheim, W. Germany (*1,140,000)...318,000
Melbourne, Australia (*1,960,000)......76,000
Mexico City, Mexico (*5,150,000).....2,775,000
Miami, Florida (*1,330,000)...........296,000
Milan, Italy (*2,575,000)............1,590,000
Milwaukee, Wisconsin (*1,285,000).....750,000
Minneapolis, Minnesota (*1,505,000)....480,000
Montevideo, Uruguay (*1,175,000)....1,070,000
Montreal, Canada (*2,150,000)........1,200,000
Moscow, Soviet Union (*8,200,000)....6,275,000
Mukden, China (*2,600,000)..........2,600,000
Munich, W. Germany (*1,450,000)....1,135,000
Nagoya, Japan (*2,025,000)..........1,655,000
Nanking, China (*1,600,000)..........1,600,000
Naples, Italy (*1,700,000)...........1,183,000
Newcastle, England (*1,145,000).......266,000
New York, New York (*15,775,000)...7,775,000
Novosibirsk, Soviet Union (*1,065,000)..1,005,000
Osaka, Japan (*8,350,000)...........3,125,000
Paris, France (*7,750,000)...........3,050,000
Peking, China (6,800,000▲)..........*4,000,000
Philadelphia, Pennsylvania
   (*4,100,000)........................1,995,000
Pittsburgh, Pennsylvania (*1,990,000)...595,000
Prague, Czechoslovakia (*1,060,000)...1,005,000
Pusan, S. Korea (*1,185,000).........1,185,000
Recife, Brazil (*1,100,000)...........830,000
Rio de Janeiro, Brazil (*4,900,000)...3,425,000
Rome, Italy (*2,325,000).............2,175,000
Rotterdam, Netherlands (*1,000,000)....729,000
Saigon, S. Vietnam (*1,700,000)......1,500,000
St. Louis, Missouri (*2,115,000)........730,000
San Diego, California (*1,165,000).....610,000
San Francisco, California (*3,500,000)...745,000
Santiago, Chile (*2,225,000)..........645,000
São Paulo, Brazil (*4,900,000)........4,100,000
Seattle, Washington (*975,000)........635,000
Seoul, S. Korea (*2,700,000).........2,550,000
Shanghai, China (10,700,000▲)......*7,800,000
Sian, China (*1,600,000).............1,600,000
Singapore, Singapore (*1,720,000).....1,040,000
Stockholm, Sweden (*1,140,000)........806,000
Stuttgart, W. Germany (*1,375,000).....645,000
Surabaja, Indonesia (*1,075,000)......1,000,000
Sverdlovsk, Soviet Union (*1,000,000)...860,000
Sydney, Australia (*2,265,000)........171,000
Taipei, Taiwan (*1,075,000)...........925,000
Taiyüan, China (*1,200,000)..........1,200,000
Tashkent, Soviet Union (*1,135,000)...1,000,000
Tehrān, Iran (*1,850,000)............1,750,000
Tientsin, China (3,600,000▲)........*3,200,000
Tōkyō, Japan (*14,700,000)..........8,600,000
Toronto, Canada (*1,860,000)..........673,000
Tsingtao, China (*1,275,000).........1,275,000
Turin, Italy (*1,255,000)............1,030,000
Victoria, Hong Kong (*2,850,000).....1,150,000
Vienna, Austria (*2,005,000).........1,630,000
Warsaw, Poland (*1,515,000)..........1,170,000
Washington, D.C. (*2,140,000)........755,000
Wuhan, China (*2,500,000)...........2,500,000
Yawata, Japan (*1,370,000)............345,000
Yokohama, Japan (*Tōkyō)..........1,435,000

* *Population of metropolitan area, including suburbs. See headnote.*
▲ *Population of entire municipality, including rural area. Starred population in these entries refers to urban portion of municipality only.*

SUPPLEMENTARY READING LIST

Alexander, Lewis M. *World Political Patterns.* Chicago: Rand McNally, 1957.

Blumenstock, David I. *The Ocean of Air.* New Brunswick, N.J.: Rutgers University Press, 1959.

Butland, G. J. *Latin America: A Regional Geography.* New York: Wiley, 1960.

Carlson, Fred A. *Geography of Latin America.* Englewood Cliffs, N.J.: Prentice-Hall, 1951.

Chisholm, Michael. *Rural Settlement and Land Use.* New York: Hillary House, 1962.

Cressey, George B. *Asia's Lands and Peoples.* New York: McGraw-Hill, 1951.

————. *Crossroads: Land and Life in Southwest Asia.* Philadelphia: Lippincott, 1960.

————. *Land of the 500 Million: A Geography of China.* New York: McGraw-Hill, 1955.

Crone, G. R. *Maps and Their Makers.* New York: Hillary House, 1953.

Cumberland, Kenneth B. *Southwest Pacific.* New York: McGraw-Hill, 1956.

Dury, G. H. *The Face of the Earth.* New York: Atheneum, 1959.

East, William Gordon and Moodie, A. E. *The Changing World.* London: Harrap, 1956.

East, William Gordon and Spate, O. H. K. *Changing Map of Asia.* New York: Dutton, 1959.

Espenshade, Edward B. (ed.). *Goode's World Atlas.* Chicago: Rand McNally, 1962.

Estall, R. C. and Buchanan, R. O. *Industrial Activity and Economic Geography.* New York: Hillary House, 1961.

Fisher, W. B. *The Middle East: A Physical, Social and Regional Geography.* New York: Dutton, 1961.

Fitzgerald, Walter. *Africa: A Social, Economic and Political Geography of its Major Regions.* New York: Dutton, 1955.

Freeman, Otis W. *Geography of the Pacific.* New York: Wiley, 1951.

Freeman, T. W. *Geography and Planning.* New York: Hillary House, 1958.

Gottmann, Jean. *Geography of Europe.* New York: Holt, Rinehart and Winston, 1962.

Griffin, Paul F. *Anglo-America: A Regional Geography of the United States and Canada.* San Francisco: Fearon, 1962.

Hoffman, George W. et al. *Geography of Europe.* New York: Ronald, 1961.

James, Preston E. *Latin America.* New York: Odyssey, 1959.

Kimble, George H. T. *Tropical Africa.* New York: 20th Century Fund, 1960.

Kimble, George H. T. and Good, D. *Geography of the Northlands.* New York: Wiley, 1955.

Lebon, J. H. G. *An Introduction to Human Geography.* New York: Hillary House, 1952.

Murphey, Rhoads, *An Introduction to Geography.* Chicago: Rand McNally, 1961.

Pounds, Norman J. G. *Europe and the Mediterranean.* New York: McGraw-Hill, 1953.

Cosmopolitan World Atlas. Chicago: Rand McNally, 1962.

Shabad, Theodore. *China's Changing Map.* New York: Praeger, 1956.

————. *Geography of the USSR.* New York: Columbia University Press, 1951.

Shackleton, M. R. *Europe: A Regional Geography.* New York: Wiley, 1958.

Shaw, Earl B. *Anglo-America: A Regional Geography.* New York: Wiley, 1959.

Shimer, John A. *This Sculptured Earth: The Landscape of America.* New York: Columbia University Press, 1959.

Smailes, A. E. *The Geography of Towns.* New York: Hillary House, 1953.

Sparks, B. W. *Geomorphology.* New York: Wiley, 1960.

Stamp, Lawrence Dudley. *Africa: A Study in Tropical Development.* New York: Wiley, 1953.

————. *Asia: A Regional and Economic Geography.* New York: Dutton, 1962.

————. *Australia and New Zealand.* New York: Wiley, 1958.

————. *Land for Tomorrow.* Bloomington: Indiana University Press, 1952.

Thiel, Erich. *The Soviet Far East: A Survey of its Physical and Economic Geography.* New York: Praeger, 1957.

Thompson, Warren. *Population and Progress in the Far East.* Chicago: University of Chicago Press, 1959.

White, Charles L. and Foscue, E. J. *Regional Geography of Anglo-America.* Englewood Cliffs, N.J.: Prentice-Hall, 1954.

Wood, Gordon L. and McBride, P. *Pacific Basin: A Human Aid to Economic Geography.* New York: Oxford University Press, 1955.

Yates, Paul Lamartine. *Food, Land and Manpower in Western Europe.* New York: St. Martin's, 1961.

Zimmerman, Erich W. *World Resources and Production.* New York: Harper, 1951.

INDEX

A

Abādān, Iran, 363
Aberdeen, Scotland, 274
Abidjan, Ivory Coast, 494
Abilene, Kansas, U.S.A., 176
Absaroka Mountains, 185
Acapulco, Mexico, 120, 218, 247
Accra, Ghana, 119, 481
Acropolis, 339
Adams, Mount, 190
Addis Ababa, Ethiopia, 499
Adelaide, South Australia, Australia, 522, 531, 535
Aden, 362, 378
Adirondack Mountains, 154, 196, 198
Adria, Italy, 331
Adriatic Sea, 333 ff., 464
Aegean Sea, 341
Afghanistan, 379-380, 449
Africa, 469-517; agriculture, 492 ff., 321, 329; Europeans in, 329, 478-485, 490, 500-501, 504, 507, 512; exploration, 469-471; independence in, 482-483; Indians in, 507, 508; lakes, 472; migration to, 565-566; minerals, 473, 474, 494 ff.; 514; national income, 516; Northwest, 344; plateaus, 496-497, 500; population, 479-480, 516; Portuguese colonies, 329; relief, 471, 472-473; rising expectations, 492; rivers, 471, 472; Sahara, 485-487; states, 139-140; trade, 493 ff.; vegetation, 476-477; Veld, 477; water power, 516
Africa, Central, 502-506; climate, 502; government, 505; minerals, 503; relief, 502; see also Africa
Africa, East, 496-502; agriculture, 498 ff.; Arabs in, 502; Gezira, 498, 499; relief, 496-498; see also Africa
Africa, Offshore, 514-515; see also Africa
Africa, South, 506-511; Boers, 507-508; climate, 506-507, 514; minerals, 508; plateau, 506; Portuguese in, 512, 513; relief, 506-507; tribes, 508; Veld, 477, 506, 507; see also Africa
Africa, West, 487-496; colonies, 560; rivers, 487, states, 489 ff.; see also Africa
Agra, India, 388
Agriculture: and climate, 87 ff.; and environment, 107; equatorial, 112; land use, 555 ff., 557-8; and population, 103-115, 565; production methods, 150, 555 ff.; savanna, 113; see also under names of countries
Aid, technical, 561-564; see also Economic Growth
Air: movement of, 78, 81; pressure, 76; "front," 77, 79-81; jet streams, 81; see also Atmosphere; Winds
Alabama, U.S.A., 165, 180
Alaska, U.S.A., 202, 206-207
Alaska Highway, 204
Alaska Mountains, 206
Albania, 337, 449, 465-466
Albany, New York, U.S.A., 166
Albert Canal, Belgium, 291
Albert, Lake, 472
Alberta, Canada, 185, 195, 199, 202
Albuquerque, New Mexico, U.S.A., 157
Aleppo, Syria, 357
Aleutian Islands, 185, 206
Alexandria, Egypt, 351
Algiers, Algeria, 345-346
Algeria, 345-346
Algoa Bay, 478
Alhambra, Spain, 325

Alice Springs, Western Australia, Australia, 537
Allegheny Front, 165
Allegheny Plateau, 165
Allegheny River, 166
Alliance for Progress, 563
Alluvial plains, 56, 105, 179, 224, 407
Alpine mountain systems, 262-263, 299-300, 318, 330; Dinaric Alps, 318, 336, 464; French Alps, 288; Swabian Alps, 298; Transylvanian Alps, 318, 457; Southern Alps, 538
Alpine states, see Switzerland; Austria
Altai Mountains, 368, 408
Altiplano, 235
Amazon: agriculture, 104-105; delta, 225; forests, 84-85, 224-225; plain, 224-225, 232; river, 224-225; tribes, 128; valley, 219
Amiens, France, 286
Amman, Jordan, 355
Amoy, China, 410
Amritsar, India, 388
Amsterdam, Netherlands, 292, 293
Amu Darya River, 431
Amundsen, Roald, 154, 542
Amur River, 423
Anatolian Plateau, 343
Anchorage, Alaska, U.S.A., 206
Ancona, Italy, 333
Andalusia, Spain, 324
Andes Mountains, 143, 218, 219, 229, 232, 234, 238
Angkor Thom, Cambodia, 393
Angkor Wat, 393
Anglo-America, 153-162, 193, 208-209, 215; area, 153; culture, 157-158, 208; exploration, 154-159; immigration, 159; population, 153, 154; settlement, 156-159; unity, 208-209; see also Canada; United States
Angola, 484, 512, 513
Ankara, Turkey, 343
Annam Mountains, 393
Antarctica, 49, 245, 541-544, 558
Antibes, France, 287
Antwerp, Belgium, 290, 291
Apartheid, 509, 512
Apennine Mountains, 56, 330, 332
Appalachian Mountains, 165, 168, 169, 170
Aquitaine, France, 286
Arab League, 321
Arabian-American Oil Co., 361
Arabian Desert, 359-362
Arabian Sea, 384
Arabs, 345, 481, 502
Arafura Sea, 519
Aragon, Spain, 324
Arakan Mountains, 370, 389
Aral Sea, 423, 431
Ararat, Mount, 363
Archangel (Arkhangelsk), Soviet Union, 443
Arctic Circle, 307, 311
Arctic Ocean, 49, 98, 199, 442
Arctic region, 558
Ardennes Plateau, 288, 291
Argentina: cities, 242, 244; farming, 242-243; irrigation, 242; oases, 242; pampas, 242; population, 243, 244; rainfall, 242; size, 241
Argos, Greece, 338
Aristotle, 552
Arizona, U.S.A., 157, 186
Arkansas, U.S.A., 181
Arkansas River, 114, 176
Armenia, 318, 447

I

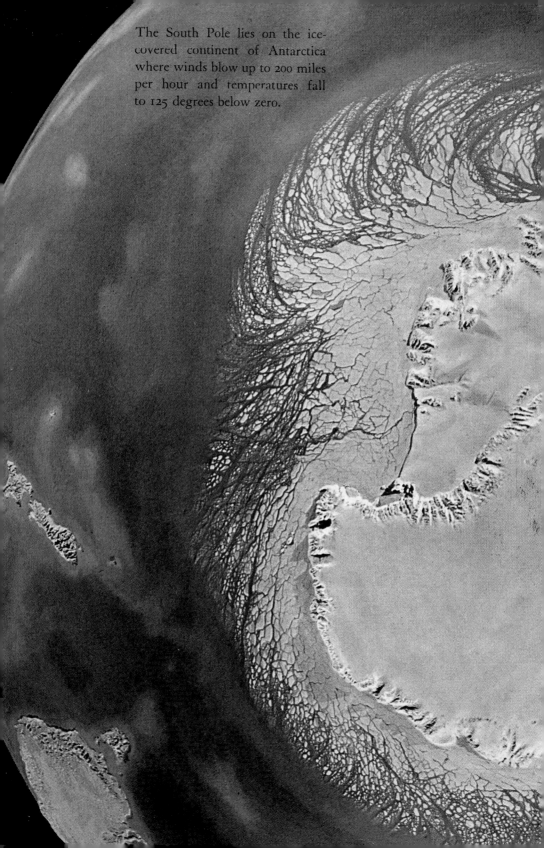

The South Pole lies on the ice-
covered continent of Antarctica
where winds blow up to 200 miles
per hour and temperatures fall
to 125 degrees below zero.